ADAPTIVE FILTERING

Edited by **Lino García Morales**

AF752207

INTECHOPEN.COM

Adaptive Filtering
Edited by Lino García Morales

Published by InTech
Janeza Trdine 9, 51000 Rijeka, Croatia

Edition 2014
Copyright © 2011 InTech
All chapters are distributed under the Creative Commons Non Commercial Share Alike Attribution 3.0 license, which permits to copy, distribute, transmit, and adapt the work in any medium, so long as the original work is properly cited. After this work has been published by InTech, authors have the right to republish it, in whole or part, in any publication of which they are the author, and to make other personal use of the work. Any republication, referencing or personal use of the work must explicitly identify the original source.

Statements and opinions expressed in the chapters are these of the individual contributors and not necessarily those of the editors or publisher. No responsibility is accepted for the accuracy of information contained in the published articles. The publisher assumes no responsibility for any damage or injury to persons or property arising out of the use of any materials, instructions, methods or ideas contained in the book.

Publishing Process Manager Petra Zobic

Technical Editor Teodora Smiljanic

Cover Designer InTech Design Team

Image Copyright Designus, 2010. Used under license from Shutterstock.com

Additional hard copies can be obtained from orders@intechopen.com

Adaptive Filtering, Edited by Lino García Morales
p. cm.
ISBN 978-953-307-158-9

INTECH

open science | open minds

Contents

Preface IX

Part 1 Fundamentals, Convergence, Performance 1

Chapter 1 Convergence Evaluation of a Random Step-Size NLMS Adaptive Algorithm in System Identification and Channel Equalization 3
Shihab Jimaa

Chapter 2 Steady-State Performance Analyses of Adaptive Filters 19
Bin Lin and Rongxi He

Chapter 3 The Ultra High Speed LMS Algorithm Implemented on Parallel Architecture Suitable for Multidimensional Adaptive Filtering 47
Marwan Jaber

Chapter 4 An LMS Adaptive Filter Using Distributed Arithmetic - Algorithms and Architectures 89
Kyo Takahashi, Naoki Honma and Yoshitaka Tsunekawa

Part 2 Complex Structures, Applications and Algorithms 107

Chapter 5 Adaptive Filtering Using Subband Processing: Application to Background Noise Cancellation 109
Ali O. Abid Noor, Salina Abdul Samad and Aini Hussain

Chapter 6 Hirschman Optimal Transform (HOT) DFT Block LMS Algorithm 135
Osama Alkhouli, Victor DeBrunner and Joseph Havlicek

Chapter 7 Real-Time Noise Cancelling Approach on Innovations-Based Whitening Application to Adaptive FIR RLS in Beamforming Structure 153
Jinsoo Jeong

Chapter 8 **Adaptive Fuzzy Neural Filtering for Decision Feedback Equalization and Multi-Antenna Systems 169**
Yao-Jen Chang and Chia-Lu Ho

Chapter 9 **A Stereo Acoustic Echo Canceller Using Cross-Channel Correlation 195**
Shigenobu Minami

Chapter 10 **EEG-fMRI Fusion: Adaptations of the Kalman Filter for Solving a High-Dimensional Spatio-Temporal Inverse Problem 233**
Thomas Deneux

Chapter 11 **Adaptive-FRESH Filtering 259**
Omar A. Yeste Ojeda and Jesús Grajal

Chapter 12 **Transient Analysis of a Combination of Two Adaptive Filters 297**
Tõnu Trump

Chapter 13 **Adaptive Harmonic IIR Notch Filters for Frequency Estimation and Tracking 313**
Li Tan, Jean Jiang and Liangmo Wang

Chapter 14 **Echo Cancellation for Hands-Free Systems 333**
Artur Ferreira and Paulo Marques

Chapter 15 **Adaptive Heterodyne Filters 359**
Michael A. Soderstrand

Preface

A digital filter is a structure that transforms sequences of numbers to others from its input to its output (signals) and models thus the behavior of a real system. The model or transfer function is a simplified mathematical representation of the system. The structure of the filter consists of a few elements: delays, multipliers, adders and, less often, functions whose magnitude, combination and number determine its characteristics. An adaptive filter, however, is able to self-adjust the parameters of such elements in time (the coefficients of the multipliers for example) according to certain algorithm and thus the relationship between the input and output sequences to adapt itself to the changes of the complex system that represents. This update takes place, usually, by minimizing a cost function in an iterative scheme.

Digital adaptive filters are, therefore, very popular in any implementation of signal processing where the system modelled and/or the input signals are time-variants; such as the echo cancellation, active noise control, blind channel equalization, etc., corresponding to problems of system identification, inverse modeling, prediction, interference cancellation, etc.

Any design of an adaptive filter focuses its attention on some of its components: structure (transversal, recursive, lattice, systolic array, non-linear, transformed domain, etc.), cost function (mean square error, least squares), coefficient update algorithm (no memory, block, gradient, etc.); to get certain benefits: robustness, speed of convergence, misalignment, tracking capacity, computational complexity, delay, etc.

This book is composed of 15 motivating chapters written by researchers and professionals that design, develop and analyze different combinations or variations of the components of the adaptive filter and apply them to different areas of knowledge. The first part of the book is devoted to the adaptive filtering fundamentals and evaluation of their performances while the second part presents structures and complex algorithms in specific applications.

This information is very interesting not only for all those who work with technologies based on adaptive filtering but also for teachers and professionals interested in the digital signal processing in general and in how to deal with the complexity of real systems in particular: non-linear, time-variants, continuous, and unknown.

Lino García Morales
Audiovisual Engineering and Communication Department
Polytechnic University of Madrid
Spain

Part 1

Fundamentals, Convergence, Performance

1

Convergence Evaluation of a Random Step-Size NLMS Adaptive Algorithm in System Identification and Channel Equalization

Shihab Jimaa
Khalifa University of Science, Technology and Research (KUSTAR)
Faculty of Engineering, Dept. of Communications Engineering
Sharjah Campus, Sharjah
United Arab Emirates

1. Introduction

Adaptive filtering algorithms have been widely applied to solve many problems in digital communication systems [1- 3]. So far, the Least Mean Square (LMS) and its normalized version (NLMS) adaptive algorithms have been the most commonly adopted approaches owing to the clarity of the mean-square-error cost function in terms of statistical concept and the simplicity for computation. It is known that the NLMS algorithm gives better convergence characteristics than the LMS because it uses a variable step-size parameter in which the variation is achieved due to the division, at each iteration, of the fixed step size by the input power. However, a critical issue associated with both algorithms is the choice of the step-size parameter that is the trade-off between the steady-state misadjustment and the speed of adaptation. Recent studies have thus presented the idea of variable step-size NLMS algorithm to remedy this issue [4-7]. Also, many other adaptive algorithms [8, 9] have been defined and studied to improve the adaptation performance. In this work, the proposed approach of randomizing the NLMS algorithm's step-size has been introduced in the adaptation process of both channel equalisation and system identification, and tested over a defined communication channels. The proposed random step-size approach yields an algorithm with good convergence rate and steady state stability.

The objective of this chapter is analyzing and comparing the proposed random step-size NLMS and the standard NLMS algorithms that were implemented in the adaptation process of two fundamental applications of adaptive filters, namely adaptive channel equalization and adaptive system identification. In particular, we focus our attention on the behavior of Mean Square Error (MSE) of the proposed and the standard NLMS algorithms in the two mentioned applications. From the MSE performances we can determine the speed of convergence and the steady state noise floor level. The key idea in this chapter is that a new and simple approach to adjust the step-size (μ) of the standard NLMS adaptive algorithm has been implemented and tested. The value of μ is totally controlled by the use of a Pseudorandom Noise (PRN) uniform distribution that is defined by values from 0 to 1. Randomizing the step-size eliminates much of the trade-off between residual error and convergence speed compared with the fixed step-size. In this case, the adaptive filter will change its coefficients according to the NLMS algorithm in which its step-size is controlled by the PRN to pseudo randomize the step size. Also this chapter covers the most popular advances in adaptive filtering which include adaptive algorithms, adaptive channel equalization, and adaptive system identification.

In this chapter, the concept of using random step-size approach in the adaptation process of the NLMS adaptive algorithm will be introduced and investigated. The investigation includes calculating and plotting the MSE performance of the proposed algorithm in system identification and channel equalization and compares the computer simulation results with that of the standard NLMS algorithm.

The organization of this chapter is as follows: In Section 2 an overview of adaptive filters and their applications is demonstrated. Section 3 describes the standard NLMS and the proposed random step size NLMS algorithms. In Sections 4 the performance analysis of adaptive channel equalization and adaptive system identification are given. Finally the conclusion and the list of references are given in Sections 5 and 6, respectively.

2. Overview of adaptive filters and applications

An adaptive filter generally consists of two distinct parts: a filter, whose structure is designed to perform a desired processing function, and an adaptive algorithm for adjusting the coefficients of that filter. The ability of an adaptive filter to operate satisfactory in an unknown environment and track time variations of input statistics make the adaptive filter a powerful device for signal processing and control applications [1].

Adaptive filters are self learn. As the signal into the filter continues, the adaptive filter coefficients adjust themselves to achieve the desired result, such as identifying an unknown filter or cancelling noise in the input signal. Figure 1 represents the adaptive filter, comprising the adaptive filter and the adaptive weight control mechanism. An adaptive Finite Impulse Response (FIR) filter or Infinite Impulse Response (IIR) filter designs itself based on the characteristics of the input signal to the filter and a signal which represent the desired behavior of the filter on its input. Designing the filter does not require any other frequency response information or specification. To define the self learning process the filter uses, you select the adaptive algorithm used to reduce the error between the output signal $y(k)$ and the desired signal $d(k)$. When the least mean square performance criteria for $e(k)$ has achieved its minimum value through the iterations of the adapting algorithm, the adaptive filter is finished and its coefficients have converged to a solution. Now the output from the adaptive filter matches closely the desired signal $d(k)$. When the input data characteristics changes, sometimes called the filter environment, the filter adapts to the new environment by generating a new set of coefficients for the new data. Notice that when $e(k)$ goes to zero and remains there you achieve perfect adaptation; the ideal result but not likely in the real world.

The ability of an adaptive filter to operate satisfactorily in an unknown environment and track time variations of input statistics make the adaptive filter a powerful device for signal processing and control applications [12]. In fact, adaptive filters have been successfully applied in such diverse fields as communications, radar, sonar, seismology, and biomedical engineering. Although these applications are quite different in nature, however, they have one basic common aspect: an input vector and a desired response are used to compute an estimation error, which is in turn used to control the values of a set of adjustable filter coefficients. The fundamental difference between the various applications of adaptive filtering arises in the way in which the desired response is extract.

In many applications requiring filtering, the necessary frequency response may not be known beforehand, or it may vary with time. (for example; suppression of engine harmonics in a car stereo). In such applications, an adaptive filter which can automatically design itself and which can track system variations in time is extremely useful. Adaptive filters are used extensively in a wide variety of applications, particularly in telecommunications. Despite that adaptive filters have been successfully applied in many communications and signal processing fields including adaptive system identification, adaptive channel equalization, adaptive interference (Noise) cancellation, and adaptive echo cancellation, the focus here is on their applications in adaptive channel equalisation and adaptive system identification.

3. Adaptive algorithms

Adaptive filter algorithms have been used in many signal processing applications [1]. One of the adaptive filter algorithms is the normalized least mean square (NLMS), which is the most popular one because it is very simple but robust. NLMS is better than LMS because the weight vector of NLMS can change automatically, while that of LMS cannot [2]. A critical issue associated with all algorithms is the choice of the step-size parameter that is the trade-off between the steady-state misadjustment and the speed of adaptation. A recent study has presented the idea of variable step-size LMS algorithm to remedy this issue [4]. Nevertheless, many other adaptive algorithms based upon non-mean-square cost function can also be defined to improve the adaptation performance. For example, the use of the error to the power Four has been investigated [8] and the Least-Mean-Fourth adaptive algorithm (LMF) results. Also, the use of the switching algorithm in adaptive channel equalization has also been studied [9].

General targets of an adaptive filter are rate of convergence and misadjustment. The fast rate of convergence allows the algorithm to adapt rapidly to a stationary environment of unknown statistics, but quantitative measure by which the final value of mean-square error (MSE) is averaged over an ensemble of adaptive filters, deviates from the minimum MSE more severely as the rate of convergence becomes faster, which means that their trade-off problem exists.

3.1 NLMS algorithm

The least mean square (LMS) algorithm has been widely used for adaptive filters due to its simplicity and numerical robustness. On the other hand, NLMS algorithm is known that it gives better convergence characteristics than the LMS, because the NLMS uses a variable step-size parameter in which, in each iteration, a step-size fixed parameter is divided by the input power. Depending on the value of the fixed step-size parameter, however, the LMS and NLMS algorithms result in a trade-off between the convergence speed and the mean square error (MSE) after convergence [5].

3.1.1 Adaptive filter

A general form of the adaptive filter is shown in Figure 1, where an input signal $u(n)$ produces an output signal $y(n)$, then the output signal $y(n)$ is subtracted from the desired response $d(n)$ to produce an error signal $e(n)$. The input signal $u(n)$ and error signal $e(n)$ are combined together into an adaptive weight-control mechanism. The weight controller applies a weight adjustment to the transversal filter so as to minimize MSE value [11]. This process is repeated for a number of iterations until the filter reaches to a steady-state. In summary, the purpose of the adaptive system is to filter the input signal *u(n)* so that it resembles the desired signal input *d(n)*. The filter could be any type but the most widely used is the *N* tap FIR filter because of its simplicity and stability.

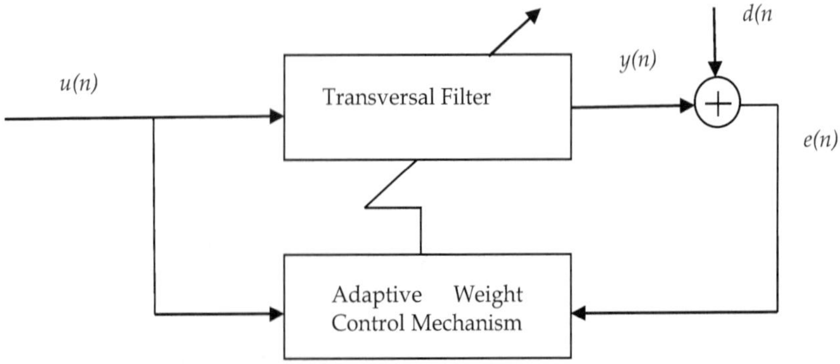

Fig. 1. Block diagram of adaptive transversal filter

3.1.2 Algorithm's operation

The weight vector of an adaptive filter should be changed in a minimal manner, subject to a constraint imposed on the updated filter's output. The NLMS adaptive filter is a manifestation of the principal of minimal disturbance from one iteration to the next [10]. To describe the meaning of NLMS as an equation, let *w(n)* be the old weight vector of the filter at iteration *n* and *w(n+1)* is its updated weight vector at iteration *n+1*. We may then formulate the criterion for designing the NLMS filter as that of constrained optimization: the input vector *u(n)* and desired response *d(n)* determine the updated tap-weight vector *w(n+1)* so as to minimize the squared Euclidean norm of the change as:

$$\delta w(n+1) = w(n+1) - w(n) \tag{1}$$

Subject to the constraint

$$d(n) = w^H(n+1)u(n) \tag{2}$$

The method of the lagrange multiplier is used to solve this problem as:

$$w(n+1) = w(n) + \frac{1}{2}\lambda\, u(n) \tag{3}$$

The unknown multiplier, λ, can be obtained by substituting (3) into (2):

$$\lambda = \frac{2e(n)}{\|u(n)\|^2} \tag{4}$$

Where $e(n)$ is the error signal and is given by:

$$e(n)=d(n)-w^H(n)u(n) \tag{5}$$

Then, combining (3) and (4) to formulate the optimal value of the incremental change, $\delta w(n+1)$, we obtain:

$$w(n+1)-w(n)=\frac{\mu}{\|u(n)\|^2}u(n)e(n) \tag{6}$$

Equation (6) can be written as:

$$w(n+1)=w(n)+\frac{\mu}{\alpha+\|u(n)\|^2}u(n)e(n) \tag{7}$$

Where the constant α is added to the denominator to avoid that $w(n+1)$ cannot be bounded when the tap-input vector $u(n)$ is too small.

3.1.3 Step-size

The stability of the NLMS algorithm depends on the value of its step-size, and thus its optimization criterion should be found [12]. The desired response has been set as follows:

$$d(n)=w^H(n)u(n)+v(n) \tag{8}$$

Where $v(n)$ is an unknown disturbance. An estimate of the unknown parameter w is calculated from the tap-weight vector $w(n)$. The weight-error vector is given below:

$$\varepsilon(n)=w-w(n) \tag{9}$$

Substituting (9) into (7) yields:

$$\varepsilon(n+1)=\varepsilon(n)-\frac{\mu}{\|u(n)\|^2}u(n)e(n) \tag{10}$$

To study the stability performance of adaptive filters, the mean-square deviation may be identified [11].

$$\xi(n)=E[|\varepsilon(n)|^2] \tag{11}$$

Where E denotes expectation. Substituting (10) into (11) yields:

$$\xi(n+1)-\xi(n)=\mu^2 E\left[\frac{|e(n)|^2}{\|u(n)\|^2}\right]-2\mu E\left\{\mathrm{Re}\left[\frac{\lambda_u(n)e(n)}{\|u(n)\|^2}\right]\right\} \tag{12}$$

where $\lambda_u(n)$ is the undisturbed error signal defined by:

$$\lambda_u(n)=\varepsilon^H(n)u(n) \tag{13}$$

The bounded range of the normalized step-size parameter can be found from (12) as:

$$0<\mu<2\frac{\mathrm{Re}\left\{E\left[\lambda_u(n)e(n)/\|u(n)\|^2\right]\right\}}{E\left[|e(n)|^2/\|u(n)\|^2\right]} \tag{14}$$

For the case of real-valued data, the following equation can be used:

$$E\left[|\lambda_u(n)|^2\right]=E\left[|u(n)|^2\right]\xi(n) \tag{15}$$

Substituting (15) into (14) yields:

$$0<\mu<2\frac{E\left[|u(n)|^2\right]\xi(n)}{E\left[|e(n)|^2\right]} \tag{16}$$

or

$$0<\mu<2\mu_{opt} \tag{17}$$

where $E\left[|e(n)|^2\right]$ is the estimation of the error signal power, $E\left[|u(n)|^2\right]$ is the estimation of the input signal power, $\xi(n)$ is the estimation of the mean-square deviation, and μ_{opt} is the optimal step-size parameter.

3.2 The random step-size algorithm

Using the proposed idea of randomizing the step size, the step-size for the NLMS algorithm is changed into a variable one, where the fixed step size is multiplied by PN (pseudo random number generator) being a selection from random numbers of uniform distribution [0 1] at each iteration time. Formulating the Pseudo-random NLMS algorithm results:

$$w[n+1]=w[n]+e(n)u(n)\frac{PN[n]\mu}{\alpha+||u[n]||^2} \tag{18}$$

Where *w(n)* is the previous weight of the filter and *w(n+1)* is the new weight.
The step-size μ directly affects how quickly the adaptive filter will converge toward the unknown system. If μ is very small, then the coefficients change only a small amount at each update, and the filter converges slowly. With a larger step-size, more gradient information is included in each update, and the filter converges more quickly; however, when the step-size is too large, the coefficients may change too quickly and the filter will diverge. (It is possible in some cases to determine analytically the largest value of μ ensuring convergence). In summary, within that margin given in (17), the larger μ the faster the convergence rate is but less stability around the minimum value. On the other hand, the smaller μ the slower the convergence rate but will be more stable around the optimum value.

4. Performance analysis

4.1 Adaptive channel equalization

Adaptive channel equalization in digital communication systems is perhaps the most heavily exploited area of application for adaptive filtering algorithms. Adaptive filtering algorithms have been widely applied to solve the problem of channel equalization in digital communication systems. This is because, firstly, the adaptation of tap weights of an equalizer is necessary to perform channel equalization tasks successfully and secondly, the development of an adaptive algorithm that allows fast weight modification, while improving the estimation performance of the equalizer, will enhance the capability of such equalization systems in real applications.

4.1.1 System model

The block diagram of the considered system is shown in Figure 2 below:

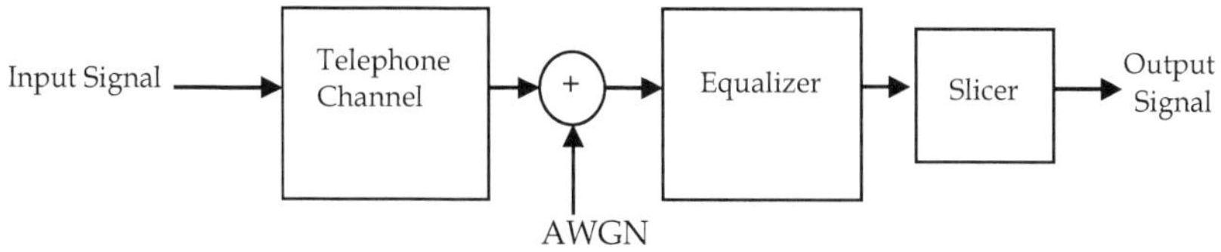

Fig. 2. The block diagram of the considered system

The input signal is Binary phase shift keying which has two phases (0 and π) so the signal is limited between 1 and -1. The general equation for a sum of weighted time delayed Telephone channel impulse responses can be written as

$$H(z) = h_0+h_1z^{-1}+h_2z^{-2}+....h_nz^{-n} \tag{19}$$

Two types of channels are considered here, the minimum phase (CH-1) and the non-minimum phase (CH-2) channels, which are given, respectively, below:

$$H(z) = 1.0 + 0.5z^{-1} \tag{20}$$

$$H(z) = 0.5 + z^{-1} \tag{21}$$

The discrete time model for the adaptive channel equalization considered in this paper is depicted in Figure 3.

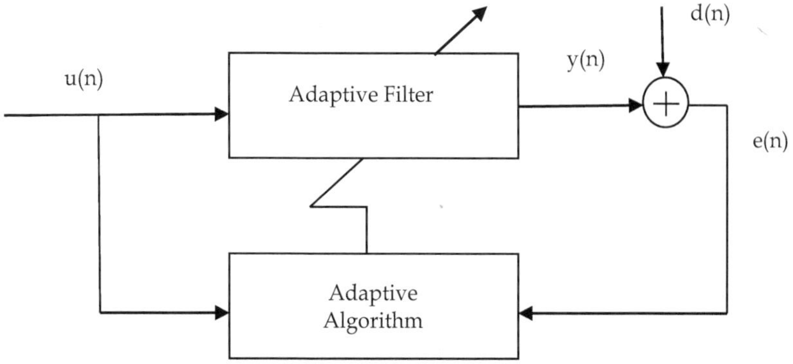

Fig. 3. The block diagram of the adaptive channel equalization

In a transversal adaptive filter, the input vector U_n and the weight vector W_n at the time of nth iteration are defined as follows:

$$U_n = [u_n, u_{n-1}, ..., u_{n-M+1}]^T \tag{22}$$

$$W_n = [w_0, w_1, ..., w_{M-1}]^T \tag{23}$$

Where u_n is the filter input and w_i, (i=0, 1, …, M-1) is the weight vector which corresponds to the filter length. The filter output is obtained as follows:

$$y_n = W_n^T U_n \tag{24}$$

The error signal e(k), involved in the adaptive process, is defined by

$$e(k) = d(k) - y(k) \tag{25}$$

$$= d(k) - w^H(k)\, u(k) \tag{26}$$

Where w(k) is the tap-weight vector of the adaptive filter assumed to have a transversal structure.

4.2 Adaptive system identification

This section introduces adaptive filters through the application of system identification using the NLMS and the random step-size NLMS algorithms. The adaptive filter adjusts its coefficients to minimize the mean-square error between its output and that of an unknown system. The objective is to change (adapt) the coefficients of an FIR filter to match as closely as possible the response of an unknown system.

4.2.1 System model

Consider the system identification problem illustrated in Figure 4. The Figure shows the discrete time model for the FIR system identification. One common application is to use adaptive filters to identify an unknown system, such as the response of an unknown communications channel. An unknown FIR system with N-point impulse response vector $w(n)$ has an input sequence $\{u(n)\}$ and an output sequence $\{d(n)\}$. The input signal is binary phase shift keying (BPSK) which has two phases (0 andπ) so the signal is limited between 1 and -1. The general formula for a sum of weighted time delayed channel impulse response can be written as:

$$H(z) = h_0 + h_1 z^{-1} + h_2 z^{-2} + \dots h_n z^{-n} \tag{27}$$

The desired response $d(n)$, providing a frame of reference for the adaptive filter, is defined by:

$$d(n) = W^H(n)\, U(n) + v(n) \tag{28}$$

Where $U(n)$ is the input vector, which is common to both the unknown system and the adaptive filter and v(n) is the Additive White Gaussian Noise (AWGN) with zero mean and variance σ^2. First the error signal, e (n), is computed which measures the difference between the output of the adaptive filter and the output of the unknown system. On the basis of this measure, the adaptive filter will change its coefficients in an attempt to reduce the error.

Hence the error signal, *e(n)*, involved in the adaptive process, is defined by:

$$e(n) = d(n) - y(n) \tag{29}$$

$$= W^{H}(n)\, U(n) + v(n) - W^{\wedge H}(n)\, U(n) \tag{30}$$

where $W^{\wedge}(n)$ is the tap-weight vector of the adaptive filter assumed to have a transversal structure.

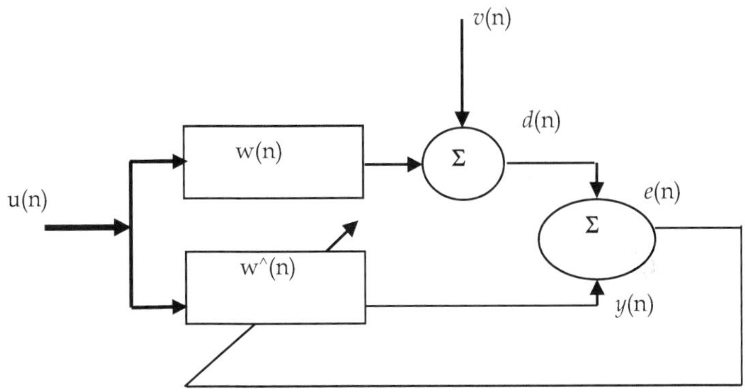

Fig. 4. System identification model using linear transversal adaptive filter

Clearly, when *e(n)* is very small, the adaptive filter response is close to the response of the unknown system. Application of the Wiener filter to this problem involves constructing an estimate *y(n)* of the observed output *d(n)* by passing the observed input sequence *u(n)* through a system modeling filter with impulse response vector *w(n)*. The impulse response of the system model is chosen to minimize the MSE. It is assumed that the adaptive filter has the same number of taps as the unknown system represented by *w(n)*.

4.3 Computer simulation results

4.3.1 Adaptive channel equalization

This section presents the computer simulations results of the performance of the non-linear transversal equalizer adapted by NLMS algorithm and the proposed pseudo-randomized NLMS algorithm [13]. The system was tested over both minimum phase and non-minimum phase channels, which are defined, respectively, as follows:

$$H_1(z) = 1.0 + 0.5z^{-1} \tag{31}$$

$$H_2(z) = 0.5 + z^{-1} \tag{32}$$

The digital signal transmitted through the channel was bipolar BPSK with values of ± 1 and the channel was corrupted by AWGN with SNR = 30dB. The order of the filter was set to 12 for both minimum phase, $H_1(z)$, and non-minimum phase, $H_2(z)$, channels. The step size for the NLMS algorithm was chosen from (0.01) to (0.1) and the number of transmitted bits equals to 2500 bits. The comparison between the two algorithms, the standard NLMS and the pseudo random step size NLMS, is done by first choosing the best step size that gives fast convergence and then uses this step size for the comparison.

Figure 5, shown below, shows that the step size with a value of 0.05 gives the fast convergence rate over the minimum phase channel (CH-1) while over the non-minimum phase channel (CH-2) the step size with a value of 0.01 gives the fast convergence rate. The comparison also looks at the effects of decreasing the SNR from 25 dB to 5 dB. While Figures 6 - 8, shown below, show the performances of the mean square error against the number of iterations for various values of signal-to-noise ratios using non-linear transversal equalizer over the minimum phase channel. From these figures it is clear that the speed of convergence has approximately the same convergence rate for both algorithms but the ground noise floor level decreases when the SNR decreases in the case of using the random step-size NLMS algorithm. The same conclusion has been noticed in the case of using the non-minimum phase channel that defined in (32) above. This is due to that the step-size parameter of the proposed random NLMS algorithm is designed based on utilizing the random distribution which made the error sequence accelerates the level of the noise floor to a much lower value compared to that of the standard NLMS algorithm with a fixed step-size value. Results for CH-2 are not included here due to space limitation.

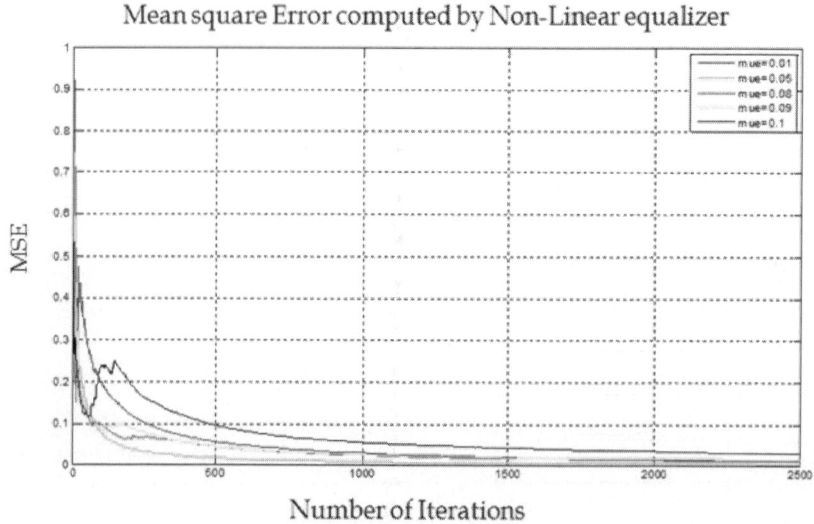

Fig. 5. MSE performances of the NLMS for various step-sizes over CH-1

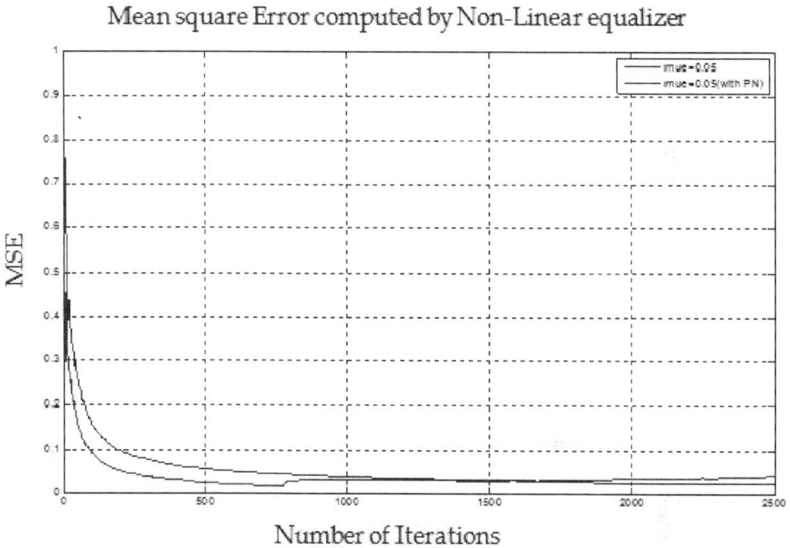

Fig. 6. MSE performances of the two algorithms for SNR=15dB over CH-1

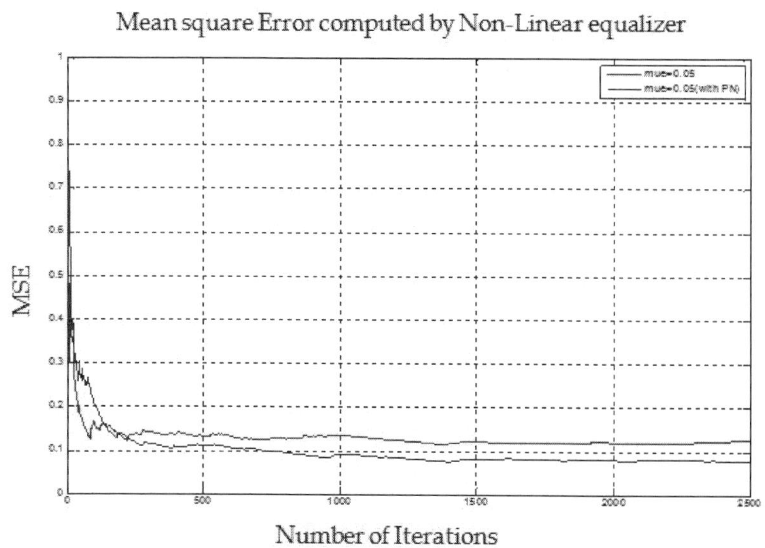

Fig. 7. MSE performances of the two algorithms for SNR=10 dB over CH-1

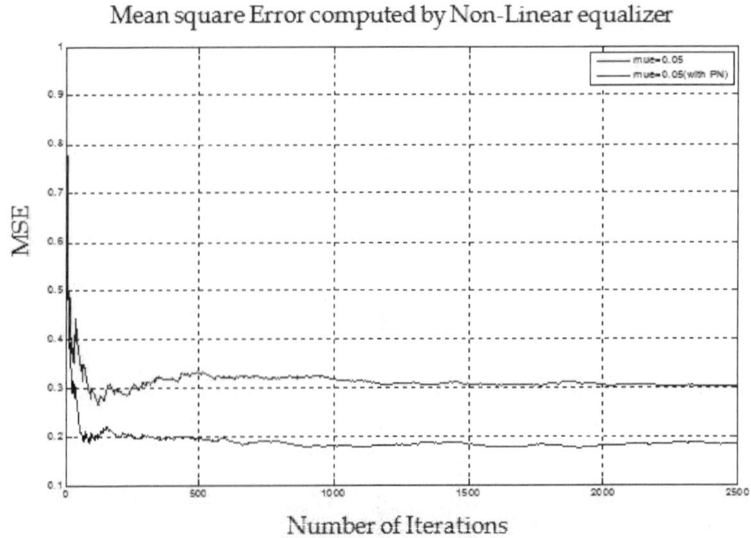

Fig. 8. MSE performances of the two algorithms for SNR=5 dB over CH-1

4.3.2 Adaptive system identification

This section presents the computer simulations results of the performance of fixed and random step-size NLMS algorithms used in system identification [14]. The following two equations represent the coefficient vector of the unknown system (to be identified by the adaptive filter) and its transfer function, respectively.

$$W^{*T} = [0.1, 0.3, 0.5, 0.3, 0.1] \tag{33}$$

$$H(z)=0.1+0.3z^{-1}+0.5z^{-2}+0.3z^{-3}+0.1z^{-4} \tag{34}$$

The unknown system output is disturbed by an uncorrelated zero-mean white Gaussian noise. The digital message applied to the channel is in random bipolar with the values of ± 1. The channel output is corrupted by a white Gaussian noise with zero mean and a variance of 0.01. The performance is determined by taking an average of 100 independent experimental simulations to demonstrate the mean-square error (MSE) performance of the proposed algorithm. The signal to noise ratio is set to 20 dB. Finally, the simulated systems have been implemented using Matlab codes. Figs. 9 & 10 show the MSE performances of the NLMS algorithm for various fixed step-sizes.

On the other hand Figs. 11-13, compare the MSE performances of the NLMS algorithm in the cases of fixed step-sizes of 0.5, 0.9, and 1.3 against the random step-size NLMS algorithm. It is clearly shown that the MSE performance of the NLMS algorithm using random step-size approach outperforms the fixed step-size algorithm's performance, especially with large step-sizes.

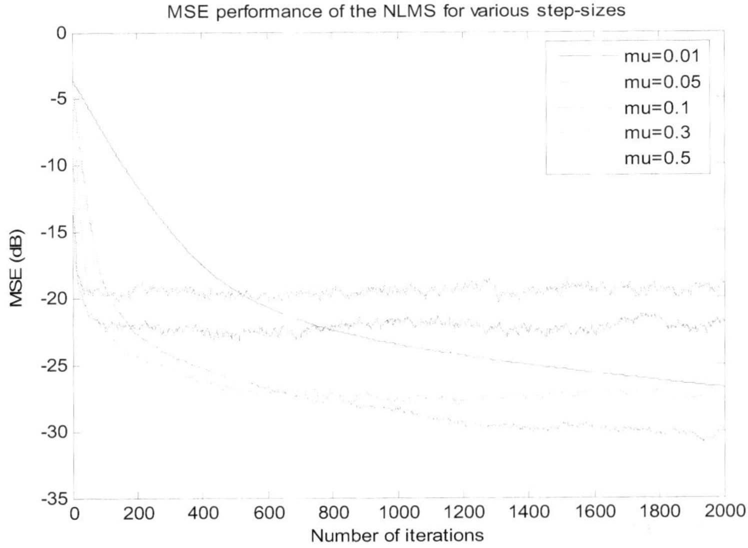

Fig. 9. MSE performance of the NLMS algorithm for various step-sizes (mu)

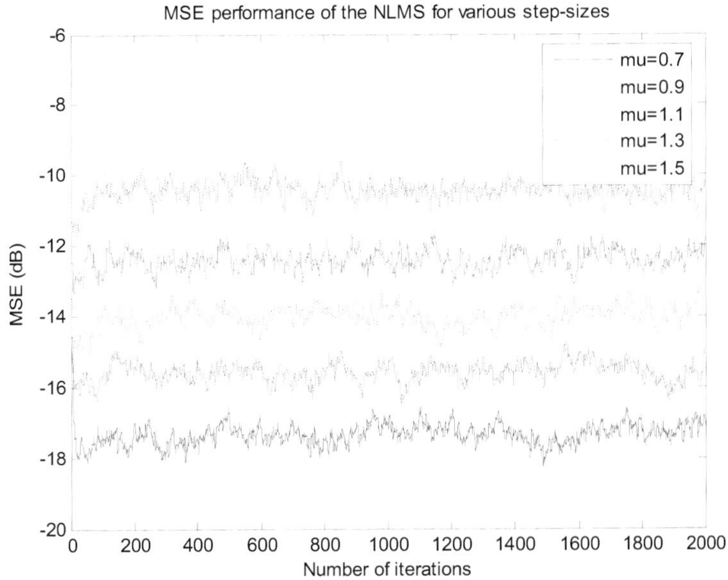

Fig. 10. MSE performance of the NLMS algorithm for various step-sizes (mu)

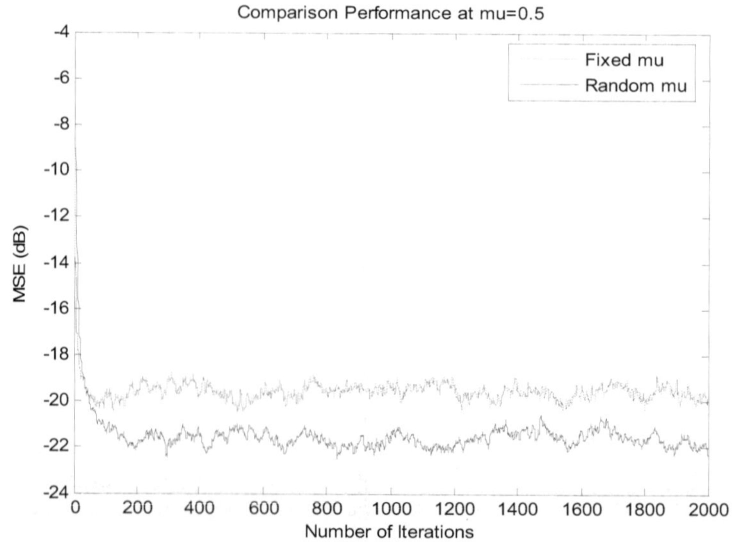

Fig. 11. MSE performances of fixed and random step-size NLMS algorithms

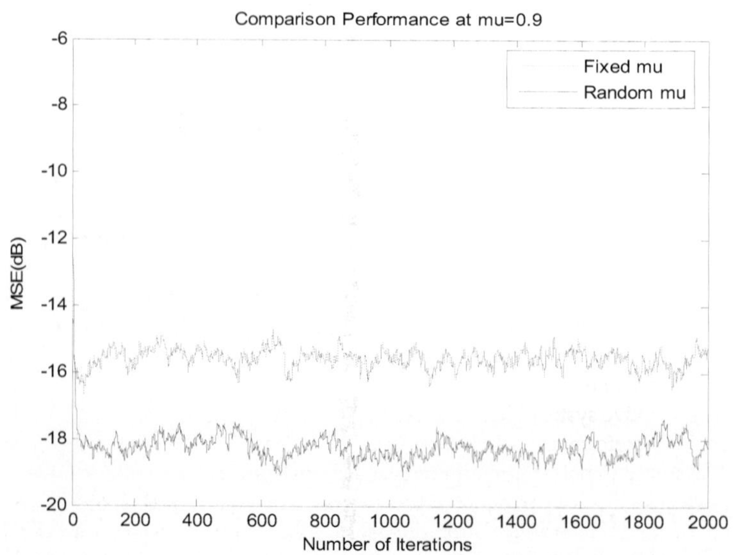

Fig. 12. MSE performances for fixed and random step-size NLMS algorithms

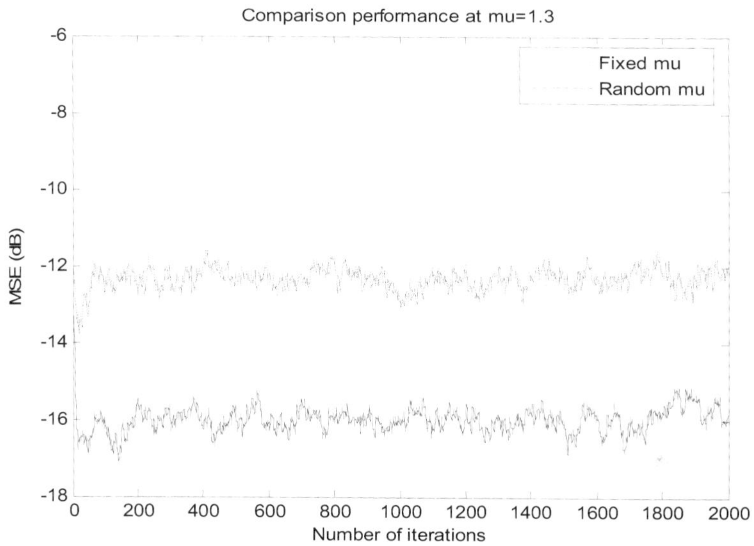

Fig. 13. MSE performances for fixed and random step-size NLMS algorithms

5. Conclusion

The proposed idea of using random step-size approach in the adaptation of the NLMS algorithm has been implemented and tested in the adaptation process of both channel equalization and system identification. The tests measure the MSE performance of using both the standard NLMS and the random step-size NLMS algorithms in the above mentioned applications. An extensive investigation, to determine the NLMS algorithm's best fixed step size, has been carried out over the defined channels. And a comparison between the performances of using the NLMS with a fixed step-size and a pseudo random step-size approaches has been carried out which shows the trade off between the convergence speed and the noise floor level.

It can be concluded, in the case of adaptive channel equalization, that the performance of using the random step-size outperforms the performance of the fixed step-size by achieving much lower ground noise floor, especially at low signal-to-noise ratios while maintaining a similar convergence rate.

In the case of adaptive system identification, the performance of using the random step-size outperforms the performance of that of fixed step-size NLMS adaptive algorithm and achieved lower ground noise floor, especially at larger step-sizes.

The values of the step-size parameter of the proposed random NLMS algorithm are based on utilizing the random uniform distribution which made the error sequence accelerates the MSE's level of the noise floor to a much lower value compared to that of the standard NLMS algorithm with a fixed step-size value.

6. Acknowledgment

The author would like to acknowledge the contributions of Mr. N. Al-Saeedi [Ref. 13] towards getting some results related to the channel equalization and Dr. T. Shimamura [Ref. 14] for his contribution towards discussing the idea of using the random step-size approach in system identification.

7. References

[1] Simon Haykin," *Adaptive Filter Theory*", Prentice- hall, 2002

[2] C.F.N.Cowan and P.M.Grant, *Adaptive Filters*, Prentice Hall, Englewood Cliffs, 1985.

[3] B.Widrow and S.D.Stearns, *Adaptive Signal Processing*, Prentice Hall, Englewood Cliffs, NJ, 1988.

[4] A. I. Sulyman and A. Zerguine, *Convergence and steady-state analysis of a variable step-size NLMS algorithm*, ELSEVIER Signal Processing, Vol. 83, , pp. 1255-1273, 2003.

[5] H. Takekawa. T. Shimamura, and S. A. Jimaa, "An efficient and effective variable step size NLMS algorithm", *42nd Asilomar conference on signals, systems and computers*, CA, USA, October 26-29, 2008.

[6] Ling Quin and M. G. Bellanger," Convergence analysis of a variable step-size normalized adaptive filter algorithm", *Proc. EUSIPCO, Adaptive Systems*, PAS.4, 1996.

[7] Y. Wang, C. Zhang, and Z. Wang," A new variable step-size LMS algorithm with application to active noise control", *Proc. IEEE ICASSP*, Vol. 5, pp. 573-575, 2003.

[8] E.Walach and B.Widrow, The Least Mean Fourth (LMF) Adaptive Algorithm and its Family" *IEEE Transactions on Information Theory*, 30(2), 275-283, 1984.

[9] S.A. Jimaa, C.F.N. Cowan and M.J.J. Holt," Adaptive Channel Equalisation Using Least Mean Switched Error Norm Algorithm", *IEE 16th Saraga Colloquium on Digital and Analogue Filters and Filtering Systems*, London, 9 Dec. 1996.

[10] Y. Wang, C. Zhang, and Z. Wang, "A new variable step-size LMS Algorithm with application to active noise control", *Proc. IEEE ICASSP*, pp. 573-575, 2003.

[11] T. Arnantapunpong, T. Shimamura, and S. A. Jimaa," A New Variable Step Size for Normalized LMS Algorithm", *NCSP'10 - 2010 RISP International Workshop on Nonlinear Circuits, Communications and Signal Processing*, Honolulu, Hawaii, USA March 3-5, 2010.

[12] Simon Haykin, *Adaptive Filter Theory*, Prentice- hall, 3rd Edition, 1996

[13] S. A. Jimaa, N. Al Saeedi, S. Al-Araji, and R. M. Shubair, Performance Evaluation of Random Step-Size NLMS in Adaptive channel equalization, *IFIP Wireless days conference*, Dubai, UAE, November 2008.

[14] S. A. Jimaa and T. Shimamura, Convergence Evaluation of a Random Step-Size NLMS Adaptive Algorithm in System Identification, *The 10th IEEE International Conference on Signal Processing ICSP 2010*, Beijing, China, Oct.24-28, 2010.

2

Steady-State Performance Analyses of Adaptive Filters

Bin Lin and Rongxi He
College of Information Science and Technology, Dalian Maritime University, Dalian, China

1. Introduction

Adaptive filters have become a vital part of many modern communication and control systems, which can be used in system identification, adaptive equalization, echo cancellation, beamforming, and so on [l]. The least mean squares (LMS) algorithm, which is the most popular adaptive filtering algorithm, has enjoyed enormous popularity due to its simplicity and robustness [2] [3]. Over the years several variants of LMS have been proposed to overcome some limitations of LMS algorithm by modifying the error estimation function from linearity to nonlinearity. Sign-error LMS algorithm is presented by its computational simplicity [4], least-mean fourth (LMF) algorithm is proposed for applications in which the plant noise has a probability density function with short tail [5], and the LMMN algorithm achieves a better steady state performance than the LMS algorithm and better stability properties than the LMF algorithm by adjusting its mixing parameter [6], [7].
The performance of an adaptive filter is generally measured in terms of its transient behavior and its steady-state behavior. There have been numerous works in the literature on the performance of adaptive filters with many creationary results and approaches [3]-[20]. In most of these literatures, the steady-state performance is often obtained as a limiting case of the transient behavior [13]-[16]. However, most adaptive filters are inherently nonlinear and time-variant systems. The nonlinearities in the update equations tend to lead to difficulties in the study of their steady-state performance as a limiting case of their transient performance [12]. In addition, transient analyses tend to require some more simplifying assumptions, which at times can be restrictive. Using the energy conservation relation during two successive iteration update , N. R. Yousef and A. H. Sayed re-derived the steady-state performance for a large class of adaptive filters [11],[12], such as sign-error LMS algorithm, LMS algorithm, LMMN algorithm, and so on, which bypassed the difficulties encountered in obtaining steady-state results as the limiting case of a transient analysis. However, it is generally observed that most works for analyzing the steady-state performance study individual algorithms separately. This is because different adaptive schemes have different nonlinear update equations, and the particularities of each case tend to require different arguments and assumptions. Some authors try to investigate the steady-state performance from a general view to fit more adaptive filtering algorithms, although that is a challenge task. Based on Taylor series expansion (TSE), S. C. Douglas and T. H. Meng obtained a general expression for the steady-state MSE for adaptive filters with error

nonlinearities [10]. However, this expression is only applicable for the cases with the real-valued data and small step-size. Also using TSE, our previous works have obtained some analytical expressions of the steady-state performance for some adaptive algorithms [8], [17], [19], [28]. Using the Price's theory, T. Y. Al-Naffouri and A. H. Sayed obtained the steady-state performance as the fixed-point of a nonlinear function in EMSE [11], [18]. For a lot of adaptive filters with error nonlinearities, their closed-form analytical expressions can not be obtained directly, and the Gaussion assumption condition of Price's theory is not adaptable for other noise. Recently, as a limiting case of the transient behavior, a general expression of the steady state EMSE was obtained by H. Husøy and M. S. E. Abadi [13]. Observing from the Table 1 in [13], we can see that this expression holds true only for the adaptive filters with most kinds of the preconditioning input data, and can not be used to analyze the adaptive filters with error nonlinearities.

These points motivate the development in this paper of a unified approach to get their general expressions for the steady-state performance of adaptive filters. In our analyses, second-order TSE will be used to analyze the performance for adaptive algorithms for real-valued cases. But for complex-valued cases, a so-called *complex Brandwood-form series expansion* (BSE), derived by G. Yan in [22], will be utilized. This series expansion is based on Brandwood's derivation operators [21] with respect to the complex-valued variable and its conjugate, and was used to analyze the MSE for Bussgang algorithm (BA) in noiseless environments [19], [20]. Here, the method is extended to analyze other adaptive filters in complex-valued cases.

1.1 Notation

Throughout the paper, the small boldface letters are used to denote vectors, and capital boldface letters are used to denote matrices, e.g., $\mathbf{w}_i$ and $\mathbf{R}_u$. All vectors are *column vectors*, except for the input vector $\mathbf{u}_i$, which is taken to be a row vector for convenience of notation. In addition, the following notations are adopted:

$\|\cdot\|$ Euclidean norm of a vector; $\mathrm{Tr}(\cdot)$ Trace of a matrix;

$\mathrm{E}\{\cdot\}$ Expectation operator; $\mathrm{Re}(\cdot)$ The real part of a complex-valued data;

$\mathbf{I}_{M\times M}$ $M\times M$ Identity matrix; $(\cdot)^*$ Complex conjugation for scalars;

! Factorial; !! Double factorial;

$f_x^{(1)}(a)$ 1th derivative of the function $f(x)$ with respect to x at the value a;

$f_{x,y}^{(2)}(a,b)$ 2th partial derivative of the function $f(x,y)$ with respect to x and y at the value (a,b) [1];

$C^i(D)$ The set of all functions for which $f^{(i)}(x)$ is continuous in definition domain D for each natural number i.

1.2 System model

Consider the following stochastic gradient approach for adaptive filters function [10]-[12][2]

$$\mathbf{w}_{i+1} = \mathbf{w}_i + \mu g(\mathbf{u}_i)\mathbf{u}_i^{\mathrm{H}} f(e_i, e_i^*), \tag{1}$$

[1] Similar notations can be used for $f_{x,x}^{(2)}(a,b)$ and $f_{y,y}^{(2)}(a,b)$.

[2] If e is complex-valued, the estimation error function $f(e,e^*)$ has two independent variables: e and e^*. In addition, due to $e = e^*$, $f(e,e^*)$ can be replaced by $f(e)$ if e is real-valued. Here, we use the general form $f(e,e^*)$.

$$e_i = d_i - \mathbf{u}_i \mathbf{w}_i , \tag{2}$$

$$d_i = \mathbf{u}_i \mathbf{w}_{o,i} + v_i , \tag{3}$$

where

μ step-size;

H conjugate and transpose;

e_i scalar-valued error signal;

$\mathbf{u}_i$ $(1 \times M)$ row input (regressor) vector;

$\mathbf{w}_i$ $(M \times 1)$ weight vector;

d_i scalar-valued noisy measurement;

$g(\mathbf{u}_i)$ scalar variable factor for step-size.

$\mathbf{w}_{o,i}$ $(M \times 1)$ unknown column vector at constant *i* that we wish to estimate;

v_i accounts for both measurement noise and modeling errors, whose support region is D_v.

$f(e_i, e_i^*)$ memoryless nonlinearity function acting upon the error e_i and its complex conjugate e_i^*. Different choices for $f(e_i, e_i^*)$ result in different adaptive algorithms. For example, Table 1 defines $f(e_i, e_i^*)$ for many well-known special cases of (1) [10]-[12].

The rest of the paper is organized as follows. In the next section, the steady-state performances for complex and real adaptive filters are derived, which are summarized in Theorem 1 based on separation principle and Theorem 2 for white Gaussian regressor, respectively. In section 3, based on Theorem 1 and Theorem 2, the steady-state performances for the real and complex least-mean *p*-power norm (LMP) algorithm, LMMN algorithm and their normalized algorithms, are investigated, respectively. Simulation results are given in Section 4, and conclusions are drawn in Section 5.

Algorithms	Estimation errors
LMP	$\lvert e_i \rvert^{p-2} e_i$
LMMN	$e_i\left(\delta + (1-\delta)\lvert e_i \rvert^2\right)$
ε - NLMP	$\lvert e_i \rvert^{p-2} e_i \Big/ \left(\varepsilon + \lVert \mathbf{u} \rVert^2\right)$
ε - LMMN	$e_i\left(\delta + (1-\delta)\lvert e_i \rvert^2\right) \Big/ \left(\varepsilon + \lVert \mathbf{u} \rVert^2\right)$

Notes:

1. The parameter p is the order of the cost function of LMP algorithm, which includes LMS ($p = 2$), LMF ($p = 4$) algorithms.
2. The parameter δ, such that $0 \le \delta \le 1$, is the mixing paramter of LMMN algorithms. $\delta = 1$ results in the LMS algorithm and $\delta = 0$ results in the LMF algorithm.
3. The parameter ε of ε - NLMP algorithm or ε - LMMN algorithm is a small positive real value.

Table 1. Examples for the estimation error

2. Steady-state performance analyses

Define so-call *a priori* estimation error $e_a(i) = \mathbf{u}_i \tilde{\mathbf{w}}_i$, where $\tilde{\mathbf{w}}_i = \mathbf{w}_{o,i} - \mathbf{w}_i$ is the weight-error vector. Then, under (2) and (3), the relation between e_i and $e_a(i)$ can be expressed as

$$e_i = e_a(i) + v_i . \tag{4}$$

The steady-state MSE for an adaptive filter can be written as $\zeta_{MSE} = \lim_{i\to\infty} \mathrm{E}|e_i|^2$. To get ζ_{MSE}, we restrict the development of statistical adaptive algorithm to a small step-size, long filter length, an appropriate initial conditions of the weights and finite input power and noise variance in much of what follows[3], which is embodied in the following two assumptions:

A.1: The noise sequence $\{v_i\}$ with zero-mean and variance σ_v^2 is independent identically distributed (i.i.d.) and statistically independent of the regressor sequence $\{\mathbf{u}_i\}$.

A.2: The a priori estimation error $e_a(i)$ with zero-mean is independent of v_i. And for complex-valued cases, it satisfies the circularity condition, namely, $\mathrm{E}e_a^2(i) = 0$.

The above assumptions are popular, which are commonly used in the steady-state performance analyses for most of adaptive algorithms [11]-[14]. Then, under A.1 and A.2, the steady-state MSE can be written as $\zeta_{MSE} = \sigma_v^2 + \zeta$, where ζ is the steady-state EMSE, defined by

$$\zeta = \lim_{i\to\infty} \mathrm{E}|e_a(i)|^2 . \tag{5}$$

That is to say, getting ζ is equivalent to getting the MSE.

A first-order random-walk model is widely used to get the tracking performance in nonstationary environments [11], [12], which assumes that $\mathbf{w}_{o,i}$ appearing in (3) undergoes random variations of the form

$$\mathbf{w}_{o,i+1} = \mathbf{w}_{o,i} + \mathbf{q}_i , \tag{6}$$

where $\mathbf{q}_i$ is $(M\times 1)$ column vector and denotes some random perturbation.

A.3: The stationary sequence $\{\mathbf{q}_i\}$ is i.i.d., zero-mean, with $(M\times M)$ covariance matrix $\mathrm{E}\left(\mathbf{q}_i\mathbf{q}_i^{\mathrm{H}}\right) = \mathbf{Q}$, which is independent of the regressor sequences $\{\mathbf{u}_i\}$ and weight-error vector $\tilde{\mathbf{w}}_i$.

In stationary environments, the iteration equation of (6) becomes $\mathbf{w}_{o,i+1} = \mathbf{w}_{o,i}$, i.e., $\mathbf{w}_{o,i}$ does not change during the iteration because of $\{\mathbf{q}_i\}$ being a zero sequence. Here, the covariance matrix of $\{\mathbf{q}_i\}$ becomes $\mathrm{E}\left(\mathbf{q}_i\mathbf{q}_i^{\mathrm{H}}\right) = \mathbf{0}$, where $\mathbf{0}$ is a $(M\times M)$ zero matrix.

Substituting (6) and the definition of $\tilde{\mathbf{w}}_i$ into (1), we get the following update

$$\tilde{\mathbf{w}}_{i+1} = \tilde{\mathbf{w}}_i - \mu g(\mathbf{u}_i)\mathbf{u}_i^{\mathrm{H}} f\left(e_i, e_i^*\right) + \mathbf{q}_i \tag{7}$$

By evaluating the energies of both sides of the above equation, we obtain

$$\begin{aligned} \|\tilde{\mathbf{w}}_{i+1}\|^2 &= \|\tilde{\mathbf{w}}_i\|^2 - \mu\tilde{\mathbf{w}}_i^{\mathrm{H}}\mathbf{u}_i^{\mathrm{H}} g(\mathbf{u}_i) f\left(e_i, e_i^*\right) - \mu\mathbf{u}_i\tilde{\mathbf{w}}_i g^*(\mathbf{u}_i) f^*\left(e_i, e_i^*\right) \\ &+ \mu^2\|\mathbf{u}_i\|^2 |g(\mathbf{u}_i)|^2 \left|f\left(e_i, e_i^*\right)\right|^2 + \tilde{\mathbf{w}}_i^{\mathrm{H}}\mathbf{q}_i + \mathbf{q}_i^{\mathrm{H}}\tilde{\mathbf{w}}_i - \mu\mathbf{q}_i^{\mathrm{H}}\mathbf{u}_i^{\mathrm{H}} g(\mathbf{u}_i) f\left(e_i, e_i^*\right) \\ &- \mu\mathbf{u}_i\mathbf{q}_i g^*(\mathbf{u}_i) f^*\left(e_i, e_i^*\right) + \|\mathbf{q}_i\|^2 \end{aligned} \tag{8}$$

[3] As described in [25] and [26], the convergence or stability condition of an adaptive filter with error nonlinearity is related to the initial conditions of the weights, the step size, filter length, input power and noise variance. Since our works mainly focus on the steady-state performances of adaptive filters, the above conditions are assumed to be satisfied.

Taking expectations on both sides of the above equation and using A.3 and $e_a(i)=\mathbf{u}_i\tilde{\mathbf{w}}_i$, we get

$$\begin{aligned}\mathrm{E}\|\tilde{\mathbf{w}}_{i+1}\|^2 &= \mathrm{E}\|\tilde{\mathbf{w}}_i\|^2-\mu\mathrm{E}\left[e_a^*(i)g(\mathbf{u}_i)f(e_i,e_i^*)\right]-\mu\mathrm{E}\left[e_a(i)g^*(\mathbf{u}_i)f^*(e_i,e_i^*)\right]\\ &+\mu^2\mathrm{E}\left[\|\mathbf{u}_i\|^2\|g(\mathbf{u}_i)\|^2 f(e_i,e_i^*)|^2\right]+\mathrm{E}\|\mathbf{q}_i\|^2\end{aligned} \qquad (9)$$

At steady state, the adaptive filters hold $\lim_{i\to\infty}\mathrm{E}\|\tilde{\mathbf{w}}_{i+1}\|^2=\lim_{i\to\infty}\mathrm{E}\|\tilde{\mathbf{w}}_i\|^2$ [11], [12]. Then, the variance relation equation (9) can be rewritten compactly as

$$2\mathrm{Re}\,\mathrm{E}\left[e_a^*g(\mathbf{u})f(e,e^*)\right]=\mu\mathrm{E}\left[\|\mathbf{u}\|^2|g(\mathbf{u})|^2|f(e,e^*)|^2\right]+\mu^{-1}\mathrm{Tr}(\mathbf{Q}). \qquad (10)$$

where $\mathrm{Tr}(\mathbf{Q})=\mathrm{E}\|\mathbf{q}_i\|^2$, and the time index '*i*' has been omitted for the easy of reading. Specially, in stationary environments, the second term in the light-hand side of (10) will be removed since $\{\mathbf{q}_i\}$ is a zero sequence (i.e., $\mathrm{Tr}(\mathbf{Q})=0$).

2.1 Separation principle

At steady-state, since the behavior of e_a in the limit is likely to be less sensitive to the input data when the adaptive filter is long enough, the following assumption can be used to obtain the steady-state EMSE for adaptive filters, i.e.,
A.4: $\|\mathbf{u}\|^2$ and $g(\mathbf{u})$ are independent of e_a.
This assumption is referred to as the *separation principle* in [11]. Under the assumptions A.2 and A.4, and using (4), we can rewrite (10) as

$$\alpha_u\mathrm{E}\varphi(e,e^*)=\mu\beta_u\mathrm{E}q(e,e^*)+\mu^{-1}\mathrm{Tr}(\mathbf{Q}) \qquad (11)$$

where

$$\begin{aligned}&\alpha_u=\mathrm{E}g(\mathbf{u}),\quad \beta_u=\mathrm{E}\left[\|\mathbf{u}\|^2|g(\mathbf{u})|^2\right]\\ &\varphi(e,e^*)=2\mathrm{Re}\left[e_a^*f(e,e^*)\right],\quad q(e,e^*)=|f(e,e^*)|^2\end{aligned} \qquad (12)$$

Lemma 1 If e is complex-valued, and $\phi(e,e^*)$ and $q(e,e^*)$ are defined by (12), then[4]

$$\begin{aligned}&\varphi(v,v^*)=0,\quad \varphi^{(2)}_{e,e^*}(v,v^*)=2\mathrm{Re}\,f_e^{(1)}(v,v^*),\quad q^{(2)}_{e,e^*}(v,v^*)=\left|f_e^{(1)}(v,v^*)\right|^2\\ &+\left|f_{e^*}^{(1)}(v,v^*)\right|^2+2\mathrm{Re}\left[f^*(v,v^*)f^{(2)}_{e,e^*}(v,v^*)\right]\end{aligned} \qquad (13)$$

The proofs of Lemma 1 and all subsequent lemmas in this paper are given in the APPENDIXS.

---

[4] Since e and e^* are assumed to be two independent variables, all $f(e,e^*)$ in Table 1 can be considered as a 'real' function with respect to e and e^*, although $f(e,e^*)$ may be complex-valued. Then, the accustomed rules of derivative with respect to two variables e and e^* can be used directly.

Lemma 2 If e is real-valued, and $\varphi(e)$ and $q(e)$ are defined by (12)[5], then

$$\varphi(v)=0,\quad \varphi_{e,e}^{(2)}(v)=4f_e^{(1)}(v),\quad q_{e,e}^{(2)}(v)=2\left|f_e^{(1)}(v)\right|^2+2f(v)f_{e,e}^{(2)}(v). \tag{14}$$

Theorem 1—Steady-state performance for adaptive filters by separation principle: Consider adaptive filters of the form (1) - (3), and suppose the assumptions A.1-A.4 are satisfied and $f(e,e^*)\in C^2(D_v)$. Then, if the following condition is satisfied, i.e.,
C.1 $A\alpha_u > \mu B\beta_u$,
the steady-state EMSE (ζ_{EMSE}), tracking EMSE (ζ_{TEMSE}), and the optimal step-size (μ_{opt}) for adaptive filters can be approximated by

$$\zeta_{EMSE}=\frac{\mu C\beta_u}{A\alpha_u-\mu B\beta_u} \tag{15}$$

$$\zeta_{TEMSE}=\frac{\mu^{-1}\mathrm{Tr}(\mathbf{Q})+\mu C\beta_u}{A\alpha_u-\mu B\beta_u} \tag{16}$$

$$\mu_{opt}=\sqrt{\left[\frac{B\mathrm{Tr}(\mathbf{Q})}{AC\alpha_u}\right]^2+\frac{\mathrm{Tr}(\mathbf{Q})}{C\beta_u}}-\frac{B\mathrm{Tr}(\mathbf{Q})}{AC\alpha_u} \tag{17}$$

where

$$\begin{aligned}&A=2\mathrm{Re}\,\mathrm{E}f_e^{(1)}(v,v^*),\quad B=\mathrm{E}\left\{\left|f_e^{(1)}(v,v^*)\right|^2+\left|f_{e^*}^{(1)}(v,v^*)\right|^2+2\mathrm{Re}\left[f^*(v,v^*)f_{e,e^*}^{(2)}(v,v^*)\right]\right\},\\&C=\mathrm{E}\left|f(v,v^*)\right|^2\end{aligned} \tag{18a}$$

for complex-valued data cases, and

$$A=2\mathrm{E}f_e^{(1)}(v),\quad B=\mathrm{E}\left|f_e^{(1)}(v)\right|^2+\mathrm{E}\left[f(v)f_{e,e}^{(2)}(v)\right],\quad C=\mathrm{E}\left|f(v)\right|^2 \tag{18b}$$

for real-valued data cases, respectively.
Proof:
First, we consider the complex-valued cases. The complex BSE of the function $\varphi(e,e^*)$ with respect to (e,e^*) around (v,v^*) can be written as [19]-[22]

$$\begin{aligned}\varphi(e,e^*)&=\varphi(v,v^*)+\varphi_e^{(1)}(v,v^*)e_a+\varphi_{e^*}^{(1)}(v,v^*)e_a^*\\&+\frac{1}{2}\left[\varphi_{e,e}^{(2)}(v,v^*)e_a^2+\varphi_{e^*,e^*}^{(2)}(v,v^*)\left(e_a^*\right)^2+2\varphi_{e,e^*}^{(2)}(v,v^*)\left|e_a\right|^2\right]+\mathbf{O}(e_a,e_a^*)\end{aligned} \tag{19}$$

[5] In real-valued cases, $f(e,e^*)$ can be simplified to $f(e)$ since $e=e^*$, and $\varphi(e,e^*)$ and $q(e,e^*)$ can also be replaced by their simplified forms $\varphi(e)$ and $q(e)$, respectively.

where $\mathbf{O}(e_a, e_a^*)$ denotes third and higher-power terms of e_a or e_a^*. Ignoring $\mathbf{O}(e_a, e_a^*)$ [6], and taking expectations of both sides of the above equation, we get

$$\begin{aligned}\mathrm{E}\varphi(e,e^*) &= \mathrm{E}\varphi(v,v^*) + \mathrm{E}\left[\varphi_e^{(1)}(v,v^*)e_a\right] + \mathrm{E}\left[\varphi_{e^*}^{(1)}(v,v^*)e_a^*\right] \\ &+ \frac{1}{2}\mathrm{E}\left[\varphi_{e,e}^{(2)}(v,v^*)e_a^2\right] + \frac{1}{2}\mathrm{E}\left[\varphi_{e^*,e^*}^{(2)}(v,v^*)(e_a^*)^2\right] + \mathrm{E}\left[\varphi_{e,e^*}^{(2)}(v,v^*)|e_a|^2\right]\end{aligned} \quad (20)$$

Under A.2, (i.e. $\{v, e_a\}$ are mutually independent, and $\mathrm{E}e_a = \mathrm{E}e_a^2 = 0$), we obtain

$$\mathrm{E}\varphi(e,e^*) = \mathrm{E}\varphi(v,v^*) + \mathrm{E}\varphi_{e,e^*}^{(2)}(v,v^*)\zeta_{TEMSE} \quad (21)$$

where ζ_{TEMSE} is defined by (5). Here, to distinguish two kinds of steady-state EMSE, we use different subscripts for ζ, i.e., ζ_{EMSE} for steady-state MSE and ζ_{TEMSE} for tracking performance. Similarly, replacing $\varphi(e,e^*)$ in (20) by $q(e,e^*)$ and using A.2, we get

$$\mathrm{E}q(e,e^*) = \mathrm{E}q(v,v^*) + \mathrm{E}q_{e,e^*}^{(2)}(v,v^*)\zeta_{TEMSE}\,. \quad (22)$$

Substituting (21) and (22) into (11) yields

$$\left[\alpha_u \mathrm{E}\varphi_{e,e^*}^{(2)}(v,v^*) - \mu\beta_u \mathrm{E}q_{e,e^*}^{(2)}(v,v^*)\right]\zeta_{TEMSE} = \alpha_u \mathrm{E}\varphi(v,v^*) + \mu\beta_u \mathrm{E}q(v,v^*) + \mu^{-1}\mathrm{Tr}(\mathbf{Q})\,. \quad (23)$$

Under Lemma 1, the above equation can be rewritten as

$$[A\alpha_u - \mu B\beta_u]\zeta_{TEMSE} = \mu\beta_u C + \mu^{-1}\mathrm{Tr}(\mathbf{Q})\,. \quad (24)$$

where parameters A, B, C are defined by (18a). Since $\mu C\mathrm{Tr}(\mathbf{R}_u) \geq 0$, $\mu^{-1}\mathrm{Tr}(\mathbf{Q}) \geq 0$, and $\zeta_{TEMSE} \geq 0$, if the condition C.1 is satisfied[7], i.e., $A\alpha_u > \mu B\beta_u$, removing the coefficient of ζ_{TEMSE} in (24) to the right-hand side, we can obtain (16) for the tracking EMSE in nonstationary environments in complex-valued cases.

Next, we consider the real-valued cases. The TSE of $\varphi(e)$ with respect to e around v can be written as

$$\varphi(e) = \varphi(v) + \varphi_e^{(1)}(v)e_a + \frac{1}{2}\varphi_{e,e}^{(2)}(v)e_a^2 + \mathbf{O}(e_a) \quad (25)$$

---

[6] At steady-state, since the *a priori* estimation error e_a becomes small if step size is small enough, ignoring $\mathbf{O}(e_a, e_a^*)$ is reasonable, which has been used in to analyze the steady-state performance for adaptive filters [11], [12], [19], [20].

[7] The restrictive condition C.1 can be used to check whether the expressions (15) - (17) are able to be used for a special case of adaptive filters. In the latter analyses, we will show that C.1 is not always satisfied for all kinds of adaptive filters. In addition, due to the influences of the initial conditions of the weights, step size, filter length, input power, noise variance and the residual terms $\mathrm{O}(e_a, e_a^*)$ having been ignored during the previous processes, C.1 can not be a strict mean square stability condition for an adaptive filter with error nonlinearity.

where $O(e_a)$ denotes third and higher-power terms of e_a. Neglecting $O(e_a)$ and taking expectations of both sides of (25) yields

$$\mathrm{E}\varphi(e) = \mathrm{E}\varphi(v) + \mathrm{E}\left[\varphi_e^{(1)}(v)e_a\right] + \frac{1}{2}\mathrm{E}\left[\varphi_{e,e}^{(2)}(v)e_a^2\right] \tag{26}$$

Under A.2, we get

$$\mathrm{E}\varphi(e) = \mathrm{E}\varphi(v) + \frac{1}{2}\mathrm{E}\varphi_{e,e}^{(2)}(v)\zeta_{TEMSE} \tag{27}$$

where ζ_{TEMSE} is defined by (5). Similarly, replacing $\varphi(e)$ in (26) by $q(e)$ and using A.2, we get

$$\mathrm{E}q(e) = \mathrm{E}q(v) + \frac{1}{2}\mathrm{E}q_{e,e}^{(2)}(v)\zeta_{TEMSE} \tag{28}$$

Substituting (27) and (28) into (11), and using Lemma 2, we can obtain (24), where parameters A, B, C are defined by (18b). Then, if the condition C.1 is satisfied, we can obtain (16) for real-valued cases.

In stationary environments, letting $\mathrm{Tr}(\mathbf{Q}) = 0$ in (16), we can obtain (15) for the steady-state EMSE, i.e., ζ_{EMSE}.

Finally, Differentiating both-hand sides of (16) with respect to μ, and letting it be zero, we get

$$\left.\frac{\partial}{\partial\mu}\zeta_{TEMSE}\right|_{\mu=\mu_{opt}} = \frac{\partial}{\partial\mu}\left[\frac{\mu^{-1}\mathrm{Tr}(\mathbf{Q}) + \mu C\beta_u}{A\alpha_u - \mu B\beta_u}\right]_{\mu=\mu_{opt}} = 0 . \tag{29}$$

Simplifying the above equation, we get

$$\mu_{opt}^2 + \frac{2B\mathrm{Tr}(\mathbf{Q})}{A\alpha_u C}\mu_{opt} - \frac{\mathrm{Tr}(\mathbf{Q})}{C\beta_u} = 0 . \tag{30}$$

Solving the above equality, we can obtain the optimum step-size expressed by (17). Here, we use the fact $\mu > 0$. This ends the proof of Theorem 1.

Remarks:

1. Substituting (17) into (16) yields the minimum steady-state TEMSE.
2. Observing from (18), we can find that the steady-state expressions of (15) ~ (17) are all second-order approximate.
3. In view of the step-size μ being very small, $\mu B\beta_u << A\alpha_u$, and the expressions (15) ~ (17) can be simplified to

$$\zeta_{EMSE} = \frac{\mu\beta_u C}{A\alpha_u}, \tag{31}$$

$$\zeta_{TEMSE} = \frac{\mu^{-1}\mathrm{Tr}(\mathbf{Q}) + \mu C\beta_u}{A\alpha_u}, \tag{32}$$

$$\mu_{opt} = \sqrt{\frac{\mathrm{Tr}(\mathbf{Q})}{C\beta_u}} \tag{33}$$

Substituting (33) into (32) yields the minimum steady-state TEMSE

$$\zeta_{\min} = \frac{2}{A\alpha_u}\sqrt{C\beta_u \mathrm{Tr}(\mathbf{Q})}\,. \tag{34}$$

In addition, since $\mu B\beta_u$ in the denominator of (15) has been ignored, C.1 can be simplified to $A > 0$, namely $\mathrm{Re}\,\mathrm{E}f_e^{(1)}(v,v^*) > 0$ for complex-valued data cases, and $\mathrm{E}f_e^{(1)}(v) > 0$ for real-valued data cases, respectively. Here, the existing condition of the second-order partial derivative of $f(e,e^*)$ can be weakened, i.e., $f(e,e^*) \in C^1(D_v)$.

4. For fixed step-size cases, substituting $g(\mathbf{u}) = 1$ into (12), we get

$$\alpha_u = 1, \beta_u = \mathrm{E}\|\mathbf{u}\|^2 = \mathrm{Tr}(\mathbf{R}_u)\,. \tag{35}$$

Substituting (35) into (31) yields $\zeta_{EMSE} = \mu C \mathrm{Tr}(\mathbf{R}_u)/A$. For the real-valued cases, this expression is the same as the one derived by S. C. Douglas and T. H.-Y. Meng in [10] (see e.g. Eq. 35). That is to say, Eq. 35 in [10] is a special case of (15) with small step-size, $g(\mathbf{u}) = 1$, and real-valued data.

2.2 White Gaussian regressor

Consider $g(\mathbf{u}_i) = 1$, and let M-dimensions regressor vector $\mathbf{u}$ have a circular Gaussian distribution with a diagonal covariance matrix, namely,

$$\mathbf{R}_u = \sigma_u^2 \mathbf{I}_{M\times M}\,. \tag{36}$$

Under the following assumption (see e.g. 6.5.13) in [11] at steady state, i.e.,

A.5 $\tilde{\mathbf{w}}$ *is independence of* $\mathbf{u}$,

the term $\mathrm{E}\left[\|\mathbf{u}\|^2 q(e,e^*)\right]$ that appears in the right-hand side of (10) can be evaluated explicitly without appealing to the separation assumption (e.g. A.4), and its steady-state EMSE for adaptive filters can be obtained by the following theorem.

Theorem 2 —Steady-state performance for adaptive filters with white Gaussian regressor: Consider adaptive filters of the form (1) - (3) with white Gaussian regressor and $g(\mathbf{u}_i) = 1$, and suppose the assumptions A.1 - A.3, and A.5 are satisfied. In addition, $f(e,e^*) \in C^2(D_v)$. Then, if the following condition is satisfied, i.e.,

C.2 $A > \mu B(M+\gamma)\sigma_u^2$,

the steady-state EMSE, TEMSE and the optimal step-size for adaptive filters can be approximated by

$$\zeta_{EMSE} = \frac{\mu C M \sigma_u^2}{A - \mu B(M+\gamma)\sigma_u^2}, \tag{37}$$

$$\zeta_{TEMSE} = \frac{\mu^{-1}\mathrm{Tr}(\mathbf{Q}) + \mu M C \sigma_u^2}{A - \mu B(M+\gamma)\sigma_u^2}, \tag{38}$$

$$\mu_{opt} = \sqrt{\left[\frac{B(M+\gamma)\mathrm{Tr}(Q)}{AMC}\right]^2 + \frac{\mathrm{Tr}(\mathbf{Q})}{MC\sigma_u^2}} - \frac{B(M+\gamma)\mathrm{Tr}(\mathbf{Q})}{AMC}, \tag{39}$$

where $\gamma = 1$, *A*, *B* and *C* are defined by (18a) for complex-valued data, and $\gamma = 2$, *A*, *B* and *C* are defined by (18b) for real-valued data, respectively.
The proofs of Theorem 2 is given in the APPENDIX D.
For the case of μ being small enough, the steady-state EMSE, TEMSE, the optimal step-size, and the minimum TEMSE can be expressed by (31) ~ (33), respectively, if we replace $\mathrm{Tr}(\mathbf{R}_u)$ by $M\sigma_u^2$ and $g(\mathbf{u}_i) = 1$. That is to say, when the input vector $\mathbf{u}$ is Gaussian with a diagonal covariance matrix (36), the steady-state performance result obtained by separation principle coincides with that under A.5 for the case of μ being small enough.

3. Steady-state performance for some special cases of adaptive filters

In this section, based on Theorem 1 and Theorem 2 in Section II, we will investigate the steady-state performances for LMP algorithm with different choices of parameter *p*, LMMN algorithm, and their normalized algorithms, respectively. To begin our analysis, we first introduce a lemma for the derivative operation about a complex variable.
Lemma 3: Let z be a complex variable and p be an arbitrary real constant number except zero, then

$$\frac{\partial}{\partial z}|z|^p = \frac{p}{2}|z|^{p-2} z^*,$$
$$\frac{\partial}{\partial z^*}|z|^p = \frac{p}{2}|z|^{p-2} z$$

3.1 LMP algorithm

The estimation error signal of LMP algorithm can be expressed as [23]

$$f(e,e^*) = |e|^{p-2} e = (ee^*)^{(p-2)/2} e \tag{40}$$

where $p > 0$ is a positive integral. $p = 2$ results in well-known LMS algorithm, and $p = 4$ results in LMF algorithm. Here, we only consider $p \ge 2$.
Using (40) and Lemma 3, we can obtain the first-order and second-order partial derivatives of $f(e,e^*)$, expressed by

$$\begin{aligned} f_e^{(1)}(e) &= (p-1)|e|^{p-2} \\ f_{e,e}^{(2)}(e) &= (p-1)(p-2)|e|^{p-4} e \end{aligned} \tag{41a}$$

in real-valued cases, and

$$\begin{aligned} f_e^{(1)}(e,e^*) &= \frac{p}{2}|e|^{p-2} \\ f_{e^*}^{(1)}(e,e^*) &= \frac{p-2}{2}|e|^{p-4} e^2 \\ f_{e,e^*}^{(2)}(e,e^*) &= \frac{p(p-2)}{4}|e|^{p-4} e \end{aligned} \tag{41b}$$

in complex-valued cases, respectively. Substituting (41) into (18a) and (42) into (18b), respectively, we get

$$\begin{aligned} A &= a\xi_v^{p-2} \\ B &= b\xi_v^{2p-4} \\ C &= \xi_v^{2p-2} \end{aligned} \tag{42}$$

where $\xi_v^k = \mathrm{E}|v|^k$ denote the k-order absolute moment of v, and

$$\begin{aligned} &a = 2(p-1),\ b = (p-1)(2p-3) \quad \text{real-valued cases} \\ &a = p,\ b = (p-1)^2 \quad \text{complex-valued cases} \end{aligned} \tag{43}$$

Then, under Theorem 1, the condition C.1 becomes

$$\xi_v^{p-2} > \frac{\mu b \beta_u}{a\alpha_u}\xi_v^{2(p-2)}, \tag{44}$$

and the steady-state performance for real LMP algorithms can be written as

$$\zeta_{EMSE} = \frac{\mu\beta_u\xi_v^{2p-2}}{a\alpha_u\xi_v^{p-2} - \mu b\beta_u\xi_v^{2(p-2)}}. \tag{45a}$$

$$\zeta_{TEMSE} = \frac{\mu\beta_u\xi_v^{2p-2} + \mu^{-1}\mathrm{Tr}(\mathbf{Q})}{a\alpha_u\xi_v^{p-2} - \mu b\beta_u\xi_v^{2(p-2)}} \tag{45b}$$

$$\mu_{opt} = -\frac{b\xi_v^{2p-4}\mathrm{Tr}(\mathbf{Q})}{a\xi_v^{p-2}\xi_v^{2p-2}\alpha_u} + \sqrt{\left[\frac{b\xi_v^{2p-4}\mathrm{Tr}(\mathbf{Q})}{a\xi_v^{p-2}\xi_v^{2p-2}\alpha_u}\right]^2 + \frac{\mathrm{Tr}(\mathbf{Q})}{\xi_v^{2p-2}\beta_u}}. \tag{45c}$$

Similarly, substituting (42) into Theorem 2, we can also obtain the corresponding expressions for the steady-state performance of LMP algorithms with white Gaussian regressor.

Example 1: For LMS algorithm, substituting $p = 2$ and (35) into (45a) ~ (45c), and substituting (42) and $p = 2$ into Theorem 2, yield the same steady-state performance results (see e.g. Lemma 6.5.1 and Lemma 7.5.1) in [11]. For LMF algorithm, substituting $p = 4$ and (34) into (45a) ~ (45c), and substituting (42) and $p = 4$ into Theorem 2, yield the same steady-state performance results (see e.g. Lemma 6.8.1 and Lemma 7.8.1 with $\delta = 0$ [8]) in [11]. That is to say, the results of Lemma 6.5.1, Lemma 7.5.1, Lemma 6.8.1 and Lemma 7.8.1 in [11] are all second-order approximate.

Example 2: Consider the real-valued data in Gaussian noise environments. Based on the following formula, described in [23]

---

[8] The parameters a,b,c in (44)-(45) are different from those in Lemma 6.8.1 and Lemma 7.8.1 in [11].

$$\xi_v^k = \begin{cases} (k-1)!!\sigma_v^k & k\text{:even} \\ \sqrt{\frac{2^k}{\pi}}\left(\frac{k-1}{2}\right)!\sigma_v^k & k\text{:odd} \end{cases}, \tag{46}$$

where $(k-1)!! = 1\cdot3\cdot5\cdots(k-1)$, (42) becomes

$$\left.\begin{aligned} A &= 2(p-1)(p-3)!!\sigma_v^{p-2} \\ B &= (p-1)(2p-3)!!\sigma_v^{2p-4} \\ C &= (2p-3)!!\sigma_v^{2p-2} \end{aligned}\right\} \quad p\text{: even}$$
$$\left.\begin{aligned} A &= \sqrt{2^p/\pi}(p-1)\left[(p-3)/2\right]!\sigma_v^{p-2} \\ B &= (p-1)(2p-3)!!\sigma_v^{2p-4} \\ C &= (2p-3)!!\sigma_v^{2p-2} \end{aligned}\right\} \quad p\text{: odd} \quad . \tag{47}$$

Then, substituting (47) into Theorem 1 and Theorem 2 or substituting (46) into (45a) - (45c), yield the steady-state performance results for real LMP algorithm in Gaussian noise environments. Here, we only give the expression for EMSE

$$\zeta_{EMSE} = \begin{cases} \dfrac{\mu(2p-3)!!\sigma_v^p\beta_u}{2(p-1)(p-3)!!\alpha_u - \mu(p-1)(2p-3)!!\sigma_v^{p-2}\beta_u}, & p\text{:even} \\ \dfrac{\mu(2p-3)!!\sigma_v^p\beta_u}{\sqrt{\frac{2^p}{\pi}}(p-1)\left(\frac{p-3}{2}\right)!\alpha_u - \mu(p-1)(2p-3)!!\sigma_v^{p-2}\beta_u}, & p\text{:odd} \end{cases}. \tag{48}$$

The above expression is also applicable for LMS algorithm by means of $(-1)!! = 1$.

Example 3: Consider the real-valued data in uniformly distributed noise environments, whose interval is $[-\Delta, \Delta]$ and k-order absolute moment can be written as

$$\xi_v^k = \frac{\Delta^k}{k+1}. \tag{49}$$

Substituting the above equation into (42), we get

$$\begin{aligned} A &= 2\Delta^{p-2} \\ B &= (p-1)\Delta^{2p-4} \\ C &= \frac{\Delta^{2p-2}}{2p-1} \end{aligned}. \tag{50}$$

Then, substituting (50) into Theorem 1 and Theorem 2 yields the steady-state performance for real LMP algorithm in uniformly distributed noise environments. Here, we also only give the EMSE expression, expressed by

$$\zeta_{EMSE} = \frac{\mu\Delta^p \beta_u}{2(2p-1)\alpha_u - \mu(2p-1)(p-1)\Delta^{p-2}\beta_u}. \tag{51}$$

Example 4: In complex Gaussian noise environments, using the following formula, summarized from [24]

$$\xi_v^k = \mathrm{E}|v|^k = \begin{cases} \frac{k}{2}!\sigma_v^k & k\text{:even} \\ 0 & k\text{:odd} \end{cases}, \tag{52}$$

(42) becomes

$$\begin{aligned} A &= p\left(\frac{p-2}{2}\right)!\sigma_v^{p-2} \\ B &= (p-1)(p-1)!\sigma_v^{2p-4}. \\ C &= (p-1)!\sigma_v^{2p-2}, \end{aligned} \tag{53}$$

for even p. Then, substituting (53) into Theorem 1 and Theorem 2 or substituting (52) into (45a) ~ (45c), we can obtain the steady-state performances for complex LMP algorithms with even p in Gaussian noise environments. For instance, the EMSE expression can be written as

$$\zeta_{EMSE} = \frac{\mu(p-1)!\sigma_v^p \beta_u}{p\left(\frac{p-2}{2}\right)!\alpha_u - \mu(p-1)(p-1)!\sigma_v^{p-2}\beta_u}. \tag{54}$$

But for odd p, substituting (40) and (52) into (18a) yields $A = 0$, which leads to the conditions C.1 and C.2 being not satisfied again. That is to say, the proposed theorems are unsuitable to analyze the steady-state performances in this case.

Example 5: Tracking performance comparison with LMS

We now compare the ability of the LMP algorithm with $p > 2$ to track variations in nonstationary environments with that of the LMS algorithm. The ratio of the minimum achievable steady-state EMSE of each of the LMS algorithm is used as a performance measure. In addition, the step-size of this minimum value is often sufficient small, which leads to that (34) can be used directly. Substituting (42) into (34), we obtain the minimum TEMSE for LMP algorithm, expressed as

$$\zeta_{\min}^{LMP} = \gamma\frac{\sqrt{\xi_v^{2p-2}\beta_u \mathrm{Tr}(\mathbf{Q})}}{\alpha_u \xi_v^{p-2}}. \tag{55}$$

where $\gamma = 2/p$ for complex-valued cases, and $\gamma = 1/(p-1)$ for real-valued cases. Then the ratio between $\zeta_{\min}^{LMS} = \sigma_v\sqrt{\mathrm{Tr}(\mathbf{R}_u)\mathrm{Tr}(\mathbf{Q})}$ (which can be obtained by substituting $p = 2$ and (35) into (55)) and $\zeta_{\min}^{LMP}$ can be written as

$$\frac{\zeta_{\min}^{LMS}}{\zeta_{\min}^{LMP}} = \frac{\alpha_u \xi_v^{p-2}\sigma_v\sqrt{\mathrm{Tr}(\mathbf{R}_u)}}{\gamma\sqrt{\beta_u \xi_v^{2p-2}}}. \tag{56}$$

For the case of LMF algorithm, substituting $p = 4$ and (35) into (56), we can obtain the same result (see e.g. Eq.7.9.1) in [11].

3.2 LMMN algorithm

The estimation error of the LMMN algorithm is [6], [7], [11], [12]

$$f\left(e,e^*\right) = e\left(\delta + \bar{\delta}|e|^2\right), \tag{57}$$

where $0 \le \delta \le 1$ and $\bar{\delta} = 1 - \delta$. $\delta = 1$ results in the LMS algorithm and $\delta = 0$ results in the LMF algorithm.
Using (57) and Lemma 3, we get

$$\begin{aligned} f_e^{(1)}\left(e,e^*\right) &= \delta + 2\bar{\delta}|e|^2 \\ f_{e^*}^{(1)}\left(e,e^*\right) &= \bar{\delta}|e|^2 \\ f_{e,e^*}^{(2)}\left(e,e^*\right) &= 2\bar{\delta}e \end{aligned} \tag{58a}$$

for complex-valued cases, and

$$\begin{aligned} f_e^{(1)}(e) &= \delta + 3\bar{\delta}e^2 \\ f_{e,e}^{(2)}(e) &= 6\bar{\delta}e \end{aligned}. \tag{58b}$$

for real-valued cases, respectively. Substituting (58a) into (18a), or substituting (58b) into (18b), respectively, we get

$$\begin{aligned} A &= 2\left(\delta + k_0\bar{\delta}\xi_v^2\right) \\ B &= \delta^2 + k_1\delta\bar{\delta}\xi_v^2 + k_2\bar{\delta}^2\xi_v^4 \\ C &= \delta^2\xi_v^2 + 2\delta\bar{\delta}\xi_v^4 + \bar{\delta}^2\xi_v^6 \end{aligned}. \tag{59}$$

where $k_0 = 3, k_1 = 12, k_2 = 15$ for real-valued cases $k_0 = 2, k_1 = 8, k_2 = 9$ for complex-valued cases. Then, under Theorem 1, the condition C.1 becomes

$$\alpha_u > \frac{\mu\beta_u\left(\delta^2 + k_1\delta\bar{\delta}\xi_v^2 + k_2\bar{\delta}^2\xi_v^4\right)}{2\left(\delta + k_0\bar{\delta}\xi_v^2\right)}, \tag{60}$$

and the steady-state performance for LMMN algorithms (here, we only give the expression for EMSE) can be written as

$$\zeta_{EMSE} = \frac{\mu\beta_u\left(\delta^2\xi_v^2 + 2\delta\bar{\delta}\xi_v^4 + \bar{\delta}^2\xi_v^6\right)}{2\left(\delta + k_0\bar{\delta}\xi_v^2\right)\alpha_u - \mu\beta_u\left(\delta^2 + k_1\delta\bar{\delta}\xi_v^2 + k_2\bar{\delta}^2\xi_v^4\right)}. \tag{61}$$

Example 6: Consider the cases with $g(\mathbf{u}) = 1$. Substituting (35) and $A = 2b`, C = a`, B = c`$ or $A = 2b, C = a, B = c$ into (15) - (17) yields the steady-state performances for real and complex

LMMN algorithms, which coincide with the results (see e.g. Lemma 6.8.1 and Lemma 7.8.1) in [11].

Example 7: In Gaussian noise environments, based on (46) and (52), we can obtain

$$\zeta_{EMSE} = \frac{\mu\beta_u\left(\delta^2\sigma_v^2 + k_3\delta\bar{\delta}\sigma_v^4 + k_4\bar{\delta}^2\sigma_v^6\right)}{2\left(\delta + k_0\bar{\delta}\sigma_v^2\right)\alpha_u - \mu\beta_u\left(\delta^2 + k_1\delta\bar{\delta}\sigma_v^2 + k_2\bar{\delta}^2\sigma_v^4\right)}. \quad (62)$$

where $k_0 = 3, k_1 = 12, k_2 = 45, k_3 = 6, k_4 = 15$ for real-valued cases, $k_0 = 2, k_1 = 8, k_2 = 18$, $k_3 = 4, k_4 = 6$ for complex-valued cases.

3.3 Normalized type algorithms

Being similar with LMF algorithm [25]-[27], there are the stability and convergence problems in the LMP algorithm with $p > 2$, LMMN algorithm, and other adaptive filters with error nonlinearities. In this subsection, ε-normalized method, extended from ε-normalized LMS (ε-NLMS) algorithm [11], will be introduced for the LMP algorithm and LMMN algorithm, which are so-called ε-NLMP algorithm and ε-NLMMN algorithm.

The estimation errors for ε-NLMP algorithm and ε-NLMMN algorithm are expressed by (40) and (57), respectively, and its variable factor for step-size can be written as

$$g(\mathbf{u}) = \frac{1}{\varepsilon + \|\mathbf{u}\|^2}. \quad (63)$$

Substituting (63) into (12), we get

$$\alpha_u = \mathrm{E}\left(\frac{1}{\varepsilon + \|\mathbf{u}\|^2}\right), \quad \beta_u = \mathrm{E}\left[\frac{\|\mathbf{u}\|^2}{\left(\varepsilon + \|\mathbf{u}\|^2\right)^2}\right]. \quad (64)$$

In general, $\varepsilon << \|\mathbf{u}\|^2$, so α_u equals to β_u, and can be expressed as

$$\alpha_u = \beta_u = \mathrm{E}\left(\frac{1}{\|\mathbf{u}\|^2}\right). \quad (65)$$

Substituting (65) into (15) yields a simplified expression for steady-state EMSE

$$\zeta_{EMSE} = \frac{\mu C}{A - \mu B} \quad (66)$$

Observing from the above equation, we can find that ζ_{EMSE} is no longer related to the regressor.

4. Simulation results

In section III, some well-known real and complex adaptive algorithms, such as LMS algorithm, LMF algorithm and LMMN algorithm have shown the accuracy of the corresponding analysis results. In this section, we will give the computer simulation for the steady-state performance of real LMP algorithm with odd parameter $p > 2$ (here $p = 3$), ε-NLMP and ε-NLMMN algorithms (here $\delta = 0.5$), which have not been involved in the previous literatures.

4.1 Simulation model

In all the cases, a 11-tap adaptive filter with tap-centered initialization is used. The data are generated according to model (3), the experimental value for different step-size is obtained by running adaptive algorithm for different iteration number and averaging the squares-error curve over 60 experiments in order to generate the ensemble-average curve. The average of the last 4×10^4 entries of the ensemble-average curve is then used as the experimental value for the MSE. The noise with variance $\sigma_v^2 = 0.001$ is used, which is generated as the following two models:

N.1 $\sigma_v \text{randn}(\ )$ is used in Gaussian noise environments;

N.2 $\sigma_v\left[-1+2\text{rand}(\ )\right]$ is used in uniformly distributed noise environments, whose distributed interval is $\left[-1,1\right]$, i.e. $\Delta = 1$.

Here, the function $\text{randn}(\ )$ is used to generate the normally distributed (Gaussian) sequence with zero mean and unit covariance in Matlab software, and $\text{rand}(\ )$ is used to generate the uniformly distributed sequence.

The regressors $\{\mathbf{u}_i\}$ are generated as the following two models.

M.1 The regressors $\{\mathbf{u}_i\}$ are generated as independent realizations of a Gaussian distribution with a covariance matrix $\mathbf{R}_u$ (a diagonal unit matrix).

M.2 The regressors $\{\mathbf{u}_i\}$ have shift structure, and are generated by feeding correlated data into a tapped delay time, which are expressed as [11]

$$u(i+1) = au(i) + \sqrt{1-a^2}s(i), \tag{67}$$

where $\mathbf{u}_i = \left[u(i), u(i-1), \cdots, u(i-L+1)\right]$, and $s(i)$ is a unit-variance i.i.d. Gaussian random process. Here, we set $a = 0.8$.

4.2 MSE and tracking performance simulation

Fig. 1 - Fig. 4 show the theoretical and simulated MSE curves for real LMP algorithm, Fig. 5 for real ε-NLMP algorithm, Fig. 6 for real ε-NLMMN algorithm, and Fig. 7 for complex ε-NLMMN algorithm. Fig. 8 ~ Fig. 11 show the theoretical and simulated tracking MSE curves for real LMP algorithm. The range of step-size are all set from 0.001 to 0.1 except for ε-NLMP algorithm, which is from 0.001 to 0.6. Other conditions (including the regressor model and the noise model) for these figures are shown in Table 2. In addition, Fig. 1, Fig. 2, Fig. 8 and Fig. 9 show two theoretical curves, one curve is plotted under Theorem 1, another under Theorem 2.

From these figures (Fig. 1 ~ Fig. 11), we can see that the simulation and theoretical results are matched reasonable well. Specially, as shown in Fig. 1, Fig. 2, Fig. 8, and Fig. 9, there is a marginal difference between the MSE values based on Theorem 1 and the values based on Theorem 2 for white Gaussian regressors. For the tracking performance, Fig. 8 ~ Fig.

11, whose corresponding σ_q are $\left(5\times10^{-5}, 1\times10^{-5}, 1\times10^{-5}, 1\times10^{-5}\right)$, where $Q=\sigma_q^2\mathbf{I}$, also show the optimal step-sizes, at which the steady-state MSE possess minimum values. These tracking figures show that these minimum values are in good agreement with the corresponding theoretical values, written by $(0.0283,\ 0.0074,\ 0.0058,\ 0.0074)$, respectively.

Figures	Regressor models	Noise models
Fig. 1	M.1	N.1
Fig. 2	M.1	N.2
Fig. 3	M.2	N.1
Fig. 4	M.2	N.2
Fig. 5	M.2	N.1
Fig. 6	M.2	N.1
Fig. 7	M.2	N.1
Fig. 8	M.1	N.1
Fig. 9	M.1	N.2
Fig. 10	M.2	N.1
Fig. 11	M.2	N.2

Table 2. Conditions for simulation examples

4.3 Tracking ability comparison with LMS algorithm

Consider the real-valued cases with $g(\mathbf{u}_i)=1$. Substituting (35), (46) and (49) into (56), we can obtain

$$\frac{\zeta_{\min}^{LMS}}{\zeta_{\min}^{LMP}}=\begin{cases}(p-3)!!(p-1)\Big/\sqrt{(2p-3)!!}\,, & p\text{:even}\\ \sqrt{\dfrac{2^{(p-2)}}{\pi}}\left(\dfrac{p-3}{2}\right)!(p-1)\Big/\sqrt{(2p-3)!!}\,, & p\text{:odd}\end{cases}. \tag{68}$$

in Gaussian noise environments, and

$$\frac{\zeta_{\min}^{LMS}}{\zeta_{\min}^{LMP}}=\frac{\sqrt{2p-1}}{\sqrt{3}}, \tag{69}$$

in uniformly distributed noise environments, respectively. Under different parameter p (from 2 to 6), Fig. 12 shows two curves for the ratio of $\zeta_{\min}^{LMS}/\zeta_{\min}^{LMP}$ (dB) in Gaussian noise environments and uniformly distributed noise environments. From the figure, we can observe that the superiority of the LMS algorithm over LMP with $p>2$ for tracking nonstationary systems in Gaussian noise environments ($\zeta_{\min}^{LMS}/\zeta_{\min}^{LMP}(\text{dB})<0$), and inferiority in uniformly distributed noise environments ($\zeta_{\min}^{LMS}/\zeta_{\min}^{LMP}(\text{dB})>0$). Similar analyses can be done for the complex-valued cases.

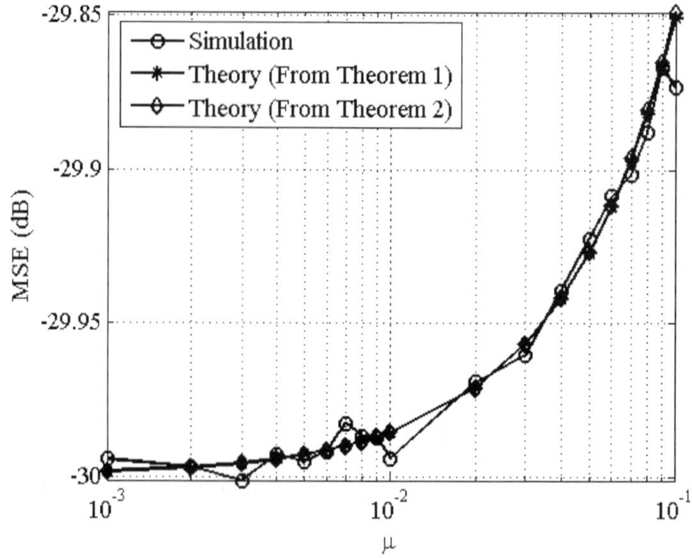

Fig. 1. Two theoretical (Theorem 1 and Theorem 2) and simulated MSEs for real LMP algorithm under the regressor model M.1 and the noise model N.1.

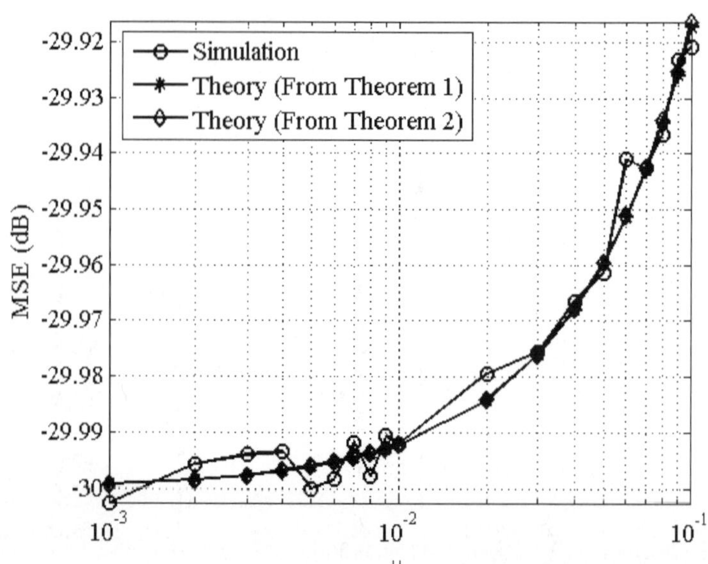

Fig. 2. Two theoretical (Theorem 1 and Theorem 2) and simulated MSEs for real LMP algorithm under the regressor model M.1 and the noise model N.2.

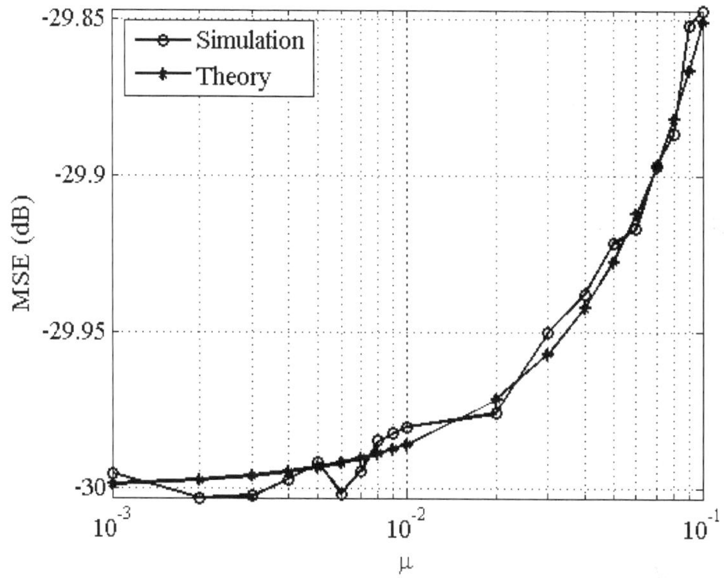

Fig. 3. Theoretical and simulated MSEs for real LMP algorithm under the regressor model M.2 and the noise model N.1.

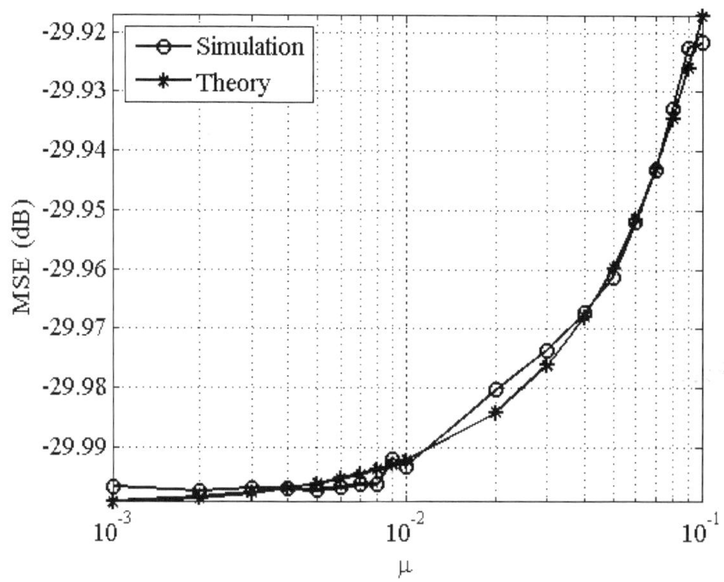

Fig. 4. Theoretical and simulated MSEs for real LMP algorithm under the regressor model M.2 and the noise model N.2.

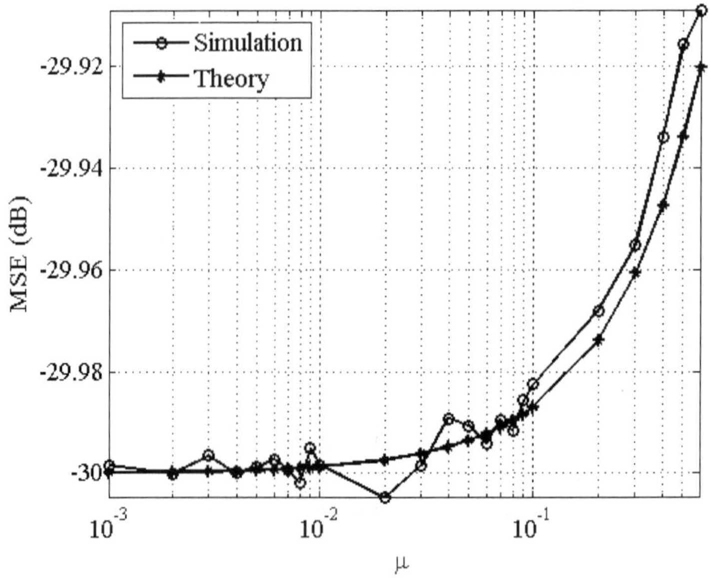

Fig. 5. Theoretical and simulated MSEs for real NLMP algorithm under the regressor model M.2 and the noise model N.1.

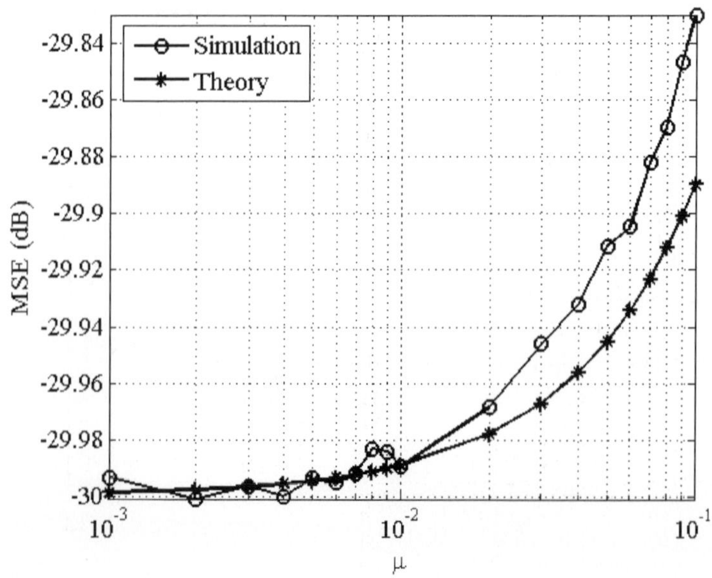

Fig. 6. Theoretical and simulated MSEs for real LMMN algorithm under the regressor model M.2 and the noise model N.1

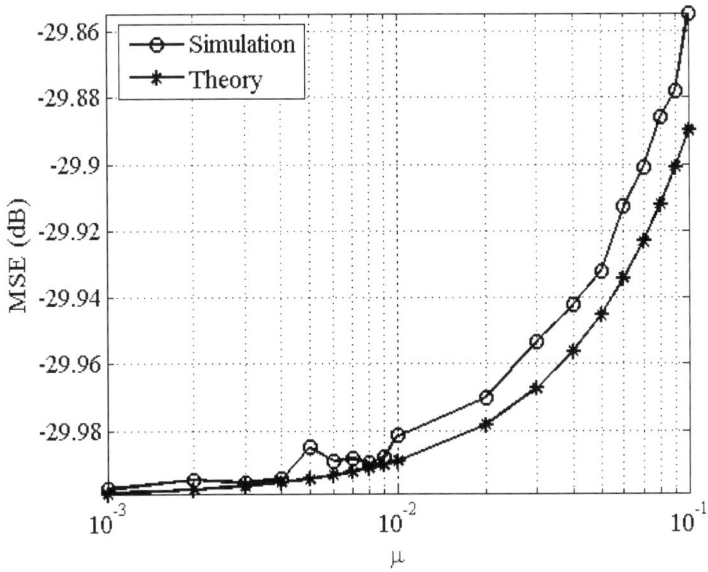

Fig. 7. Theoretical and simulated MSEs for complex LMMN algorithm under the regressor model M.2 and the noise model N.1.

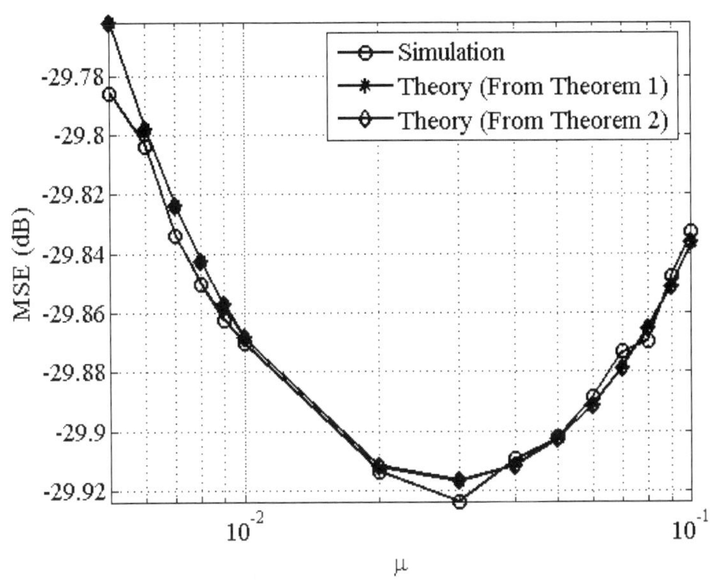

Fig. 8. Two theoretical (Theorem 1 and Theorem 2) and simulated tracking MSEs for real LMP algorithm under the regressor model M.1 and the noise model N.1.

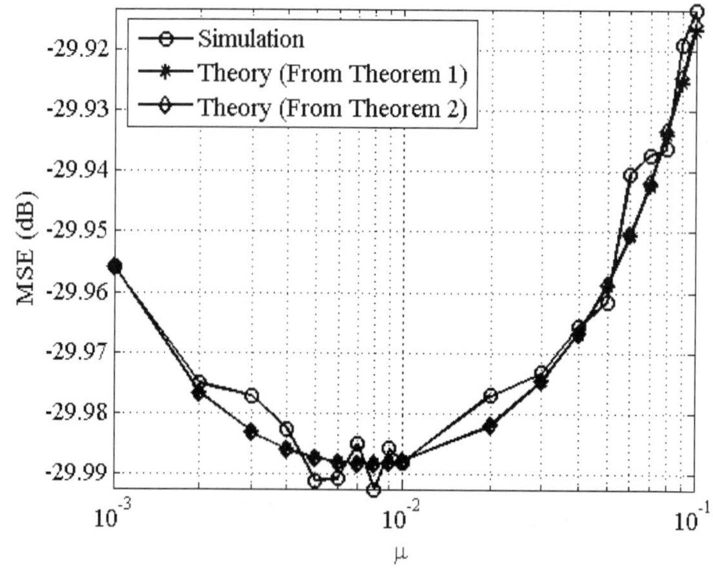

Fig. 9. Two theoretical (Theorem 1 and Theorem 2) and simulated tracking MSEs for real LMP algorithm under the regressor model M.1 and the noise model N.2.

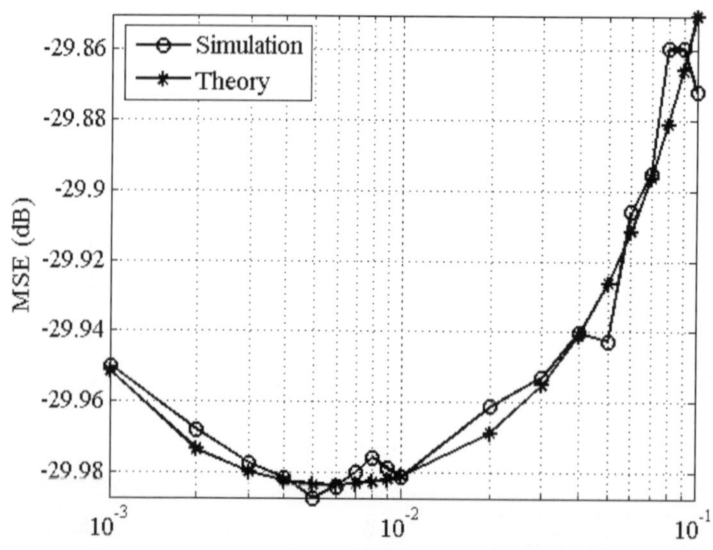

Fig. 10. Theoretical and simulated tracking MSEs for real LMP algorithm under the regressor model M.2 and the noise model N.1.

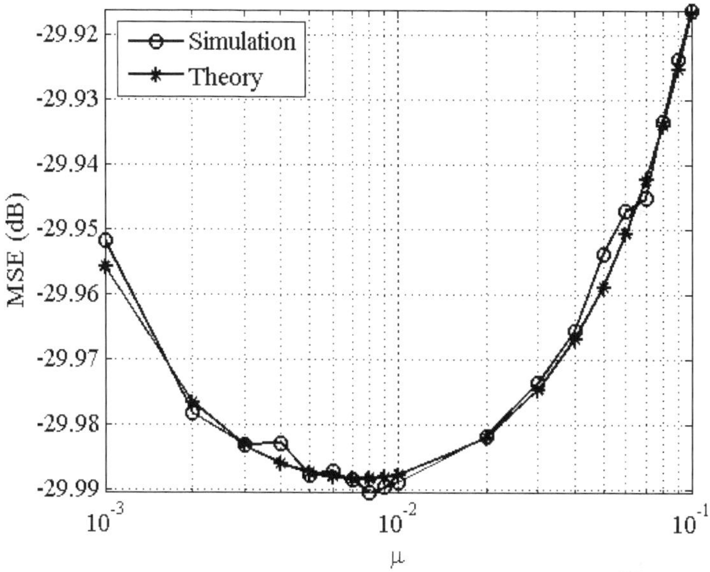

Fig. 11. Theoretical and simulated tracking MSEs for real LMP algorithm under the regressor model M.2 and the noise model N.2.

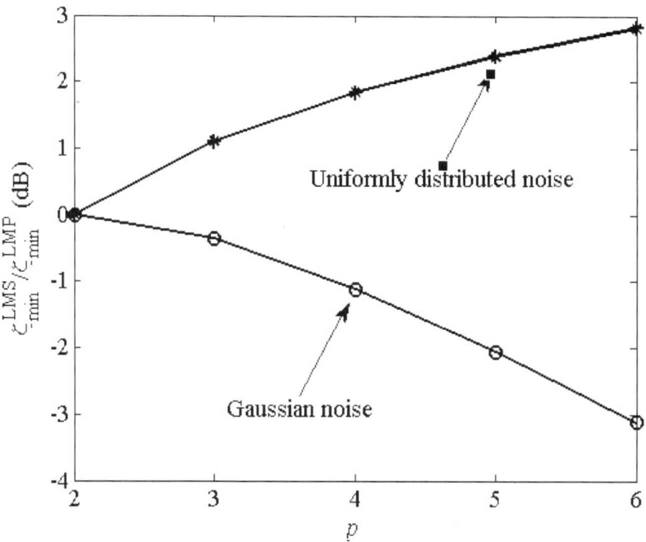

Fig. 12. Comparisons of the tracking performance between LMS algorithm and LMP algorithm in Gaussian noise environments and uniformly distributed noise environments.

5. Conclusions

Based on the Taylor series expansion (TSE) and so-called *complex Brandwood-form series expansion* (BSE), this paper develops a unified approach for the steady-state mean-square-error (MSE) and tracking performance analyses of adaptive filters. The general closed-form analytical expressions for the steady-state mean square error (MSE), tracking performance, optimal step-size, and minimum MSE are derived. These expressions are all second-order approximate. For some well-known adaptive algorithms, such as least-mean-square (LMS) algorithm, least-mean-forth (LMF) algorithm and least-mean-mixed norm (LMMN) algorithm, the proposed results are all the same as those summarized by A. H. Sayed in [11]. For least-mean p-power (LMP) algorithm, the normalized type LMMN algorithm and LMP algorithm (i.e., ε-NLMMN and ε-NLMP), their steady-state performances are also investigated. In addition, comparisons with tracking ability between LMP algorithm with $p>2$ and LMS algorithm, show that the superiority of the LMS algorithm over LMP algorithm in Gaussian noise environments, and inferiority in uniformly distributed noise environments. Extensive computational simulations show the accuracy of our analyses.

APPENDIX A. Proof of lemma 1

Under (4), we have $e_a = e - v$. Then, substituting this result into (12), we get

$$\varphi(v,v^*) = 2\operatorname{Re}\left[e_a^* f(e,e^*)\right]\Big|_{e=v,e^*=v^*} = 2\operatorname{Re}\left[(e^*-v^*) f(e,e^*)\right]\Big|_{e=v,e^*=v^*} = 0. \tag{A.1}$$

$$\begin{aligned}
\varphi^{(2)}_{e,e^*}(v,v^*) &= \frac{\partial^2}{\partial e \partial e^*} 2\operatorname{Re}\left[e_a^* f(e,e^*)\right]\Big|_{\substack{e=v,\\ e^*=v^*}} = \frac{\partial^2}{\partial e \partial e^*}\left[(e-v)^* f(e,e^*) + (e-v) f(e,e^*)^*\right]\Big|_{\substack{e=v,\\ e^*=v^*}} \\
&= \frac{\partial}{\partial e^*}\left[(e-v)^* f^{(1)}_e(e,e^*) + f(e,e^*)^* + (e-v) f^{(1)}_e(e,e^*)^*\right]\Big|_{\substack{e=v,\\ e^*=v^*}} \\
&= f^{(1)}_e(e,e^*) + f^{(1)}_{e^*}(e,e^*)^* + (e-v)^* f^{(2)}_{e,e^*}(e,e^*) + (e-v) f^{(2)}_{e,e^*}(e,e^*)^*\Big|_{\substack{e=v,\\ e^*=v^*}} \\
&= 2\operatorname{Re} f^{(1)}_e(v,v^*).
\end{aligned} \tag{A.2}$$

$$\begin{aligned}
q^{(2)}_{e,e^*}(v,v^*) &= \frac{\partial}{\partial e^* \partial e}\left|f(e,e^*)\right|^2\Big|_{e=v,e^*=v^*} = \frac{\partial}{\partial e^* \partial e}\left[f(e,e^*) f(e,e^*)^*\right]\Big|_{e=v,e^*=v^*} \\
&= \frac{\partial}{\partial e^*}\left[f(e,e^*) f^{(1)}_e(e,e^*)^* + f(e,e^*)^* f^{(1)}_e(e,e^*)\right]\Big|_{e=v,e^*=v^*} \\
&= f^{(1)}_{e^*}(e,e^*) f^{(1)}_e(e,e^*)^* + f^{(1)}_e(e,e^*) f^{(1)}_{e^*}(e,e^*)^* \\
&\quad + f(e,e^*) f^{(2)}_{e,e^*}(e,e^*)^* + f(e,e^*)^* f^{(2)}_{e,e^*}(e,e^*)\Big|_{e=v,e^*=v^*} \\
&= \left|f^{(1)}_e(v,v^*)\right|^2 + \left|f^{(1)}_{e^*}(v,v^*)\right|^2 + 2\operatorname{Re}\left[f^*(v,v^*) f^{(2)}_{e,e^*}(v,v^*)\right]
\end{aligned} \tag{A.3}$$

Here, we use two equalities: $\left[f_e^{(1)}(e,e^*)\right]^* = f_{e^*}^{(1)}(e,e^*)^*$ and $\left[f_{e,e^*}^{(2)}(e,e^*)\right]^* = f_{e,e^*}^{(2)}(e,e^*)^*$.

APPENDIX B. Proof of lemma 2

Consider the real-valued cases. Substituting $e_a = e - v$ into (12), we get

$$\varphi(v) = 2\left[e_a f(e)\right]\Big|_{e=v} = 2\left[(e-v)f(e)\right]\Big|_{e=v} = 0. \tag{B.1}$$

$$\begin{aligned}\varphi_{e,e}^{(2)}(v) &= \frac{\partial^2}{\partial e \partial e} 2\left[e_a f(e)\right]\Big|_{e=v} = 2\frac{\partial}{\partial e}\left[(e-v)f_e^{(1)}(e) + f(e)\right]\Big|_{e=v} \\ &= 2\left[f_e^{(1)}(e) + (e-v)f_{e,e}^{(2)}(e) + f_e^{(1)}(e)\right]\Big|_{e=v} = 4f_e^{(1)}(v)\end{aligned} \tag{B.2}$$

$$\begin{aligned}q_{e,e}^{(2)}(v) &= \frac{\partial^2}{\partial e \partial e} f^2(e)\Big|_{e=v} = \frac{\partial}{\partial e}\left[2f(e)f_e^{(1)}(e)\right]\Big|_{e=v} \\ &= 2\left|f_e^{(1)}(e)\right|^2 + 2f(e)f_{e,e}^{(2)}(e)\Big|_{e=v} = 2\left[\left|f_e^{(1)}(v)\right|^2 + f(v)f_{e,e}^{(2)}(v)\right]\end{aligned} \tag{B.3}$$

APPENDIX C. Proof of lemma 3

Let $z = x + jy$, where x and $y \neq 0$ are all real variables, then

$$\begin{aligned}\frac{\partial}{\partial z}|z|^p &= \frac{\partial}{\partial z}\left(|z|^2\right)^{p/2} = \frac{1}{2}\left(\frac{\partial}{\partial x} - j\frac{\partial}{\partial y}\right)\left(x^2+y^2\right)^{p/2} \\ &= \frac{p}{4}\left(x^2+y^2\right)^{p/2-1}2x - j\frac{p}{4}\left(x^2+y^2\right)^{p/2-1}2y \\ &= \frac{p}{2}|z|^{p-2}(x-jy) = \frac{p}{2}|z|^{p-2}z^*\end{aligned} \tag{C.1}$$

Likewise, we can obtain $\frac{\partial}{\partial z^*}|z|^p = \frac{p}{2}|z|^{p-2}z$. Here, we use the Brandword's derivation operators [21].

APPENDIX D. Proof of theorem 2

First, we consider the complex-valued cases. Substituting the complex BSE of $q(e,e^*)$ (i.e., replacing $\varphi(e,e^*)$ in (19) by $q(e,e^*)$) into $\mathrm{E}\left[\|\mathbf{u}\|^2 q(e,e^*)\right]$, and neglecting $\mathrm{O}(e_a,e_a^*)$, we obtain

$$\begin{aligned}\mathrm{E}\left[\|\mathbf{u}\|^2 q(e,e^*)\right] &= \mathrm{E}\left[\|\mathbf{u}\|^2 q(v,v^*)\right] + \mathrm{E}\left[\|\mathbf{u}\|^2 q_e^{(1)}(v,v^*)e_a\right] + \mathrm{E}\left[\|\mathbf{u}\|^2 q_{e^*}^{(1)}(v,v^*)e_a^*\right] \\ &+ \frac{1}{2}\mathrm{E}\left[\|\mathbf{u}\|^2 q_{e,e}^{(2)}(v,v^*)e_a^2\right] + \frac{1}{2}\mathrm{E}\left[\|\mathbf{u}\|^2 q_{e^*,e^*}^{(2)}(v,v^*)\left(e_a^*\right)^2\right] + \mathrm{E}\left[\|\mathbf{u}\|^2 q_{e,e^*}^{(2)}(v,v^*)|e_a|^2\right]\end{aligned} \tag{D.1}$$

Due to v being independent of e_a and $\mathbf{u}$ (i.e., A.1 and A.2), the above equation can be rewritten as

$$\begin{aligned}\mathrm{E}\left[\|\mathbf{u}\|^2 q(e,e^*)\right] &= \mathrm{E}\|\mathbf{u}\|^2 \mathrm{E}q(v,v^*) + \mathrm{E}\left(\|\mathbf{u}\|^2 e_a\right)\mathrm{E}q_e^{(1)}(v,v^*) + \mathrm{E}\left(\|\mathbf{u}\|^2 e_a^*\right)\mathrm{E}q_{e^*}^{(1)}(v,v^*)\\ &+\frac{1}{2}\mathrm{E}\left(\|\mathbf{u}\|^2 e_a^2\right)\mathrm{E}q_{e,e}^{(2)}(v,v^*) + \frac{1}{2}\mathrm{E}\left[\|\mathbf{u}\|^2 \left(e_a^*\right)^2\right]\mathrm{E}q_{e^*,e^*}^{(2)}(v,v^*)\\ &+\mathrm{E}\left(\|\mathbf{u}\|^2 |e_a|^2\right)\mathrm{E}q_{e,e^*}^{(2)}(v,v^*)\end{aligned} \quad . \quad \text{(D.2)}$$

Using $e_a = \mathbf{u}\tilde{\mathbf{w}}$ and A.5, we get

$$\mathrm{E}\left(\|\mathbf{u}\|^2 e_a\right) = \mathrm{E}\left(\|\mathbf{u}\|^2 e_a^*\right) = \mathrm{E}\left(\|\mathbf{u}\|^2 e_a^2\right) = \mathrm{E}\left[\|\mathbf{u}\|^2 \left(e_a^*\right)^2\right] = 0\,. \quad \text{(D.3)}$$

Hence, substituting (D.3) into (D.2) and using Lemma 1, we can obtain

$$\mathrm{E}\left[\|\mathbf{u}\|^2 q(e,e^*)\right] = C\mathrm{E}\|\mathbf{u}\|^2 + B\mathrm{E}\left(\|\mathbf{u}\|^2 |e_a|^2\right) \quad \text{(D.4)}$$

where B and C are defined by (18a). Substituting the following formula [see e.g. 6.5.18] in [11], i.e.,

$$\mathrm{E}\left(\|\mathbf{u}\|^2 |e_a|^2\right) = (M+1)\sigma_u^2 \mathrm{E}|e_a|^2 \quad \text{(D.5)}$$

into (D.4), and using (5) and $\mathrm{E}\|\mathbf{u}\|^2 = M\sigma_u^2$, we have

$$\mathrm{E}\left[\|\mathbf{u}\|^2 q(e,e^*)\right] = CM\sigma_u^2 + B(M+1)\sigma_u^2 \zeta_{TEMSE}\,. \quad \text{(D.6)}$$

Then, substituting (21) and (D.6) into (10) yields

$$\left[A - \mu B(M+1)\sigma_u^2\right] \zeta_{TEMSE} = \mu CM\sigma_u^2 + \mu^{-1}\mathrm{Tr}(\mathbf{Q})\,. \quad \text{(D.7)}$$

where A is defined by (18a). Obviously, if the condition C.2 is satisfied, the tracking EMSE expression of (38) can be obtained while in nonstationary environments.
Next, we consider the real-valued cases. Similarly, substituting the TSE of $q(e)$ (i.e., replacing $\varphi(e)$ in (25) by $q(e)$) into $\mathrm{E}\left[\|\mathbf{u}\|^2 q(e)\right]$, neglecting $\mathrm{O}(e_a)$, and using A.1, A.2 and A.5, we get

$$\mathrm{E}\left[\|\mathbf{u}\|^2 q(e)\right] = C\mathrm{E}\|\mathbf{u}\|^2 + B\mathrm{E}\left(\|\mathbf{u}\|^2 |e_a|^2\right). \quad \text{(D.8)}$$

where B and C are defined by (18b). Using $\mathrm{E}\|\mathbf{u}\|^2 = M\sigma_u^2$ and substituting the following formula [see e.g. 6.5.20] in [11], i.e.,

$$\mathrm{E}\left(\|\mathbf{u}\|^2 |e_a|^2\right) = (M+2)\sigma_u^2 \mathrm{E}|e_a|^2 \tag{D.9}$$

into (D.8), we obtain

$$\mathrm{E}\left[\|\mathbf{u}\|^2 q(e)\right] = CM\sigma_u^2 + B(M+2)\sigma_u^2 \zeta_{TEMSE}. \tag{D.10}$$

Hence, substituting (27) and (D.10) into the real-form equation of (10) yields

$$\left[A - \mu B(M+2)\sigma_u^2\right] \zeta_{TEMSE} = \mu CM\sigma_u^2 + \mu^{-1}\mathrm{Tr}(\mathbf{Q}). \tag{D.11}$$

where A is defined by (18b). Then, if the condition C.2 is satisfied, we can obtain (37) and (38) while $\gamma = 2$, respectively.

Next, letting $\mathrm{Tr}(\mathbf{Q}) = 0$, we can obtain the EMSE expression of (37) in stationary environments.

Finally, differentiating both-hand sides of (38) with respect to μ, and letting it be zero, we get

$$\mu_{opt}^2 + \frac{2B(M+\gamma)\mathrm{Tr}(\mathbf{Q})}{AMC}\mu_{opt} - \frac{\mathrm{Tr}(\mathbf{Q})}{MC\sigma_u^2} = 0 \tag{D.12}$$

Then, we can obtain (39) by solving the above equation. This ends the proof of Theorem 2.

6. References

[1] S. Haykin, *Adaptive Filter Theory*. 4th edn. Englewood Cliffs, NJ: Prentice Hall 2002.

[2] B. Widrow and M. E. Hoff, Jr., "Adaptive switching circuits," *IRE WESCON Conv. Rec.*, Pt. 4, pp. 96-104, 1960.

[3] B. Windrow, J. M. Mccool, M. G. Larimore, and C. R. Hohnson, "Stationary and nonstationary learning characteristics of the LMS adaptive filter, " *Proc. IEEE*, vol.46, pp. 1151-1161, 1976.

[4] V. J. Mathews and S. Cho, "Improved convergence analysis of stochastic gradient adaptive filters using the sign algorithm," *IEEE Trans. Acoust., Speech, Signal Processing*, vol. 35, pp. 450-454, 1987.

[5] E. Walah and B. Widrow, "The least-mean fourth (LMF) adaptive algorithm and its family," *IEEE Trans. Information Theory*, vol. 30, pp. 275-283, 1984.

[6] J. A. Chambers, O. Tanrikulu and A. G. Constantinides, "Least mean mixed-norm adaptive filtering," *Electron. Lett.*, vol. 30, pp. 1574-1575, 1994.

[7] O. Tanrikulu and J. A. Chambers, "Convergence and steady-state properties of the least-mean mixed-norm (LMMN) adaptive algorithm," *IEE Proceedings- Vision, Image Signal Processing*, vol. 143, pp137-142, 1996.

[8] B. Lin, R. He, X. Wang and B. Wang, "Excess MSE analysis of the concurrent constant modulus algorithm and soft decision-directed scheme for blind equalization," *IET Signal Processing*, vol. 2, pp. 147-155, Jun., 2008.

[9] D. L. Duttweiler, "Adaptive filter performance with nonlinearities in the correlation multiplier," *IEEE Trans. Acoust., Speech, Signal Processing*, vol. ASSP-30, pp.578-586, Aug., 1982.

[10] S. C. Douglas and T. H.-Y. Meng, "Stochastic gradient adaptation under general error criteria," *IEEE Trans. Signal Processing*, vol.42, pp.1335-1351, Jun., 1994.

[11] A. H. Sayed, *Fundamentals of adaptive filtering*, New York:Wiley, 2003.

[12] N. R. Yousef and A. H. Sayed, "A unified approach to the steady-state and tracking analyses of adaptive filters", *IEEE Trans. Signal Processing*, vol. 49, pp. 314-324, Feb., 2001.

[13] J. H. Husøy and M. S. E. Abadi, "Unified approach to adaptive filters and their performance," *IET Signal Processing*, vol. 2, pp. 97-109, Jun., 2008.

[14] T. Y. Al-Naffouri and A. H. Sayed, "Transient analysis of adaptive filters with error nonlinearities," *IEEE Trans. Signal Processing*, vol. 51, pp. 653-663, Mar., 2003.

[15] O. Dabeer, and E. Masry, "Analysis of mean-square error and transient speed of the LMS adaptive algorithm," *IEEE Trans. Information Theory*, vol. 48, pp. 1873-1894, July, 2002.

[16] N. J. Bershad, J. C. M. Bermudez and J. Y. Tourneret, "An affine combination of two LMS adaptive filters-transient mean-square analysis," *IEEE Trans. Signal Processing*, vol. 56, pp. 1853-1864, May, 2008.

[17] B. Lin, R. He, L. Song and B. Wang, "Steady-state performance analysis for adaptive filters with error nonlinearities," *Proc. of ICASSP*, Taibei, Taiwan, pp. 3093-3096, Apr., 2009.

[18] N. R. Yousef and A. H. Sayed, "Fixed-point steady-state analysis of adaptive filters," *Int. J. Contr. Signal Processing*, vol. 17, pp. 237-258, 2003.

[19] B. Lin, R. He, X. Wang and B. Wang, "The excess mean square error analyses for Bussgang algorithm," *IEEE Signal Processing Letters*, vol. 15, pp. 793-796, 2008.

[20] A. Goupil and J. Palicot, "A geometrical derivation of the excess mean square error for Bussgang algorithms in a noiseless environment", *ELSEVIER Signal Processing*, vol. 84, pp. 311-315, May, 2004.

[21] D. H. Brandwood, "A complex gradient operator and its application in adaptive array theory," *Proc. Inst. Elect. Eng. F, H*, vol. 130, pp. 11-16, Feb., 1983.

[22] G. Yan and H. Fan, "A Newton-like algorithm for complex variables with applications in blind equalization," *IEEE Trans. Signal Processing*, vol. 48, pp. 553-556, Feb., 2000.

[23] S. C. Pei, and C. C. Tseng, "Least mean *p*-power error criterion for adaptive FIR filter," *IEEE Journal on Selected Areas in Communications*, vol. 12, pp. 1540-1547, Dec. 1994.

[24] I. S. Reed, "On a moment theorem for complex Gaussian process," *IRE Trans. Information Theory*, pp. 194-195, April, 1962.

[25] V. H. Nascimento and J. C. M. Bermudez, "Probability of divergence for the least-mean fourth (LMF) algorithm," *IEEE Trans. Signal Processing*, vol. 54, pp. 1376-1385, Apr., 2006.

[26] J. C. M. Bermudez and V. H. Nascimento, "A mean-square stability analysis of the least mean fourth adaptive algorithm," *IEEE Trans. Signal Processing*, vol. 55, pp. 4018-4028, Apr., 2007.

[27] A. Zerguine, "Convergence and steady-state analysis of the normalized least mean fourth algorithm," *Digital Signal Processing*, vol. 17 (1), pp. 17-31, Jan., 2007.

[28] B. Lin, R. He, X. Wang and B. Wang, "The steady-state mean square error analysis for least mean *p*-order algorithm," *IEEE Signal Processing Letter*, vol. 16, pp. 176-179, 2009.

3

The Ultra High Speed LMS Algorithm Implemented on Parallel Architecture Suitable for Multidimensional Adaptive Filtering

Marwan Jaber
Université du Québec à Trois-Rivières
Canada

1. Introduction

Over the past decades a number of new adaptive filter algorithms have been elaborated and applied to meet demands for faster convergence and better tracking properties than earlier techniques could offer. The Filtered LMS algorithm is currently the most popular method for adapting a filter, due to its simplicity and robustness, which have made it widely adopted in many applications. Applications include adaptive channel equalization, adaptive predictive speech coding, Noise Suppression and on-line system identification. Recently, because of the progress of digital signal processors, a variety of selective coefficient update of gradient-based adaptive algorithms could be implemented in practice. Different types of adaptive algorithms have been developed and used in conventional adaptive filters such as, filtered LMS algorithms [1], [2], [3] and [4], filtered X-LMS algorithms [1], [2], [5], and [6], filtered NLMS algorithms and RLS algorithms [1] and [2]. As a result, this chapter surveys sequential filter adaptation techniques and some applications for transversal FIR filter.
In other words filters are devices or systems that processes (or reshapes) the input signal according to some specific rules to generate an output signal Figure 1.

Fig. 1. Filter Representation

Filters could be classified in two categories linear and non-linear filters where in linear filters there is a linear relationship between input and output of the filter that satisfy the following property:

$$\begin{aligned} &x_1 \rightarrow y_1 \\ &x_2 \rightarrow y_2 \\ &\text{then } ax_1 + bx_2 = ay_1 + by_2 \end{aligned} \tag{1}$$

meanwhile in non-linear filters; there is a nonlinearity between input and output of the filter that satisfy the following property:

$$x_1 \rightarrow y_1 = x_1^2$$
$$x_2 \rightarrow y_2 = x_2^2 \qquad (2)$$
$$\text{then } x_1 + x_2 = (x_1 + x_2)^2$$

In this chapter we will be focusing on adaptive filtering which could automatically adjust (or adapt) in the face of changing environments and changing system requirements by training them to perform specific filtering or decision-making tasks and in which they should be some "adaptation algorithm" for adjusting the system's parameters figure (2) [7].

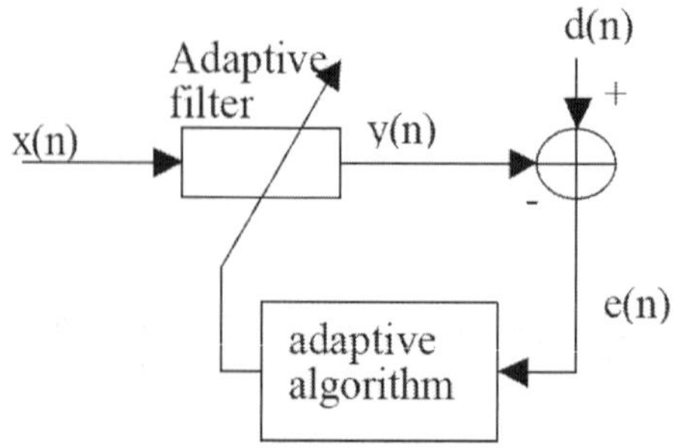

Fig. 2. General Adaptive Filter Configuration.

Different filter structures could be implemented in the adaptive filter of figure 2 such as:

- Transversal Filter Structure (FIR)
- IIR Filter Structure
- Lattice Filter Structure
- Non-Linear Filter Structure (Volterra Filter)

in which the adaptation approaches are based on:

- Wiener filter theory where the optimum coefficients of a linear filter are obtained by minimization of its mean-square error (MSE)
- Method of least squares where The performance index is the sum of weighted error squares

The main objective of the adaptation algorithm is to set the filter parameters, $\overline{\theta_{(n)}}$ in such a way that its output tries to minimize a meaningful objective function F (cost function in some literatures) involving the reference signal (or desired signal) which will be based on

- Mean Square Error
- Least Square Error
- weighted least square
- instantaneous square value

and the minimization algorithms are based on the following methods:

- Newton's method
- Quasi-Newton method
- Steepest-descent method

2. Signals

Before pursuing the study of adaptive systems, it is important to refresh our memory with some useful definitions from the stochastic process theory. The representation of signals could fall into two categories:

- Deterministic Signals
- Random Signals

2.1 Deterministic signals

A deterministic discrete-time signal is characterized by a defined mathematical function of the time index n, with $n= 0, \pm1, \pm2, \cdots$, such as:

$$x_{(n)} = e^{-\alpha n}\cos(wn) + u_{(n)} \tag{3}$$

where $u_{(n)}$ is the unit-step sequence and The response of a linear time-invariant filter to an input $x_{(n)}$ is given by:

$$y_{(n)} = x_{(n)} * h_{(n)} = \sum_{k=-\infty}^{\infty} x_{(k)} h_{(n-k)} \tag{4}$$

where $h_{(n)}$ is the impulse response of the filter. Knowing that The Z-transform and its inverse of a given sequence $x_{(n)}$ is defined as:

$$\begin{aligned} Z\left(x_{(n)}\right) &= X(Z) = \sum_{n=-\infty}^{\infty} x_{(n)} Z^{-n} \\ x_{(n)} &= \frac{1}{2\pi j}\oint_{c} X(Z) Z^{n-1} dZ \end{aligned} \tag{5}$$

where C is a counter clockwise closed contour in the region of convergence of $X(z)$ and encircling the origin of the z-plane as a result; by taking the Z-transform of both sides of equation (4), we will obtain

$$Y(Z) = H(Z) \times X(Z) \tag{6}$$

For finite finite-energy waveform, it is convenient to use the discrete-time Fourier transform defined as:

$$F(x_n) = X\left(e^{jw}\right) = \sum_{n=-\infty}^{\infty} x_{(n)} e^{-jwn} \tag{7}$$

2.2 Random signals

In many real life situations, observations are made over a period of time and they are influenced by random effects, not just at a single instant but throughout the entire interval of time or sequence of times. In a "rough" sense, a random process is a phenomenon that varies to some degree unpredictably as time goes on. If we observed an entire time-sequence of the process on several different occasions, under presumably "identical" conditions, the resulting observation sequences, in general, would be different. A random variable (RV) is a rule (or function) that assigns a real number to every outcome of a random experiment, while a stochastic random process is a rule (or function) that assigns a time function to every outcome of a random experiment. The elements of a stochastic process, $\{x_{(n)}\}$, for different value of time-index n, are in general complex-valued random variable that are characterized by their probability distribution functions. A stochastic random process is called stationary in the strict sense if all of its (single and joint) distribution function is independent of a shift in the time origin.

In this subsection we will be reviewing some useful definitions in stochastic process:

- Stochastic Average

$$m_x = E\left[x_{(n)}\right] \tag{8}$$

where E is the expected value of $\boldsymbol{x_{(n)}}$.

- Autocorrelation function for a stochastic process $\boldsymbol{x_{(n)}}$

$$\phi_{xx}(n,m) = E\left[x_{(n)}x^*_m\right] \tag{9}$$

where $\boldsymbol{x^*}$ denotes the complex conjugate of $\boldsymbol{x}$ and the symmetry properties of correlation function is:

$$\phi_{xx}(k) = \phi^*_{xx}(-k) \tag{10}$$

Furthermore a stochastic random process is called stationary in the wide sense if m_x and $\phi_{xx}(n,m)$ are independent of a shift in the time origin for any k, m, and n therefore,

$$m_x(n) = m_x(n+k) = \text{constant for all } n \tag{11}$$

and

$$\phi_{xx}(n,m) = \phi_{xx}(n+k,m+k) \tag{12}$$

which means $\phi_{xx}(n,m)$ depends only on the difference $\boldsymbol{n - m}$ or

$$\phi_{xx}(k) = E\left[x_{(n)}x^*_{(n-k)}\right] \tag{13}$$

Special case

$$\phi_{xx}(0) = E\left[\left|x_{(n)}\right|^2\right] = \text{mean square of } x_{(n)} \tag{14}$$

The Z-transform of $\phi_{xx}(k)$ is given by

$$\Phi_{xx}(Z) = \sum_{k=-\infty}^{\infty} \phi_{xx}(k) Z^{-k} \tag{15}$$

where it can be easily shown that

$$\Phi_{xx}(Z) = \Phi^*_{xx}\left(\frac{1}{Z^*}\right) \tag{16}$$

Equation (16) implies that if $\Phi_{xx}(Z)$ is a rational function of z, then its poles and zeros must occur in complex-conjugate reciprocal pairs. Moreover, the points that belong to the region of convergence of $\Phi_{xx}(Z)$ also occur in complex-conjugate pairs which suggest that the region of convergence of $\Phi_{xx}(Z)$ must be of the form $|a| \prec |z| \prec \frac{1}{|a|}$ which will cover the unit circle $|z| = 1$. By assuming that $\Phi_{xx}(Z)$ is convergent on the unit circle's contour C and by letting $\mathbf{Z} = e^{jw}$ then,

$$\phi_{xx}(0) = \frac{1}{2\pi}\int_{-\pi}^{\pi} \Phi_{xx}\left(e^{jw}\right)dw \tag{17}$$

and if $m_x = 0$, we will have

$$\sigma_x^2 = E\left[\left|x_{(n)}\right|^2\right] = \frac{1}{2\pi}\int_{-\pi}^{\pi} \Phi_{xx}\left(e^{jw}\right)dw \tag{18}$$

- Cross-correlation function for two stochastic processes $x_{(n)}$ and $y_{(n)}$

$$\phi_{xy}(n,m) = E\left[x_{(n)}y_m^*\right] \tag{19}$$

and the symmetry properties of the correlation function is:

$$\phi_{xy}(k) = \phi_{yx}^*(-k) \tag{20}$$

The Z-transform of $\phi_{xy}(k)$ is given by

$$\Phi_{xy}(Z) = \sum_{k=-\infty}^{\infty} \phi_{xy}(k)Z^{-k} \tag{21}$$

where it can be easily shown that

$$\Phi_{xy}(Z) = \Phi_{xy}^*\left(\frac{1}{Z^*}\right) \tag{22}$$

- Auto-covariance function for stationary process is defined as:

$$\gamma_{xx}(k) = E\left[\left(x_{(n)} - m_x\right)\left(x_{(n-k)} - m_x\right)^*\right] = \phi_{xx}(k) - |m_x|^2 \tag{23}$$

and the symmetry properties of auto-covariance function

$$\gamma_{xx}(k) = \gamma_{xx}^*(-k) \tag{24}$$

Special case

$$\gamma_{xx}(0) = \sigma_x^2 = \text{variance of } x_{(n)} \tag{25}$$

- Cross-covariance function is defined as:

$$\gamma_{xy}(k) = E\left[\left(x_{(n)} - m_x\right)\left(y_{(n-k)} - m_y\right)^*\right] = \phi_{xy}(k) - m_x m_y^* \tag{26}$$

and the symmetry properties of the cross-covariance function is:

$$\gamma_{xy}(k) = \gamma_{yx}^*(-k) \tag{27}$$

2.2.1 Power spectral density

Consider the wide-sense stationary random process $\{x_{(n)}\}$ from which we will consider a window of $2N+1$ elements of $x_{(n)}$ such as

$$x_{N_{(n)}} = \begin{cases} x_{(n)}, -N \le n \le N \\ 0, otherwise \end{cases} \tag{28}$$

and the discrete-time Fourier transform of $x_{N_{(n)}}$ is computed as:

$$X_N\left(e^{jw}\right) = \sum_{n=-\infty}^{\infty} x_{N_{(n)}} e^{-jwn} = \sum_{n=-N}^{N} x_{(n)} e^{-jwn} \tag{29}$$

By conjugating both sides of equation 29 with:

$$X_N^*\left(e^{jw}\right) = \sum_{n=-N}^{N} x_{(m)}^* e^{jwm} \tag{30}$$

we will obtain

$$\left|X_M\left(e^{jw}\right)\right|^2 = \sum_{n=-N}^{N} \sum_{m=-N}^{N} x_{(n)} x_{(m)}^* e^{-jw(n-m)} \tag{31}$$

and by taking the expected value of equation 31, we will have:

$$E\left[\left|X_M\left(e^{jw}\right)\right|^2\right] = \sum_{n=-N}^{N} \sum_{m=-N}^{N} E\left[x_{(n)} x_{(m)}^*\right] e^{-jw(n-m)} \tag{32}$$

which after simplification by imposing $k = n - m$ will yield:

$$\frac{1}{2N+1} E\left[\left|X_N\left(e^{jw}\right)\right|^2\right] = \sum_{k=-2N}^{2N} \left(1 - \frac{|k|}{2N+1}\right) \phi_{xx}(k) e^{-jwk} \tag{33}$$

By assuming that the summation on the right hand side of equation 33 will converge for large k then

$$\lim_{N\to\infty}\left(\frac{1}{2N+1} E\left[\left|X_N\left(e^{jw}\right)\right|^2\right]\right) = \sum_{k=-2N}^{2N} \phi_{xx}(k) e^{-jwk} = \Phi_{xx}\left(e^{jw}\right) \tag{34}$$

The function $\Phi_{xx}\left(e^{jw}\right)$ is called the power spectral density of the stochastic, wide-sense stationary process $\{x_{(n)}\}$ which is always real and non-negative.

2.2.2 Response of linear system to stochastic processes

Given the Linear Time-Invariant System (LTI) illustrated in figure 3 where we will assume that $\phi_{xx}(k)$ is known therefore, the Z-transform of $\phi_{xy}(k)$ could be elaborated as:

$$\Phi_{xy}(Z) = \sum_{k=-\infty}^{\infty} \phi_{xy}(k) Z^{-k} = \sum_{k=-\infty}^{\infty} E\left[x_{(n)} y^{*}_{(n-k)}\right] Z^{-k} \tag{35}$$

and

$$y_{(n)} = \sum_{l=-\infty}^{\infty} h_{(l)} x_{(n-l)} \tag{36}$$

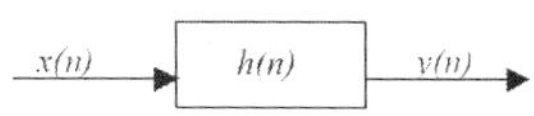

$x(n)$: input (stochastic process)

$y(n)$: output (stochastic process)

$h(n)$: system impulse response

Fig. 3. Structure of LTI system

To be noted that the following expressions could be easily derived:

$$\Phi_{yy}(Z) = H(Z) H^{*}\left(\tfrac{1}{Z}\right) \Phi_{xx}(Z) \tag{37}$$

and

$$\begin{aligned} \Phi_{xy}\left(e^{jw}\right) &= H^{*}\left(e^{jw}\right) \Phi_{xx}\left(e^{jw}\right) \\ \Phi_{yx}\left(e^{jw}\right) &= H\left(e^{jw}\right) \Phi_{xx}\left(e^{jw}\right) \\ \Phi_{yy}\left(e^{jw}\right) &= \left|H\left(e^{jw}\right)\right| \Phi_{xx}\left(e^{jw}\right) \end{aligned} \tag{38}$$

3. Regression

Data fitting is one of the oldest adaptive systems which are a powerful tool, allowing predictions of the present or future events to be made based on information about the past or present events. The two basic types of regression are linear regression and multiple regressions.

3.1 Linear regression

The goal of linear regression is to adjust the values of slope and intercept to find the line that best predicts d from x (Figure 4) or in other words linear regression estimates how much d changes when x changes by one unit.

The slope quantifies the steepness of the line which is equals to the change in d for each unit change in x. If the slope is positive, d increases as d increases. If the slope is negative, d

decreases as d increases. The d intercept is the d value of the line when x equals zero. It defines the elevation of the line.

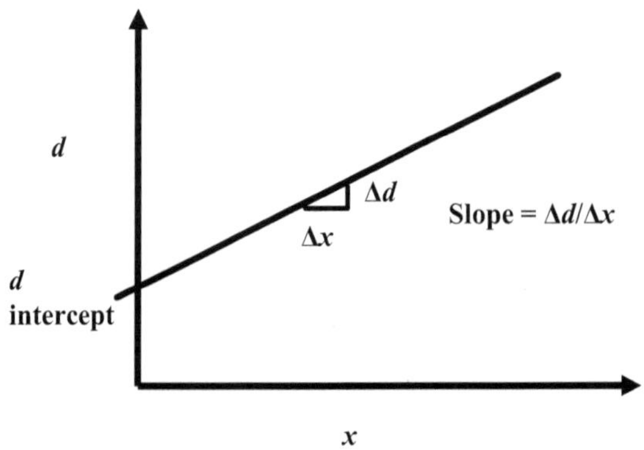

Fig. 4. Slope and Intercept.

The deviation from the straight line which represents the best linear fits of a set of data as shown in figure 5 is expressed as:

$$d \approx w \times x + b \tag{39}$$

or more specifically,

$$d_{(n)} = w \times x_{(n)} + b + e_{(n)} = y_{(n)} + e_{(n)} \tag{40}$$

where $e_{(n)}$ is the instantaneous error that is added to $y_{(n)}$ (the linearly fitted value), w is the slope and b is the y intersect (or bias). More precisely, the goal of regression is to minimize the sum of the squares of the vertical distances of the points from the line. The problem can be solved by a linear system with only two free parameters, the slope w and the bias b.

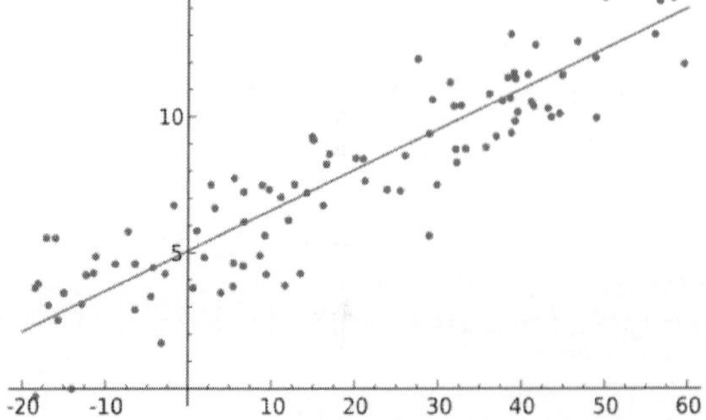

Fig. 5. Example of linear regression with one independent variable

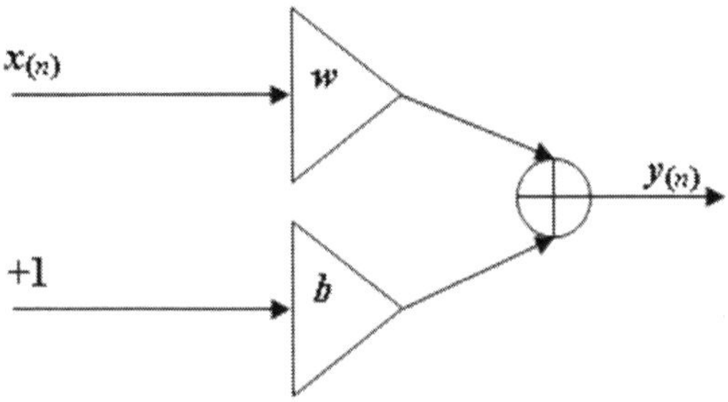

Fig. 6. Linear Regression Processing Element.

Figure 6 is called the Linear Regression Processing Element (LRPE) which is built from two multipliers and one adder. The multiplier w *scales the input*, and the multiplier b *is a simple bias*, which can also be thought of as an extra input connected to the value +1.The parameters (b, w) have different functions in the solution.

3.1.1 Least squares for linear model

Least squares solves the problem by finding the best fitted line to a set of data; for which the sum of the square deviations (or residuals) in the d direction are minimized (figure 7).

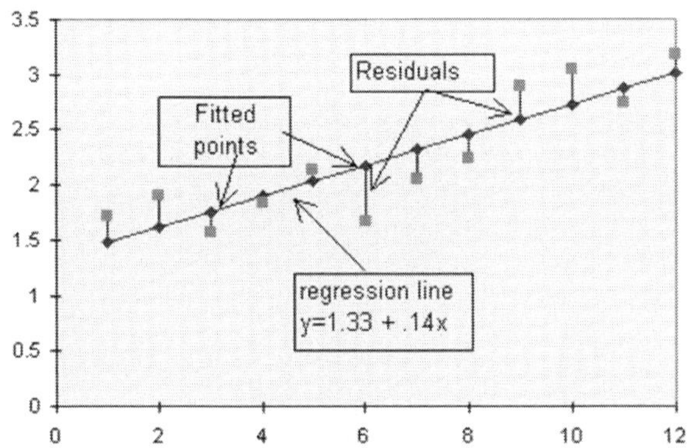

Fig. 7. Regression line showing the deviations.

The goal is to find a systematic procedure to find the constants b and w which minimizes the error between the true value $d_{(n)}$ and the estimated value $y_{(n)}$ which is called the linear regression.

$$d_{(n)} - (b + wx_{(n)}) = d_{(n)} - y_{(n)} = e_{(n)} \tag{41}$$

The best fitted line to the data is obtained by minimizing the error $e_{(n)}$ which is computed by the mean square error (MSE) that is a widely utilized as performance criterion

$$\xi = \frac{1}{2N}\sum_{n=1}^{N} e_{(n)}^2 \tag{42}$$

where N in the number of observations and ξ is the mean square error.
Our goal is to minimize ξ analytically, which can be achieved by taking the partial derivative of this quantity with respect to the unknowns and equate the resulting equations to zero, i.e.

$$\begin{cases} \dfrac{\delta \xi}{\delta b} = 0 \\ \dfrac{\delta \xi}{\delta w} = 0 \end{cases} \tag{43}$$

which yields after some manipulation to:

$$b = \frac{\sum_n x_{(n)}^2 \sum_n d_{(n)} - \sum_n x_{(n)} \sum_n x_{(n)} d_{(n)}}{N\left[\sum_n \left(x_{(n)} - \bar{x}\right)^2\right]} \quad w = \frac{\sum_n \left(x_{(n)} - \bar{x}\right)\left(d_{(n)} - \bar{d}\right)}{\sum_n \left(x_{(n)} - \bar{x}\right)^2} \tag{44}$$

where the bar over the variable means the mean value and the procedure to determine the coefficients of the line is called the least square method.

3.1.2 Search procedure

The purpose of least squares is to find parameters (b, w_1, w_2, …, w_p) that minimize the difference between the system output $y_{(n)}$ and the desired response $d_{(n)}$. *So, regression is effectively computing the optimal parameters of an interpolating system* which predicts the value of d from the value of x.
Figure 8 shows graphically the operation of adapting the parameters of the linear system in which the system output y is always a linear combination of the input x with a certain bias b according to the equation $y = wx + b$. Changing b modifies the y intersect, while changing w modifies the slope. The goal of linear regression is to adjust the position of the line such that the average square difference between the y values (on the line) and the cloud of points $d_{(n)}$ i.e. the error $e_{(n)}$, is minimized.

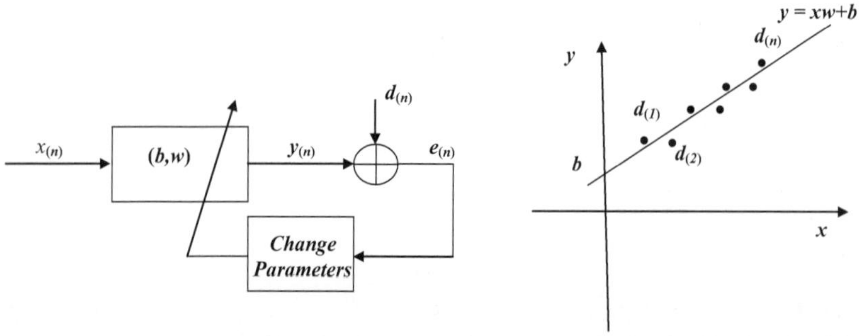

Fig. 8. Regression as a linear system design problem.

The key point is to recognize the information transmitted by the error which can be used to optimally place the line and this could be achieved by including a subsystem that accepts the error and modifies the parameters of the system. Thus, the *error* $e_{(n)}$ *is fed-back to the system* and indirectly affects the output through a change in the parameters (b,w). With the incorporation of the mechanism that automatically modifies the system parameters, a very powerful linear system can be built that will constantly seek optimal parameters. Such systems are called Adaptive systems, and are the focus of this chapter.

3.2 Multiple regression

With the same reasoning as above, the regression for multiple variables could be derived as:

$$e_{(i)} = d_{(i)} - \left(b + \sum_{k=0}^{p} w_{(k)} x_{(i,k)} \right) = d_{(i)} - \sum_{k=0}^{p} w_{(k)} x_{(i,k)} \tag{45}$$

where for this case is to find the coefficient vector W that minimizes the MSE of $e_{(i)}$ over the i samples (Figure 9).

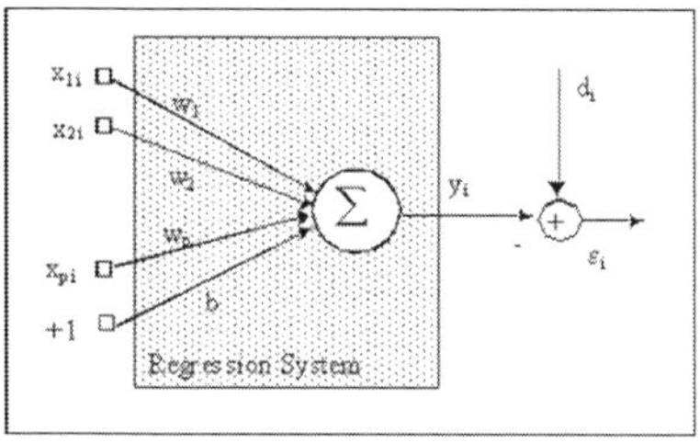

Fig. 9. Regression system for multiple inputs.

The mean square error (MSE) becomes for this case:

$$\xi = \frac{1}{2N} \sum_{n} \left(d_{(n)} - \sum_{k=0}^{p} w_{(k)} x_{(n,k)} \right)^2 \tag{46}$$

where the solution of this equation can be found by taking the derivatives of ξ with respect to the unknowns $(w_{(k)})$, and equating the result to zero which will yield to the famous *normal matrix equation* expressed as:

$$\sum_{n} x_{(n,j)} d_{(n)} = \sum_{k=0}^{p} w_{(k)} \sum_{n} x_{(n,k)} x_{(n,j)} \tag{47}$$

for $j = 0, 1, \ldots, p$.
By defining:

$$R_{(n,j)} = \frac{1}{N} \sum_{n} x_{(n,k)} x_{(n,j)} \tag{48}$$

as the autocorrelation function,

$$P_{(j)} = \frac{1}{N} \sum_{n} x_{(n,j)} d_{(n)} \tag{49}$$

as the cross-correlation of the input x for index j and the desired response y and substituting these definitions into Eq. (47), the set of normal equations can be written simply as:

$$P = RW^* \quad \text{or } W^* = R^{-1}P \tag{50}$$

where W is a vector with the p+1 weights w_i in which W^* represents the value of the vector for the optimum (minimum) solution. The solution of the multiple regression problems can be computed analytically as the product of the inverse of the autocorrelation of the input samples multiplied by the cross-correlation vector of the input and the desired response.
All the concepts previously mentioned for linear regression can be extended to the multiple regression case where J in matrix notation is illustrated as:

$$\xi = \left[W^T RW - 2P^T W + \sum_n \frac{d_{(n)}^2}{N} \right] \tag{51}$$

where T means the transpose and the values of the coefficients that minimize the solution are:

$$\nabla \xi = 0 = RW - P \quad \text{or } W^* = R^{-1}P \tag{52}$$

4. Wiener filters

The Wiener filter is a filter proposed by Norbert Wiener during the 1940s and published in 1949 [8]. Its purpose was to reduce the amount of noise present in a signal in comparison with an estimation of the desired noiseless signal. This filter is an MSE-optimal stationary linear filter which was mainly used for images degraded by additive noise and blurring. The optimization of the filter is achieved by minimizing mean square error defined as the difference between the output filter and the desired response (Figure 10) which is known as the cost function expressed as:

$$\xi = E\left[\left| e_n \right|^2 \right] \tag{53}$$

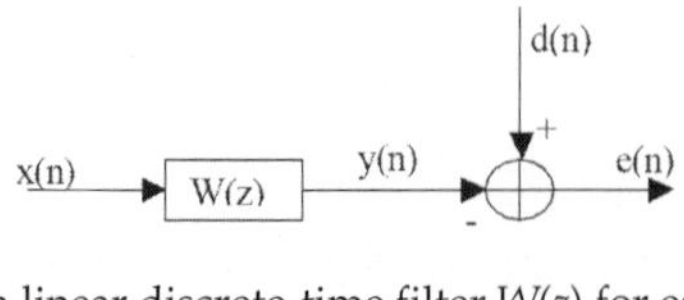

Fig. 10. block schematic of a linear discrete-time filter $W(z)$ for estimating a desired signal $d_{(n)}$ based on an excitation $x_{(n)}$ where $d_{(n)}$ and $x_{(n)}$ are random processes.

In signal processing, a causal filter is a linear and time-invariant causal system. The word *causal* indicates that the filter output depends only on past and present inputs. A filter whose output also depends on future inputs is non-causal. As a result two cases should be considered for the optimization of the cost function (equation 53).

- The filter $W(Z)$ is causal and or FIR (Finite Impulse Response).
- The filter $W(Z)$ is non-causal and or IIR (Infinite Impulse Response Filter).

4.1 Wiener filter - the transversal filter

Let $\overline{W}$ be the transversal filter's tap weights illustrated in figure 11 which is defined as:

$$\overline{W} = \begin{bmatrix} w_0 & w_1 & \cdots & w_{N-1} \end{bmatrix}^T \tag{54}$$

where T denotes the vector transpose and

$$\overline{X} = \begin{bmatrix} x_0 & x_1 & \cdots & x_{N-1} \end{bmatrix}^T \tag{55}$$

be the input vector signal where two cases should be treated separately depending on the required application:

- Real valued input signal
- Complex valued input signal

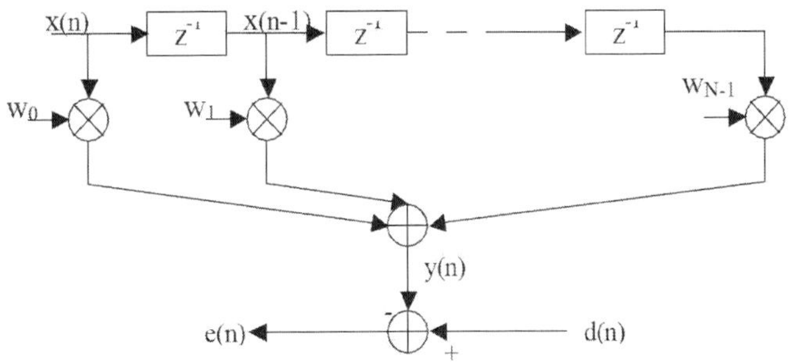

Fig. 11. Block Diagram of the Transversal Filter.

4.1.1 Wiener filter - the transversal filter - real-valued input signal

The output filter could be expressed as:

$$y_{(n)} = \sum_{i=0}^{N-1} w_i x_{(n-i)} = \overline{W}^T \overline{X_{(n)}} = \overline{X_{(n)}}^T \overline{W} \tag{56}$$

Where

$$e_{(n)} = d_{(n)} - y_{(n)} = d_{(n)} - \overline{X_{(n)}}^T \overline{W} \tag{57}$$

The performance or cost function expressed in equation 53 could be elaborated as:

$$\begin{aligned} \xi &= E\left[|e_n|^2\right] = E\left[\left(d_{(n)} - \overline{W}^T \overline{X_{(n)}}\right)\left(d_{(n)} - \overline{X_{(n)}}^T \overline{W}\right)\right] \\ &= E\left[d_{(n)}^2\right] - \overline{W}^T E\left[\overline{X_{(n)}} d_{(n)}\right] - E\left[\overline{X_{(n)}}^T d_{(n)}\right]\overline{W} + \overline{W}^T E\left[\overline{X_{(n)}}\,\overline{X_{(n)}}^T\right]\overline{W} \end{aligned} \tag{58}$$

By examining equation 58 we could easily notice that $E\left[\overline{X_{(n)}} d_{(n)}\right]$ is the cross correlation function which will be defined as:

$$\overline{P} \equiv E\left[\overline{X_{(n)}d_{(n)}}\right] = \begin{bmatrix} p_0 & p_1 & \cdots & p_{N-1} \end{bmatrix}^T \tag{59}$$

and with the same reasoning as above the autocorrelation function $E\left[\overline{X_{(n)}}\,\overline{X_{(n)}}^T\right]$ could be expressed as:

$$R \equiv E\left[\overline{X_{(n)}}\,\overline{X_{(n)}}^T\right] = \begin{bmatrix} r_{0,0} & r_{0,1} & \cdots & r_{0,N-1} \\ r_{1,0} & r_{1,1} & \cdots & r_{1,N-1} \\ \vdots & \vdots & \vdots & \vdots \\ r_{N-1,0} & r_{N-1,1} & \cdots & r_{N-1,N-1} \end{bmatrix} \tag{60}$$

Knowing that $E\left[d_{(n)}\overline{X_{(n)}}^T\right] = \overline{P}^T$ and $\overline{W}^T\overline{P} = \overline{P}^T\overline{W}$ therefore, the cost function would be:

$$\xi = E\left[d_{(n)}^2\right] - 2\overline{W}^T\overline{P} + \overline{W}^T R\overline{W} \tag{61}$$

where $\overline{W}$ in the quadratic function expressed in equation 47 will have a global minimum if and only if R is a positive definite Matrix.

The gradient method is the most commonly used method to compute the tap weights that minimizes the cost function therefore,

$$\nabla\xi = \frac{\partial\xi}{\partial w_i} = \begin{bmatrix} \frac{\partial\xi}{\partial w_0} & \frac{\partial\xi}{\partial w_1} & \cdots & \frac{\partial\xi}{\partial w_{N-1}} \end{bmatrix} = 0 \tag{62}$$

which yield after expanding equation 61 to:

$$\begin{aligned} &\frac{\partial\xi}{\partial w_i} = 0 \\ &0 = -2p_i + \sum_{l=0}^{N-1} w_l\left(r_{li} + r_{il}\right) \\ &\sum_{l=0}^{N-1} w_l\left(r_{li} + r_{il}\right) = 2p_i \end{aligned} \tag{63}$$

where we have assumed in the expanded equation $\xi = E\left[d_{(n)}^2\right] - 2\sum_{l=0}^{N-1} p_l w_l + \sum_{l=0}^{N-1}\sum_{m=0}^{N-1} w_l w_l r_{lm}$ that:

$$\sum_{l=0}^{N-1}\sum_{m=0}^{N-1} w_l w_l r_{lm} = \sum_{\substack{l=0 \\ l\neq i}}^{N-1}\sum_{\substack{m=0 \\ m\neq i}}^{N-1} w_l w_l r_{lm} + w_i \sum_{\substack{m\neq 0 \\ l\neq i}}^{N-1} w_m r_{im} + w_i^2 r_{ii} \tag{64}$$

Knowing that $r_{li} = r_{il}$ due to the symmetry property of the autocorrelation function of real-valued signal equation 49 could be expressed as:

$$\sum_{l=0}^{N-1} w_l r_{il} = p_i \tag{65}$$

for $i = 0, 1, \ldots, N-1$ which could be expressed in matrix notation as:

$$R\overline{W}_{op} = \overline{P} \tag{66}$$

known as Weiner-Hopf equation, whose solution for the optimal tap-weight vector $\overline{W}_{op}$ and by assuming that R has an inverse matrix, is:

$$\overline{W}_{op} = R^{-1}\overline{P} \tag{67}$$

Finally, the minimum value of the cost function can be expressed as:

$$\xi_{\min} = E\left[d_{(n)}^2\right] - \overline{W}_{op}^T \overline{P} = E\left[d_{(n)}^2\right] - \overline{W}_{op}^T R \overline{W}_{op} = E\left[d_{(n)}^2\right] - \overline{P}^T R^{-1} \overline{P} \tag{68}$$

4.1.2 Wiener filter - the transversal filter - complex-valued input signal

The data transmission of the basebands QPSK and the QAM is complex valued random signals where the filter's tap weight vector is also assumed to be complex therefore, the cost function for this case could be expressed as:

$$\xi = E\left[\left|e_{(n)}\right|^2\right] = E\left[e_{(n)} e_{(n)}^*\right] \tag{69}$$

and the gradient of the cost function would be:

$$\nabla_{w_i}^c = E\left[e_{(n)} \nabla_{w_i}^c e_{(n)}^* + \nabla_{w_i}^c e_{(n)}^* e_{(n)}\right] \tag{70}$$

By examining figure 11 we could easily notice that equation 57 could be formulated as:

$$e_{(n)} = d_{(n)} - \sum_{k=0}^{N-1} w_{(k)} x_{(n-k)} \tag{71}$$

and since d is independent of w and since

$$\begin{aligned} \nabla_{w_i}^c e_{(n)} &= -x_{(n-i)} \nabla_{w_i}^c w_i \\ \nabla_{w_i}^c e_{(n)}^* &= -x_{(n-i)}^* \nabla_{w_i}^c w_i^* \\ \nabla_{w_i}^c w_i &= \frac{\partial w_i}{\partial w_{i,R}} + j\frac{\partial w_i}{\partial w_{i,I}} = 1 + j(j) = 0 \\ \nabla_{w_i}^c w_i^* &= \frac{\partial w_i^*}{\partial w_{i,R}^*} + j\frac{\partial w_i^*}{\partial w_{i,I}^*} = 1 + j(-j) = 2 \end{aligned} \tag{72}$$

Where the sub-indices R and I refers to the real part and imaginary part of the complex number therefore, the gradient of the cost function (Equation 70) would be:

$$\nabla_{w_i}^c \xi = -2E\left[e_{(n)} x_{(n-i)}^*\right] \tag{73}$$

The optimum filter's tap-weights $e_{0(n)}$ are obtained by setting the complex gradient of equation 73 to zero yielding:

$$E\left[e_{o(n)}x^{*}_{(n-i)}\right]=0 \tag{74}$$

By defining

$$\begin{aligned}\overline{x}_{(n)} &\equiv \left[x_{(n)} \quad x_{(n-1)} \quad \cdots \quad x_{(n-N+1)}\right]^{T} \equiv \left[x^{*}_{(n)} \quad x^{*}_{(n-1)} \quad \cdots \quad x^{*}_{(n-N+1)}\right]^{H} \\ \overline{w}_{(n)} &\equiv \left[w^{*}_{0} \quad w^{*}_{1} \quad \cdots \quad w^{*}_{N-1}\right]^{T} \equiv \left[w_{(0)} \quad w_{1} \quad \cdots \quad x_{N-1}\right]^{H}\end{aligned} \tag{75}$$

where H denotes the complex-conjugate transpose or Hermitian and by re-writing equation 71 as:

$$e_{(n)}=d_{(n)}-\overline{w}_{o}^{H}x_{(n)} \tag{76}$$

whose solution is:

$$R\overline{w}_{o}=\overline{p} \tag{77}$$

where

$$\begin{aligned}R &= E\left[\overline{x}_{(n)}\overline{x}^{H}_{(n)}\right] \\ \overline{p} &= E\left[\overline{x}_{(n)}d^{*}_{(n)}\right]\end{aligned} \tag{78}$$

Equation 77 is known as Weiner-Hopf equation for the complex valued signals and the minimum of the cost function will be:

$$\xi_{\min}=E\left[d^{2}_{(n)}\right]-\overline{w}_{o}^{H}R\overline{w}_{o} \tag{79}$$

5. Least Mean Square algorithm (LMS algorithm)

The purpose of least squares is to is to find the optimal filter's tap weights that that minimize the difference between the system output $y_{(n)}$ and the desired response $d_{(n)}$ or in other words to minimize the cost function. Instead of solving the Weiner-Hopf equation in order to obtain the optimal filter's tap weights as seen previously, their exists other iterative methods which employ an iterative search method that starts with an *arbitrary initial weight* $\overline{W}_{(0)}$, then a recursive search method that may require many iterations in order to converge to the optimal filter's tap weights $\overline{W}_{o}$. The most important iterative methods are the gradient based iterative methods which are listed below:

- Steepest Descent Method
- Newton's Method

5.1 Steepest descent method

The steepest descent method (also known as the gradient method) is the simplest example of a gradient based method that *minimizes a function of several variables.* This process is employing an iterative search method that starts with an *arbitrary initial weight* $\overline{W}_{(0)}$, and then at the kth iteration $\overline{W}_{(k)}$ is updated according to the following equation:

$$\overline{W}_{(k+1)} = \overline{W}_{(k)} - \mu \nabla_k \xi \tag{80}$$

where μ is positive known as the step size and $\nabla_k \xi$ denotes the gradient vector $\nabla \xi = 2R\overline{W} - 2\overline{p}$ evaluated at the point $\overline{W} = \overline{W}_{(k)}$. Therefore, equation 80 could be formulated as:

$$\overline{W}_{(k+1)} = \overline{W}_{(k)} - 2\mu\left(R\overline{W}_{(k)} - \overline{p}_{(k)}\right) = (1 - 2\mu R)\left(\overline{W}_{(k)} - \overline{W}_0\right) \tag{81}$$

Knowing that the auto-correlation matrix R may be diagonalized by using the unitary similarity decomposition:

$$R = Q\Lambda Q^T \tag{82}$$

where Λ is a diagonal matrix consisting of the auto-correlation matrix R eigenvalues $\lambda_0\ \lambda_1 \cdots \lambda_{N-1}$ and the columns of Q contain the corresponding orthonormal eigenvectors and by defining the vector $\overline{v}_{(k)}$ as:

$$\overline{v}_{(k)} = \overline{W}_{(k)} - \overline{W}_0 \tag{83}$$

As a result equation 81 could be expressed as:

$$\overline{v}_{(k+1)} = \left(I - 2\mu Q\Lambda Q^T\right)\overline{v}_{(k)} \tag{84}$$

which after mathematical manipulation and by using the vector transformation $\overline{v}'_{(k)} = Q^T \overline{v}_{(k)}$ could be written as:

$$v'_{i_{(k+1)}} = (1 - 2\mu\lambda_i) v'_{i_{(k)}} \tag{85}$$

For $i = 0, 1, 2, \dots, N-1$ and $\overline{v}'_{(k)} = \left[v'_{0_{(k)}} \quad v'_{1_{(k)}} \quad \cdots \quad v'_{N-1_{(k)}} \right]$ that yields:

$$v'_{i_{(k)}} = (1 - 2\mu\lambda_i)^k v'_{i_{(0)}} \tag{86}$$

Equation 86 converges to zero if and only if the step-size parameter μ is selected so that:

$$|1 - 2\mu\lambda_i| \prec 1 \tag{87}$$

which means

$$0 \prec \mu \prec \lambda_i \tag{88}$$

for all i or equivalently

$$0 \prec \mu \prec \lambda_{\max} \tag{89}$$

where λ_{max} is the maximum of the eigenvalues $\lambda_0\ \lambda_1 \cdots \lambda_{N-1}$.

5.2 Newton's method

By replacing the scalar step-size μ with a matrix step-size given by μR^{-1}in the steepest descent algorithm (equation 81) and by using $\bar{p} = R\overline{W}_0$, the resulting algorithm is:

$$\overline{W}_{(k+1)} = \overline{W}_{(k)} - \mu R^{-1}\nabla_k \xi \tag{90}$$

Substituting $\nabla \xi = 2R\overline{W} - 2\bar{p}$ in equation 90 we will get:

$$\begin{aligned}\overline{W}_{(k+1)} &= \overline{W}_{(k)} - 2\mu R^{-1}\left(R\overline{W}_{(k)} - \bar{p}\right) \\ &= (1-2\mu)\overline{W}_{(k)} + 2\mu R^{-1}\bar{p} \\ &= (1-2\mu)\overline{W}_{(k)} + 2\mu\overline{W}_0\end{aligned} \tag{91}$$

and by subtracting $\overline{W}_0$ from both sides of equation 91 will yield:

$$\overline{W}_{(k+1)} - \overline{W}_0 = (1-2\mu)\left(\overline{W}_{(k)} - \overline{W}_0\right) \tag{92}$$

where in actual implementation of adaptive filters, the exact values of $\nabla_k \xi$ and R^{-1} are not available and have to be estimated.

5.3 Least Mean Square (LMS) algorithm

The LMS algorithm is a practical scheme for realizing Wiener filters, without explicitly solving the Wiener-Hopf equation and this was achieved in the late 1960's by Widrow [2] who proposed an extremely elegant algorithm to estimate the gradient that revolutionized the application of gradient descent procedures by *using the instantaneous value of the gradient as the estimator for the true quantity* which means replacing the cost function $\xi = E\left[e^2_{(n)}\right]$ by its instantaneous coarse estimate $\hat{\xi} = e^2_{(n)}$ into steepest descent algorithm. By doing so, we will obtain

$$\overline{W}_{(n+1)} = \overline{W}_{(n)} - \mu \nabla e^2_{(n)} \tag{93}$$

where $\overline{W}_{(n)} = \begin{bmatrix} w_{0_{(n)}} & w_{1_{(n)}} & \cdots & w_{N-1_{(n)}} \end{bmatrix}^T$ and $\nabla = \begin{bmatrix} \dfrac{\partial}{\partial w_0} & \dfrac{\partial}{\partial w_1} & \cdots & \dfrac{\partial}{\partial w_{N-1}} \end{bmatrix}^T$.

The ith element of the gradient vector $\nabla e^2_{(n)}$ is:

$$\frac{\partial e^2_{(n)}}{\partial w_i} = 2e_{(n)}\frac{\partial e_{(n)}}{\partial w_i} = -2e_{(n)}\frac{\partial y_{(n)}}{\partial w_i} = -2e_{(n)}x_{(n-i)} \tag{94}$$

which leads to:

$$\nabla e^2_{(n)} = -2e_{(n)}\bar{x}_{(n)} \tag{95}$$

that will be replaced in equation 93 to obtain:

$$\overline{W}_{(n+1)} = \overline{W}_{(n)} + 2\mu e_{(n)}\bar{x}_{(n)} \tag{96}$$

where $\bar{x}_{(n)} = \begin{bmatrix} x_{(n)} & x_{(n-1)} & \cdots & x_{(n-N+1)} \end{bmatrix}^T$.

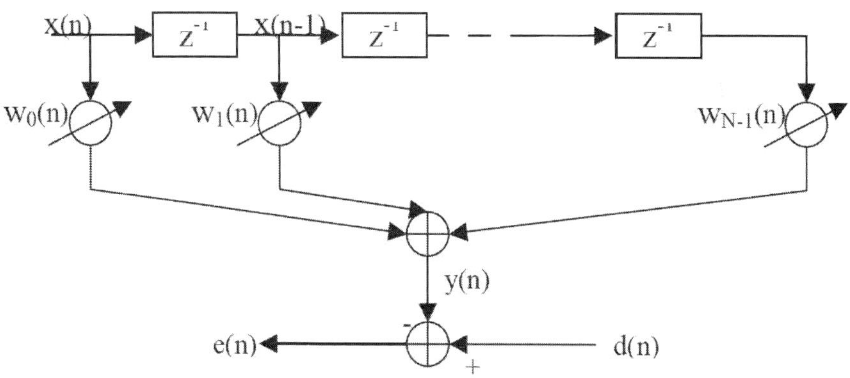

Fig. 12. LMS Filter Structure

Equation 96 is known as the LMS recursion and the summary of the LMS algorithm illustrated on figure 12 will be as follow:

- Input
- tap-weight vector, $\overline{W}_{(n)}$
- input vector, $\bar{x}_{(n)}$
- desired output, $d_{(n)}$
- Output
- Filter output, $y_{(n)}$
- Tap-weight vector update, $\overline{W}_{(n+1)}$

1. Filtering: $y_{(n)} = \overline{W}^T_{(n)}\bar{x}_{(n)}$
2. Error estimation: $e_{(n)} = d_{(n)} - y_{(n)}$
3. Tap-weight vector adaptation: $\overline{W}_{(n+1)} = \overline{W}_{(n)} + 2\mu e_{(n)}\bar{x}_{(n)}$

6. Classifying adaptive filtering applications

Various applications of adaptive filtering differ in the manner in which the desired response is extracted. In this context, we may distinguish four basic classes of adaptive filtering applications (depicted in Figures 13 to 16, which follow):

- Identification
- Inverse Modeling
- Prediction
- Interference Cancelling

Adaptive Filtering Class	Application
Identification	System Identification
	Layered Earth Modeling
Inverse Modeling	Predictive Convolution
	Adaptive Equalization
Prediction	Linear Prediction Coding
	Adaptive Differential PCM
	Auto Regressive Spectrum Analysis
	Signal Detection
Interference Cancelling	Adaptive Noise Cancelling
	Echo Cancellation
	Radar Polarimetry
	Adaptive Beam-forming

Table 1. Adaptive Filtering Applications

The following notations are used in Figures 11-15:
u = input applied to the adaptive filter
y = output of the adaptive filter
d = desired response
e = d - y = estimation error
The functions of the four basic classes of adaptive filtering applications are summarized as follow:

- Identification (Figure 13).

The notion of a mathematical model is fundamental to sciences and engineering. In the class of applications dealing with identification, an adaptive filter is used to provide a linear model that represents the best fit to an unknown plant. The plant and the adaptive filter are driven by the same input. The plant output supplies the desired responses for the adaptive filter. If the plant is dynamic in nature, the model will be time varying.

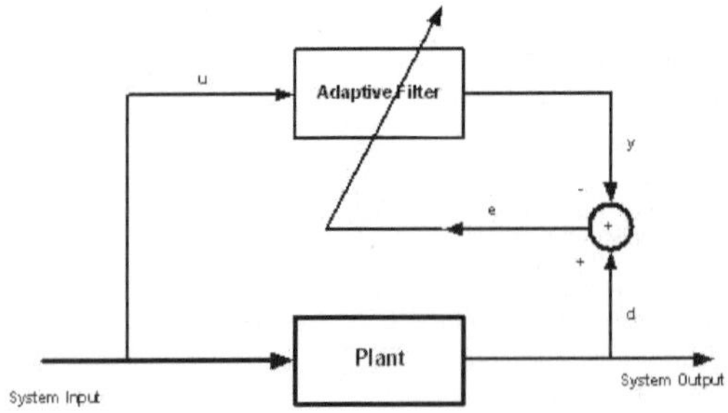

Fig. 13. Identification

- Inverse Modeling (Figure 14).

In this second class of applications, the adaptive filter provides an inverse model representing the best fit to an unknown noisy plant. Ideally, the inverse model has a transfer function equal to the reciprocal of the plant's transfer function. A delayed version of the plant input constitutes the desired response for the adaptive filter. In some applications, the plant input is used without delay as the desired response.

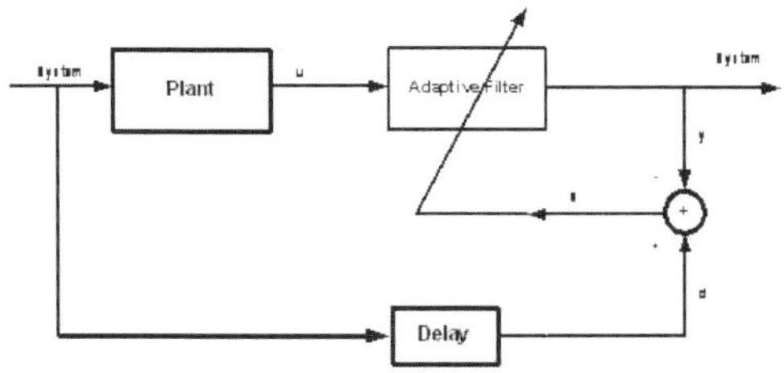

Fig. 14. Inverse Modeling

- Prediction (Figure 15).

In this example, the adaptive filter provides the best prediction of the present value of a random signal. The present value of the signal serves the purpose of a desired response for the adaptive filter. Past values of the signal supply the input applied to the adaptive filter. Depending on the application of interest, the adaptive filter output or the estimation error may service as the system output. In the first case, the system operates as a predictor; in the latter case, it operates as a prediction error filter.

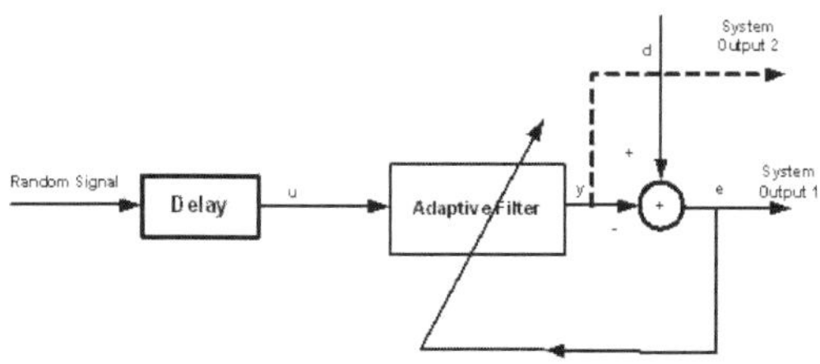

Fig. 15. Prediction

- Interference Cancelling (Figure 16).

In this final class of applications, the adaptive filter is used to cancel unknown interference contained in a primary signal, with the cancellation being optimized in some sense. The primary signal serves as the desired response for the adaptive filter. A reference signal is employed as the input to the adaptive filter. The reference signal is derived from a sensor or set of sensors located in relation to the sensor(s) supplying the primary signal in such a way that the information-bearing signal component is weak or essentially undetectable.

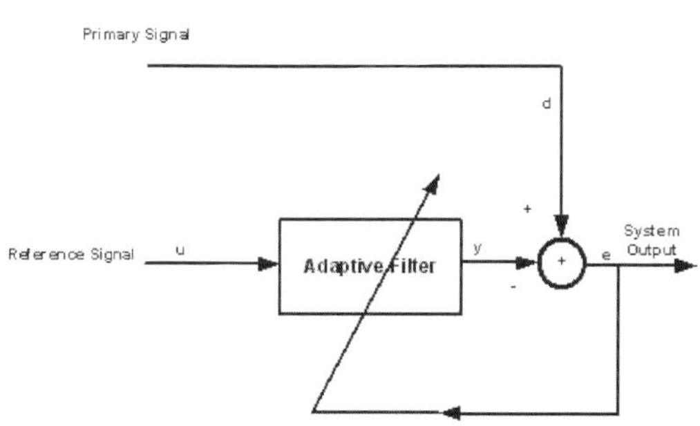

Fig. 16. Interference Cancelling

7. Active noise suppressor ANC

In this subsection we propose a new approach of noise control named ANS, where we propose stability-guaranteed algorithm for an adaptive filters, which can be derived on a basis of the strictly positive real property of the error model treated in adaptive system theory. It is important to assure the stability of the adaptive system especially in presence of unknown disturbances and mismatch in the order of the adaptive filter. Experimental results, performed on real mining noise, validate the effectiveness of the proposed stable algorithm [9].

7.1 Sounds and hearing

When sound waves from a point source strike a plane wall, they produce reflected circular wave fronts as if there were an "image" of the sound source at the same distance on the other side of the wall. If something obstructs the direct sound from the source from reaching your ear, then it may sound as if the entire sound is coming from the position of the "image" behind the wall. This kind of sound imaging follows the same laws of reflection as your image in a plane mirror (figure 17). The reflection of sound follows the law "angle of incidence equals angle of reflection" as the light does and other waves or the bounce of a billiard ball off the bank of a table figure (18).

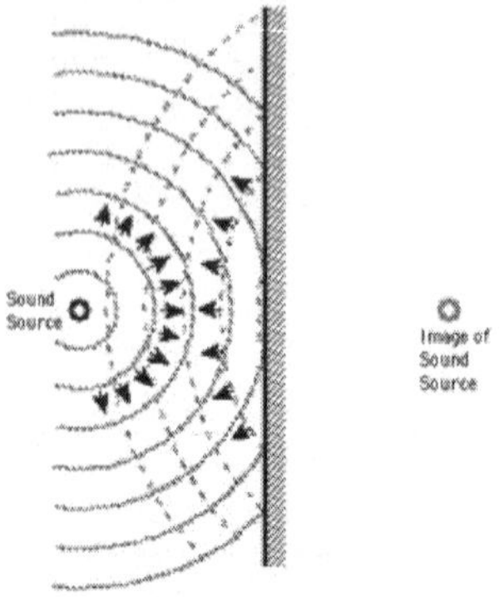

Fig. 17. Point source of sound reflecting from a plane surface.

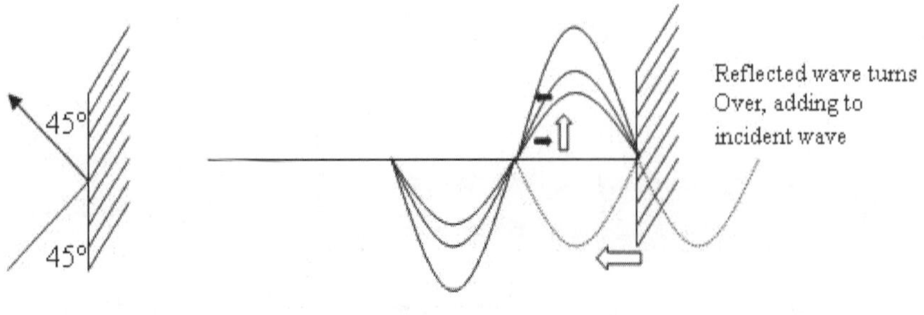

Fig. 18. Wave reflection

The main item of note about sound reflections off of hard surfaces is the fact that they undergo a 180-degree phase change upon reflection. This can lead to resonance such as standing waves in rooms. It also means that the sound intensity near a hard surface is enhanced because the reflected wave adds to the incident wave, giving pressure amplitude that is twice as great in a thin "pressure zone" near the surface. This is used in pressure zone microphones to increase sensitivity. The doubling of pressure gives a 6-decibel increase in the signal picked up by the microphone figure (19). Since the reflected wave and the incident wave add to each other while moving in opposite directions, the appearance of propagation is lost and the resulting vibration is called a standing wave. The modes of vibration associated with resonance in extended objects like strings and air columns have characteristic patterns called standing waves. These standing wave modes arise from the combination of reflection and interference such that the reflected waves interfere constructively with the incident waves. An important part of the condition for this constructive interference is the fact that the waves change phase upon reflection from a fixed end. Under these conditions, the medium appears to vibrate in segments or regions and the fact that these vibrations are made up of traveling waves is not apparent - hence the term "standing wave" figure (19).

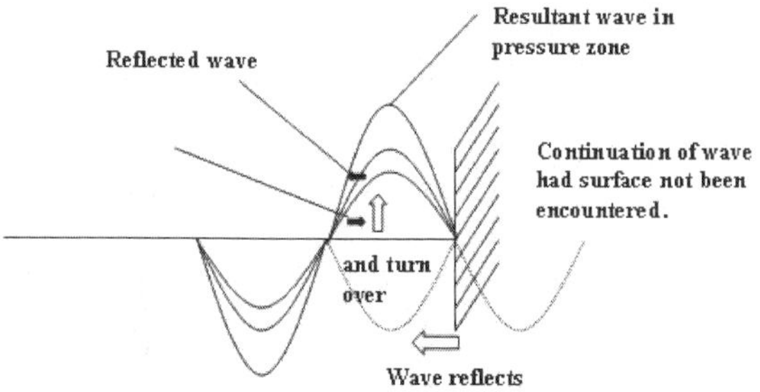

Fig. 19. Resultant wave in pressure zone.

Two traveling waves, which exist in the same medium, will interfere with each other figure (20). If their amplitudes add, the interference is said to be constructive interference, and destructive interference if they are "out of phase" and subtract figure (21). Patterns of destructive and constructive interference may lead to "dead spots" and "live spots" in auditorium acoustics.

Interference of incident and reflected waves is essential to the production of resonant standing waves figure (22).

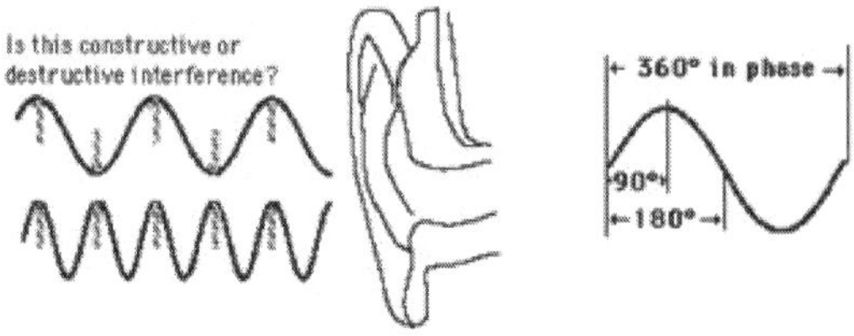

Fig. 20. Interference of Sound

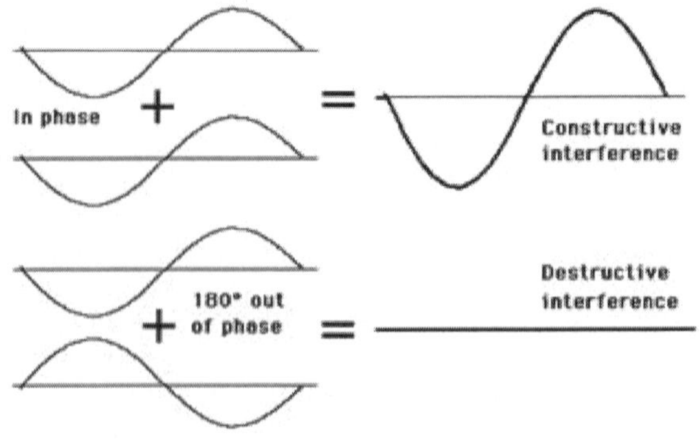

Fig. 21. Interference and Phase

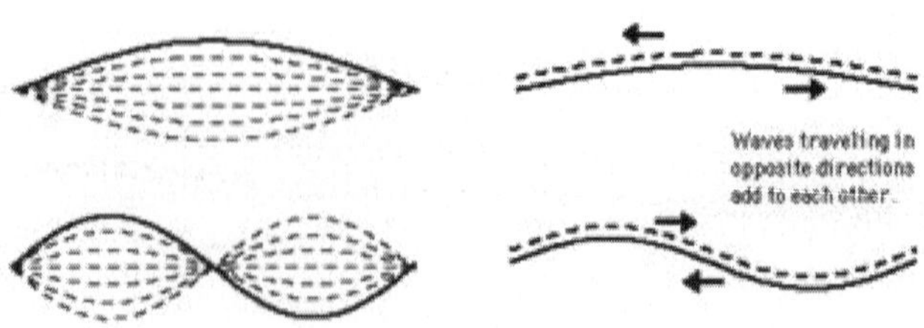

Fig. 22. The fundamental and second harmonic standing waves for a stretched string.

The sound intensity from a point source of sound will obey the inverse square law if there are no reflections or reverberation figure (23). Any point source, which spreads its influence equally in all directions without a limit to its range, will obey the inverse square law. This comes from strictly geometrical considerations. The intensity of the influence at any given radius r is the source strength divided by the area of the sphere. Being strictly geometric in its origin, the inverse square law applies to diverse phenomena. Point sources of gravitational force, electric field, light, sound or radiation obey the inverse square law.

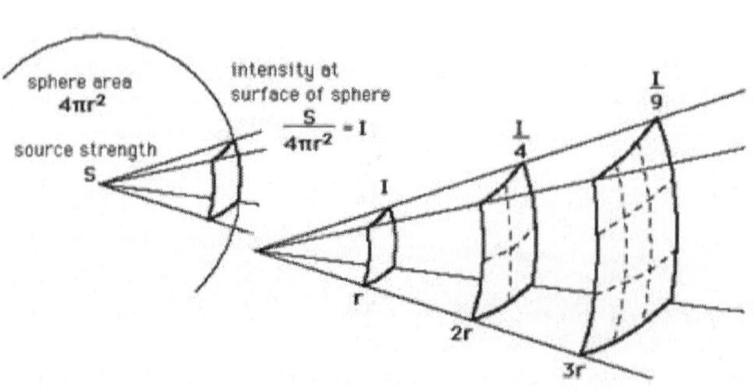

Fig. 23. Inverse Square Law

A plot of this intensity drop shows that it drops off rapidly figure (24). A plot of the drop of sound intensity according to the inverse square law emphasizes the rapid loss associated with the inverse square law. In an auditorium, such a rapid loss is unacceptable. The reverberation in a good auditorium mitigates it. This plot shows the points connected by straight lines but the actual drop is a smooth curve between the points.

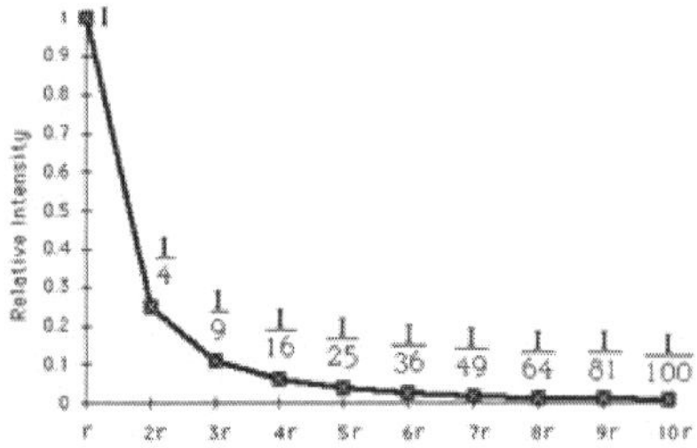

Fig. 24. Inverse Square Law Plot

Reverberation is the collection of reflected sounds from the surfaces in an enclosure like an auditorium. It is a desirable property of auditoriums to the extent that it helps to overcome the inverse square law drop-off of sound intensity in the enclosure. However, if it is excessive, it makes the sounds run together with loss of articulation - the sound becomes muddy, garbled figure (25).

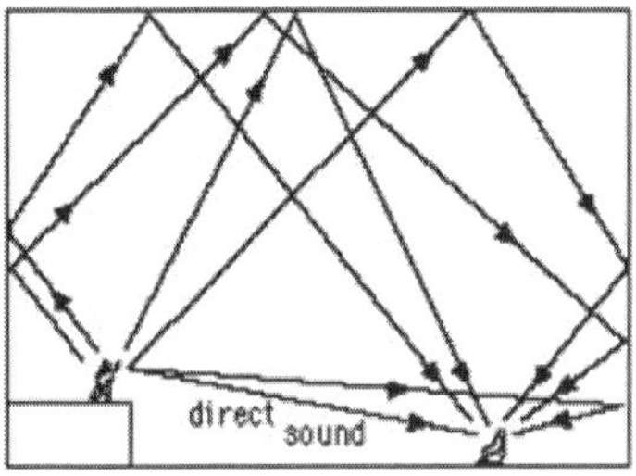

Fig. 25. Reverberant sound is the collection of all the reflected sounds in an auditorium.

7.2 ANC

In order to cancel unwanted noise, it is necessary to obtain an accurate estimate of the noise to be cancelled. In an open environment, where the noise source can be approximated as a point source, microphones can be spaced far apart as necessary and each will still receive a substantially similar estimate of the background noise. However in a confined environment containing reverberation noise caused by multiple sound reflections, the sound field is very complex and each point in the environment has a very different background noise signal. The further apart the microphones are, the more dissimilar the sound field. As a result, it is difficult to obtain an accurate estimate of the noise to be cancelled in a confined environment by using widely spaced microphones.

The proposed model is embodied in a dual microphone noise suppression system in which the echo between the two microphones is substantially cancelled or suppressed.

Reverberations from one microphone to the other are cancelled by the use of first and second line echo cancellers. Each line echo canceller models the delay and transmission characteristics of the acoustic path between the first and second microphones Figure (26).

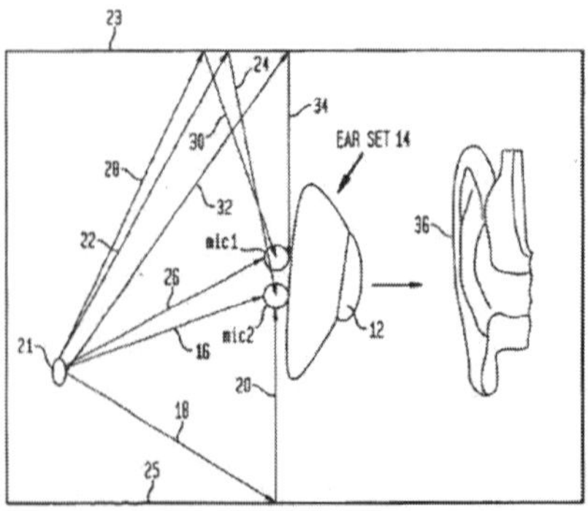

Fig. 26. A pictorial representation of the sound field reaching an ear set in accordance with the proposed model intended to be worn in the human ear.

If the two microphones are moved closer together, the second microphone should provide a better estimate of the noise to be cancelled in the first microphone. However, if the two microphones are placed very close together, each microphone will cause an additional echo to strike the other microphone. That is, the first microphone will act like a speaker (a sound source) transmitting an echo of the sound field striking the second microphone. Similarly, the second microphone will act like a speaker (a sound source) transmitting an echo of the sound field striking the first microphone. Therefore, the signal from the first microphone contains the sum of the background noise plus a reflection of the background noise, which results in a poorer estimate of the background noise to be cancelled figures (27) and (28).

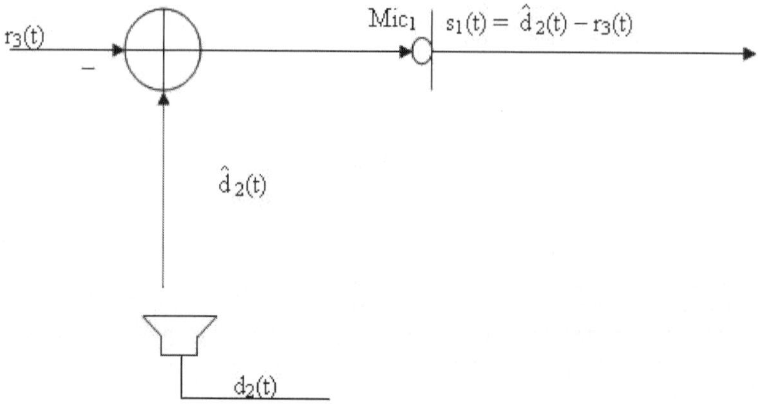

Fig. 27. Simplified model for one direction.

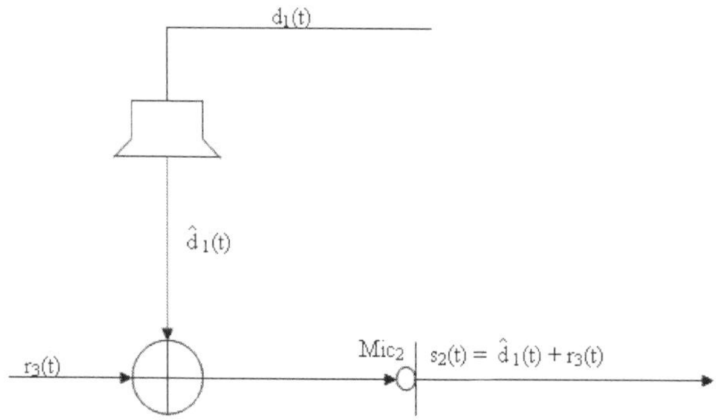

Fig. 28. Simplified model for the opposite direction.

In a first embodiment, a noise suppression system in accordance with the proposed model acts as an ear protector, cancelling substantially all or most of the noise striking the dual microphones of the ear set figure (29). In a second embodiment, a noise suppression system in accordance with the present invention acts a noise suppression communication system, suppressing background noise while allowing communication signals to be heard by the wearer figures (30 and 31).

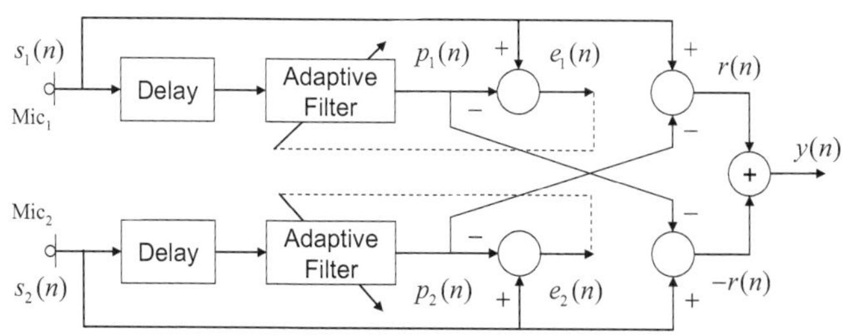

Fig. 29. A noise suppression System in accordance with a first embodiment of the proposed model.

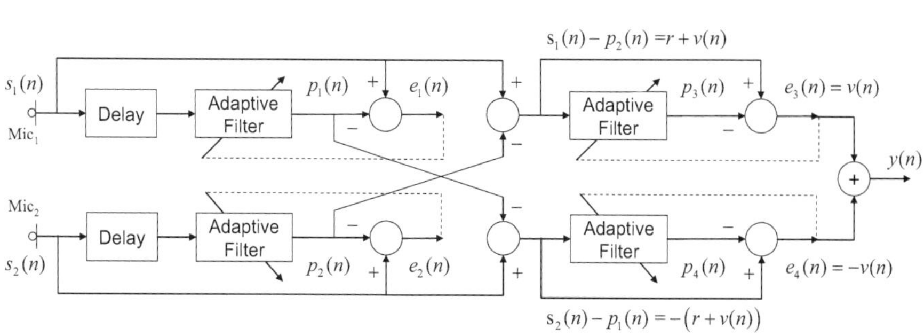

Fig. 30. A noise suppression communications system in accordance with a second embodiment of the proposed model.

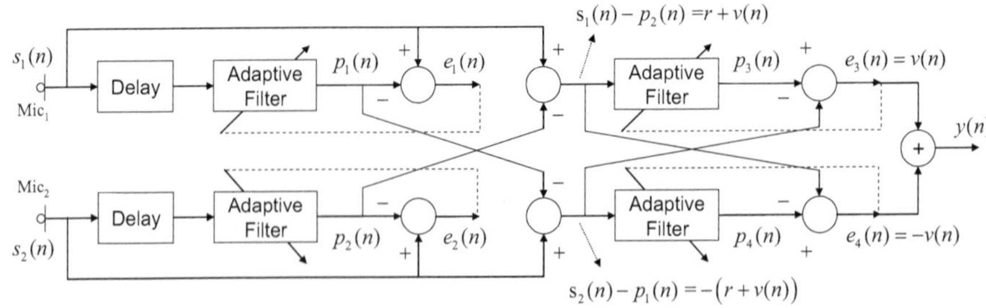

Fig. 31. An alternate scheme for a noise suppression communications system in accordance with a second embodiment of the proposed model.

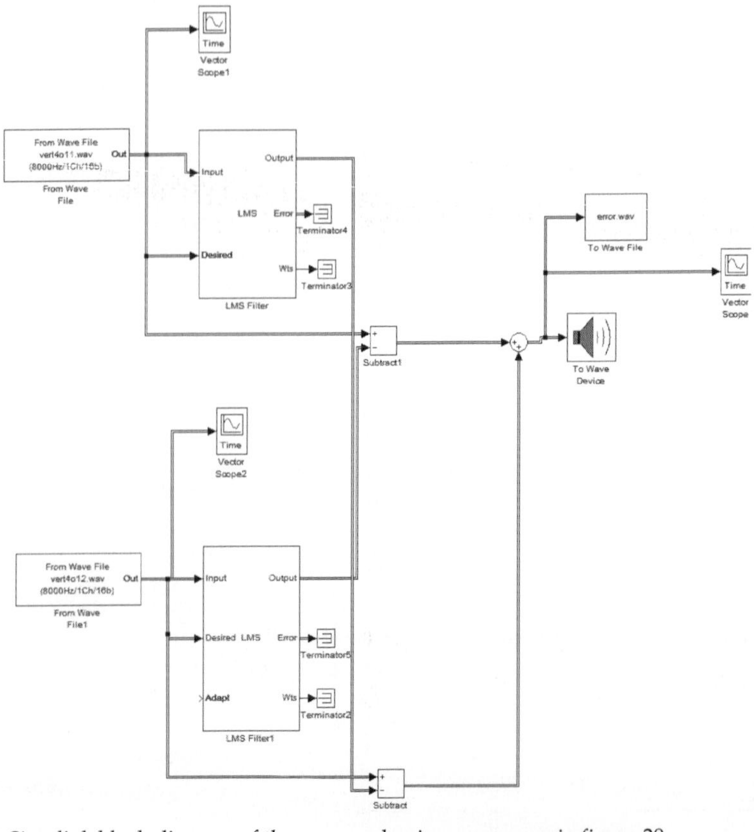

Fig. 32. Simulink block diagram of the proposed noise suppressor in figure 29.

The conceptual key to this proposed model is that the signals received at two closely spaced microphones in a multi-path acoustic environment are each made up of a sum of echoes of

the signal received at the other one. This leads to the conclusion that the difference between the two microphone signals is a sum of echoes of the acoustic source in the environment. In the absence of a speech source, the ANS scheme proposed by Jaber first attempts to isolate the difference signal at each of the microphones by subtracting from it an adaptively predicted version of the other microphone signal. It then attempts to adaptively cancel the two difference signals. When speech is present (as detected by some type of VAD-based strategy), the adaptive cancellation stage has its adaptivity turned off (i.e. the impulse responses of the two FIR filters, one for each microphone, are unchanged for the duration of the speech). The effect here is that the adaptive canceller does not end up cancelling the speech signal contained in the difference between the two microphone signals.
The Simulink implementation of the noise suppression system illustrated in figure 29 is displayed in figure 32 where figures 33 and 34 display the noise captured by Mic.1 and Mic. 2 respectively, meanwhile figure 35 shows the filter output.

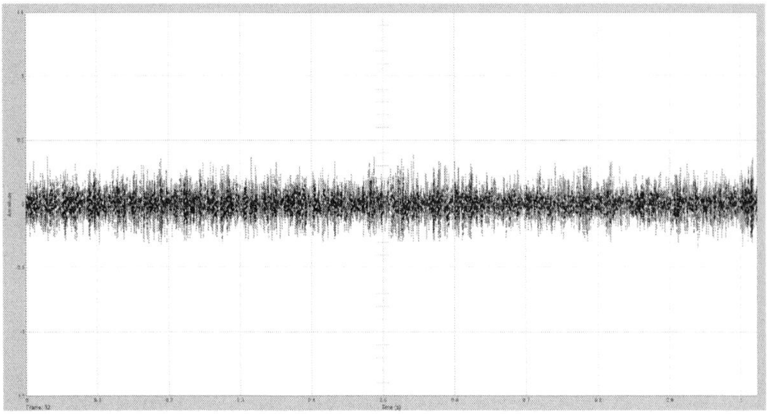

Fig. 33. Noise Captured by Mic. 1.

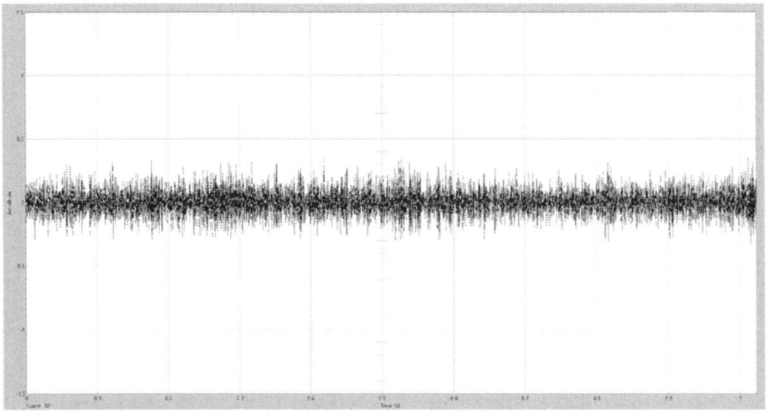

Fig. 34. Noise Captured By Mic. 2.

The Simulink implementation of the Active Noise Suppressor illustrated in Figure 30 with no Voice Activity Detection (VAD) attached is sketched in 36 and the taking off plane's noise captured by Mic.1 and Mic. 2 are presented in figures 37 and 38 respectively meanwhile figure 39 shows the system output.

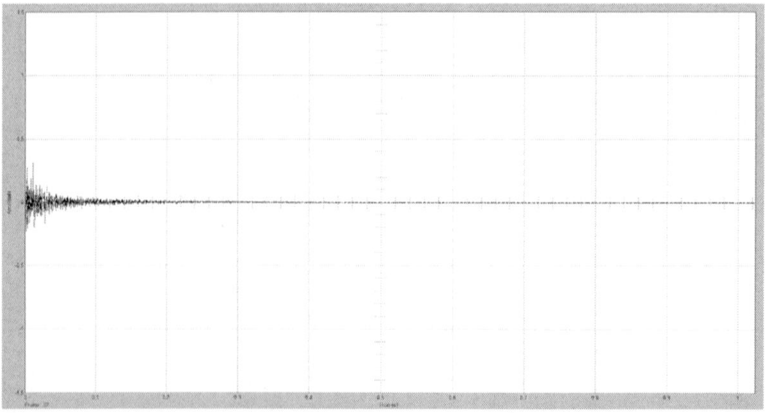

Fig. 35. The Filtered Noise output.

With an accurate front-point and end-point detection VAD algorithm [10] implemented in our proposed models illustrated in figures 30-31, an active noise suppressor is obtained.
The simulation results have been obtained from 25 seconds of noisy voice conditions as shown in Fig. 40 at Mic. 1 and the clean speech of our output filter is shown in figure 41 mean while figure 42 will illustrate the clean speech on a reduced scale [11].

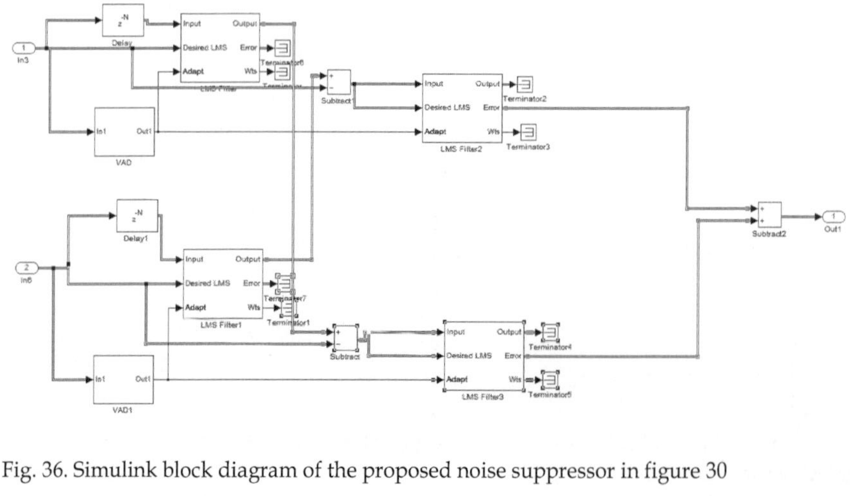

Fig. 36. Simulink block diagram of the proposed noise suppressor in figure 30

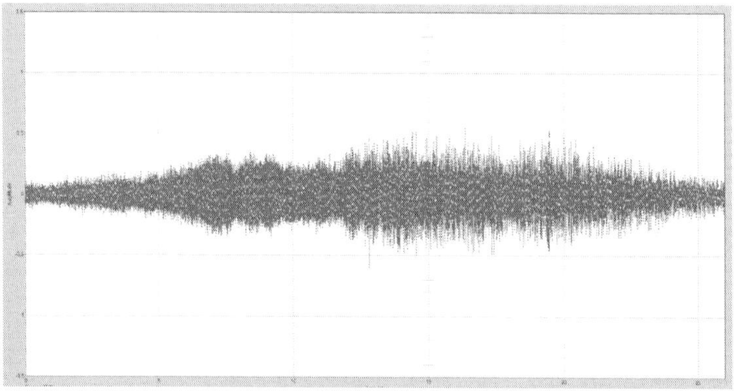

Fig. 37. Taking off Airplane's Noise Captured by Mic. 1.

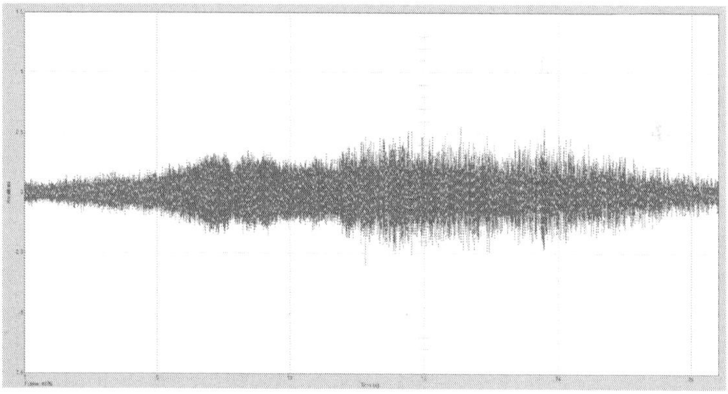

Fig. 38. Taking off Airplane's Noise Captured by Mic. 2.

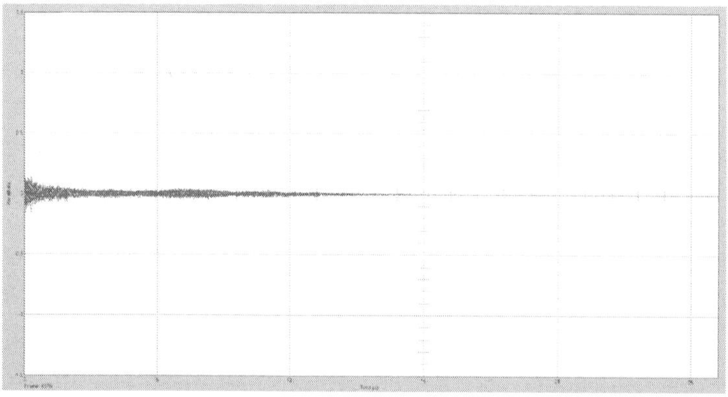

Fig. 39. The system's output

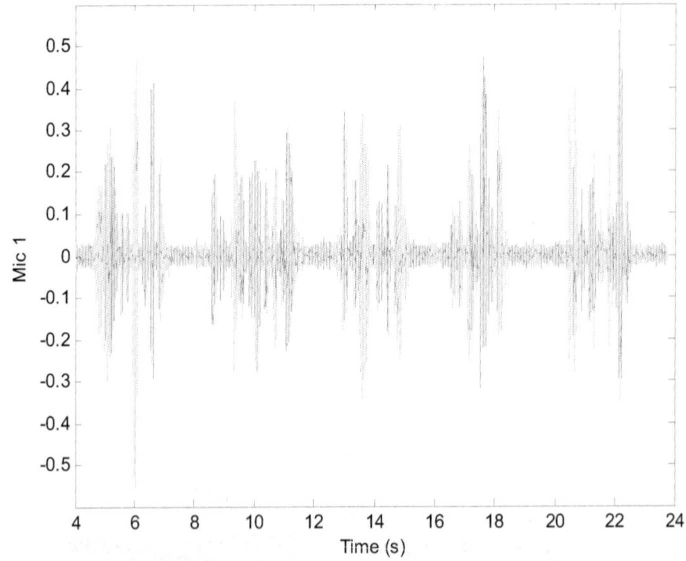

Fig. 40. Noisy speech captured by Mic 1.

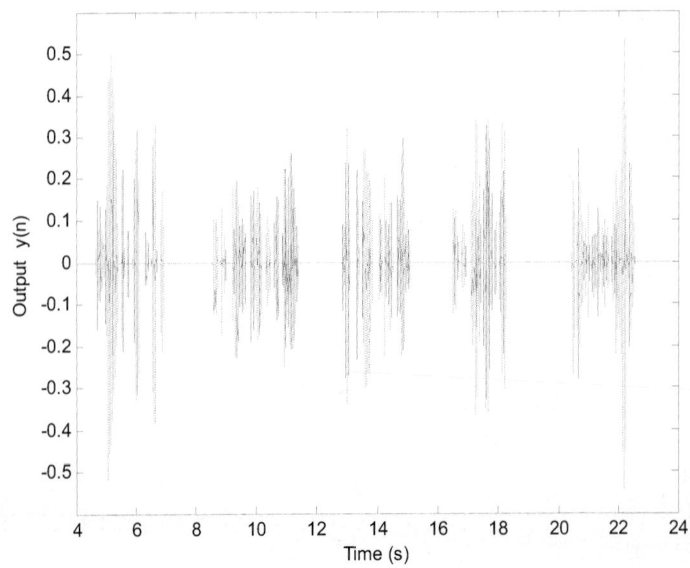

Fig. 41. The clean speech obtained at the output of our proposed ANC (Fig. 30) by using a VAD.

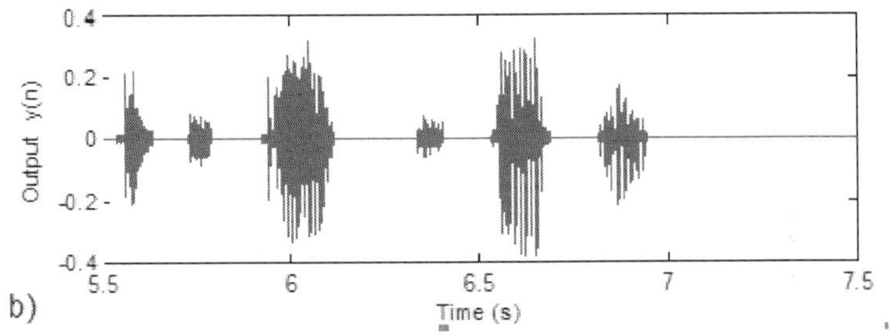

Fig. 42. The clean speech obtained at the output of our proposed ANC (Fig. 30) by reducing the time scale

8. The ultra high speed LMS algorithm implemented on parallel architecture

There are many problems that require enormous computational capacity to solve, and therefore the success of computational science to accurately describe and model the real world has helped to fuel the ever increasing demand for cheap computing power. Scientists are eager to find ways to test the limits of theories, using high performance computing to allow them to simulate more realistic systems in greater detail. Parallel computing offers a way to address these problems in a cost effective manner. **Parallel Computing** deals with the development of programs where multiple concurrent processes cooperate in the fulfilment of a common task. Finally, in this section we will develop the theory of the parallel computation of the widely used algorithms named the least-mean-square (LMS) algorithm[1] by its originators, Widrow and Hoff (1960) [2].

8.1 The spatial radix-*r* factorization

This section will be devoted in proving that discrete signals could be decomposed into ***r*** partial signals and whose statistical properties remain invariant therefore, given a discrete signal $\boldsymbol{x_n}$ of size **N**

$$x_n = \left[x_0 \; x_1 \; x_2 \; \cdots \; x_{(N-1)} \right] \tag{97}$$

and the identity matrix $\boldsymbol{I_r}$ of size ***r***

$$I_r = \begin{bmatrix} 1 & 0 & \dots & 0 \\ 0 & 1 & \dots & 0 \\ \dots & \dots & \dots & \dots \\ 0 & 0 & \dots & 1 \end{bmatrix} = \left[I_{(l,c)} \right] = \begin{cases} 1 & for\ l = c \\ 0 & elsewhere \end{cases} \tag{98}$$

for $l = c = 0, 1, \ldots, r-1$.

Based on what was proposed in [2]-[9]; we can conclude that for any given discrete signal $\boldsymbol{x_{(n)}}$ we can write:

[1] M Jaber "Method and apparatus for enhancing processing speed for performing a least mean square operation by parallel processing" US patent No. 7,533,140, 2009

$$x_{(l,n)} = \left[I_{(l,c)} \right] \times \left[x_{(rn)} \ x_{(rn+1)} \ \cdots \ x_{(rn+p)} \right] \tag{99}$$

is the product of the identity matrix of size **r** by **r** sets of vectors of size **N/r** (**n** = 0,1, .., **N/r** -1) where the lth element of the nth product is stored into the memory address location given by

$$l = (rn + p) \tag{100}$$

for $p = 0, 1, \ldots, r - 1$.
The mean (or Expected value) of x_n is given as:

$$E[x] = \frac{\sum_{n=0}^{N-1} x_n}{N} \tag{101}$$

which could be factorizes as:

$$\begin{aligned} E[x] &= \frac{\sum_{n=0}^{(N/r)-1} x_{(rn)} + \cdots + \sum_{n=0}^{(N/r)-1} x_{(rn+(r-1))}}{N} = \mu_{(x)} \\ &= \frac{\frac{1}{r} \times \sum_{n=0}^{(N/r)-1} x_{(rn+p)}}{\frac{N}{r}} = \frac{\mu_{(x(rn+p))}}{r} \end{aligned} \tag{102}$$

therefore, the mean of the signal x_n is equal to sum of the means of its r partial signals divided by r for $p = 0, 1, \ldots, r - 1$.
Similarly to the mean, the variance of the signal x_n equal to sum of the variances of its r partial signals according to:

$$\begin{aligned} Var(x) &= \sigma_x^2 = E\left[(x-\mu)^2 \right] = \sum_{n=0}^{N-1} \left(x_{(n)} - \mu \right)^2 \\ &= \sum_{n=0}^{(N/r)-1} \left(x_{(rn)} - \mu_{(rn)} \right)^2 + \cdots + \sum_{n=0}^{(N/r)-1} \left(x_{(rn+(r-1))} - \mu_{(rn+(r-1))} \right)^2 \\ &= \sum_{p=0}^{r-1} \sigma_{x(rn+p)}^2 \end{aligned} \tag{103}$$

8.2 The parallel implementation of the least squares method

The method of least squares assumes that the best-fit curve of a given type is the curve that has the minimal sum of the deviations squared (*least square error*) from a given set of data. Suppose that the N data points are $(x_0, y_0), (x_1, y_1) \ldots (x_{(n-1)}, y_{(n-1)})$, where x is the independent variable and y is the dependent variable. The fitting curve d has the deviation (error) σ from each data point, i.e., $\sigma_0 = d_0 - y_0$, $\sigma_1 = d_1 - y_1 \ldots \sigma_{(n-1)} = d_{(n-1)} - d_{(n-1)}$ which could be re-ordered as:

$$\begin{aligned} &\sigma_0 = d_0 - y_0, \sigma_r = d_r - y_r, \sigma_{2r} = d_{2r} - y_{2r}, \ldots, \\ &\sigma_{rn} = d_{rn} - y_{rn}, \sigma_1 = d_1 \ \ y_1, \ldots, \sigma_{(rn+1)} = d_{(rn+1)} - y_{(rn+1)}, \ldots, \sigma_{(rn+(r-1))} = d_{(rn+(r-1))} - y_{(rn+(r-1))} \end{aligned} \tag{104}$$

for $n = 0, 1, \ldots, (N/r) - 1$.

According to the method of least squares, the best fitting curve has the property that:

$$\begin{aligned} J &= \sigma_0^2 + \ldots + \sigma_m^2 + \sigma_1^2 + \ldots + \sigma_{(m+1)}^2 + \ldots + \sigma_{(m+(r-1))}^2 \\ &= \sum_{j0=0}^{r-1} \sum_{n=0}^{(N/r)-1} \left[d_{(m+j0)} - y_{(m+j0)} \right]^2 \\ &= \sum_{j0=0}^{r-1} \sum_{n=0}^{(N/r)-1} \sigma_{(m+j0)}^2 = \text{a minimum} \end{aligned} \tag{105}$$

The parallel implementation of the least squares for the linear case could be expressed as:

$$\begin{aligned} e_{(n)} &= d_{(n)} - \left(b + wx_{(n)}\right) = d_{(n)} - y_{(n)} \\ &= \left(I_r \times \left[d_{(m+j0)} - y_{(m+j0)} \right]\right) \\ &= \left(I_r \times \left[e_{(m+j0)} \right]\right) \end{aligned} \tag{106}$$

for $j_0 = 1, \ldots, r-1$ and in order to pick the line which best fits the data, we need a criterion to determine which linear estimator is the "best". The sum of square errors (also called the mean square error (MSE)) is a widely utilized performance criterion.

$$\begin{aligned} J &= \frac{1}{2N} \sum_{n=0}^{N-1} e_{(n)}^2 \\ &= \left(1/r\right) \sum_{j0=0}^{r-1} \left(1/2(N/r) \right) \sum_{n=0}^{(N/r)-1} \left(\left(I_r \times \left[e_{(m+j0)} \right] \right) \right)^2 \end{aligned} \tag{107}$$

which yields after simplification to:

$$\begin{aligned} J &= \left(1/r\right) \sum_{j0=0}^{r-1} \left(I_r \times \left[\left(\frac{1}{2(N/r)} \right) \sum_{n=0}^{(N/r)-1} e_{(m+j0)}^2 \right] \right) \\ &= \left(1/r\right) \sum_{j0=0}^{r-1} \left(I_r \times \left[J_{j0} \right] \right) = \left(1/r\right) \sum_{j0=0}^{r-1} J_{j0} \end{aligned} \tag{108}$$

where J_0 is the partial MSE applied on the subdivided data.

Our goal is to minimize J analytically, which according to Gauss can be done by taking its partial derivative with respect to the unknowns and equating the resulting equations to zero:

$$\begin{cases} \dfrac{\partial J}{\partial b} = 0 \\ \dfrac{\partial J}{\partial w} = 0 \end{cases} \tag{109}$$

which yields:

$$\begin{cases} \dfrac{\partial J}{\partial b} = \dfrac{\partial\left((1/r)\sum_{j0=0}^{r-1}\left(I_r \times \left[J_{j0} \right] \right) \right)}{\partial b} = (1/r)\sum_{j0=0}^{r-1}\dfrac{\partial\left(J_{j0} \right)}{\partial b} = 0 \\ \dfrac{\partial J}{\partial w} = \dfrac{\partial\left((1/r)\sum_{j0=0}^{r-1}\left(I_r \times \left[J_{j0} \right] \right) \right)}{\partial w} = (1/r)\sum_{j0=0}^{r-1}\dfrac{\partial\left(J_{j0} \right)}{\partial w} = 0 \end{cases} \quad (110)$$

With the same reasoning as above the MSE could be obtained for multiple variables by:

$$\begin{aligned} J &= \frac{1}{2N}\sum_{n}\left(d_{(n)} - \sum_{k=0}^{p} w_{(k)} x_{(n,k)} \right)^2 \\ &= \frac{1}{r}\left(\sum_{j0=0}^{r-1} \frac{1}{2\left(N/r\right)} \sum_{n=0}^{(N/r)-1}\left[d_{(rn+j0)} - \sum_{k=0}^{p} w_{((rn+j0),k)} x_{((rn+j0),k)} \right]^2 \right) \\ &= \frac{1}{r}\sum_{j0=0}^{r-1} J_{j0} \end{aligned} \quad (111)$$

for $j_0 = 1, \ldots, r-1$ and where J_{j_0} is the partial MSE applied on the subdivided data.

The solution to the extreme (minimum) of this equation can be found in exactly the same way as before, that is, by taking the derivatives of J_{j_0} with respect to the unknowns (w_k), and equating the result to zero.

Instead of solving equations 110 and 111 analytically, a gradient adaptive system can be used which is done by estimating the derivative using the difference operator. This estimation is given by:

$$\nabla_w J = \frac{\delta J}{\delta w} \quad (112)$$

where in this case the bias b is set to zero.

8.3 Search of the performance surface with steepest descent

The method of steepest descent (also known as the gradient method) is the simplest example of a gradient based method for *minimizing a function of several variables* [12]. In this section we will be elaborating the linear case.

Since the performance surface for the linear case implemented in parallel, are r paraboloids each of which has a single minimum, an alternate procedure to find the best value of the coefficient $w_{j0(k)}$ is to search in parallel the performance surface instead of computing the best coefficient analytically by Eq. 110. The search for the minimum of a function can be done efficiently using a broad class of methods that *use gradient information*. The gradient has two main advantages for search.

- The gradient can be computed locally.
- The gradient always points in the direction of maximum change.

If the goal is to reach the minimum in each parallel segment, the search must be in the direction opposite to the gradient. So, the overall method of search can be stated in the following way:

Start the search with an *arbitrary initial weight* $w_{j0(0)}$, where the *iteration* is denoted by the index in parenthesis (Fig 43). Then compute the gradient of the performance surface at $w_{j0(0)}$, and modify the initial weight proportionally to the negative of the gradient at $w_{j0(0)}$. This changes the operating point to $w_{j0(1)}$. Then compute the gradient at the new position $w_{j0(1)}$, and apply the same procedure again, i.e.

$$w_{j0(k+1)} = w_{j0(k)} - \eta \nabla J_{j0(k)} \tag{113}$$

where η is a small constant and $\nabla J_{j0(k)}$ denotes the gradient of the performance surface at the kth iteration of j_0 parallel segment. η is used to maintain stability in the search by ensuring that the operating point does not move too far along the performance surface. This search procedure is called the steepest descent method (fig 43)

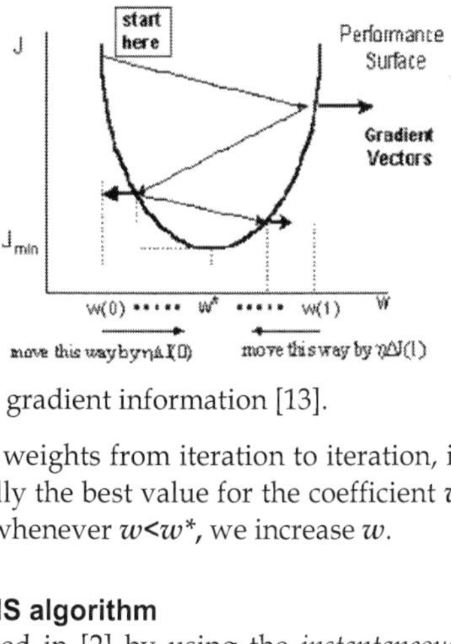

Fig. 43. The search using the gradient information [13].

If one traces the path of the weights from iteration to iteration, intuitively we see that if the constant η is small, eventually the best value for the coefficient w^* will be found. Whenever $w>w^*$, we decrease w, and whenever $w<w^*$, we increase w.

8.4 The radix- *r* parallel LMS algorithm

Based on what was proposed in [2] by using the *instantaneous value of the gradient as the estimator for the true quantity* which means by dropping the summation in equation 108 and then taking the derivative with respect to w yields:

$$\begin{aligned}
\nabla J_{(k)} &= \nabla\left(\frac{1}{r}\times\left(I_r\times\left[J_{j0(k)}\right]\right)\right) \\
&= \frac{\partial}{\partial w}J_{(k)} = \frac{\partial}{\partial w}\left(\frac{1}{r}\times\left(I_r\times\left[J_{j0(k)}\right]\right)\right) \\
&\approx \frac{\partial}{\partial w}\frac{1}{2Nr}\sum e^2 = \frac{\partial}{\partial w}\frac{1}{2Nr}\sum_{j0=0}^{r-1}\sum_{n=0}^{\left(\frac{N}{r}\right)-1}\left(I_r\times\left[e_{(rn+j0)}\right]\right)^2 \\
&\approx \frac{1}{r}\frac{\partial}{\partial w}\left(I_r\times\left[e_{(rn+j0)(k)}x_{(rn+j0)(k)}\right]\right)
\end{aligned} \tag{114}$$

What this equation tells us is that an *instantaneous estimate of the gradient is simply the product of the input to the weight times the error at iteration k.* This means that with one multiplication per weight the gradient can be estimated. This is the gradient estimate that leads *to the famous Least Means Square (LMS) algorithm* (Fig 44).
If the estimator of Eq.114 is substituted in Eq.113, the steepest descent equation becomes

$$I_r \times \left[w_{j0_{(k+1)}} \right] = I_r \times \left(w_{j0_{(k)}} + \left(\left(\frac{1}{r} \right) \left(\eta_{j0} e_{(rn+j0)_{(k)}} x_{(rn+j0)_{(k)}} \right) \right) \right) \tag{115}$$

for $j_0 = 0,1, \ldots, r-1$.
This equation is the ***r*** Parallel ***LMS** algorithm,* which is used as predictive filter, is illustrated in Figure 45. The small constant **η** is called the step size *or the learning rate.*

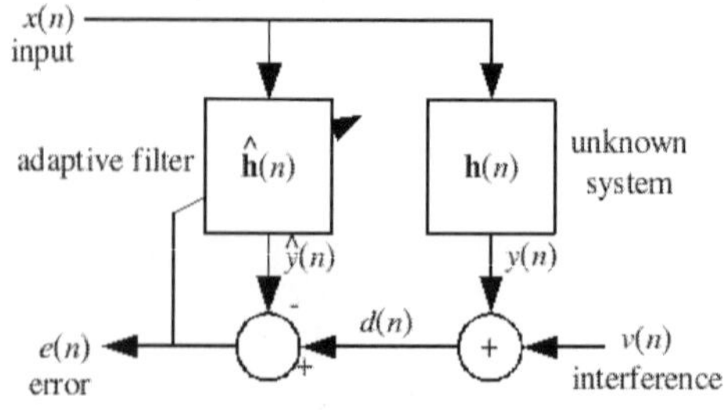

Fig. 44. LMS Filter

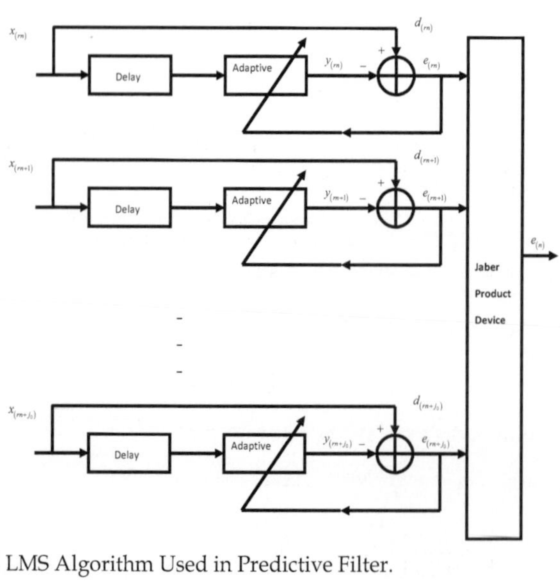

Fig. 45. *r* Parallel LMS Algorithm Used in Predictive Filter.

8.5 Simulation results

The notion of a mathematical model is fundamental to sciences and engineering. In class of applications dealing with identification, an adaptive filter is used is used to provide a linear model that represents the best fit (in some sense) to an unknown signal. The LMS Algorithm which is widely used is an extremely simple and elegant algorithm that is able to minimize the external cost function by using local information available to the system parameters. Due to its computational burden and in order to speed up the process, this paper has presented an efficient way to compute the LMS algorithm in parallel where it follows from the simulation results that the stability of our models relies on the stability of our r parallel adaptive filters. It follows from figures 47 and 48 that the stability of r parallel LMS filters (in this case $r = 2$) has been achieved and the convergence performance of the overall model is illustrated in figure 49. The complexity of the proposed method will be reduced by a factor of r in comparison to the direct method illustrated in figure 46. Furthermore, the simulation result of the channel equalization is illustrated in figure 50 in which the blue curves represents our parallel implementation (2 LMS implemented in parallel) compared to the conventional method where the curve is in a red colour.

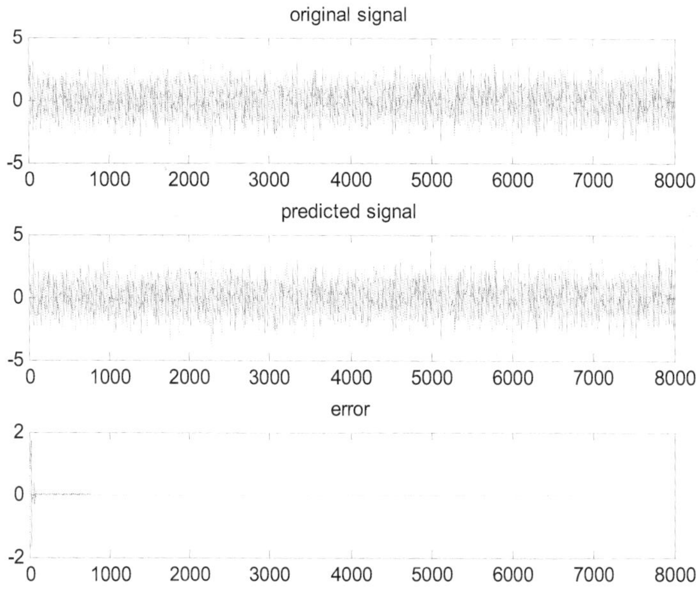

Fig. 46. Simulation Result of the original signal

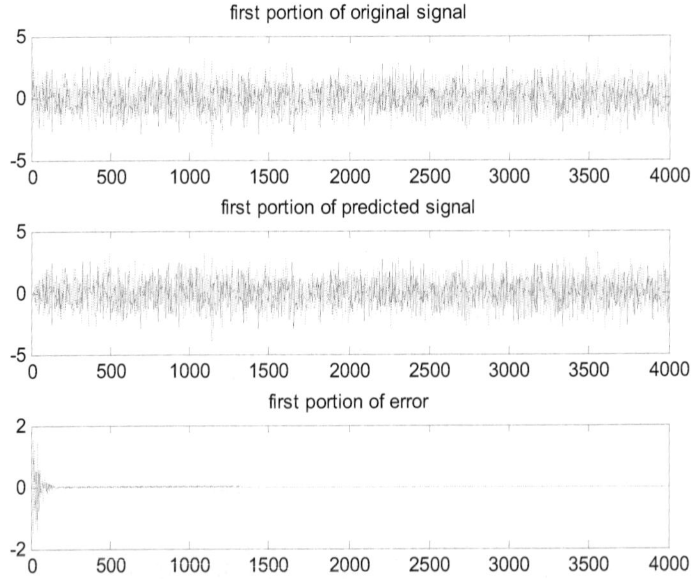

Fig. 47. Simulation Result of the first partial LMS Algorithm.

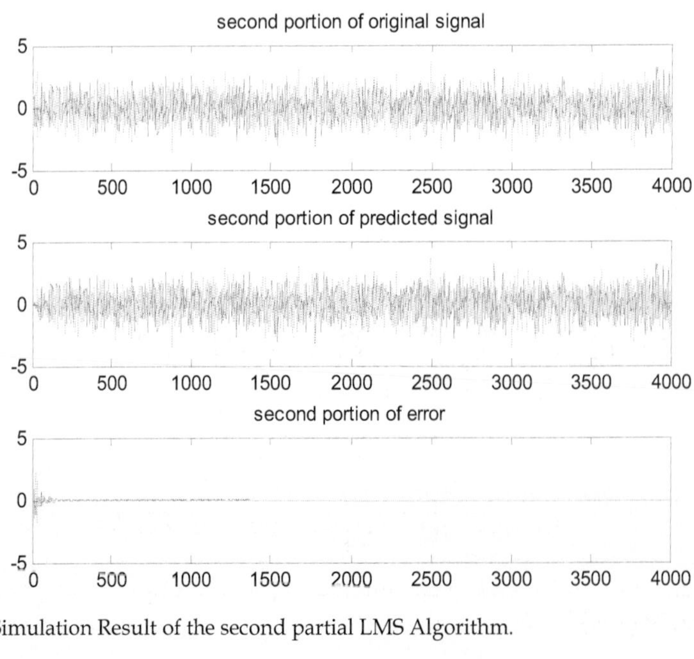

Fig. 48. Simulation Result of the second partial LMS Algorithm.

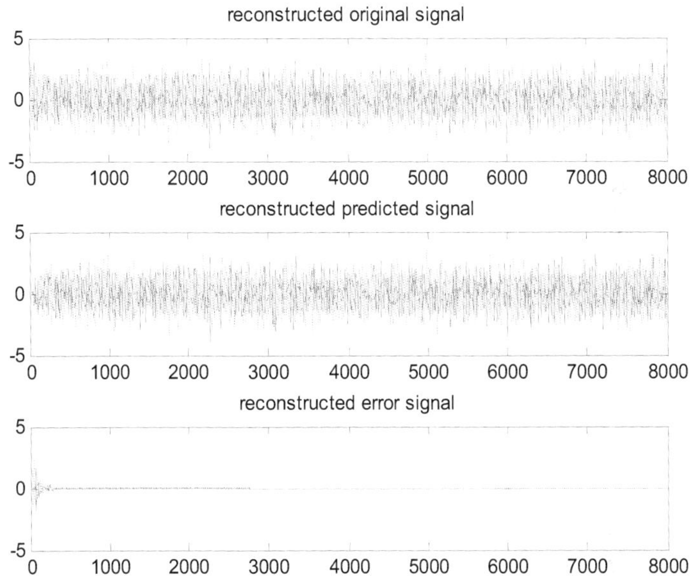

Fig. 49. Simulation Result of the Overall System.

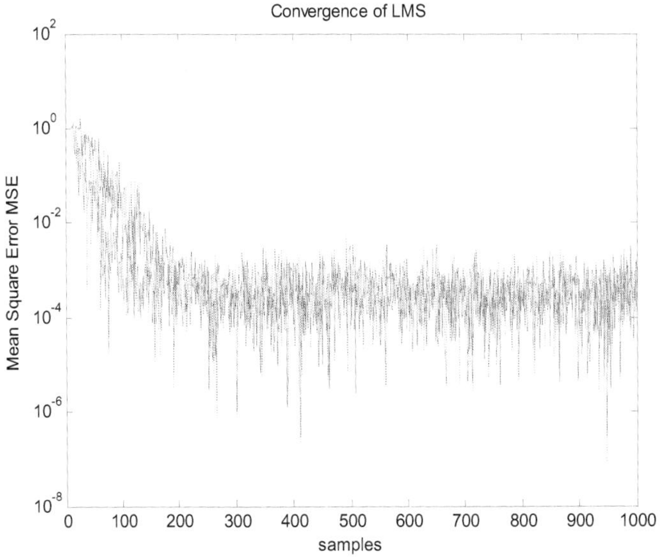

Fig. 50. Simulation Result of the channel equalization (blue curve two LMS implemented in Parallel red curve one LMS).

8. References

[1] S. Haykin, Adaptive Filter Theory, Prentice-Hall, Englewood Cliffs, NJ, 1991.

[2] Widrow and Stearns, " Adaptive Signal Processing ", Prentice Hall 195.

[3] K. Mayyas, and T. Aboulnasr, "A Robust Variable Step Size LMS-Type Algorithm: Analysis and Simulations", IEEE 5-1995, pp. 1408-1411.

[4] T. Aboulnasar, and K. Mayyas, "Selective Coefficient Update of Gradient-Based Adaptive Algorithms", IEEE 1997, pp. 1929-1932.

[5] E. Bjarnason: "Analysis of the Filtered X LMS Algorithm ", IEEE 4 1993, pp. III-511, III-514.

[6] E.A. Wan, "Adjoint LMS: An Efficient Alternative To The Filtered X LMS And Multiple Error LMS Algorithm", Oregon Graduate Institute Of Science & Technology, Department Of Electrical Engineering And Applied Physics, P.O. Box 91000, Portland, OR 97291.

[7] B. Farhang-Boroujeny: "Adaptive Filters, Theory and Applications", Wiley 1999.

[8] Wiener, Norbert (1949). *"Extrapolation, Interpolation, and Smoothing of Stationary Time Series"*, New York: Wiley. ISBN 0-262-73005-7

[9] M. Jaber "Noise Suppression System with Dual Microphone Echo Cancellation US patent no.US-6738482.

[10] M. Jaber, "Voice Activity detection Algorithm for Voiced /Unvoiced Decision and Pitch Estimation in a Noisy Speech feature Extraction", US patent application no. 60/771167, 2007.

[11] M. Jaber and D. Massicottes: "A Robust Dual Predictive Line Acoustic Noise Canceller", International Conference on Digital Signal Processing DSP 2009 Santorini Greece.

[12] M. Jaber, D. Massicotte, "A New FFT Concept for Efficient VLSI Implementation: Part I - Butterfly Processing Element", 16th International Conference on Digital Signal Processing (DSP'09), Santorini, Greece, 5-7 July 2009.

[13] J.C. Principe, W.C. Lefebvre, N.R. Euliano, *"Neural Systems: Fundamentals through Simulation"*, 1996.

4

An LMS Adaptive Filter Using Distributed Arithmetic - Algorithms and Architectures

Kyo Takahashi[1], Naoki Honma[2] and Yoshitaka Tsunekawa[2]
[1]*Iwate Industrial Research Institute*
[2]*Iwate University*
Japan

1. Introduction

In recent years, adaptive filters are used in many applications, for example an echo canceller, a noise canceller, an adaptive equalizer and so on, and the necessity of their implementations is growing up in many fields. Adaptive filters require various performances of a high speed, lower power dissipation, good convergence properties, small output latency, and so on. The echo-canceller used in the videoconferencing requires a fast convergence property and a capability to track the time varying impulse response (Makino & Koizumi, 1988). Therefore, implementations of very high order adaptive filters are required. In order to satisfy these requirements, highly-efficient algorithms and architectures are desired. The adaptive filter is generally constructed by using the multipliers, adders and memories, and so on, whereas, the structure without multipliers has been proposed.

The LMS adaptive filter using distributed arithmetic can be realized by using adders and memories without multipliers, that is, it can be achieved with a small hardware. A Distributed Arithmetic (DA) is an efficient calculation method of an inner product of constant vectors, and it has been used in the DCT realization. Furthermore, it is suitable for time varying coefficient vector in the adaptive filter. Cowan and others proposed a Least Mean Square (LMS) adaptive filter using the DA on an offset binary coding (Cowan & Mavor, 1981; Cowan et al, 1983). However, it is found that the convergence speed of this method is extremely degraded (Tsunekawa et al, 1999). This degradation results from an offset bias added to an input signal coded on the offset binary coding. To overcome this problem, an update algorithm generalized with 2's complement representation has been proposed (Tsunekawa et al, 1999), and the convergence condition has been analyzed (Takahashi et al, 2002). The effective architectures for the LMS adaptive filter using the DA have been proposed (Tsunekawa et al, 1999; Takahashi et al, 2001). The LMS adaptive filter using distributed arithmetic is expressed by DA-ADF. The DA is applied to the output calculation, i.e., inner product of the input signal vector and coefficient vector. The output signal is obtained by the shift and addition of the partial-products specified with the bit patterns of the N-th order input signal vector. This process is performed from LSB to MSB direction at the every sampling instance, where the B indicates the word length. The B partial-products used to obtain the output signal are updated from LMB to MSB direction. There exist 2^N partial-products, and the set including all the partial-products is called Whole Adaptive Function Space (WAFS). Furthermore, the DA-ADF using multi-memory block structure that uses the divided WAFS (MDA-ADF) (Wei & Lou, 1986; Tsunakawa et al, 1999) and the MDA-ADF using half-memory algorithm based on the pseudo-odd symmetry property of the WAFS (HMDA-ADF) have been proposed (Takahashi et al, 2001). The divided WAFS is expressed by DWAFS.

In this chapter, the new algorithm and effective architecture of the MDA-ADF are discussed. The objectives are improvements of the MDA-ADF permitting the increase of an amount of hardware and power dissipation. The convergence properties of the new algorithm are evaluated by the computer simulations, and the efficiency of the proposed VLSI architecture is evaluated.

2. LMS adaptive filter

An N-tap input signal vector S(k) is represented as

$$\mathbf{S}(k)=\left[s(k),s(k-1),\cdots,s(k-N+1)\right]^T, \tag{1}$$

where, s(k) is an input signal at k time instance, and the T indicates a transpose of the vector. The output signal of an adaptive filter is represented as

$$y(k)=\mathbf{S}^T(k)\mathbf{W}(k), \tag{2}$$

where, W(k) is the N-th coefficient vector represented as

$$\mathbf{W}(k)=\left[w_0(k),w_1(k),\cdots,w_{N-1}(k)\right]^T, \tag{3}$$

and the $w_i(k)$ is an i-th tap coefficient of the adaptive filter.

The Widrow's LMS algorithm (Widrow et al, 1975) is represented as

$$\mathbf{W}(k+1)=\mathbf{W}(k)+2\mu e(k)\mathbf{S}(k), \tag{4}$$

where, the e(k), μ and d(k) are an error signal, a step-size parameter and the desired signal, respectively. The step-size parameter deterimines the convergence speed and the accuracy of the estimation. The error signal is obtained by

$$\mathrm{e(k)=d(k)-y(k)}. \tag{5}$$

The fundamental structure of the LMS adaptive filter is shown in Fig. 1. The filter input signal s(k) is fed into the delay-line, and shifted to the right direction every sampling instance. The taps of the delay-line provide the delayed input signal corresponding to the depth of delay elements. The tap outputs are multiplied with the corresponding coefficients, the sum of these products is an output of the LMS adaptive filter. The error signal is defined as the difference between the desired signal and the filter output signal. The tap coefficients are updated using the products of the input signals and the scaled error signal.

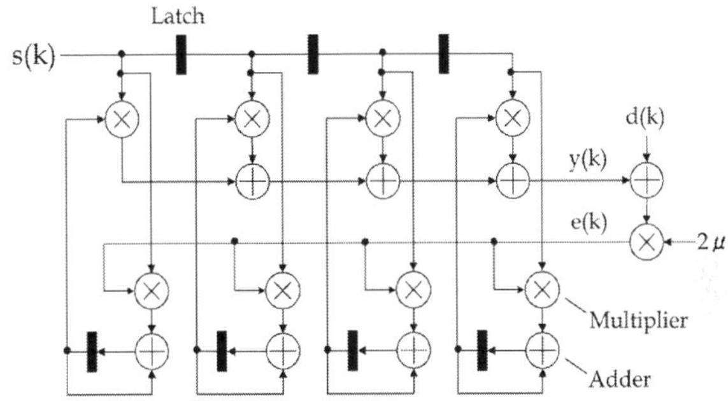

Fig. 1. Fundamental Structure of the 4-tap LMS adaptive filter.

3. LMS adaptive filter using distributed arithmetic

In the following discussions, the fundamentals of the DA on the 2's complement representation and the derivation of the DA-ADF are explained. The degradation of the convergence property and the drastic increase of the amount of hardware in the DA-ADF are the serious problems for its higher order implementation. As the solutions to overcome the problems, the multi-memory block structure and the half-memory algorithm based on the pseudo-odd symmetry property of WAFS are explained.

3.1 Distributed arithmetic

The DA is an efficient calculation method of an inner product by a table lookup method (Peled &Liu, 1974). Now, let's consider the inner product

$$y = \mathbf{a}^T \mathbf{v} = \sum_{i=1}^{N} a_i v_i \tag{6}$$

of the N-th order constant vector

$$\mathbf{a} = \left[a_0, a_1, \cdots a_{(N-1)}\right]^T \tag{7}$$

and the variable vector

$$\mathbf{v} = \left[v_0, v_1, \cdots v_{(N-1)}\right]^T . \tag{8}$$

In Eq.(8), the v_i is represented on B-bit fixed point and 2's complement representation, that is,

$$-1 \le v_i < 1$$

and

$$v_i = -v_i^0 + \sum_{k=1}^{B-1} v_i^k 2^{-k} , \quad i = 0,1,\cdots,N-1 . \tag{9}$$

In the Eq.(9), v_i^k indicates the k-th bit of v_i, i.e., 0 or 1. By substituting Eq.(9) for Eq.(6),

$$y = -\Phi\left(v_0^0, v_1^0, \cdots, v_{N-1}^0\right) + \sum_{k=1}^{B-1} \Phi\left(v_0^k, v_1^k, \cdots, v_{N-1}^k\right) 2^{-k} \tag{10}$$

is obtained. The function Φ which returns the partial-product corresponding argument is defined by

$$\Phi\left(v_0^k, v_1^k, \cdots, v_{N-1}^k\right) \equiv \sum_{i=0}^{N-1} a_i v_i^k . \tag{11}$$

Eq.(10) indicates that the inner product of y is obtained as the weighted sum of the partial-products. The first term of the right side is weighted by -1, i.e., sign bit, and the following terms are weighted by the 2^{-k}. Fig.2 shows the fundamental structure of the FIR filter using the DA (DA-FIR). The function table is realized using the Read Only Memory (ROM), and the right-shift and addition operation is realized using an adder and register. The ROM previously includes the partial-products determined by the tap coefficient vector and the bit-pattern of the input signal vector. From above discussions, the operation time is only depended on the word length B, not on the number of the term N, fundamentally. This means that the output latency is only depended on the word length B. The FIR filter using the DA can be implemented without multipliers, that is, it is possible to reduce the amount of hardware.

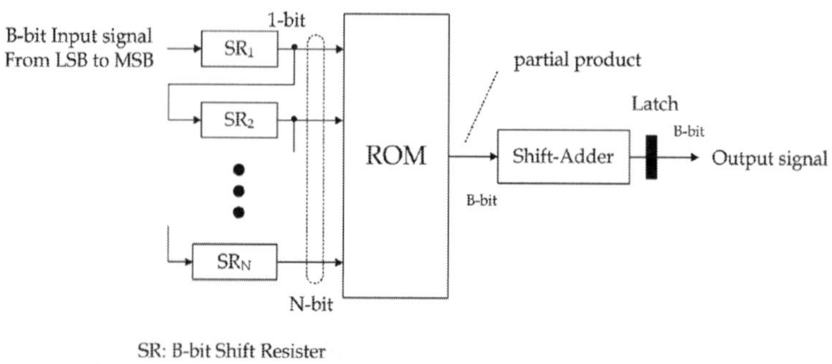

Fig. 2. Fundamental structure of the FIR filter using distributed arithmetic.

3.2 Derivation of LMS adaptive algorithm using distributed arithmetic

The derivation of the LMS algorithm using the DA on 2's complement representation is as follows. The N-th order input signal vector in Eq.(1) is defined as

$$\mathbf{S}(k) \equiv \mathbf{A}(k)\mathbf{F} . \tag{12}$$

Using this definition, the filter output signal is represented as

$$y(k) = \mathbf{S}^T(k)\mathbf{W}(k) = \mathbf{F}^T\mathbf{A}^T(k)\mathbf{W}(k) . \tag{13}$$

In Eq.(12) and Eq(13), an address matrix which is determined by the bit pattern of the input signal vector is represented as

$$\mathbf{A}(k)=\begin{bmatrix} b_0(k) & b_0(k-1) & \cdots & b_0(k-N+1) \\ b_1(k) & b_1(k-1) & \cdots & b_1(k-N+1) \\ \vdots & \vdots & \ddots & \vdots \\ b_{B-1}(k) & b_{B-1}(k-1) & \cdots & b_{B-1}(k-N+1) \end{bmatrix}^T, \tag{14}$$

and a scaling vector based on the 2's complement representation is represented as

$$\mathbf{F}=\left[-2^0,2^{-1},\cdots,2^{B-1}\right]^T, \tag{15}$$

where, $b_i(k)$ is an i-th bit of the input signal s(k). In Eq.(13), $A^T(k)W(k)$ is defined as

$$\mathbf{P}(k)\equiv\mathbf{A}^T(k)\mathbf{W}(k), \tag{16}$$

and the filter output is obtained as

$$y(k)=\mathbf{F}^T\mathbf{P}(k). \tag{17}$$

The P(k) is called adaptive function space (AFS), and is a B-th order vector of

$$\mathbf{P}(k)=\left[p_0(k),p_1(k),\cdots,p_{B-1}(k)\right]^T. \tag{18}$$

The P(k) is a subset of the WAFS including the elements specified by the row vectors (access vectors) of the address matrix. Now, multiplying both sides by $A^T(k)$, Eq.(4) becomes

$$\mathbf{A}^T(k)\mathbf{W}(k+1)=\mathbf{A}^T(k)\{\mathbf{W}(k)+2\mu e(k)\mathbf{A}(k)\mathbf{F}\}$$

$$=\mathbf{A}^T(k)\mathbf{W}(k)+2\mu e(k)\mathbf{A}^T(k)\mathbf{A}(k)\mathbf{F}. \tag{19}$$

Furthermore, by using the definitions described as

$$\mathbf{P}(k)\equiv\mathbf{A}^T(k)\mathbf{W}(k)$$

and

$$\mathbf{P}(k+1)\equiv\mathbf{A}^T(k)\mathbf{W}(k+1), \tag{20}$$

the relation of them can be explained as

$$\mathbf{P}(k+1)=\mathbf{P}(k)+2\mu e(k)\mathbf{A}^T(k)\mathbf{A}(k)\mathbf{F}. \tag{21}$$

It is impossible to perform the real-time processing because of the matrix multiplication of $A^T(k)A(k)$ in Eq.(21).

To overcome this problem, the simplification of the term of $A^T(k)A(k)F$ in Eq.(21) has been also achieved on the 2's complement representation (Tsunekawa et al, 1999). By using the relation

$$E\left[\mathbf{A}^T(k)\mathbf{A}(k)\mathbf{F}\right] = 0.25N\mathbf{F}\,, \tag{22}$$

the simplified algorithm becomes

$$\mathbf{P}(k+1) = \mathbf{P}(k) + 0.5\mu Ne(k)\mathbf{F}\,, \tag{23}$$

where, the operator E[ ] denotes an expectation. Eq.(23) can be performed by only shift and addition operations without multiplications using approximated μN with power of two, that is, the fast real-time processing can be realized. The fundamental structure is shown in Fig.3, and the timing chart is also shown in Fig.4. The calculation block can be used the fundamental structure of the DA-FIR, and the WAFS is realized by using a Random Access Memory (RAM).

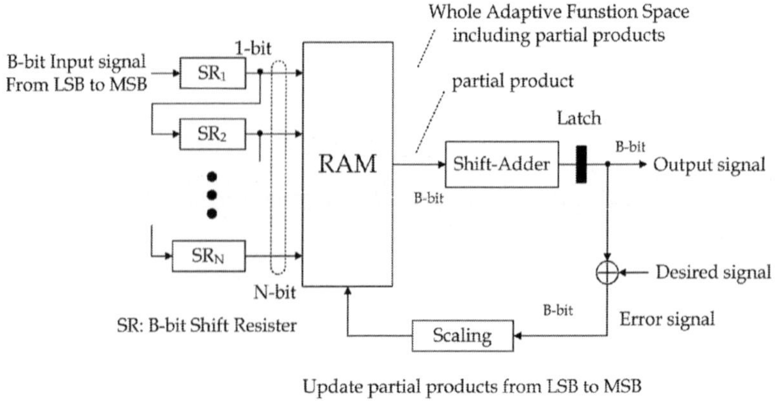

Fig. 3. Fundamental structure of the DA-ADF.

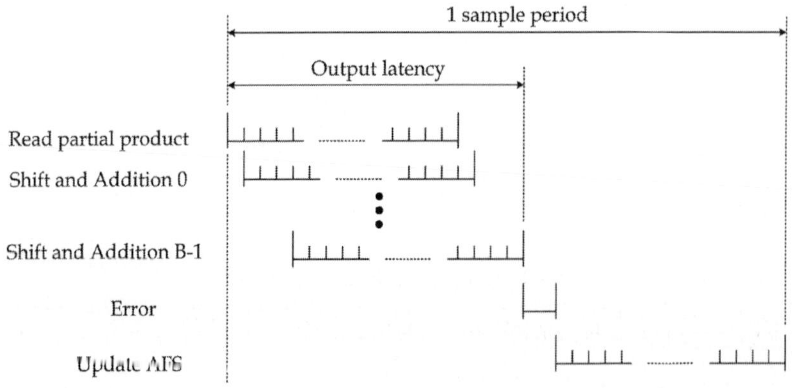

Fig. 4. Timing chart of the DA-ADF.

3.3 Multi-memory block structure

The structure employing the DWAFS to guarantee the convergence speed and the small

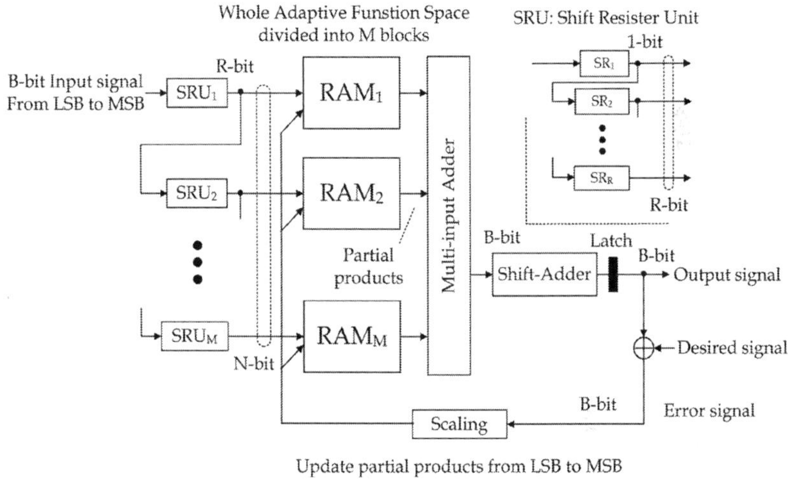

Fig. 5. Fundamental structure of the MDA-ADF.

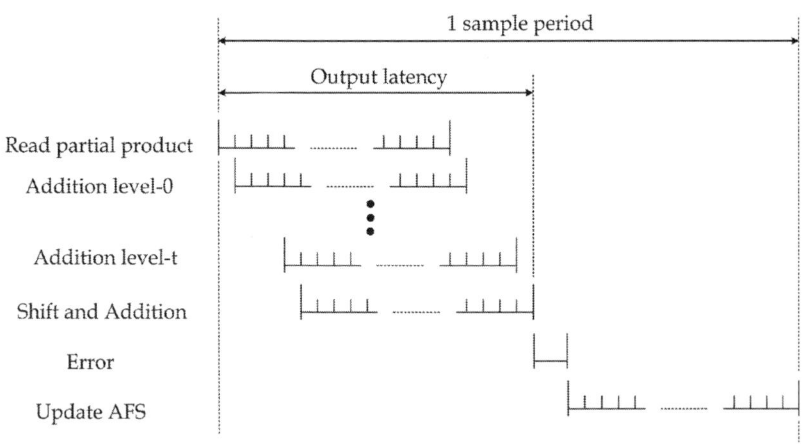

Fig. 6. Timing chart of the MDA-ADF.

hardware for higher order filtering has been proposed (Wei & Lou, 1986; Tsunakawa et al, 1999). The DWAFS is defined for the divided address-line of R bit. For a division number M, the relation of N and R is represented as

$$R = N / M .$$

The capacity of the individual DWAFS is 2^R words, and the total capacity becomes smaller $2^R M$ words than the DA's 2^N words. For the smaller WAFS, the convergence of the algorithm can be achieved by smaller iterations. The R-th order coefficient vector and the related AFS is represented as

$$\mathbf{W}_m(k) = \left[w_{m0}(k), w_{m1}(k), \cdots, w_{m(R-1)}(k) \right]^T, \tag{24}$$

$$\mathbf{P}_m(k) = \left[p_{m0}(k), p_{m1}(k), \cdots, p_{m(B-1)}(k) \right]^T, \tag{25}$$

$$(m = 0,1,\cdots,M-1\,;\, R = N/M),$$

where, the AFS is defined as

$$\mathbf{P}_m(k) \equiv \mathbf{A}_m^T(k)\mathbf{W}_m(k) \cdot \tag{26}$$

Therefore, the filter output signal is obtained by

$$y(k) = \sum_{m=1}^{M} F^T \mathbf{P}_m(k), \tag{27}$$

where, the address matrix is represented as

$$\mathbf{A}_m(k) = \begin{bmatrix} b_{m0}(k) & b_{m0}(k-1) & \cdots & b_{m0}(k-R+1) \\ b_{m1}(k) & b_{m1}(k-1) & \cdots & b_{m1}(k-R+1) \\ \vdots & \vdots & \ddots & \vdots \\ b_{m(B-1)}(k) & b_{m(B-1)}(k-1) & \cdots & b_{m(B-1)}(k-R+1) \end{bmatrix}^T . \tag{28}$$

The update formula of the MDA-ADF is represented as

$$\mathbf{P}_m(k+1) = \mathbf{P}_m(k) + 0.5\mu \mathrm{Re}(k)\mathbf{F} . \tag{29}$$

The fundamental structure and the timing chart are shown in Fig.5 and 6, respectively.

3.4 Half-memory algorithm using pseudo-odd symmetry property

It is known that there exists the odd symmetry property of the WAFS in the conventional DA-ADF on the offset binary coding (Cowan et al, 1983). Table 1 shows the example of the odd symmetry property in case of R=3. The stored partial-product for the inverted address has an equal absolute values and a different sign. Using this property, the MDA-ADF is can be realized with half amount of capacity of the DWAFS. This property concerned with a property of the offset binary coding. However, the pseudo-odd symmetry property of WAFS on the 2's complement representation has been found (Takahashi et al, 2001). The stored partial-product for the inverted address is a nearly equal absolute value and a different sign. The MDA algorithm using this property is called half-memory algorithm, and the previous discussed MDA algorithm is called full-memory algorithm. The access method of the DWAFS is represented as follows (Takahashi et al, 2001).

Address	Stored partial-product
000	$-0.5w_0 -0.5w_1 -0.5w_2$
001	$-0.5w_0 -0.5w_1 +0.5w_2$
010	$-0.5w_0 +0.5w_1 -0.5w_2$
011	$-0.5w_0 +0.5w_1 +0.5w_2$
100	$+0.5w_0 -0.5w_1 -0.5w_2$
101	$+0.5w_0 -0.5w_1 +0.5w_2$
110	$+0.5w_0 +0.5w_1 -0.5w_2$
111	$+0.5w_0 +0.5w_1 +0.5w_2$

Table 1. Example of the odd-symmetry property of the WAFS on the offset binary coding. This property is approximately achieved on the 2's complement representation.

```
Read the partial-products
begin
  for i:=1 to B do
  begin
     if addressMSB = 0 then
        Read the partial-product using R-1 bits address;
     if addressMSB = 1 then
        Invert the R-1 bits of address;
        Read the partial products using inverted R-1 bits address;
        Obtain the negative read value;
  end
end
Update the WAFS
begin
  for i:=1 to B do
  begin
     if addressMSB = 0 then
        Add the partial-product and update value;
     if addressMSB = 1 then
        Invert the R-1 bits of address;
        Obtain the negative update value;
        Add the partial-product and the negative update value;
  end
end
```

The expression of "addressMSB" indicates the MSB of the address. Fig.7 shows the difference of the access method between MDA and HMDA. The HMDA accesses the WAFS with the R-1 bits address-line without MSB, and the MSB is used to activate the 2's complementors located both sides of the WAFS. Fig. 8 shows the comparison of the convergence properties of the LMS, MDA, and HMDA. Results are obtained by the computer simulations. The simulation conditions are shown in Table 2. Here, IRER represents an impulse response error ratio. The step-size parameters of the algorithms were adjusted so as to achieve a final IRER of -49.5 [dB]. It is found that both the MDA(R=1) and the HMDA(R=2) achieve a good convergence properties that is equivalent to the LMS's one. Since both the MDA(R=1) and the HMDA(R=2) access the DWAFS with 1 bit address, the DWAFS is the smallest size and defined for every tap of the LMS. The convergence speed of the MDA is degraded by increasing R (Tsunekawa et al, 1999). This means that larger capacity of the DWAFS needs larger iteration for the convergence. Because of smaller capacity, the convergence speed of the HMDA(R=4) is faster than the MDA(R=4)'s one (Takahashi et al, 2001). The HMDA can improve the convergence speed and reduce the capacity of the WAFS, i.e., amount of hardware, simultaneously.

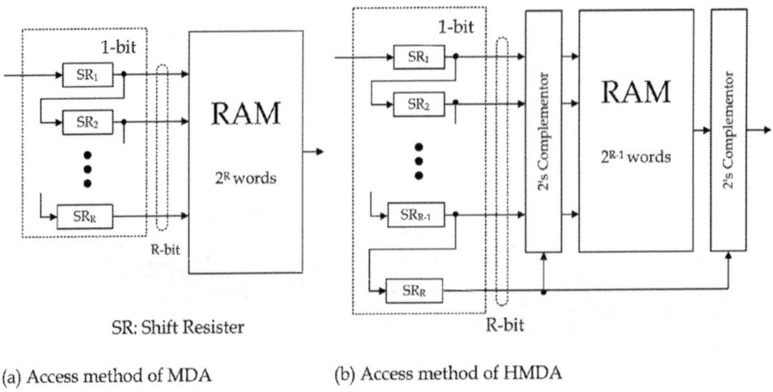

Fig. 7. Comparison of the access method for the WAFS. (a) Full-memory algorithm (b) Half-memory algorithm.

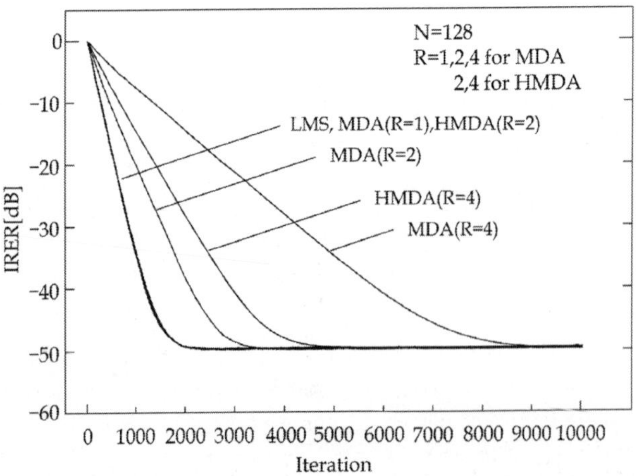

Fig. 8. Comparison of the Convergence properties.

Simulation Model	System identification problem
Unknown system	128 taps low-pass FIR filter
Method	LMS, MDA, and HMDA
Measurement	Impulse Response Error Ratio(IRER)
Number of taps	128
Number of address-line	1, 2, 4 for MDA, 2 and 4 for HMDA
Input signal	White Gaussian noise, variance=1.0, average=0.0
Observation noise	White Gaussian noise independent to the input signal, 45dB

Table 2. Computer simulation conditions.

4. New algorithm and architecture

The new algorithm and effective architecture can be obtained by applying the following techniques and ideas. 1) In the DA algorithm based on 2's complement representation, the pseudo-odd symmetry property of WAFS is applied to the new algorithm and architecture from different point of view on previously proposed half-memory algorithm. 2) A pipelined structure with separated output calculation and update procedure is applied. 3) The delayed update method (Long, G. Et al, 1989, 1992; Meyer & Agrawal, 1993; Wang, 1994) is applied. 4) To reduce the pitch of pipeline, two partial-products are pre-loaded before addition in update procedure. 5) The multi-memory block structure is applied to reduce an amount of hardware for higher order. 6) The output calculation procedure is performed from LSB to MSB, whereas, the update procedure is performed with reverse direction.

4.1 New algorithm with delayed coefficient adaptation

To achieve a high-speed processing, the parallel computing of the output calculation and the update in the MDA-ADF is considered. It is well known that the delayed update method enables the parallel computation in the LMS-ADF permitting the degradation of the convergence speed. This method updates the coefficients using previous error signal and input signal vector in the LMS-ADF.

Now, let's apply this method to the MDA-ADF. In the MDA and the HMDA, both of the output calculation and the update are performed from LSB to MSB. However, in this new algorithm, the output calculation procedure is performed from LSB to MSB, whereas, the update procedure is performed with reverse direction. Here, four combinations of the direction for the two procedures exist. However, it is confirmed by the computer simulations that the combination mentioned above is the best for the convergence property when the large step-size parameter close to the upper bound is selected. Examples of the convergence properties for the four combinations are shown in Fig.9. In these simulations, the step-size of 0.017 is used for the (a) and (c), and 0.051 is used for the (b) and (d) to achieve a final IRER of -38.9 [dB]. Both the (b) and (d) have a good convergence properties that is equivalent to the LMS's one, whereas, the convergence speed of the (a) and (c) is degraded. This implies that the upper bound of the (a) and (c) becomes lower than the (b) , (d) and LMS's one.

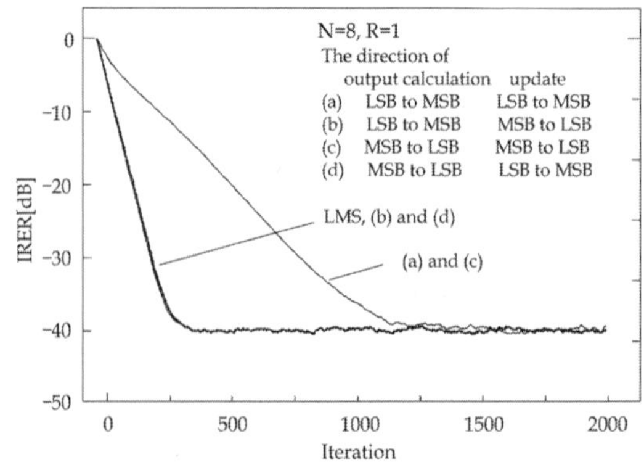

Fig. 9. Comparison of the convergence characteristics for the different combinations of the direction on the output calculation and update. The step-size of 0.017 is used for the (a) and (c), and 0.051 is used for the (b) and (d).

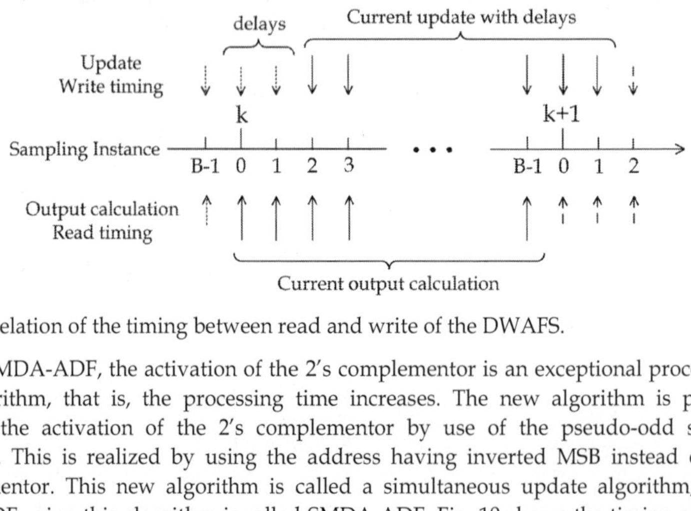

Fig. 10. Relation of the timing between read and write of the DWAFS.

In the HMDA-ADF, the activation of the 2's complementor is an exceptional processing for the algorithm, that is, the processing time increases. The new algorithm is performed without the activation of the 2's complementor by use of the pseudo-odd symmetry property. This is realized by using the address having inverted MSB instead of the 2's complementor. This new algorithm is called a simultaneous update algorithm, and the MDA-ADF using this algorithm is called SMDA-ADF. Fig. 10 shows the timing of the read and write of the DWAFS. The partial-product is read after writing the updated partial-products.

The SMDA algorithm is represented as follows. The filter output is obtained as the same manner in the MDA-ADF. The m-th output of the m-th DWAFS is

$$y_m(k) = \sum_{i=0}^{B-1} \mathbf{F}'^{T}_{B-1-i} \mathbf{P}_{m,B-1-i}(k) . \tag{30}$$

The output signal is the sum of these M outputs, and this can be expressed as

$$y(k)=\sum_{m=1}^{M} y_m(k). \tag{31}$$

The scaling vectors are

$$\mathbf{F}_0^{'}(k)=\left[2^0,0,\cdots,0\right]^T,\mathbf{F}_1^{'}(k)=\left[0,2^{-1},\cdots,0\right]^T,\cdots,\mathbf{F}_{B-1}^{'}(k)=\left[0,0,\cdots,2^{-B+1}\right]^T. \tag{32}$$

The address matrix including the inverted MSB for the output calculation is represented as

$$\mathbf{A}_m^{out}(k)=\begin{bmatrix} \bar{b}_{m0}(k) & \bar{b}_{m0}(k-1) & \cdots & \bar{b}_{m0}(k-R+1) \\ b_{m1}(k) & b_{m1}(k-1) & \cdots & b_{m1}(k-R+1) \\ \vdots & \vdots & \ddots & \vdots \\ b_{m(B-1)}(k) & b_{m(B-1)}(k-1) & \cdots & b_{m(B-1)}(k-R+1) \end{bmatrix}^T. \tag{33}$$

This algorithm updates the two partial-products according to the address and its inverted address, simultaneously. When the delays in Fig.10 is expressed by d, the address matrix for the update procedure is represented as

$$\mathbf{A}_m^{up}(k)=\begin{bmatrix} \bar{b}_{m0}(k) & \bar{b}_{m0}(k-1) & & \bar{b}_{m0}(k-R+1) \\ \vdots & \vdots & \cdots & \vdots \\ b_{m(B-1-d)}(k) & b_{m(B-1-d)}(k-1) & & b_{m(B-1-d)}(k-R+1) \\ b_{m(B-d)}(k-1) & b_{m(B-d)}(k-2) & \ddots & b_{m(B-d)}(k-R) \\ \vdots & \vdots & & \vdots \\ b_{m(B-1)}(k-1) & b_{m(B-1)}(k-2) & \cdots & b_{m(B-1)}(k-R) \end{bmatrix}^T. \tag{34}$$

The update formulas are

$$\mathbf{P}_{m,i}(k+1)=\mathbf{P}_{m,i}(k)+0.5\mu\,\mathrm{Re}(k-1)\mathbf{F}_i^{'}, \tag{35}$$

$$\overline{\mathbf{P}}_{m,i}(k+1)=\overline{\mathbf{P}}_{m,i}(k)-0.5\mu\,\mathrm{Re}(k-1)\mathbf{F}_i^{'}, \tag{36}$$

$$(\mathrm{m}=1,2,\cdots,\mathrm{M};\ \mathrm{i}=0,1,\cdots,\mathrm{B}-\mathrm{d}),$$

and

$$\mathbf{P}_{m,i}(k+1)=\mathbf{P}_{m,i}(k)+0.5\mu\,\mathrm{Re}(k-2)\mathbf{F}_i^{'}, \tag{37}$$

$$\overline{\mathbf{P}}_{m,i}(k+1)=\overline{\mathbf{P}}_{m,i}(k)-0.5\mu\,\mathrm{Re}(k-2)\mathbf{F}_i^{'}, \tag{38}$$

$$(\mathrm{m}=1,2,\cdots,\mathrm{M};\ \mathrm{i}=\mathrm{B}-\mathrm{d}-1,\cdots,\mathrm{B}-1).$$

The error signal is obtained by

$$e(k) = d(k) - y(k)$$

In Eq.(36) and Eq.(38), $\bar{\mathbf{P}}_{m,i}(k)$ is the AFS specified by the inverted addresses.

4.2 Evaluation of convergence properties

The convergence properties are evaluated by the computer simulations. Table 3 shows the simulation conditions, and Fig.11 shows the simulation results. The step-size parameters of the algorithms were adjusted so as to achieve a final IRER of -49.8 [dB]. The SMDA and the HMDA (Takahashi et al, 2001) with R=2 achieve a good convergence properties that is equivalent to the LMS's one. The convergence speed of the DLMS (LMS with 1 sample delayed update) degrades against the LMS's one because of the delayed update with 1 sample delay, whereas, in spite of the delayed update with 1 and 2 sample delays, the SMDA with R=2 can achieve a fast convergence speed.

4.3 Architecture

Fig.12 shows the block diagram of the SMDA-ADF. Examples of the sub-blocks are shown in Fig.13, Fig.14, and Fig.15. In Fig.12, the input signal register includes (2N+1)B shift-registers. The address matrix is provided to the DWAFS Module (DWAFSM) from the input register. The sum of the M-outputs obtained from M-DWAFSM is fed to the Shift-Adder.

After the shift and addition in B times, the filter output signal is obtained. The obtained two error signals, the e(k-1) and the - e(k-1), are scaled during reading the partial-products to be updated. In Fig.13, the DWAFSM includes the 2^R+2 B-bit register, 1 R-bit register, 2 decoders, 5 selectors, and 2 adders. The decoder provides the select signal to the selectors. The two elements of DWAFS are updated, simultaneously. Fig.16 shows the timing chart of the SMDA-ADF. The parallel computation of the output calculation and update procedure are realized by the delayed update method.

Simulation Model	System identification problem
Unknown system	128 taps low-pass FIR filter
Method	LMS, DLMS, SMDA , and HMDA
Measurement	Impulse Response Error Ratio(IRER)
Number of taps	128
Number of address-line	2 and 4 for DA method
Input signal	White Gaussian noise, variance=1.0, average=0.0
Observation noise	White Gaussian noise independent to the input signal, 45dB

Table 3. Simulation conditions.

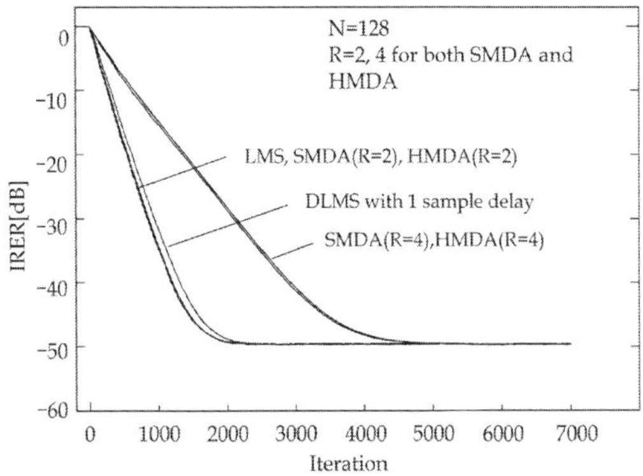

Fig. 11. Comparison of the convergence properties.

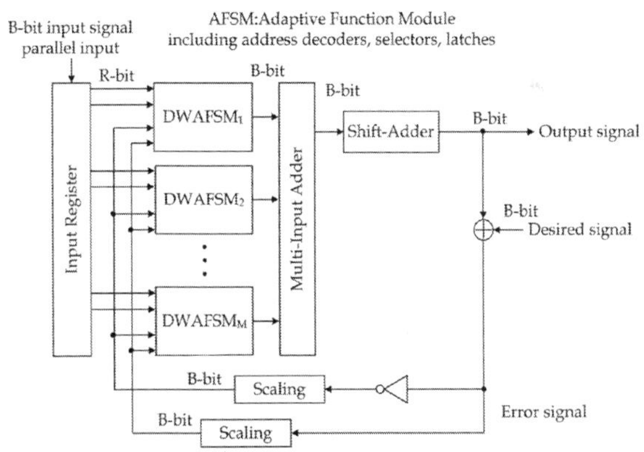

Fig. 12. Block Diagram of the SMDA-ADF.

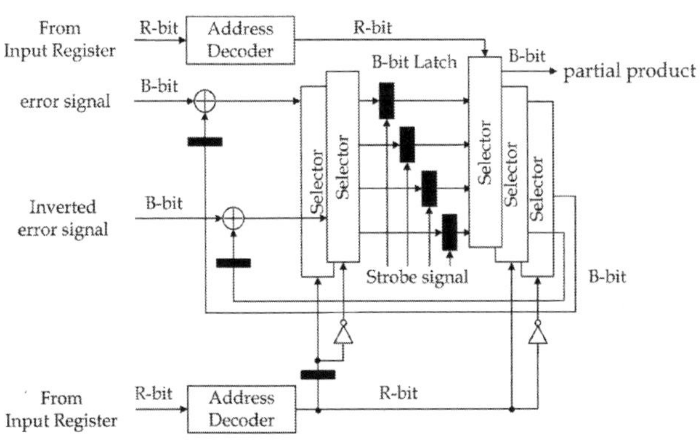

Fig. 13. Example of the DWAFS module for R=2.

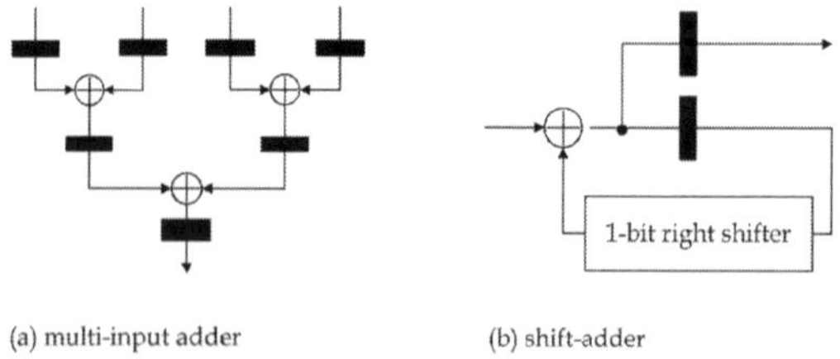

Fig. 14. Example of the multi-input register and shift-adder.

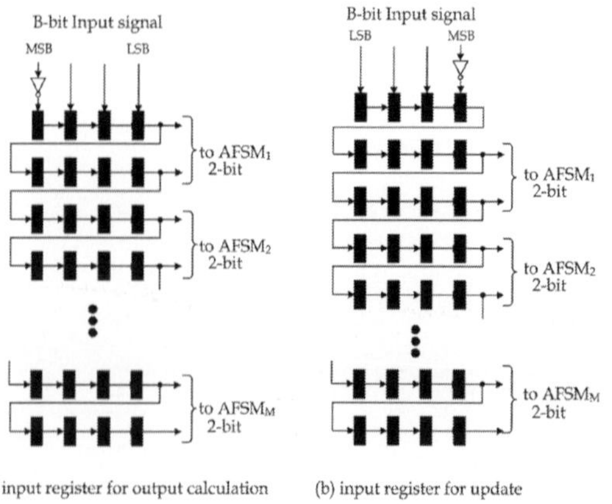

Fig. 15. Example of the input registers for B=4 and R=2. The (a) is for output calculation, and the (b) is for update.

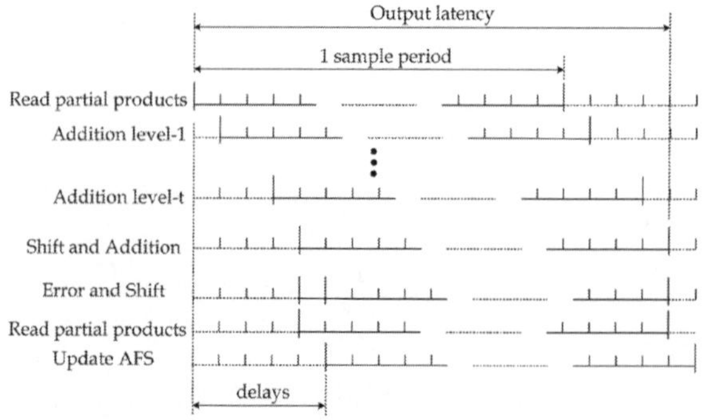

Fig. 16. Timing chart of the SMDA-ADF. The sampling period is equal to the word length of the input signal. The current update procedure begins after delays.

4.4 VLSI evaluations

The VLSI architecture of the SMDA is evaluated with comparison to the previous proposed methods using the multipliers, the MDA (Tsunakawa et al, 1999), conventional LMS, pipelined

DLMS (Meyer & Agrawal, 1993), pipelined LMS structure (Harada et al, 1998), and pipelined NCLMS (Takahashi et al, 2006). Table 4 shows the evaluation conditions. The result for the SMDA and MDA are shown in Table 5, and the others using the multipliers are shown in Table 6. These results were obtained by a VLSI design system PARTHENON (NTT DATA Corporation, 1990). It is found that the SMDA can achieve the high-sampling rate of 380% and small output latency of 67% against the MDA, whereas, the power dissipation and the area are increased. However, the improvement of the sampling rate and latency exceed the degradation of the power dissipation and the area. The methods in Table 6 need both of the very large amount of gates and the area against the SMDA. From these results, it is found that the SMDA has advantages of small amount of hardware, a sampling rate close to the LMS.

Methods	LMS, Pipelined-DLMS, Pipelined-LMS, Pipelined-NCLMS, SMDA
Number of taps	128
Word length	16 bit
Division number	64
VLSI library	0.8 micron CMOS standard cell, 5V
Adder	Carry look-ahead adder
Multiplier	Booth's encode algorithm, Wallace tree, Carry look-ahead adder

Table 4. The condition of the VLSI evaluation.

	MDA	SMDA
Machine cycle [ns]	31	21
Sampling rate [MHz]	0.79	3.00
Latency [ns]	713	479
Power dissipation [W]	6.40	16.47
Area [mm^2]	36	54
Number of gates	175,321	258,321

Table 5. Comparison of the VLSI evaluations for the MDA and the SMDA.

	LMS	Pipe-DLMS	Pipe-LMS	Pipe-NCLMS
Machine cycle [ns]	297	63	131	61
Sampling rate [MHz]	3.37	15.87	7.63	16.39
Latency [ns]	214	8,064	131	61
Power dissipation [W]	6.23	25.79	27.33	18.20
Area [mm^2]	297	205	429	187
Number of gates	1,570,084	997,760	2,082,304	916,893

Table 6. Comparison of the VLSI evaluations for ADFs employing multipliers.

5. Conclusions

In this chapter, the new LMS algorithm using distributed arithmetic and its VLSI architecture have been presented. According the discussions, we conclude as follows:

1. The SMDA-ADF can achieve the good convergence speed, higher sampling rate and small output latency than the conventional MDA-ADF.

2. The small amount of hardware is the feature of the SMDA-ADF against the ADFs employing the multipliers.
3. In spite of the delayed adaptation, the convergence speed is equivalent to the LMS's one.
4. The convergence property depends on the combination of the direction of the output and update procedure. The output calculation from LSB to MSB and the update procedure with reverse direction is the best, when the step-size parameter is close to the upper bound.

6. References

Widrow, B., Glover,J.R., McCool, J.M., Kaunitz, J., Williams, C.S., Hearn, R.H., Zeidler, J.R., Dong, E. & Goodlin, R.C. (1975). Adaptive noise cancelling: Principles and applications. Proc. IEEE, vol.63, pp.1692-1716

Makino, S. & Koizumi, N. (1988). Improvement on Adaptation of an Echo Canceller in a Room. IEICE Letter Fundamentals, Vol. J 71-A, No.12, pp.2212-2214

Tsunekawa,Y., Takahashi,K., Toyoda,S. & Miura, M. (1999). High-performance VLSI Architecture of Multiplier-less LMS Adaptive Filter Using Distributed Arithmetic. IEICE Trans. Fundamentals, Vol.J82-A, No.10, pp.1518-1528

Takahashi,K., Tsunekawa,Y., Toyoda,S. & Miura, M. (2001). High-performance Architecture of LMS Adaptive Filter Using Distributed Arithmetic Based on Half-Memory Algorithm. IEICE Trans. Fundamentals, Vol.J84-A, No.6, pp.777-787

Takahashi, K., Tsunekawa, Y., Tayama, N., Seki, K. (2002). Analysis of the Convergence Condition of LMS Adaptive Digital Filter Using Distributed Arithmetic. IEICE Trans. Fundamentals, Vol.E85-A, No.6, pp1249-1256

Takahashi, K., Kanno, D. & Tsunekawa, Y. (2006). High-Performance Pipelined Architecture of Adaptive Digital Filter Employing FIR Filter with Minimum Coefficients Delay and Output Latency. IEICE Trans. Fundamentals, Vol.J89-A, No.12, pp.1130-1141

Cowan, C.F.N. & Mavor., J. (1981). New digital adaptive-filter implementation using distributed-arithmetic techniques. IEE Proc., vol.128, Pt.F, no.4, pp.225--230

Cowan, C.F.N, Smith, S.G. & Elliott, J.H. (1983). A digital adaptive filter using a memory-accumulator architecture:theory and realization. IEEE Trans. Acoust., Speech \& Signal Process., vol.31, no.3, pp.541--549

Peled, A. & Liu, B. (1974). A new hardware realization of digital filters. IEEE Trans. Acoust., Speech \& Signal Process., vol.22, no.12, pp.456--462

Wei, C.H. & Lou, J.J. (1986). Multimemory block structure for implementing a digital adaptive filter using distributed arithmetic. IEE Proc., vol.133, Pt.G, no.1, pp.19--26

Long, G., Ling, F. & Proakis, J.G. (1989). The LMS algorithm with delayed coefficient adaptation. IEEE Trans. Acoust. Speech Signal Process., vol.37, no.9, pp.1397-1405

Long, G., Ling, F. & Proakis, J.G. (1992). Corrections to "The LMS algorithm with delayed coefficient adaptation". IEEE Trans. Acoust. Speech Signal Process., vol.40, no.1, pp.230-232

Meyer, M.D. & Agrawal, D.P. (1993). A high sampling rate delayed LMS filter architecture. IEEE Trans. Circuits \& Syst. II, vol.40, no.11, pp.727-729

Wang, C.L. (1994). Bit-serial VLSI implementation of delayed LMS transversal adaptive filters. IEEE Trans. Signal Processing, vol.42, no.8, pp.2169--2175

Harada, A., Nishikawa, K. & Kiya, H. (1998). Pipelined Architecture of the LMS Adaptive Digital Filter with the Minimum Output Latency. IEICE Trans. Fundamentals, Vol.E81-A, No.8, pp.1578-1585

NTT DATA Corporation (1990). PARTHENON User's Manual. Japan.

Part 2

Complex Structures, Applications and Algorithms

5

Adaptive Filtering Using Subband Processing: Application to Background Noise Cancellation

Ali O. Abid Noor, Salina Abdul Samad and Aini Hussain
The National University of Malaysia (UKM), Malaysia

1. Introduction

Adaptive filters are often involved in many applications, such as system identification, channel estimation, echo and noise cancellation in telecommunication systems. In this context, the Least Mean Square (LMS) algorithm is used to adapt a Finite Impulse Response (FIR) filter with a relatively low computation complexity and good performance. However, this solution suffers from significantly degraded performance with colored interfering signals, due to the large eigenvalue spread of the autocorrelation matrix of the input signal (Vaseghi, 2008). Furthermore, as the length of the filter is increased, the convergence rate of the algorithm decreases, and the computational requirements increase. This can be a problem in acoustic applications such as noise cancellation, which demand long adaptive filters to model the noise path. These issues are particularly important in hands free communications, where processing power must be kept as low as possible (Johnson et al., 2004). Several solutions have been proposed in literature to overcome or at least reduce these problems. A possible solution to reduce the complexity problem has been to use adaptive Infinite Impulse Response (IIR) filters, such that an effectively long impulse response can be achieved with relatively few filter coefficients (Martinez & Nakano 2008). The complexity advantages of adaptive IIR filters are well known. However, adaptive IIR filters have the well known problems of instability, local minima and phase distortion and they are not widely welcomed. An alternative approach to reduce the computational complexity of long adaptive FIR filters is to incorporate block updating strategies and frequency domain adaptive filtering (Narasimha 2007; Wasfy & Ranganathan, 2008). These techniques reduce the computational complexity, because the filter output and the adaptive weights are computed only after a large block of data has been accumulated. However, the application of such approaches introduces degradation in the performance, including a substantial signal path delay corresponding to one block length, as well as a reduction in the stable range of the algorithm step size. Therefore for nonstationary signals, the tracking performance of the block algorithms generally becomes worse (Lin et al., 2008).

As far as speed of convergence is concerned, it has been suggested to use the Recursive Least Square (RLS) algorithm to speed up the adaptive process (Hoge et al., 2008).The convergence rate of the RLS algorithm is independent of the eigenvalue spread. Unfortunately, the drawbacks that are associated with RLS algorithm including its $O(N^2)$ computational requirements, which are still too high for many applications, where high speed is required, or when a large number of inexpensive units must be built. The Affine Projection Algorithm (APA) (Diniz, 2008; Choi & Bae, 2007) shows a better convergence behavior, but the computational complexity increases with the factor P in relation to LMS, where P denotes the order of the APA.

As a result, adaptive filtering using subband processing becomes an attractive option for many adaptive systems. Subband adaptive filtering belongs to two fields of digital signal processing, namely, adaptive filtering and multirate signal processing. This approach uses filter banks to split the input broadband signal into a number of frequency bands, each serving as an independent input to an adaptive filter. The subband decomposition is aimed to reduce the update rate, and the length of the adaptive filters, hopefully, resulting in a much lower computational complexity. Furthermore, subband signals are usually downsampled in a multirate system. This leads to a whitening of the input signals and therefore an improved convergence behavior of the adaptive filter system is expected. The objectives of this chapter are: to develop subband adaptive structures which can improve the performance of the conventional adaptive noise cancellation schemes, to investigate the application of subband adaptive filtering to the problem of background noise cancellation from speech signals, and to offer a design with fast convergence, low computational requirement, and acceptable delay. The chapter is organized as follows. In addition to this introduction section, section 2 describes the use of Quadrature Mirror Filter (QMF) banks in adaptive noise cancellation. The effect of aliasing is analyzed and the performance of the noise canceller is examined under various noise environments. To overcome problems incorporated with QMF subband noise canceller system, an improved version is presented in section 3. The system is based on using two-fold oversampled filter banks to reduce aliasing distortion, while a moderate order prototype filter is optimized for minimum amplitude distortion. Section 4 offers a solution with reduced computational complexity. The new scheme is based on using polyphase allpass IIR filter banks at the analysis stage, while the synthesis filter bank is optimized such that an inherent phase correction is made at the output of the noise canceller. Finally, section 5 concludes the chapter.

2. Adaptive noise cancellation using QMF banks

In this section, a subband adaptive noise canceller system is presented. The system is based on using critically sampled QMF banks in the analysis and synthesis stages. A suband version of the LMS algorithm is used to control a FIR filter in the individual branches so as to reduce the noise in the input noisy signal.

2.1 The QMF bank

The design of M-band filter bank is not quite an easy job, due to the downsampling and upsampling operations within the filter bank. Therefore, iterative algorithms are often employed to optimize the filter coefficients (Bergen 2008; Hameed et al. 2006). This problem is simplified for the special case where M =2 which leads to the QMF bank as shown in Fig.1. Filters $H_0(z)$ and $G_0(z)$ are lowpass filters and $H_1(z)$ and $G_1(z)$ are highpass filters with a nominal cut off of $\frac{f_s}{4}$ or $\frac{\pi}{2}$, where f_s is the sampling frequency.

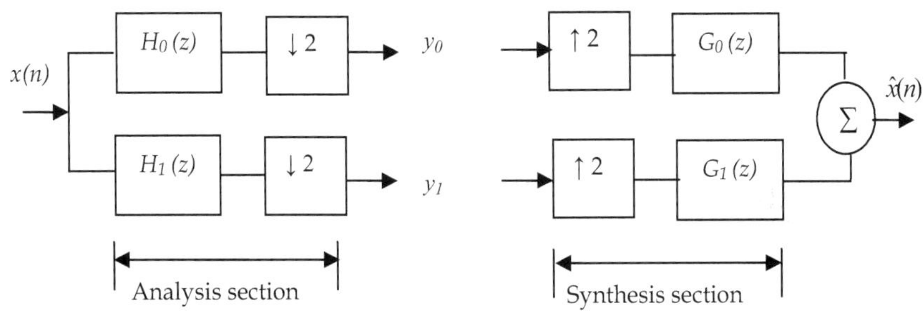

Fig. 1. The quadrature mirror filter (QMF) bank

The downsampling operation has a modulation effect on signals and filters, therefore the input to the system is expressed as follows;

$$\mathbf{X}(z) = [X(z) \;\; X(-z)]^T \tag{1}$$

where $.^T$ is a transpose operation. Similarly, the analysis filter bank is expressed as,

$$\mathbf{H}(z) = \begin{bmatrix} H_0(z) & H_0(-z) \\ H_1(z) & H_1(-z) \end{bmatrix} \tag{2}$$

The output of the analysis stage is expressed as,

$$\mathbf{Y}(z) = \mathbf{H}(z)\mathbf{X}(z) \tag{3}$$

The total input-output relationship is expressed as,

$$\hat{X}(z) = \frac{1}{2}X(z)[H_0(z)G_0(z) + H_1(z)G_1(z)] + \frac{1}{2}X(-z)[H_0(-z)G_0(z) + H_1(-z)G_1(z)] \tag{4}$$

The right hand side term of equation (4) is the aliasing term. The presence of aliasing causes a frequency shift of π in signal argument, and it is unwanted effect. However, it can be eliminated by choosing the filters as follows;

$$H_1(z) = H_0(-z) \tag{6}$$

$$G_0(z) = H_0(z) \tag{7}$$

$$G_1(z) = -H_0(-z) \tag{8}$$

By direct substitution into Equation (4), we see that the aliasing terms go to zero, leaving

$$\hat{X}(z) = \frac{1}{2}X(z)\left[H_0^2(z) + H_1^2(z)\right] \tag{9}$$

In frequency domain, replacing z by $e^{j\omega}$, where $\omega = 2\pi f$, equation (9) can be expressed as,

$$\hat{X}(e^{j\omega}) = \frac{1}{2} X(e^{j\omega}) \left[H_0^2(e^{j\omega}) + H_1^2(^{j\omega}) \right] \tag{10}$$

Therefore, the objective is to determine $H_0^2(e^{j\omega})$ such that the overall system frequency approximates $e^{j\omega.n_0}$, i.e. approximates an allpass function with constant group delay n_0. All four filters in the filter bank are specified by a length L lowpass FIR filter.

2.2 Efficient implementation of the QMF bank

An efficient implementation of the preceding two-channel QMF bank is obtained using polyphase decomposition and the noble identities (Milic, 2009). Thus, the analysis and synthesis filter banks can be redrawn as in Fig.2. The downsamplers are now to the left of the polyphase components of $H_0(z)$, namely $F_0(z)$ and $F_1(z)$, so that the entire analysis bank requires only about $L/2$ multiplications per unit sample and $L/2$ additions per unit sample, where L is the length of $H_0(z)$.

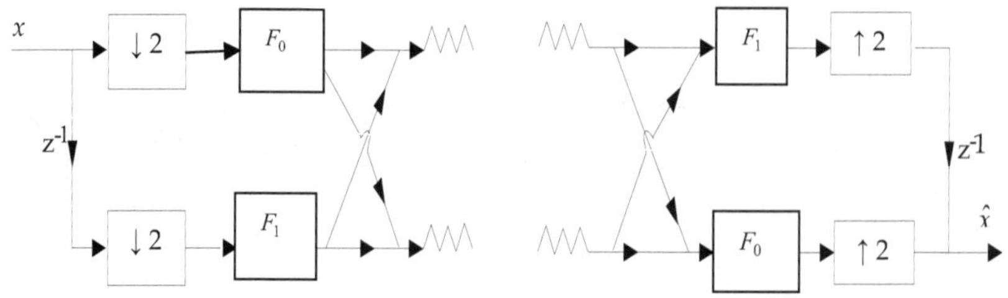

Fig. 2. Polyphase implementation of QMF bank

2.3 Distortion elimination in QMF banks

Let the input-output transfer function be $T(z)$, so that

$$T(z) = \frac{\hat{x}(z)}{x(z)} = \frac{1}{2}\left[H_0(z)G_0(z) + H_1(z)G_1(z)\right] \tag{11}$$

which represents the distortion caused by the QMF bank. *T(z)* is the overall transfer function (or the distortion transfer function). The processed signal $\hat{x}(n)$ suffers from amplitude distortion if $\left|T(e^{j\omega})\right|$ is not constant for all ω, and from phase distortion if *T(z)* does not have linear phase. To eliminate amplitude distortion, it is necessary to constrain *T(z)* to be allpass, whereas to eliminate phase distortion, we have to restrict *T(z)* to be FIR with linear phase. Both of these distortions are eliminated if and only if *T(z)* is a pure delay, i.e.

$$T(z) = cz^{n_0} \tag{12}$$

where c is a scalar constant, or, equivalently,

$$\hat{x}(n) = cx(n - n_0) \tag{13}$$

Systems which are alias free and satisfy (12) are called perfect reconstruction (PR) systems. For any pair of analysis filter, the choice of synthesis filters according to (7) and (8) eliminates aliasing distortion, the distortion can be expressed as,

$$T(z)\frac{1}{2}[H_0(z)H_1(-z)+H_1(z)H_0(z)] \tag{14}$$

The transfer function of the system in (14) can be expressed in terms of polyphase components as,

$$T(z)=\frac{1}{2}\left[H_0^2(z)-H_0^2(-z)\right]=2z^{-1}F_0(z^2)F_1(z^2) \tag{15}$$

Since $H_0(z)$ is restricted to be FIR, this is possible if and only if $F_0(z)$ and $F_1(z)$ are delays, which means $H_0(z)$ must have the form;

$$H_0(z)=c_0z^{-2n_0}+c_1z^{-(2n_1+1)} \tag{16}$$

For our purpose of adaptive noise cancellation, frequency responses are required to be more selective than (16). So, under the constraint of (13), perfect reconstruction is not possible. However, it is possible to minimize amplitude distortion by optimization procedures. The coefficients of $H_0(z)$ are optimized such that the distortion function is made as flat as possible. The stopband energy of $H_0(z)$ is minimized, starting from the stopband frequency. Thus, an objective function of the form

$$\beta\int_{\omega s}^{\pi}\left|H_0(e^{j\omega})\right|^2 d\omega+(1-\beta)\int_0^{\pi/2}[1-\left|T(e^{j\omega})\right|^2]^2 d\omega \tag{17}$$
$$0<\beta<1$$

can be minimized by optimizing the coefficients of $H_0(z)$. The factor β is used to control the tradeoff between the stopband energy of $H_0(z)$ and the flatness of $|\ T(e^{j\omega})\ |$. The prototype filter $H_0(z)$ is constraint to have linear phase if $T(z)$ must have a linear phase. Therefore, the prototype filter $H_0(z)$ is chosen to be linear phase FIR filter with L=32 .

2.4 Adaptive noise cancellation using QMF banks

A schematic of the two-band noise canceller structure is shown at Fig.3, this is a two sensor scheme, it consists of three sections: analysis which contains analysis filters $H_o(z)$, $H_1(z)$ plus the down samplers, adaptive section contains two adaptive FIR filters with two controlling algorithms, and the synthesis section which comprises of two upsamplers and two interpolators $G_o(z)$, $G_1(z)$. The noisy speech signal is fed from the primary input, whilst, the noise $\hat{x}$ is fed from the reference input sensor, $\hat{x}$ is added to the speech signal via a transfer function *A(z)* which represents the acoustic noise path, thus $\hat{x}$ correlated with x and uncorrelated with s. In stable conditions, the noise x should be cancelled completely leaving the clean speech as the total error signal of the system. The suggested two channel adaptive noise cancellation scheme is shown in Fig.3. It is assumed in this configuration that z transforms of all signals and filters exist on the unit circle. Thus, from Fig. 3, we see that the noise *X(z)* is filtered by the noise path *A(z)*. The output of $A(z)$, $\hat{X}(z)$ is added to the speech signal, $S(z)$, and it is then split by an analysis filter bank $H_0(z)$ and $H_1(z)$ and subsampled to yield the two subband system signals V_0 and V_1.The adaptive path first splits the noise *X(z)* by an identical analysis filter bank, and then models the system in the subband domain by two independent adaptive filters, yield to the two estimated subband signals y_0 and y_1. The subband error signals are obtained as,

$$E_k(z) = V_k(z) - Y_k(z), \quad \text{for } k = 0,1 \tag{18}$$

The system output $\hat{S}$ is obtained after passing the subband error signals e_0 and e_1 through a synthesis filter bank $G_0(z)$ and $G_1(z)$. The subband adaptive filter coefficients $\hat{\mathbf{w}}_0$ and $\hat{\mathbf{w}}_1$ have to be adjusted so as to minimize the noise in the output signal, in practice, the adaptive filters are adjusted so as to minimize the subband error signals e_0 and e_1.

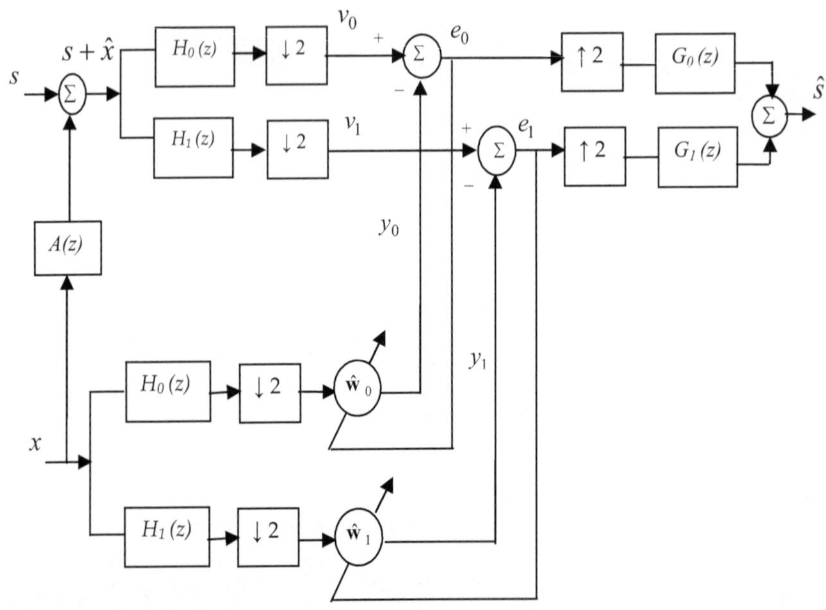

Fig. 3. The two-band noise canceller

In the adaptive section of the two-band noise canceller, a modified version of the LMS algorithm for subband adaptation is used as follows;

$$J(\hat{\mathrm{w}}) = e_0^2(n) + e_1^2(n) \tag{19}$$

where $J(\hat{w})$ is a cost function which depends on the individual errors of the two adaptive filters. Taking the partial derivatives of $J(\hat{w})$ with respect to the samples of $\hat{w}$, we get the components of the instantaneous gradient vector. Then, the LMS adaptation algorithm is expressed in the form;

$$\hat{w}_i(n) = \hat{w}_i(n-1) - \mu(n)\left[2e_0(n)\frac{\partial e_0(n)}{\partial \hat{w}_i} + 2e_1(n)\frac{\partial e_1(n)}{\partial \hat{w}_i}\right] \tag{20}$$

for $i=0,1,2..... L_w - 1$, where L_w is the length of the branch adaptive filter. The convergence of the algorithm (20) towards the optimal solution $s = \hat{s}$ is controlled by the adaptation step size μ. It can be shown that the behavior of the mean square error vector is governed by the eigenvalues of the autocorrelation matrix of the input signal, which are all strictly greater than zero (Haykin, 2002). In particular, this vector converges exponentially to zero provided that $\mu < 1/\lambda_{\max}$, where $\lambda_{\max}$ is the largest eigenvalue of the input autocorrelation matrix. This condition is not sufficient to insure the convergence of the Mean Square Error (MSE) to its minimum. Using the classical approach , a convergence condition for the MSE is stated as

$$\mu < \frac{2}{trR} = \mu_{\max} \tag{21}$$

where trR is the trace of the input autocorrelation matrix R.

2.5 The M-band case

The two-band noise canceller can be extended so as to divide the input broadband signal into M bands, each subsampled by a factor of M. The individual filters in the analysis bank are chosen as a bandpass filters of bandwidth f_s / M (if the filters are real, they will have two conjugate parts of bandwidth $f_s / 2M$ each). Furthermore, it is assumed that the filters are selective enough so that they overlap only with adjacent filters. A convenient class of such filters which has been studied for subband coding of speech is the class of pseudo-QMF filters (Deng et al. 2007). The *kth* filter of such a bank is obtained by cosine modulation of a low-pass prototype filter with cutoff frequency $f_s / 4M$. For our purpuse of noise cancellation, the analysis and synthesis filter banks are made to have a paraunitary relationship so as the following condition is satisfied.

$$\frac{1}{M}\sum_{k=0}^{M-1} G_k(z)H_k(zW_M^{-i}) = cz^{-\tau} \tag{22}$$

where c is a constant, W_M is the Mth root of unity, with $i=0,1,2,...M-1$ and τ is the analysis/synthesis reconstruction delay. Thus, the prototype filter order partly defines the signal delay in the system. The above equation is the perfect reconstruction (PR) condition in z-transform domain for causal M-channel filter banks. The characteristic feature of the paraunitary filter bank is the relation of analysis and synthesis subfilters; they are connected via time reversing. Then, the same PR-condition can be written as,

$$\frac{1}{M}\sum_{k=0}^{M-1} H_k(z^{-1})H_k(zW_M^{-i}) = cz^{-\tau} \tag{23}$$

The reconstruction delay of a paraunitary filter bank is fixed by the prototype filter order, $\tau = L$, where L is the order of the prototype filter. Amplitude response for such a filter bank is shown in Fig.4. The analysis matrix in (2) can be expressed for the M-band case as,

$$\mathbf{H}(z) = \begin{bmatrix} H_0(z) & H_0(zW) & \dots & H_0(zW^{M-1}) \\ H_1(z) & H_1(zW) & \dots & H_1(zW^{M-1}) \\ \vdots & & & \\ H_{M-1}(z) & H_{M-1}(zW) & \dots & H_{M-1}(zW^{M-1}) \end{bmatrix} \tag{24}$$

The matrix in (24) contains the filters and their modulated versions (by the Mth root of unity $W = e^{-j2\pi/M}$). This shows that there are M-1 alias components $H(zW^k)$, $k > 0$ in the reconstructed signal.

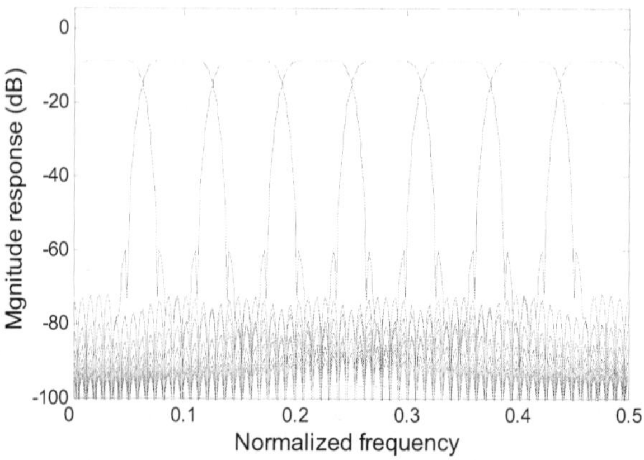

Fig. 4. Magnitude response of 8-band filter bank, with prototype order of 63

2.6 Results of the subband noise canceller using QMF banks

2.6.1 Filter bank setting and distortion calculation

The analysis filter banks are generated by a cosine modulation function. A single prototype filter is used to produce the sub-filters in the critically sampled case. Aliasing error is the parameter that most affect adaptive filtering process in subbands, and the residual noise at the system's output can be very high if aliasing is not properly controlled. Fig.5 gives a describing picture about aliasing distortion. In this figure, settings of prototype filter order are used for each case to investigate the effect of aliasing on filter banks. It is clear from Fig.5, that aliasing can be severe for low order prototype filters. Furthermore, as the number of subbands is increased, aliasing insertion is also increased. However, for low number of subbands e.g. 2 subbabds, low order filters can be afforded with success equivalent to high order ones.

2.6.2 Noise cancellation tests

Initially, the two-band noise canceller model is tested using a variable frequency sine wave contaminated with zero mean, unit variance white Gaussian noise. This noise is propagating through a noise path *A(z)*, applied to the primary input of the system. The same Gaussian noise is passed directly to the reference input of the canceller. Table 1 lists the various parameters used in the experiment.

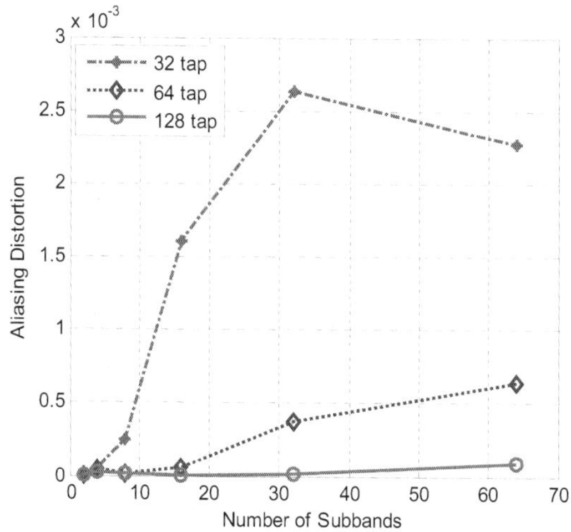

Fig. 5. Aliasing versus the number of subbands for different prototype filter length

Parameter	Value
Noise path length	92
Adaptive filter length	46
Step size μ	0.02
Sampling frequency	8kHz
Input (first test)	Variable frequency sinusoid
Noise (first test)	Gaussian white noise with zero mean and unit variance
Input (second test)	Speech of a woman
Noise (second test)	Machinery noise

Table 1. Test parameters

In a second experiment, a speech of a woman, sampled at 8 kHz, is used for testing. Machinery noise as an environmental noise is used to corrupt the speech signal. Convergence behavior using mean square error plots are used as a measure of performance. These plots are smoothed with 200 point moving average filter and displayed as shown in Fig.6 for the case of variable frequency sine wave corrupted by white Gaussian noise, and in Fig.7 for the case speech input corrupted by machinery noise.

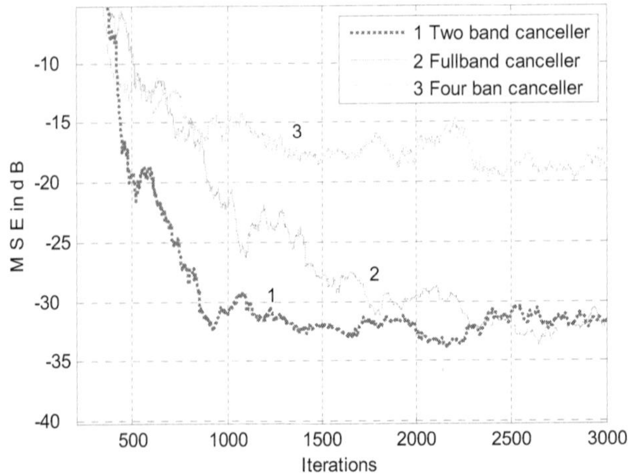

Fig. 6. MSE performance under white environment

2.7 Discussion

The use of the two-band QMF scheme, with near perfect reconstruction filter bank, should lead to approximately zero steady state error at the output of the noise cancellation scheme; this property has been experimentally verified as shown in Fig.6. The fullband adaptive filter performance as well as for a four-band critically sampled scheme are shown on the same graph for sake of comparison. The steady state error of the scheme with two-band QMF banks is very close to the error of the fullband filter, this demonstrate the perfect identification property. Those results show that the adaptive filtering process in subbands based on the feedback of the subbands errors is able to model perfectly a system. The subband plots exhibit faster initial parts; however, after the error has decayed by about 15 dB (4-band) and 30 dB (2-band), the convergence of the four-band scheme slows down dramatically. The errors go down to asymptotic values of about -30 dB (2-band) and -20 dB (4-band). The steady state error of the four-band system is well above the one of the fullband adaptive filter due to high level of aliasing inserted in the system. The improvement of the transient behavior of the four-band scheme was observed only at the start of convergence. The aliased components in the output error cannot be cancelled, unless cross adaptive filters are used to compensate for the overlapping regions between adjacent filters, this would lead to an even slower convergence and an increase in computational complexity of the system. Overall, the convergence performances of the two-band scheme are significantly better than that of the four-band scheme: in particular, the steady state error is much smaller. However, the convergence speed is not improved as such, in comparison with the fullband scheme. The overall convergence speed of the two-band scheme was not found significantly better than the one of the fullband adaptive filter. Nevertheless, such schemes would have the practical advantage of reduced computational complexity in comparison with the fullband adaptive filter.

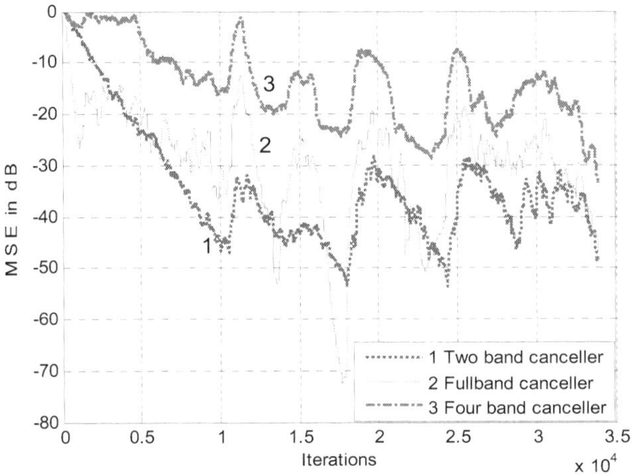

Fig. 7. MSE performance under white environment

3. Adaptive noise cancellation using optimized oversampled filter banks

Aliasing insertion in the critically sampled systems plays a major role in the performance degradation of subband adaptive filters. Filter banks can be designed alias-free and perfectly reconstructed when certain conditions are met by the analysis and synthesis filters. However, any filtering operation in the subbands may cause a possible phase and amplitude change and thereby altering the perfect reconstruction property. In a recent study, Kim et al. (2008) have proposed a critically sampled structure to reduce aliasing effect. The inter-band aliasing in each subband is obtained by increasing the bandwidth of a linear-phase FIR analysis filter, and then subtracted from the subband signal. This aliasing reduction technique introduces spectral dips in the subband signals. Therefore, extra filtering operation is required to reduce these dips.

In this section, an optimized 2-fold oversampled M-band noise cancellation technique is used to mitigate the problem of aliasing insertion associated with critically sampled schemes. The application to the cancellation of background noise from speech signals is considered. The prototype filter is obtained through optimization procedure. A variable step size version of the LMS algorithm is used to control the noise in the individual branches of the proposed canceller. The system is implemented efficiently using polyphase format and FFT/IFFT transforms. The proposed scheme offers a simplified structure that without employing cross-filters or gap filter banks reduces the aliasing level in the subbands. The issue of increasing initial convergence rate is addressed. The performance under white and colored environments is evaluated and compared to the conventional fullband method as well as to a critically sampled technique developed by Kim et al. (2008). This evaluation is offered in terms of MSE convergence of the noise cancellation system.

3.1 Problem formulation

The arrangement in Fig.3 is redrawn for the general case of M-band system downsampled with a factor of D as shown in Fig.8.

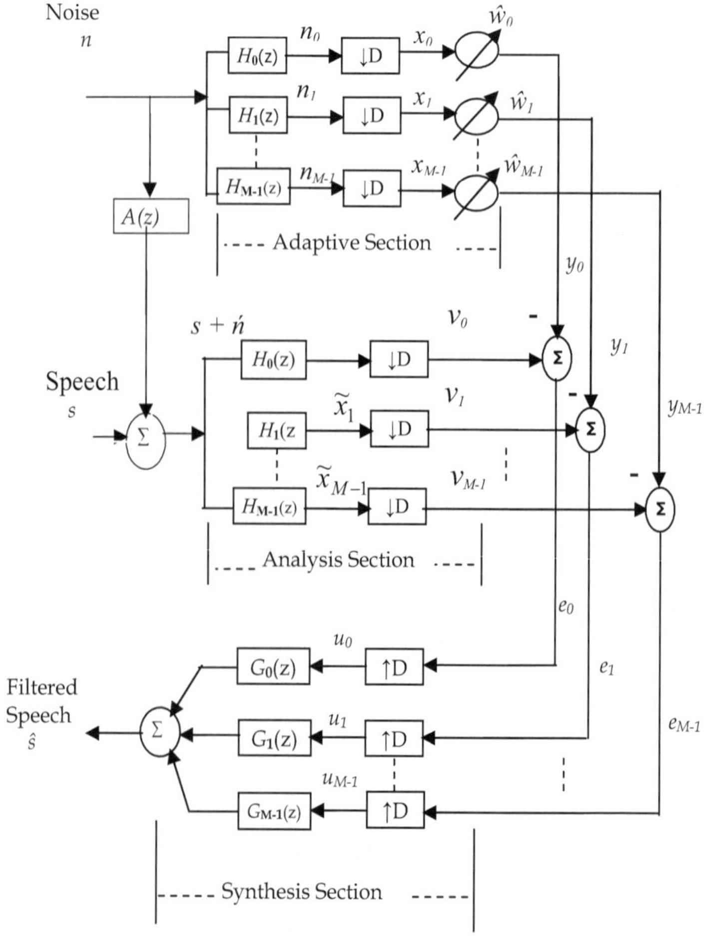

Fig. 8. The M-band noise canceller with downsampling factor set to D

Distortions due the insertion of the analysis/synthesis filter bank are expressed as follows,

$$T_0(z) \approx \frac{1}{M} \sum_{k=0}^{M-1} G_K(z) H_k(z) \tag{25}$$

$$T_i(z) \approx \frac{1}{D} \sum_{k=0}^{M-1} G_K(z) H_k(zW_D^l) \quad , \text{for } i = 1,2,.....D-1 \tag{26}$$

A critical sampling creates severe aliasing effect due to the transition region of the prototype filter. This has been discussed in section 2. When the downsampling factor decreases, the aliasing effect is gradually reduced. Optimizing the prototype filter by minimizing both

$T_0(z)$ and $T_i(z)$ may result in performance deviated toward one of them. Adjusting such an optimization process is not easy in practice, because there are two objectives in the design of the filter bank. Furthermore, minimizing aliasing distortion $T_i(z)$ using the distortion function $T_0(z)$ as a constraint is a very non-linear optimization problem and the results may not reduce both distortions. Therefore, in this section, we use 2-times oversampling factor to reduce aliasing error, and the total system distortion is minimized by optimizing a single prototype filter in the analysis and synthesis stages. The total distortion function $T_0(z)$ and the aliasing distortion $T_i(z)$ can be represented in frequency domain as,

$$T_0(e^{j\omega}) \approx \frac{1}{M}\sum_{k=0}^{M-1} G_K(e^{j\omega})H_k(e^{j\omega}) \tag{27}$$

$$T_i(e^{j\omega}) \approx \frac{1}{D}\sum_{k=0}^{M-1} G_K(e^{j\omega})H_k(e^{j\omega}W_D^l) \tag{28}$$

The objective is to find prototype filters $H_0(e^{j\omega})$, and $G_0(e^{j\omega})$, that minimize the system reconstruction error. In effect, a single lowpass filter is used as a prototype to produce the analysis and synthesis filter banks by Discrete Fourier Transform (DFT) modulation,

$$H_k(z) = H_0(ze^{2\pi k/M}) \tag{25}$$

3.2 Prototype filter optimization

Recalling that, the objective here is to find prototype filter $H_0(e^{j\omega})$ to minimize reconstruction error. In frequency domain the analysis prototype filter is given by

$$H_0(e^{j\omega}) = \sum_{n=0}^{L-1} h_0(n)e^{-j\omega n} \tag{29}$$

For a lowpass prototype filter whose stop-band stretches from ω_s to π, we minimize the total stopband energy according to the following function

$$E_s = \int_{\omega_s}^{\pi} \left|H_0(e^{j\omega})\right|^2 d\omega \tag{30}$$

For M-channel filter banks the stopband edge is expressed as,

$$\omega_s = \frac{\pi(1+\beta)}{2M} \tag{31}$$

where β is the roll-off parameter. Stopband attenuation is the measure that is used when comparing the design results with different parameters. The numerical value is the highest sidelobe given in dBs when the prototype filter passband is normalized to 0 dB. E_s is expressed with a quadratic matrix as follows;

$$E_s = \mathbf{h}^T\mathbf{\Phi}\mathbf{h} \tag{32}$$

where vector $\mathbf{h}$ contains the prototype filter impulse response coefficients, and $\mathbf{\Phi}$ is given by Nguyen (1993) as,

$$\Phi_{n,m} = \begin{cases} \pi - \omega_s & n = m \\ \dfrac{1}{n-m}(\sin((n-m)\pi) - \sin((n-k)\omega_s)) & n \neq m \end{cases} \tag{33}$$

The optimum coefficients of the FIR filter are those that minimize the energy function E_s in (30). For M-band complementary filter bank, the frequency $\omega = \pi / 2M$ is located at the middle of the transition band of its prototype filter. The pass-band covers the frequency range of $0 \leq \omega \leq \dfrac{\pi(1-\beta)}{2M}$. For a given number of subbands, M, a roll-off factor β and for a certain length of prototype filter L we find the optimum coefficients of the FIR filter. The synthesis prototype filter $G_0(e^{j\omega})$, is a time reversed version of $H_0(e^{j\omega})$. In general, it is not easy to maintain the low distortion level unless the length of the filter increases to allow for narrow transition regions. The optimization is run for various prototype filter lengths L, different number of subbands M and certain roll-off factors β. Frequency response of the final design of prototype filter is shown in Fig.9.

3.3 The adaptive process

The filter weight updating is performed using a subband version of the LMS algorithm that is expressed by the following;

$$\hat{\mathbf{w}}_k(m+1) = \hat{\mathbf{w}}_k(m) + \mu_k.\alpha_k.e_k(m)\mathbf{x}_k(m) \tag{34}$$

$$e_k(m) = v_k(m) - y_k(m) \tag{35}$$

$$y_k(m) = \hat{\mathbf{w}}_k{}^T(m)\mathbf{x}_k(m) \tag{36}$$

The filter weights in each branch are adjusted using the subband error signal belonging to the same branch. To prevent the adaptive filter from oscillating or being too slow, the step size of the adaptation algorithm is made inversely proportional to the power in the subband signals such that

$$\alpha_k = \frac{1}{\sigma + \|x_k\|^2} \tag{37}$$

where $\|x_k\|$ is the norm of the input signal and σ is a small constant used to avoid possible division by zero. On the other hand, a suitable value of the adaptation gain factor μ is deduced using trial and error procedure.

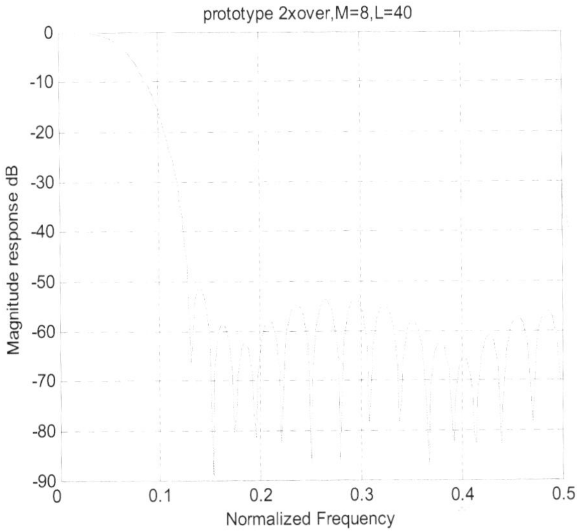

Fig. 9. Optimized prototype filter

3.4 Polyphse implementation of the subband noise canceller

The implementation of DFT modulated filter banks can be done using polyphase decomposition of a single prototype filter and a Fast Fourier Transform (FFT). A DFT modulated analysis filter bank with subsequent D-fold downsampling is implemented as a tapped delay line of size M with D-fold downsampling, followed by a structured matrix $M \times D$ containing the polyphase components of the analysis prototype filter $\mathbf{F}(z)$, and an $M \times M$ FFT matrix as shown in Fig. 10. The synthesis bank is constructed in a reversed fashion with $D \times M$ matrix containing the polyphase components of the synthesis filter bank $\tilde{\mathbf{F}}(z)$.

3.5 Results of the optimized 2-fold oversampled noise canceller

The noise path used in these tests is an approximation of a small room impulse response modeled by a FIR processor of 512 taps. To measure the convergence behavior of the oversampled subband noise canceller, a variable frequency sinusoid was corrupted with white Gaussian noise. This noise was passed through the noise path, and then applied to the primary input of the noise canceller, with white Gaussian noise is applied to the reference input. Experimental parameters are listed in Table 2. Mean square error convergence is used as a measure of performance. Plots of MSE are produced and smoothed with a suitable moving average filter. A comparison is made with a conventional fullband system as well as with a recently developed critically sampled system (Kim et al 2008) as shown in Fig.11. The optimized system is denoted by (OS), the critically sampled system is denoted by (CS) and the fullband system is denoted by (FB). To test the behavior under environmental conditions, a speech signal is then applied to the primary input of the proposed noise canceller. The speech was in the form of Malay utterance "Kosong, Satu, Dua,Tiga" spoken by a woman. The speech was sampled at 16 kHz. Engine noise is used as a background interference to corrupt the above speech. Plots of MSE are produced as shown in Fig.12. In this figure, convergence plots of a fullband and critically sampled systems are also depicted for comparison.

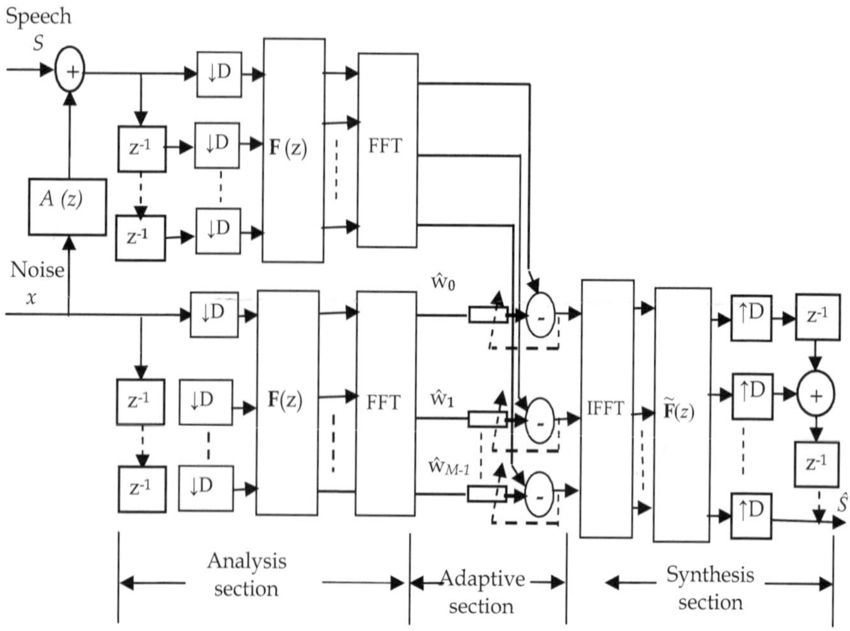

Fig. 10. Polyphase implementation of the multiband noise canceller

Parameter	Specification
Acoustic noise path	FIR processor with 512 taps
Adaptation algorithm type	Subband power normalized LMS
Primary input (first test)	Variable frequency sinusoid
Reference input (first test)	Additive white Gaussian noise
Primary input (second test)	Malay utterance, sampled at 16 kHz
Reference input (second test)	Machinery noise

Table 2. Test parameters

3.6 Discussion

From Figure 11, it is clear that the MSE plot of the proposed oversampled subband noise canceller converges faster than the fullband. While the fullband system is converging slowly, the oversampled noise canceller approaches 25 dB noise reductions in about 2500 iterations. In an environment where the impulse response of the noise path is changing over a period of time shorter than the initial convergence period, initial convergence will most affect cancellation quality. On the other hand, the CS system developed using the method by (Kim et al. 2008) needs a longer transient time than that OS system. The FB canceller needs around 10000 iterations to reach approximately a similar noise reduction level. In case of speech and machinery noise (Fig12), it is clear that the FB system converges slowly with colored noise as the input to the adaptive filters. Tests performed in this part of the experiment proved that the proposed optimized OS noise canceller does have better performance than the conventional fullband model as well as a recently developed critically sampled system. However, for white noise interference, there is still some amount of residual error on steady state as it can be noticed from a close inspection of Fig.11.

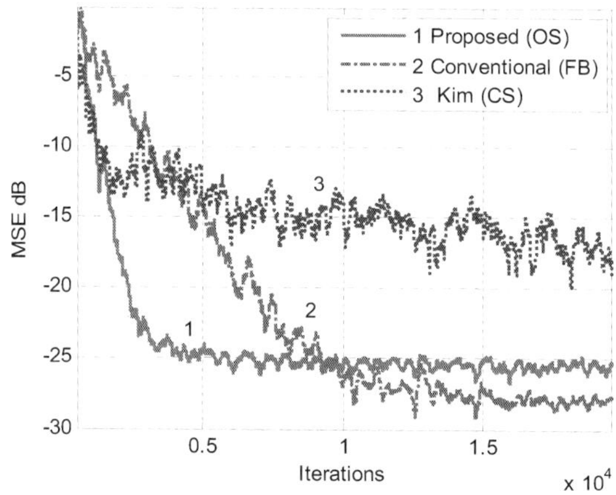

Fig. 11. MSE performance under white noise

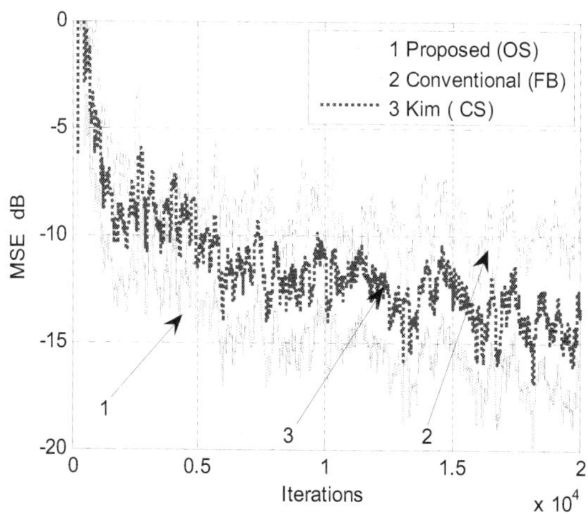

Fig. 12. MSE performance under environmental conditions

4. Low complexity noise cancellation technique

In the last section, optimized oversampled filter banks are used in the subband noise cancellation system as an appropriate solution to avoid aliasing distortion associated with the critically sampled subband noise canceller. However, oversampled systems imply higher computational requirements than critically sampled ones. In addition, it has been shown in the previous section that oversampled FIR filter banks themselves color the input signal, which leads to under modeling and hence high residual noise at system's output for white noise. Therefore, a cheaper implementation of the subband noise canceller that retains good noise reduction performance and low signal delay is sought in this section. The idea is centered on using allpass infinite impulse response filters. The filters can be good alternatives for FIR filters. Flat responses with very small transition band, can be achieved with only few filter coefficients. Aliasing distortion in the analysis filter banks can be reduced to tolerable levels with lower expenses and acceptable delay. In literature, the use of allpass IIR filter banks for echo control has been treated by Naylor et al. (1998). One shortcoming of this treatment is the spectral gaps produced as a result of using notch filtering to preprocess the subband signals at the analysis stage in an attempt to reduce the effect of nonlinearity on the processed signal. The use of notch filters by Naylor et al. (1998) has also increased processing delay. In this section, an adaptive noise cancellation scheme that uses a combination of polyphase allpass filter banks at the analysis stage and an optimized FIR filter bank at the synthesis stage is developed and tested. The synthesis filters are designed in such a way that inherent phase correction is made at the output of the noise canceller. The adaptive process is carried out as given by equations (34)-(37). Details of the design of analysis and synthesis filter banks are described in the following subsections.

4.1 Analysis filter bank design

The analysis prototype filter of the proposed system is constructed from second order allpass sections as shown in Fig.13. The transfer function of the prototype analysis filter is given by

$$H_0(z) = \frac{1}{2}\sum_{k=0}^{N-1} F_k(z^{-2})z^{-k} \tag{38}$$

where,

$$F_k(z^{-2}) = \prod_{n-1}^{L_k} F_{k,n}(z^{-2}) = \prod_{n=1}^{L_k} \frac{\alpha_{k,n} + z^{-2}}{1+\alpha_{k,n} z^{-2}} \tag{39}$$

where $\alpha_{k,n}$ is the coefficient of the kth allpass section in the nth branch L_n is the number of sections in the nth branch, and N is the order of the section. These parameters can be determined from filter specifications. The discussion in this chapter is limited to second order allpass sections, since higher order allpass functions can be built from products of such second order filters.

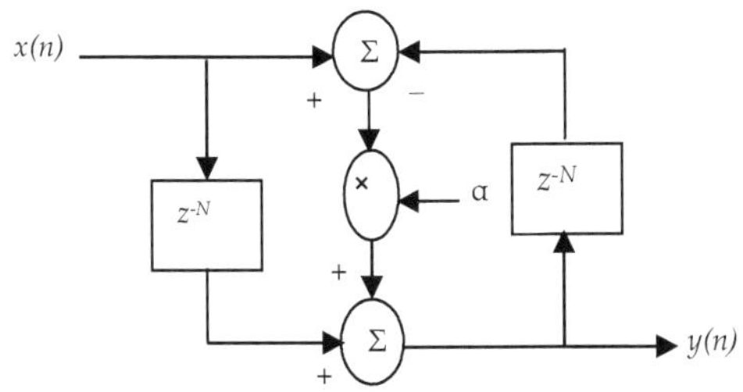

Fig. 13. The second order allpass section

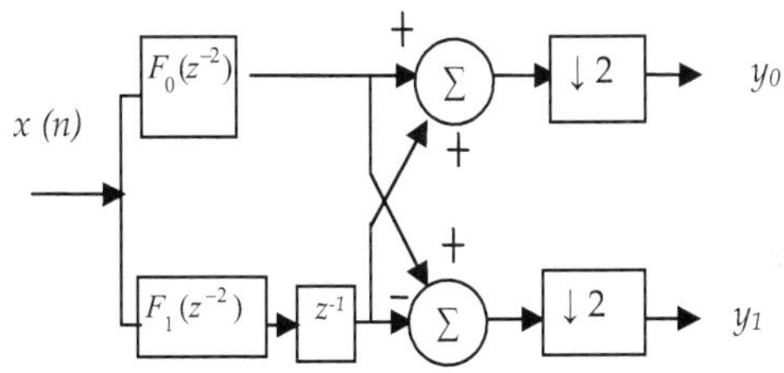

Fig. 14. Polyphase implementation

Furthermore, to maintain the performance of the filters in fixed point implementation, it is advantageous to use cascaded first or second-order sections (Mendel 1991). These filters can be used to produce multirate filter banks with high filtering quality (Milić 2009). Elliptic filters fall into this class of filters yielding very low-complexity analysis filters (Poucki et al. 2010).The two band analysis filter bank that is shown on the L.H.S. of Fig.1 can be modified to the form of the polyphase implementation(type1) as shown in Fig.14 and is given by

$$H_0(z)=\frac{1}{2}(F_0(z^2)+z^{-1}F_1(z^2)) \quad (40)$$

$$H_1(z)=\frac{1}{2}(F_0(z^2)-z^{-1}F_1(z^2)) \quad (41)$$

Filters $H_0(z)$ and $H_1(z)$ are bandlimiting filters representing lowpass and highpass respectively. This modification results in half the number of calculations per input sample and half the storage requirements. In Fig.14, y_0 and y_1 represent lowpass and highpass filter outputs, respectively. The polyphase structure can be further modified by shifting the downsampler to the input to give more efficient implementation. According to the noble identities of multirate systems, moving the downsampler to the left of the filter results in the power of z in $F_0(z^2)$ and $F_1(z^2)$ to reduced to 1 and the filters becomes $F_0(z)$ and $F_1(z)$, where $F_0(z)$ and $F_1(z)$ are causal, real, stable allpass filters. Fig15 depicts the frequency response of the analysis filter bank.

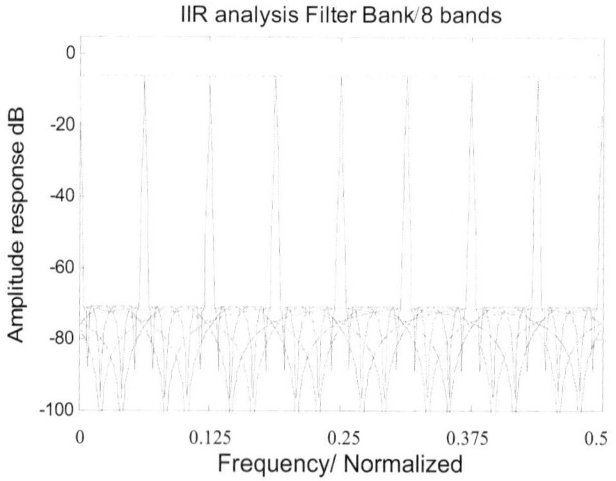

Fig. 15. Analysis filter bank magnitude frequency response

4.2 Analysis/synthesis matching

For phase correction at the noise canceller output, a relationship that relates analysis filters to synthesis filter is established as follows. The analysis prototype filter $H(z)$ can be represented in the frequency domain by,

$$H(e^{j\omega}) = \left|H(e^{j\omega})\right| e^{j\varphi(\omega)} \tag{42}$$

where $\varphi(\omega)$ is the phase response of the analysis prototype filter. On the other hand, the synthesis filter bank is based on prototype low pass FIR filter that is related to the analysis prototype filter by the following relationship

$$G_d(e^{j\omega}) = \left|G_0(e^{j\omega})\right| e^{j\psi} = \left|H_0(e^{j\omega})\right| e^{-j[\omega.\partial+\varphi\ (\omega)]} \tag{43}$$

where $G_d(e^{j\omega})$ is the desired frequency response of synthesis prototype filter and ψ is the phase of the synthesis filter. This shall compensate for any possible phase distortion at the analysis stage. The coefficients of the prototype synthesis filter $G_d(e^{j\omega})$ are evaluated by minimizing the weighted squared of the error that is given by the following

$$WSE = \sum Wt(\omega)\left|G_0(e^{j\omega}) - G_{d.}(e^{j\omega})\right|^2 \tag{44}$$

where $Wt(\omega)$ is a weighting function given by

$$Wt(\omega) = \left|\hat{G}_0(e^{j\omega}) - G_{d.}(e^{j\omega})\right|^2 \tag{45}$$

where $\hat{G}_0(e^{j\omega})$ is an approximation of the desired frequency response, it is obtained by frequency transforming the truncated impulse response of the desired prototype filter, leading to nearly perfect reconstruction up to a delay in which the amplitude, phase and aliasing distortions will be small. *WSE* is evaluated on a dense grid of frequencies linearly distributed in the fundamental frequency range. The use of FIR filter bank at the synthesis stage with prototype filter as dictated by (43) ensures a linear phase at the output, a constant group delay and a good analysis/synthesis matching. Plot of the distortion function is shown in Fig. 16. It is obvious from this figure that the distortion due the filter bank is quite low.

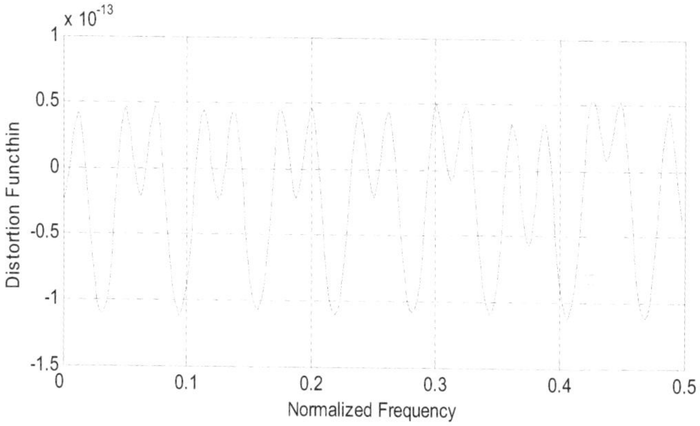

Fig. 16. Distortion function

4.3 Computational complexity and system delay analysis

The total computational complexity of the system can be calculated in three parts, analysis, adaptive and synthesis. The complexity of 8-band analysis filter bank with eight coefficients prototype filter, and for tree implementation of three stages giving a total of 28 multiplication operations per unit sample by utilizing the noble identities. The complexity of the adaptive section is calculated as the fullband adaptive filter length L_{FB} divided by the number of subbands, $L_{FB}/8$ .The complexity of the synthesis section is calculated directly by multiplying the number of filter coefficients by the number of bands, in our case, for 55 tap synthesis prototype filter, and for eight band filter bank, which gives a total to 440 multiplication operations at the synthesis stage. Therefore, the overall number of multiplication operations required is $(578+L_{FB}/8)$. Now, comparing with a system uses high order FIR filter banks at the analysis and the synthesis stages to give that equivalent performance. For an equivalent performance, the length of the prototype should be at least 128, and for 8 bands, at the analysis stage we need 1024 multiplication operations, a similar number at the synthesis stage is required. Thus, for two analysis filter banks and one synthesis filterbank total number of multiplications =$2048+L_{FB}/8$. On the other hand, the computational complexity of block updating method given by Narasimha (2007) requires three complex FFT operations, each one corresponds to $2\times L_{AF}\times\log_2 L_{AF}-L_{AF}$ multiplications, which is much higher than the proposed method. In acoustic environments, the length of the acoustic path usually few thousands of taps, making the adaptive section is the main bulk of computations. As far as system delay is concerned, the prototype analysis filter has a group delay between 2.5 and 5 samples except at the band edge where it reaches about 40 samples as shown in Fig. 17. The maximum group delay due to the analysis filter bank is 70 samples calculated as 40 samples for the first stage followed by two stages, each of them working at half the rate of the previous one. The synthesis stage has a maximum group delay of 27 samples which brings the total delay to 97 samples..

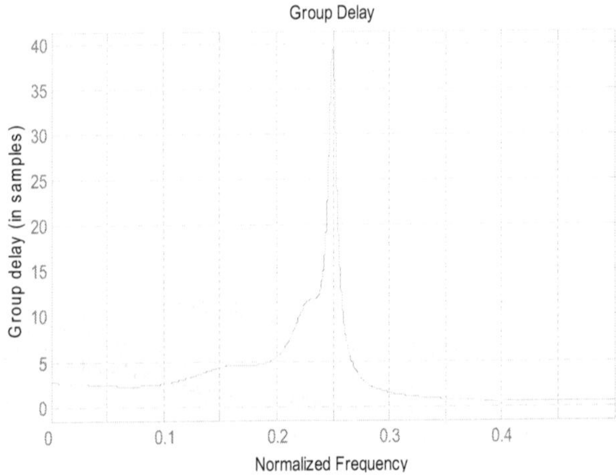

Fig. 17. Group delay of prototype analysis filter

In the technique offered by Narasimha (2007) for example, the output is calculated only after the accumulation of L_{FB} samples block. For a path length of 512 considered in these experiments, a delay by the same amount of samples is produced, which is higher than the proposed one, particularly if a practical acoustic path is considered. Therefore for tracking non-stationary signals our proposed technique offers a better tracking than that offered by Narasimha (2007). Furthermore, comparison of computational complexity of our LC system with other literature techniques is depicted in table 3.

	Kim (2008)	Narasimha (2007)	Choi&Bai (2007)	Proposed (LC)
Complexity	890	27136	2056	532
Delay/samples	430	512	128	97

Table 3. Computational complexity and delay comparison.

4.4 Results and discussion of the low complexity noise canceller

The same input signals and noise path as in in previous section are used in testing the low complexity system. In the sequel, the following notations shall be used, LC for low complexity noise canceller, OS and FB stand for oversampled and fullband systems, respectively. It is shown in Fig. 18 that mean square error plots of the OS system levels off at -25 dB after a fast initial convergence. This due to the presence of colored components as discussed in the last section. Meanwhile, the MSE plot of the proposed LC noise canceller outperforms the MSE plot of the classical fullband system during initial convergence and exhibits comparable steady state performance with a little amount of residual noise. This is probably due to some non linearity which may not be fully equalized by the synthesis stage, since the synthesis filter bank is constructed by an approximation procedure. However, subjective tests showed that the effect on actual hearing is hardly noticed. It is obvious that the LC system reaches a steady state in approximately 4000 iterations. The fullband (FB) system needs more than 10000 iterations to reach the same noise cancellation level. On the other hand, the amount of residual noise has been reduced compared to the OS FIR/FIR noise canceller. Tests performed using actual speech and ambient interference (Fig. 19) proved that the proposed LC noise canceller does have an improved performance compared to OS scheme, as well as the FB canceller. The improvement in noise reduction on steady state ranges from 15-20 dB compared to fullband case, as this is evident from Fig. 20. The improved results for the proposed LC system employing polyphase IIR analysis filter bank can be traced back to the steeper transition bands, nearly perfect reconstruction, good channel separation and very flat passband response, within each band. For an input speech sampled at 16 kHz, the adaptation time for the given channel and input signal is measured to be below 0.8 seconds. The convergence of the NLMS approaches above 80% in approximately 0.5 seconds. The LC noise canceller possesses the advantage of low number of multiplications required per input sample. To sum up, the proposed LC approach showed an improved performance for white and colored interference situations, proving usefulness of the method for noise cancellation.

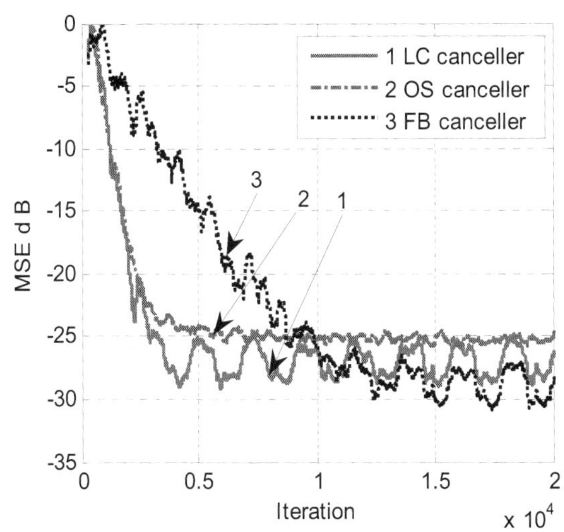

Fig. 18. MSE performance comparison of the proposed low complexity (LC) system with an equivalent oversampled (OS) and fullband (FB) cancellers under white noise interference

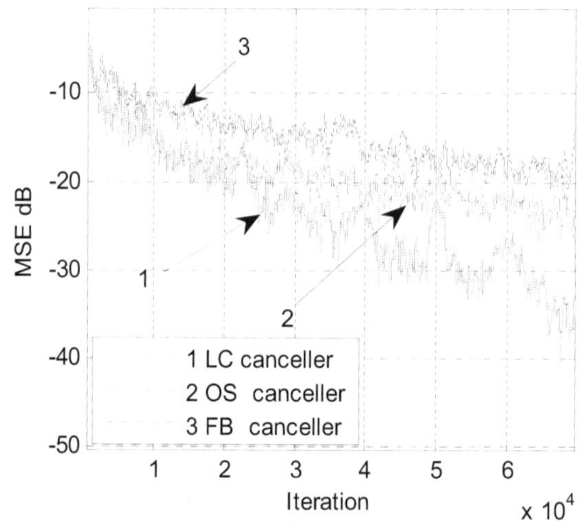

Fig. 19. MSE performance comparison of the proposed low complexity (LC) system with an equivalent oversampled (OS) and conventional fullband (FB) cancellers under ambient noise

5. Conclusion

Adaptive filter noise cancellation systems using subband processing are developed and tested in this chapter. Convergence and computational advantages are expected from using such a technique. Results obtained showed that; noise cancellation techniques using critically sampled filter banks have no convergence improvement, except for the case of two-band QMF decomposition, where the success was only moderate. Only computational advantages may be obtained in this case. An improved convergence behavior is obtained by using two-fold oversampled DFT filter bank that is optimized for low amplitude distortion. The price to be paid is the increase in computational costs. Another limitation with this technique is the coloring effect of the filter bank when the background noise is white. The use of polyphase allpass IIR filters at the analysis stage with inherent phase compensation at the synthesis stage have reduced the computational complexity of the system and showed convergence advantages. This reduction in computational power can be utilized in using more subbands for high accuracy and lower convergence time required to model very long acoustic paths. Moreover, the low complexity system offered a lower delay than that offered by other techniques. A further improvement to the current work can be achieved by using a selective algorithm that can apply different adaptation algorithms for different frequency bands. Also, the use of other transforms can be investigated.

6. References

Bergen, S.W.A. (2008). A design method for cosine-modulated filter banks using weighted constrained-least-squares filters, *Elsevier Signal Processing Journal*, Vol.18, No.3, (May 2008), pp. 282–290. ISSN 1051-2004.

Choi, H, & Bae, H.D. (2007). Subband affine projection algorithm for acoustic echo cancellation system. *EURASIP Journal on Advances in Signal Processing*, Vol. 2007. doi:10.1155/2007/75621, ISSN 1110-8657.

Deng, Y.; Mathews, V.J. & Boroujeny, B.F. (2007). Low-Delay Nonuniform Pseudo-QMF Banks With Application to Speech Enhancement, *IEEE Trans. on Signal Processing*, Vol.55, No.5, (May 2007), pp. 2110-2121, ISSN 1053-587X.

Diniz, P. S. R. (2008). *Adaptive Filtering: Algorithms and practical implementations 3rd edition*, Springer Science+Business Media, ISBN 978-0-387-3-31274-3, New York, USA.

Hameed, A.K.M. & Elias, E. (2006). M-channel cosine modulated filter banks with linear phase analysis and synthesis filters. *Elsevier Signal Processing*, Vol.86, No.12, December 2006, pp. 3842–3848.

Haykin, S. (2002). *Adaptive filter Theory*, 4thed, Prentice Hall, ISBN 0-130-90126-1, New Jersey, USA.

Hoge, S.W.; Gallego, F.; Xiao, Z. & Brooks. D.H. (2008). RLS-GRAPPA: Reconstructing parallel MRI data with adaptive filters, *Proceedings of the 5th IEEE Symposium on Biomedical Imaging* (ISBI 2008), pp. 1537-1540, ISBN 978-1-4244-2002-5,Paris, France, May 14-17, 2008.

Johnson, J.; Cornu, E.; Choy G. & Wdowiak, J. (2004). Ultra low-power sub-band acoustic echo cancellation for wireless headsets, *Proceedings of the IEEE International Conference on Acoustics, Speech and Signal Processing*, pp. V357-60, ISBN 0-7803-8484-9, Montreal, Canada, May 17-21, 2004.

Kim, S.G., Yoo, C.D. & Nguyen, T.Q. (2008). Alias-free subband adaptive filtering with critical sampling. *IEEE Transactions on Signal Processing*. Vol.56, No.5, May 2008, pp. 1894-1904. ISSN 1053-587X.

Lin, X.; Khong, A. W. H.; Doroslovaˇcki, M. & Naylor, P. A. (2008). Frequency-domain adaptive algorithm for network echo cancellation in VoIP. *EURASIP Journal on Audio, Speech, and Music Processing*. Volume 2008, Article ID 156960, 9 pages, doi:10.1155/2008/156960, ISSN 1687-4714.

Martinez, J.I.M., & Nakano, K. (2008). Cascade lattice IIR adaptive filter structure using simultaneous perturbation method for self-adjusting SHARF algorithm, *Proceedings of* SICE *Annual SICE Annual Conference*, pp. 2156-2161, ISBN 978-4-907764-30-2, Tokyo, Japan, 20-22 August 20-22, 2008.

Mendel, J.M. (1991). Tutorial on higher-order statistics (spectra) in signal processing and system theory: Theoretical results and some applications. *IEEE Transactions*, (March 1991), Vol. 79, No.3, pp. 278–305, ISSN 0018-9219.

Milić, L. (2009). *Multirate filtering for digital signal processing: MATLAB Applications*. Information Science Reference (IGI Global), ISBN 1605661783, Hershy PA 17033, USA.

Narasimha, M.J. (2007). Block adaptive filter with time-domain update using three transforms. *IEEE Signal Processing Letters*, Vol.14, No.1, (January 2007), pp51-53, ISSN 1070-9908.

Naylor, P.A., Tanrıkulu,O. & Constantinides, A.G. (1998). Subband adaptive filtering for acoustic echo control using allpass polyphase IIR filterbanks. *IEEE Transactions on Speech and Audio Processing*, Vol.6, No.2, (March 1998), pp. 143-155. ISSN 1063-6676.

Nguyen, T. Q. & Vaidyanathan, P.P. (1988). Maximally decimated perfect – reconstruction FIR filter banks with pairwise mirror-Image analysis (and synthesis) frequency response. *IEEE Trans. on Acoustics, Speech and Signal Processing, Vol.*36, No.5, (May 1988), pp. 693-706. ISSN 0096-3518.

Poucki , V.M.; Žemvaa, A. ; Lutovacb, M.D. & Karcnik, T. (2010). Elliptic IIR filter sharpening implemented on FPGA. *Elsevier Signal Processing,* Vol.20, No.1, (January 2010), pp. 13–22, ISSN 1051-2004.

Radenkovic, M. & Tamal Bose. (2001). Adaptive IIR filtering of non stationary signals. *Elsevier Signal Processing,* Vol.81, No.1, (January 2010), pp.183-195, ISSN 0165-1684.

Vaseghi, V.S. (2008). *Advanced digital signal processing and noise reduction.* 4rd Edition, John Willey and Sons Ltd, 978-0-470-75406-1, West Sussex, England.

Wasfy, M., B. & Ranganathan, R. 2008. Complex FIR block adaptive digital filtering algorithm with independent adaptation of real and imaginary filter parameters, *Proceedings of the 51st Midwest Symposium on Circuits and Systems*, pp. 854-85, ISBN 978-1-4244-2166-4, Knoxville, TN, August 10-13, 2008.

6

Hirschman Optimal Transform (HOT) DFT Block LMS Algorithm

Osama Alkhouli[1], Victor DeBrunner[2] and Joseph Havlicek[3]
[1]*Caterpillar Inc.,*
[2]*Florida State University,*
[3]*The University of Oklahoma*
USA

1. Introduction

Least mean square (LMS) adaptive filters, as investigated by Widrow and Hoff in 1960 (Widrow & Hoff, 1980), find applications in many areas of digital signal processing including channel equalization, system identification, adaptive antennas, spectral line enhancement, echo interference cancelation, active vibration and noise control, spectral estimation, and linear prediction (Farhang-Boroujeny, 1999; Haykin, 2002). The computational burden and slow convergence speed of the LMS algorithm can render its real time implementation infeasible. To reduce the computational cost of the LMS filter, Ferrara proposed a frequency domain implementation of the LMS algorithm (Ferrara, 1980). In this algorithm, the data is partitioned into fixed-length blocks and the weights are allowed to change after each block is processed. This algorithm is called the DFT block LMS algorithm. The computational reduction in the DFT block LMS algorithm comes from using the fast DFT convolution to calculate the convolution between the filer input and weights and the gradient estimate.
The Hirschman optimal transform (HOT) is a recently developed discrete unitary transform (DeBrunner et al., 1999; Przebinda et.al, 2001) that uses the orthonormal minimizers of the entropy-based Hirschman uncertainty measure (Przebinda et.al, 2001). This measure is different from the energy-based Heisenberg uncertainty measure that is only suited for continuous time signals. The Hirschman uncertainty measure uses entropy to quantify the spread of discrete-time signals in time and frequency (DeBrunner et al., 1999). Since the HOT bases are among the minimizers of the uncertainty measure, they have the novel property of being the most compact in discrete-time and frequency. The fact that the HOT basis sequences have many zero-valued samples, as well as their resemblance to the DFT basis sequences, makes the HOT computationally attractive. Furthermore, it has been shown recently that a thresholding algorithm using the HOT yields superior frequency resolution of a pure tone in additive white noise to a similar algorithm based on the DFT (DeBrunner et al., 2005). The HOT is similar to the DFT. For example, the 3^2-point HOT matrix is explicitly given below.

$$\begin{bmatrix} 1\,0\,0 & 1 & 0 & 0 & 1 & 0 & 0 \\ 0\,1\,0 & 0 & 1 & 0 & 0 & 1 & 0 \\ 0\,0\,1 & 0 & 0 & 1 & 0 & 0 & 1 \\ 1\,0\,0 & e^{-j2\pi/3} & 0 & 0 & e^{-j4\pi/3} & 0 & 0 \\ 0\,1\,0 & 0 & e^{-j2\pi/3} & 0 & 0 & e^{-j4\pi/3} & 0 \\ 0\,0\,1 & 0 & 0 & e^{-j2\pi/3} & 0 & 0 & e^{-j4\pi/3} \\ 1\,0\,0 & e^{-j4\pi/3} & 0 & 0 & e^{-j8\pi/3} & 0 & 0 \\ 0\,1\,0 & 0 & e^{-j4\pi/3} & 0 & 0 & e^{-j8\pi/3} & 0 \\ 0\,0\,1 & 0 & 0 & e^{-j4\pi/3} & 0 & 0 & e^{-j8\pi/3} \end{bmatrix} \tag{1}$$

In general, the NK-point HOT basis are generated from the N-point DFT basis as follows. Each of the DFT basis functions are interpolated by K and then circularly shifted to produce the complete set of orthogonal basis signals that define the HOT. The computational saving of any fast block LMS algorithm depends on how efficiently each of the two convolutions involved in the LMS algorithm are calculated (Clark et al., 1980; Ferrara, 1980). The DFT block LMS algorithm is most efficient when the block and filter sizes are equal. Recently, we developed a fast convolution based on the HOT (DeBrunner & Matusiak, 2003). The HOT convolution is more efficient than the DFT convolution when the disparity in the lengths of the sequences being convolved is large. In this chapter we introduce a new fast block LMS algorithm based on the HOT. This algorithm is called the HOT DFT block LMS algorithm. It is very similar to the DFT block LMS algorithm and reduces its computational complexity by about 30% when the filter length is much smaller than the block length. In the HOT DFT block LMS algorithm, the fast HOT convolution is used to calculate the filter output and update the weights.

Recently, the HOT transform was used to develop the HOT LMS algorithm (Alkhouli et al., 2005; Alkhouli & DeBrunner, 2007), which is a transform domain LMS algorithm, and the HOT block LMS algorithm (Alkhouli & DeBrunner, 2007), which is a fast block LMS algorithm. The HOT DFT block LMS algorithm presented here is different from the HOT block LMS algorithm presented in (Alkhouli & DeBrunner, 2007). The HOT DFT block LMS algorithm developed in this chapter uses the fast HOT convolution (DeBrunner & Matusiak, 2003). The main idea behind the HOT convolution is to partition the longer sequence into sections of the same length as the shorter sequence and then convolve each section with the shorter sequence efficiently using the fast DFT convolution. The relevance of the HOT will become apparent when the all of the (sub)convolutions are put together concisely in a matrix form as will be shown later in this chapter.

The following notations are used throughout this chapter. Nonbold lowercase letters are used for scalar quantities, bold lowercase is used for vectors, and bold uppercase is used for matrices. Nonbold uppercase letters are used for integer quantities such as length or dimensions. The lowercase letter k is reserved for the block index. The lowercase letter n is reserved for the time index. The time and block indexes are put in brackets, whereas subscripts are used to refer to elements of vectors and matrices. The uppercase letter N is reserved for the filter length and the uppercase letter L is reserved for the block length. The superscripts T and H denote vector or matrix transposition and Hermitian transposition, respectively. The N-point DFT matrix is denoted by $\mathbf{F}_N$ or simply by $\mathbf{F}$. The subscripts F and H are used to highlight the DFT and HOT domain quantities, respectively. The $N \times N$ identity matrix is denoted by $\mathbf{I}_{N\times N}$ or $\mathbf{I}$. The $N \times N$ zero matrix is denoted by $\mathbf{0}_{N\times N}$. The linear and

circular convolutions are denoted by $*$ and $\star$, respectively. Diag $[\mathbf{u}]$ or $\mathcal{U}$ denotes the diagonal matrix whose diagonal elements are the elements of the vector $\mathbf{u}$.
In section 2, The explicit relation between the DFT and HOT is developed. The HOT convolution is presented in Section 3. In Section 4, the HOT DFT block LMS algorithm is developed. Its computational cost is analyzed in Section 5. Section 6 contains the convergence analysis and Section 7 contains its misadjustment. Simulations are provided in Section 8 before the conclusions in Section 9

2. The relation between the DFT and HOT

In this section, an explicit relation between the DFT and HOT is derived. Let $\mathbf{u}$ be a vector of length NK. The K-band polyphase decomposition of $\mathbf{u}$ decomposes $\mathbf{u}$ into a set of K polyphase components. The kth polyphase componenet of $\mathbf{u}$ is denoted by $\tilde{\mathbf{u}}_k$ and is given by

$$\tilde{\mathbf{u}}_k = \begin{bmatrix} u_k \\ u_{k+K} \\ u_{k+2K} \\ \vdots \\ u_{k+(N-1)K} \end{bmatrix}. \tag{2}$$

The vector that combines the polyphase components of $\mathbf{u}$ is denoted by $\tilde{\mathbf{u}}$, i.e.,

$$\tilde{\mathbf{u}} = \begin{bmatrix} \tilde{\mathbf{u}}_0 \\ \tilde{\mathbf{u}}_1 \\ \tilde{\mathbf{u}}_2 \\ \vdots \\ \tilde{\mathbf{u}}_{K-1} \end{bmatrix}. \tag{3}$$

The square matrix that relates $\tilde{\mathbf{u}}$ and $\mathbf{u}$ is denoted by $\mathbf{P}$, i.e.,

$$\tilde{\mathbf{u}} = \mathbf{P}\mathbf{u}. \tag{4}$$

For example, $\mathbf{P}$ for the case of $N = 4$ and $K = 3$ is given by

$$\mathbf{P} = \begin{bmatrix} 1\,0\,0\,0\,0\,0\,0\,0\,0\,0\,0\,0 \\ 0\,0\,0\,1\,0\,0\,0\,0\,0\,0\,0\,0 \\ 0\,0\,0\,0\,0\,0\,1\,0\,0\,0\,0\,0 \\ 0\,0\,0\,0\,0\,0\,0\,0\,0\,1\,0\,0 \\ 0\,1\,0\,0\,0\,0\,0\,0\,0\,0\,0\,0 \\ 0\,0\,0\,0\,1\,0\,0\,0\,0\,0\,0\,0 \\ 0\,0\,0\,0\,0\,0\,0\,1\,0\,0\,0\,0 \\ 0\,0\,0\,0\,0\,0\,0\,0\,0\,0\,1\,0 \\ 0\,0\,1\,0\,0\,0\,0\,0\,0\,0\,0\,0 \\ 0\,0\,0\,0\,0\,1\,0\,0\,0\,0\,0\,0 \\ 0\,0\,0\,0\,0\,0\,0\,0\,1\,0\,0\,0 \\ 0\,0\,0\,0\,0\,0\,0\,0\,0\,0\,0\,1 \end{bmatrix}. \tag{5}$$

Without loss of generality, we consider the special case of $N = 4$ and $K = 3$ to find an explicit relation between the DFT and HOT. The 4×3-point HOT is given by

$$\mathbf{H} = \begin{bmatrix} 1\,0\,0 & 1 & 0 & 0 & 1 & 0 & 0 & 1 & 0 & 0 \\ 0\,1\,0 & 0 & 1 & 0 & 0 & 1 & 0 & 0 & 1 & 0 \\ 0\,0\,1 & 0 & 0 & 1 & 0 & 0 & 1 & 0 & 0 & 1 \\ 1\,0\,0 & e^{-j2\pi/4} & 0 & 0 & e^{-j4\pi/4} & 0 & 0 & e^{-j6\pi/4} & 0 & 0 \\ 0\,1\,0 & 0 & e^{-j2\pi/4} & 0 & 0 & e^{-j4\pi/4} & 0 & 0 & e^{-j6\pi/4} & 0 \\ 0\,0\,1 & 0 & 0 & e^{-j2\pi/4} & 0 & 0 & e^{-j4\pi/4} & 0 & 0 & e^{-j6\pi/4} \\ 1\,0\,0 & e^{-j4\pi/4} & 0 & 0 & e^{-j8\pi/4} & 0 & 0 & e^{-j12\pi/4} & 0 & 0 \\ 0\,1\,0 & 0 & e^{-j4\pi/4} & 0 & 0 & e^{-j8\pi/4} & 0 & 0 & e^{-12\pi/4} & 0 \\ 0\,0\,1 & 0 & 0 & e^{-j4\pi/4} & 0 & 0 & e^{-j8\pi/4} & 0 & 0 & e^{-j12\pi/4} \\ 1\,0\,0 & e^{-j6\pi/4} & 0 & 0 & e^{-j12\pi/4} & 0 & 0 & e^{-j18\pi/4} & 0 & 0 \\ 0\,1\,0 & 0 & e^{-j6\pi/4} & 0 & 0 & e^{-j12\pi/4} & 0 & 0 & e^{-j18\pi/4} & 0 \\ 0\,0\,1 & 0 & 0 & e^{-j6\pi/4} & 0 & 0 & e^{-j12\pi/4} & 0 & 0 & e^{-j18\pi/4} \end{bmatrix}. \tag{6}$$

Equation (6) shows that the HOT takes the 4-point DFTs of the 3 polyphase components and then reverses the polyphase decomposition. Therefore, the relation between the DFT and HOT can be written as

$$\mathbf{H} = \mathbf{P} \begin{bmatrix} \mathbf{F}_4 & \mathbf{0}_{4\times4} & \mathbf{0}_{4\times4} \\ \mathbf{0}_{4\times4} & \mathbf{F}_4 & \mathbf{0}_{4\times4} \\ \mathbf{0}_{4\times4} & \mathbf{0}_{4\times4} & \mathbf{F}_4 \end{bmatrix} \mathbf{P}. \tag{7}$$

Also, it can be easily shown that

$$\mathbf{H}^{-1} = \mathbf{P} \begin{bmatrix} \mathbf{F}_4^{-1} & \mathbf{0}_{4\times4} & \mathbf{0}_{4\times4} \\ \mathbf{0}_{4\times4} & \mathbf{F}_4^{-1} & \mathbf{0}_{4\times4} \\ \mathbf{0}_{4\times4} & \mathbf{0}_{4\times4} & \mathbf{F}_4^{-1} \end{bmatrix} \mathbf{P}. \tag{8}$$

3. The HOT convolution

In this section we present a computationally efficient convolution algorithm based on the HOT. Let $h(n)$ be a signal of length N and $u(n)$ be a signal of length KN. The linear convolution between $h(n)$ and $u(n)$ is given by

$$y(n) = \sum_{l=0}^{N-1} h(l)u(n-l). \tag{9}$$

According to the overlap-save method (Mitra, 2000), $y(n)$ for $0 \le n \le KN$, where K is an integer, can be calculated by dividing $u(n)$ into K overlapping sections of length $2N$ and $h(n)$ is post appended with N zeros as shown in Figure 1 for $K = 3$. The linear convolution in (9) can be calculated from the circular convolutions between and $h(n)$ and the sections of $u(n)$. Let $u_k(n)$ be the kth section of $u(n)$. Denote the $2N$-point circular convolution between $u_k(n)$ and $h(n)$ by $c_k(n) = u_k(n) \star h(n)$.

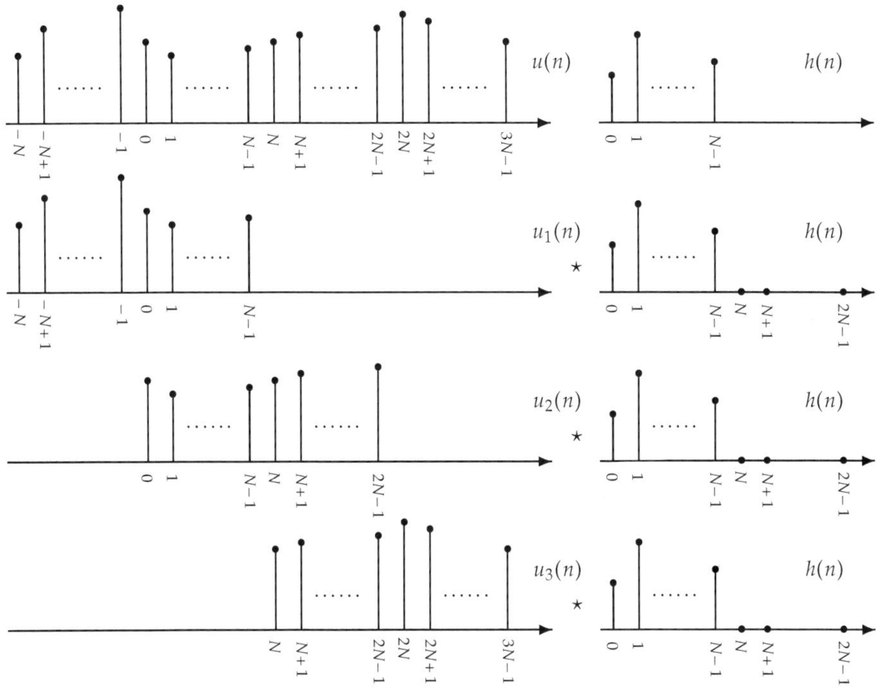

Fig. 1. Illustration of how $u(n)$ is divided into 3 overlapping sections. Each section is convolved with the the appended $h(n)$.

The circular convolution $c_k(n)$ can be calculated using the $2N$-point DFT as follows. First, form the vectors

$$\mathbf{h} = \begin{bmatrix} h(0) \\ h(1) \\ \vdots \\ h(N-1) \\ 0 \\ 0 \\ \vdots \\ 0 \end{bmatrix}, \tag{10}$$

$$\mathbf{c}_k = \begin{bmatrix} c_k(0) \\ c_k(1) \\ \vdots \\ c_k(2N-1) \end{bmatrix}, \tag{11}$$

Then the $2N$-point DFT of $\mathbf{c}_k$ is given by

$$\mathbf{F}_{2N}\mathbf{c}_k = \mathbf{F}_{2N}\mathbf{u}_k \cdot \mathbf{F}_{2N}\mathbf{h}, \tag{12}$$

where $\mathbf{u}_k$ is the vector that contains the elements of $u_k(n)$. "$\cdot$" indicates pointwise matrix multiplication and, throughout this chapter, pointwise matrix multiplication takes a lower precedence than conventional matrix multiplication. Combining all of the circular convolutions into one matrix equation, we should have

$$\begin{bmatrix} \mathbf{F}_{2N}\mathbf{c}_0 \\ \mathbf{F}_{2N}\mathbf{c}_1 \\ \vdots \\ \mathbf{F}_{2N}\mathbf{c}_{K-1} \end{bmatrix} = \begin{bmatrix} \mathbf{F}_{2N}\mathbf{h} \\ \mathbf{F}_{2N}\mathbf{h} \\ \vdots \\ \mathbf{F}_{2N}\mathbf{h} \end{bmatrix} \cdot \begin{bmatrix} \mathbf{F}_{2N}\mathbf{u}_0 \\ \mathbf{F}_{2N}\mathbf{u}_1 \\ \vdots \\ \mathbf{F}_{2N}\mathbf{u}_{K-1} \end{bmatrix}. \tag{13}$$

Using equation (7), equation (13) can be written as

$$\mathbf{H}\tilde{\mathbf{c}} = \mathbf{H}\tilde{\mathbf{u}} \cdot \mathbf{H}\tilde{\mathbf{h}}_r, \tag{14}$$

where

$$\mathbf{h}_r = \begin{bmatrix} \mathbf{h} \\ \mathbf{h} \\ \vdots \\ \mathbf{h} \end{bmatrix}, \tag{15}$$

and

$$\mathbf{u} = \begin{bmatrix} \mathbf{u}_0 \\ \mathbf{u}_1 \\ \vdots \\ \mathbf{u}_{k-1} \end{bmatrix}. \tag{16}$$

Therefore, The vector of the circular convolutions is given by

$$\mathbf{c} = \mathbf{P}\mathbf{H}^{-1}\left(\mathbf{H}\tilde{\mathbf{u}} \cdot \mathbf{H}\tilde{\mathbf{h}}_r\right). \tag{17}$$

According to the overlap-save method, only the second half of $\mathbf{c}_k$ corresponds to the kth section of the linear convolution. Denote the kth section of the linear convolution by $\mathbf{y}_k$ and the vector that contains the elements of $y(n)$ by $\mathbf{y}$. Then $\mathbf{y}_k$ can be written as

$$\mathbf{y}_k = \begin{bmatrix} \mathbf{0}_{N\times N} & \mathbf{I}_{N\times N} \end{bmatrix} \mathbf{c}_k, \tag{18}$$

and $\mathbf{y}$ as

$$\mathbf{y} = \mathbf{G}\mathbf{c}, \tag{19}$$

where

$$\mathbf{G} = \begin{bmatrix} \mathbf{0}_{N\times N}\ \mathbf{I}_{N\times N} & \mathbf{0}_{2N\times 2N} & \cdots & \mathbf{0}_{2N\times 2N} \\ \mathbf{0}_{2N\times 2N} & \mathbf{0}_{N\times N}\ \mathbf{I}_{N\times N} & \cdots & \mathbf{0}_{2N\times 2N} \\ \vdots & \vdots & \ddots & \vdots \\ \mathbf{0}_{2N\times 2N} & \mathbf{0}_{2N\times 2N} & \cdots & \mathbf{0}_{N\times N}\ \mathbf{I}_{N\times N} \end{bmatrix}. \tag{20}$$

Finally, the linear convolution using the HOT is given by

$$\mathbf{y} = \mathbf{G}\mathbf{P}\mathbf{H}^{-1}\left(\mathbf{H}\tilde{\mathbf{u}} \cdot \mathbf{H}\tilde{\mathbf{h}}_r\right). \tag{21}$$

In summery, the convolution between $(K+1)N$-point input $u(n)$ and N-point impulse response $h(n)$ can be calculated efficiently using the HOT as follows:

1. Divide $u(n)$ into K overlapping sections and combine them into one vector to from $\mathbf{u}$.
2. Perform K-band polyphase decomposition of $\mathbf{u}$ to form $\tilde{\mathbf{u}}$.
3. Take the HOT of $\tilde{\mathbf{u}}$.
4. Post append $h(n)$ with N zeros and then stack the appended $h(n)$ K times into one vector to form $\mathbf{h}_r$.
5. Perform K-band polyphase decomposition of $\mathbf{h}_r$ to form $\tilde{\mathbf{h}}_r$.
6. Take the HOT of $\tilde{\mathbf{h}}_r$.
7. Point-wise multiply the vectors from steps 3 and 6.
8. Take the inverse HOT of the vector from step 7.
9. Perform K-band polyphase decomposition of the result from step 8.
10. Multiply the result of step 9 with $\mathbf{G}$.

4. Development of the HOT DFT block LMS algorithm

Recall that in the block LMS algorithm there are two convolutions needed. The first convolution is a convolution between the filter impulse response and the filter input and is needed to calculate the output of the filter in each block. The second convolution is a convolution between the filter input and error and is needed to estimate the gradient in the filter weight update equation. If the block length is much larger than the filter length, then the fast HOT convolution developed in the previous section can be used to calculate the first convolution. However, the second convolution is a convolution between two signals of the same length and the fast HOT convolution can not be used directly without modification.
Let N be the filer length and $L = NK$ be the block length, where N, L, and K are all integers. Let

$$\hat{\mathbf{w}}(k) = \begin{bmatrix} w_0(k) \\ w_1(k) \\ \vdots \\ w_{N-2}(k) \\ w_{N-1}(k) \end{bmatrix} \tag{22}$$

be the filter tap-weight vector in the kth block and

$$\hat{\mathbf{u}}(k) = \begin{bmatrix} u\,(kL-N) \\ \vdots \\ u\,(kL) \\ u\,(kL+1) \\ \vdots \\ u\,(kL+L-1) \end{bmatrix} \tag{23}$$

be the vector of input samples needed in the kth block. To use the fast HOT convolution described in the previous section, $\hat{\mathbf{u}}(k)$ is divided is into K overlapping sections. Such sections can be formed by multiplying $\hat{\mathbf{u}}(k)$ with the following matrix:

$$\mathbf{J} = \begin{bmatrix} \mathbf{I}_{N\times N} & \mathbf{0} & \cdots & \mathbf{0} & \mathbf{0} \\ \mathbf{0} & \mathbf{I}_{N\times N} & \cdots & \mathbf{0} & \mathbf{0} \\ \mathbf{0} & \mathbf{I}_{N\times N} & \cdots & \mathbf{0} & \mathbf{0} \\ \vdots & \vdots & \ddots & \vdots & \vdots \\ \mathbf{0} & \mathbf{0} & \cdots & \mathbf{I}_{N\times N} & \mathbf{0} \\ \mathbf{0} & \mathbf{0} & \cdots & \mathbf{I}_{N\times N} & \mathbf{0} \\ \mathbf{0} & \mathbf{0} & \cdots & \mathbf{0} & \mathbf{I}_{N\times N} \end{bmatrix}. \tag{24}$$

Define the extended tap-weight vector (post appended with N zeros)

$$\mathbf{w}(k) = \begin{bmatrix} \hat{\mathbf{w}}(k) \\ 0 \\ \vdots \\ 0 \end{bmatrix}. \tag{25}$$

According the fast HOT convolution, see equation (21), the output of the adaptive filter in the kth block

$$\mathbf{y}(k) = \begin{bmatrix} y(kL) \\ y(kL+1) \\ \vdots \\ y(kL+L-2) \\ y(kL+L-1) \end{bmatrix} \tag{26}$$

is given by

$$\mathbf{y}(k) = \mathbf{GPH}^{-1}\Big(\mathbf{HPw}_r(k)\cdot\mathbf{HPJ}\hat{\mathbf{u}}(k)\Big). \tag{27}$$

The desired signal vector and the filter error in the kth block are given by

$$\hat{\mathbf{d}}(k) = \begin{bmatrix} d(kL) \\ d(kL+1) \\ \vdots \\ d(kL+L-2) \\ d(kL+L-1) \end{bmatrix} \tag{28}$$

and

$$\hat{\mathbf{e}}(k) = \begin{bmatrix} e(kL) \\ e(kL+1) \\ \vdots \\ e(kL+L-2) \\ e(kL+L-1) \end{bmatrix}, \tag{29}$$

respectively, where

$$e(n) = d(n) - y(n). \tag{30}$$

The filter update equation is given by

$$\hat{\mathbf{w}}(k+1) = \hat{\mathbf{w}}(k) + \frac{\mu}{L}\sum_{i=0}^{L-1} \begin{bmatrix} u\,(kL+i) \\ u\,(kL+i-1) \\ \vdots \\ u\,(kL+i-N+2) \\ u\,(kL+i-N+1) \end{bmatrix} e(kL+i). \tag{31}$$

The sum in equation (31) can be efficiently calculated using the $(L+N)$-point DFTs of the error vector $e(n)$ and input vector $u(n)$. However, the $(L+N)$-point DFT of $u(n)$ is not available and only the $2N$-point DFTs of the K sections of $\hat{\mathbf{u}}(k)$ are available. Therefore, the sum in equation (31) should be divided into K sections as follows:

$$\sum_{i=0}^{L-1} \begin{bmatrix} u\,(kL+i) \\ u\,(kL+i-1) \\ \vdots \\ u\,(kL+i-N+2) \\ u\,(kL+i-N+1) \end{bmatrix} e(kL+i) =$$

$$\sum_{l=0}^{K-1}\sum_{j=0}^{N-1} \begin{bmatrix} u\,(kL+lN+j) \\ u\,(kL+lN+j-1) \\ \vdots \\ u\,(kL+lN+j-N+2) \\ u\,(kL+lN+j-N+1) \end{bmatrix} e(kL+lK+j). \tag{32}$$

For each l, the sum over j can be calculated as follows. First, form the vectors

$$\mathbf{u}_l(k) = \begin{bmatrix} u(kL+lN-N) \\ \vdots \\ u(kL+lN+N-2) \\ u(kL+lN+N-1) \end{bmatrix}, \tag{33}$$

$$\mathbf{e}_l(k) = \begin{bmatrix} \mathbf{0}_{N\times 1} \\ e(kL+lN) \\ \vdots \\ e(kL+lN+N-2) \\ e(kL+lN+N-1) \end{bmatrix}. \tag{34}$$

Then the sum over j is just the first N elements of the circular convolution of $\mathbf{e}_l(k)$ and circularly shifted $\mathbf{u}_l(k)$ and it can be computed using the DFT as shown below:

$$\sum_{j=0}^{N-1} \mathbf{u}_l(k)e(kL+lK+j) = \mathbf{U}_N\left(\mathbf{u}_{lF}^{*}(k)\cdot\mathbf{e}_{lF}(k)\right), \tag{35}$$

where

$$\mathbf{U}_N = \begin{bmatrix} \mathbf{I}_{N\times N} & \mathbf{0}_{N\times N} \\ \mathbf{0}_{N\times N} & \mathbf{0}_{N\times N} \end{bmatrix}, \tag{36}$$

$$\mathbf{u}_{lF}(k) = \mathbf{F}_{2N}\mathbf{u}_l(k), \tag{37}$$

and

$$\mathbf{e}_{lF}(k) = \mathbf{F}_{2N}\mathbf{e}_l(k). \tag{38}$$

Therefore, the filter update equation for the HOT DFT block LMS algorithm can be written as

$$\mathbf{w}(k+1) = \mathbf{w}(k) + \frac{\mu}{L}\sum_{l=0}^{K-1}\mathbf{U}_N\mathbf{F}^{-1}\Big(\mathbf{u}^*_{lF}(k)\cdot\mathbf{e}_{lF}(k)\Big). \tag{39}$$

Next, we express the sum in equation (39) in terms of the HOT. Form the vectors

$$\mathbf{u}(k) = \begin{bmatrix} \mathbf{u}_0(k) \\ \mathbf{u}_1(k) \\ \vdots \\ \mathbf{u}_{K-1}(k) \end{bmatrix}, \tag{40}$$

$$\mathbf{e}(k) = \begin{bmatrix} \mathbf{e}_0(k) \\ \mathbf{e}_1(k) \\ \vdots \\ \mathbf{e}_{K-1}(k) \end{bmatrix}. \tag{41}$$

Then using equation (7), the filter update equation can be written as

$$\mathbf{w}(k+1) = \mathbf{w}(k) + \frac{\mu}{L}\mathbf{SPH}^{-1}\Big(\mathbf{H}^*\tilde{\mathbf{u}}(k)\cdot\mathbf{H}\tilde{\mathbf{e}}(k)\Big), \tag{42}$$

where the matrix $\mathbf{S}$ is given by

$$\mathbf{S} = \begin{bmatrix} \begin{matrix} \mathbf{1}_{K\times 1} & \mathbf{0}_{K\times 1} & \cdots & \mathbf{0}_{K\times 1} \\ \mathbf{0}_{K\times 1} & \mathbf{1}_{K\times 1} & \cdots & \mathbf{0}_{K\times 1} \\ \vdots & \vdots & \ddots & \vdots \\ \mathbf{0}_{K\times 0} & \mathbf{0}_{K\times 1} & \cdots & \mathbf{1}_{K\times 1} \end{matrix} & \mathbf{0}_{N\times KN} \\ \mathbf{0}_{N\times KN} & \mathbf{0}_{N\times KN} \end{bmatrix}. \tag{43}$$

Figure 2 shows the flow block diagram of the HOT DFT block LMS adaptive filter.

5. Computational cost of the HOT DFT block LMS algorithm

Before looking at the convergence analysis of the new adaptive filter, we look at its computational cost. To calculate the the output of the kth block, $2K+1$ $2N$-point DFTs are needed. Therefore, $(2K+1)2N\log_2 2N + 2NK$ multiplications are needed to calculate the output. To calculate the gradient estimate in the filter update equation, $2K$ $2N$-point DFTs are required. Therefore, $6KN\log_2 2N + 2NK$ multiplications are needed. The total multiplication count of the new algorithm is then $(4K+1)2N\log_2 2N + 4NK$. The multiplication count for the DFT block LMS algorithm is $10KN\log_2 2NK + 4NK$. Therefore, as K gets larger the HOT DFT block LMS algorithm becomes more efficient than the DFT block LMS algorithm. For example, for $N = 100$ and $K = 10$, the HOT DFT LMS algorithm is about 30% more efficient and for for $N = 50$ and $K = 20$ the HOT DFT LMS algorithm is about 40% more efficient.

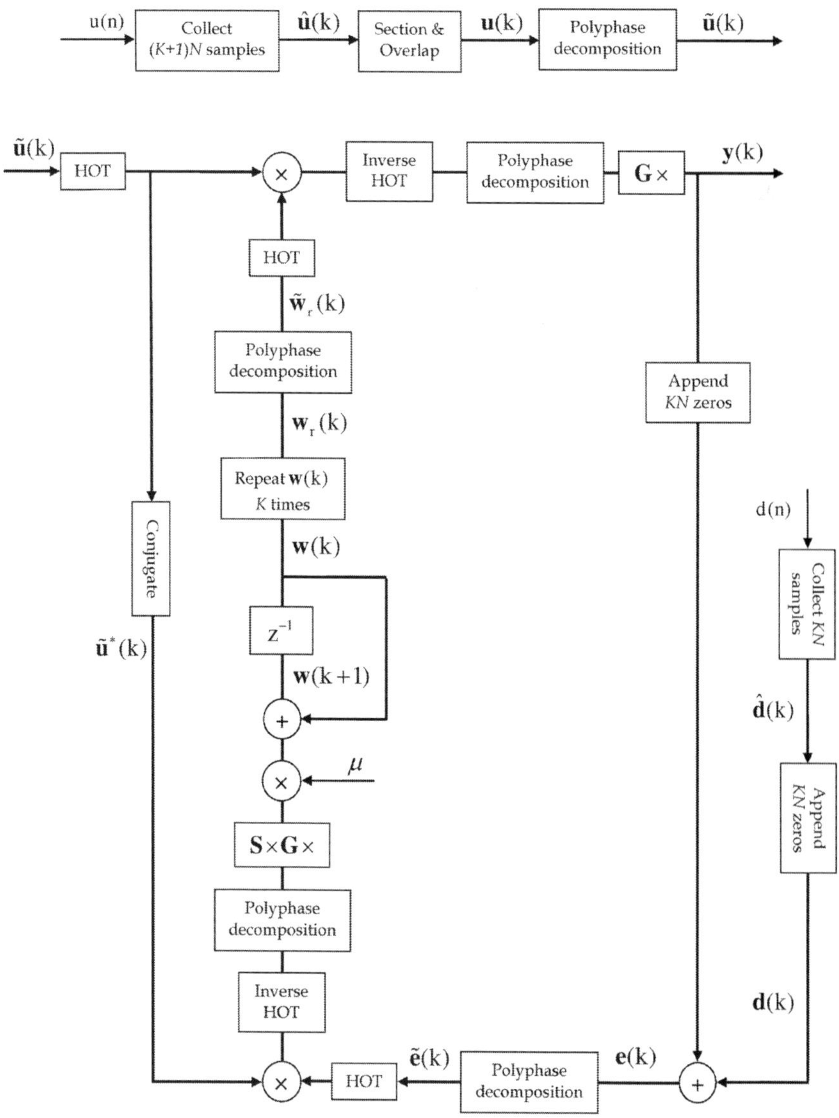

Fig. 2. The flow block diagram of the HOT DFT block LMS adaptive filter.

The ratio between the number of multiplications required for the HOT DFT block LMS algorithm and the number of multiplications required for the DFT block LMS algorithm is plotted in Figure 3 for different filter lengths. The HOT DFT block LMS filter is always more efficient than the DFT block LMS filter and the efficiency increases as the block length increases.

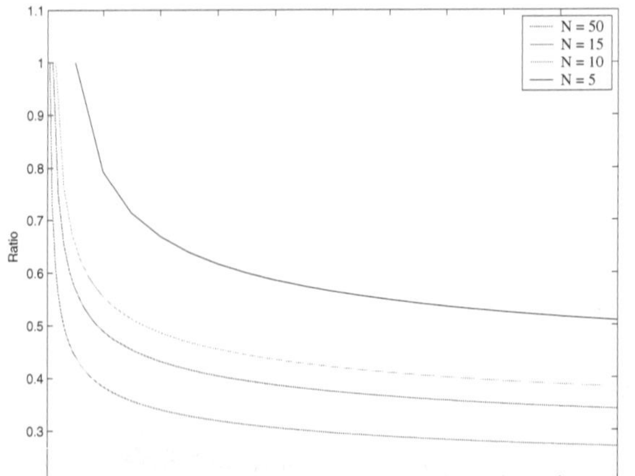

Fig. 3. Ratio between the number of multiplications required for the HOT DFT and the DFT block LMS algorithms.

6. Convergence analysis of the HOT DFT LMS algorithm

Now the convergence of the new algorithm is analyzed. The analysis is performed in the DFT domain. The adaptive filter update equation in the DFT domain is given by

$$\mathbf{w}_F(k+1) = \mathbf{w}_F(k) + \frac{\mu}{L}\sum_{l=0}^{K-1} \mathbf{F}\mathbf{U}_N\mathbf{F}^{-1}\Big(\mathbf{u}_{lF}^{*}(k)\cdot\mathbf{e}_{lF}(k)\Big). \tag{44}$$

Let the desired signal be generated using the linear regression model

$$d(n) = w^o(n) * u(n) + e^o(n), \tag{45}$$

where $w^o(n)$ is the impulse response of the Wiener optimal filter and $e^o(n)$ is the irreducible estimation error, which is white noise and statistically independent of the adaptive filter input. In the kth block, the lth section of the desired signal in the DFT domain is given by

$$\hat{\mathbf{d}}_l(k) = \begin{bmatrix}\mathbf{0}_{N\times N} & \mathbf{I}_{N\times N}\end{bmatrix}\mathbf{F}^{-1}\Big(\mathbf{w}_F^o(k)\cdot\mathbf{u}_{lF}(k)\Big) + \hat{\mathbf{e}}_l^o(k), \tag{46}$$

Therefore, the lth section of the error is given by

$$\mathbf{e}_l(k) = \mathbf{L}_N\mathbf{F}^{-1}\Big(\epsilon_F(k)\cdot\mathbf{u}_{lF}(k)\Big) + \mathbf{e}_l^o(k), \tag{47}$$

where

$$\mathbf{L}_N = \begin{bmatrix} \mathbf{0}_{N\times N} & \mathbf{0}_{N\times N} \\ \mathbf{0}_{N\times N} & \mathbf{I}_{N\times N} \end{bmatrix}, \tag{48}$$

and $\boldsymbol{\epsilon}_F(k) = \mathbf{w}_F^o - \mathbf{w}_F(k)$. Using equation (44), the error in the estimation of the adaptive filter weight vector $\boldsymbol{\epsilon}_F(k)$ is updated according to

$$\boldsymbol{\epsilon}_F(k+1) = \boldsymbol{\epsilon}_F(k) - \frac{\mu}{L}\sum_{l=0}^{K-1} \mathbf{U}_{N,F}\left(\mathbf{u}_{lF}^*(k)\cdot \mathbf{e}_{lF}(k)\right), \tag{49}$$

where

$$\mathbf{U}_{N,F} = \mathbf{F}\begin{bmatrix} \mathbf{I}_{N\times N} & \mathbf{0}_{N\times N} \\ \mathbf{0}_{N\times N} & \mathbf{0}_{N\times N} \end{bmatrix}\mathbf{F}^{-1}. \tag{50}$$

Taking the DFT of equation (47), we have that

$$\mathbf{e}_{lF}(k) = \mathbf{L}_{N,F}\left(\boldsymbol{\epsilon}_F(k)\cdot \mathbf{u}_{lF}(k)\right) + \mathbf{e}_{lF}^o(k), \tag{51}$$

where

$$\mathbf{L}_{N,F} = \mathbf{F}\begin{bmatrix} \mathbf{0}_{N\times N} & \mathbf{0}_{N\times N} \\ \mathbf{0}_{N\times N} & \mathbf{I}_{N\times N} \end{bmatrix}\mathbf{F}^{-1}. \tag{52}$$

Using equation (51), we can write

$$\mathbf{u}_{lF}^*(k)\cdot \mathbf{e}_{lF}(k) = \mathcal{U}_{lF}^*(k)\left(\mathbf{L}_{N,F}\mathcal{U}_{lF}(k)\boldsymbol{\epsilon}_F(k) + \mathbf{e}_{lF}^o(k)\right). \tag{53}$$

Using

$$\mathcal{U}_{lF}^*(k)\mathbf{L}_{N,F}\mathcal{U}_{lF}(k) = \mathbf{u}_{lF}^*(k)\mathbf{u}_{lF}^T(k)\cdot \mathbf{L}_{N,F}, \tag{54}$$

equation (53) can be simplified to

$$\mathbf{u}_{lF}^*(k)\cdot \mathbf{e}_{lF}(k) = \left(\mathbf{u}_{lF}^*(k)\mathbf{u}_{lF}^T(k)\cdot \mathbf{L}_{N,F}\right)\boldsymbol{\epsilon}_F(k) + \mathbf{u}_{lF}^*(k)\cdot \mathbf{e}_{lF}^o(k). \tag{55}$$

Substituting equation (55) into equation (49), we have that

$$\boldsymbol{\epsilon}_F(k+1) = \left(\mathbf{I} - \frac{\mu}{L}\mathbf{U}_{N,F}\sum_{l=0}^{K-1}\mathbf{u}_{lF}^*(k)\mathbf{u}_{lF}^T(k)\cdot \mathbf{L}_{N,F}\right)\boldsymbol{\epsilon}_F(k) - \frac{\mu}{L}\mathbf{U}_{N,F}\sum_{l=0}^{K-1}\mathbf{u}_{lF}^*(k)\cdot \mathbf{e}_{lF}^o(k). \tag{56}$$

Taking the expectation of the above equation yields

$$\mathrm{E}\boldsymbol{\epsilon}_F(k+1) = \left(\mathbf{I} - \frac{\mu}{N}\mathbf{U}_{N,F}\left(\mathbf{R}_{u,F}\cdot \mathbf{L}_{N,F}\right)\right)\mathrm{E}\boldsymbol{\epsilon}_F(k), \tag{57}$$

where $\mathbf{R}_{u,F} = \mathbf{F}^H\mathbf{R}_u\mathbf{F}$ and $\mathbf{R}_u$ is the $2N \times 2N$ autocorrelation matrix of $u(n)$. Equation (57) is similar to the result that corresponds to the DFT block LMS algorithm (Farhang-Boroujeny & Chan, 2000). Therefore, the convergence characteristics of the HOT DFT block LMS algorithm are similar to that of the DFT block LMS algorithm.

The convergence speed of the HOT DFT LMS algorithm can be increased if the convergence moods are normalized using the estimated power of the tap-input vector in the DFT domain. The complete HOT DFT block LMS weight update equation is given by

$$\mathbf{w}(k+1) = \mathbf{w}(k) + \frac{\mu}{L}\sum_{l=0}^{K-1}\mathbf{U}_N\mathbf{F}^{-1}\Lambda_l^{-1}(k)\left(\mathbf{u}_{lF}^*(k)\cdot \mathbf{e}_{lF}(k)\right) \tag{58}$$

and

$$\Lambda_l(k+1) = \frac{k-1}{k}\Lambda_l(k) + \frac{1}{kL}\mathrm{Diag}\left[\mathbf{u}_{lF}^*(k)\cdot \mathbf{u}_{lF}(k)\right]. \tag{59}$$

7. Misadjustment of the HOT DFT LMS algorithm

In this section, the misadjusment of the HOT DFT block LMS algorithm is derived. The mean square error of the conventional LMS algorithm is given by

$$J(n) = \mathrm{E}\left|e(n)\right|^2. \tag{60}$$

For the block LMS algorithm, the mean square error is given by

$$J(k) = \frac{1}{L}\mathrm{E}\sum_{i=0}^{L-1}\left|e(kL+i)\right|^2, \tag{61}$$

which is also equivalent to

$$J(k) = \frac{1}{2NL}\mathrm{E}\sum_{l=0}^{K-1}\mathbf{e}_{lF}^H(k)\mathbf{e}_{lF}(k). \tag{62}$$

Using equation (51), the mean square error of the HOT DFT block LMS algorithm is given by

$$J(k) = J^o + \frac{1}{2NL}\mathrm{E}\sum_{l=0}^{K-1}\left|\left|\mathbf{L}_{N,F}\mathcal{U}_{lF}(k)\epsilon(k)\right|\right|^2, \tag{63}$$

where J^o is the mean square of $e^o(n)$. Assuming that $\epsilon(k)$ and $\mathrm{Diag}[\mathbf{u}_{lF}(k)]$ are independent, the excess mean square error is given by

$$J_{\mathrm{ex}}(k) = \frac{1}{2NL}\mathrm{E}\sum_{l=0}^{K-1}\epsilon_F^H(k)\mathrm{E}\mathcal{U}_{lF}^H(k)\mathbf{L}_{N,F}\mathcal{U}_{lF}^H(k)\epsilon_F(k). \tag{64}$$

Using equation (54), the excess mean square error can be written as

$$J_{\mathrm{ex}} = \frac{K}{2NL}\mathrm{E}\epsilon_F^H(k)\left(\mathbf{R}_{u,F}\cdot\mathbf{L}_{N,F}\right)\epsilon_F(k), \tag{65}$$

or equivalently

$$J_{\mathrm{ex}} = \frac{K}{2NL}\mathrm{tr}\left[\left(\mathbf{R}_{u,F}\cdot\mathbf{L}_{N,F}\right)\mathrm{E}\epsilon_F(k)\epsilon_F^H(k)\right]. \tag{66}$$

8. Simulation of the HOT DFT block LMS algorithm

The learning curves of the HOT DFT block LMS algorithm were simulated. The desired input was generated using the linear model $d(n) = w^o(n) * u(n) + e^o(n)$, where $e^o(n)$ is the measurement white gaussian noise with variance 10^{-8}. The input was a first-order Markov signal with autocorrelation function given by $r(k) = \rho^{|k|}$. The filter was lowpass with a cutoff frequency $\pi/2$ rad.

Figure 4 shows the learning curves for the HOT DFT block LMS filter with those for the LMS and DFT block LMS filters for $N = 4$, $K = 3$, and $\rho = 0.9$. Figure 5 shows similar curves for $N = 50$, $K = 10$, and $\rho = 0.9$. Both figures show that the HOT DFT block LMS algorithm converges at the same rate as the DFT block LMS algorithm and yet is computationally more efficient. Figure 6 shows similar curves for $N = 50$ and $K = 10$ and $\rho = 0.8$. As the correlation coefficient decreases the algorithms converges faster and the HOT DFT block LMS algorithm converges at the same rate as the DFT block LMS algorithm.

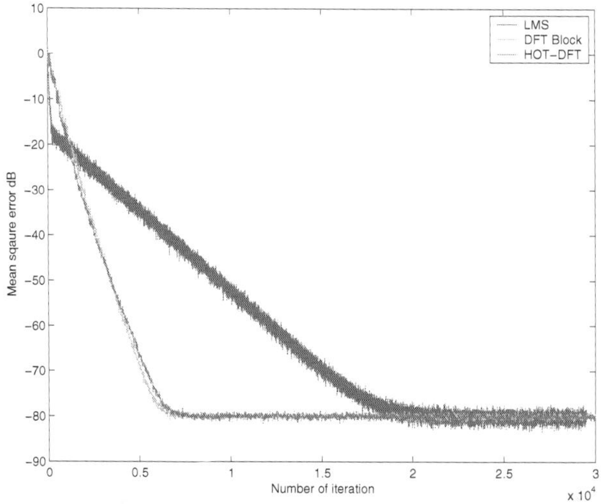

Fig. 4. Learning curves for the LMS, HOT DFT block LMS, and DFT block LMS algorithms. $N = 4$ and $K = 3$. $\rho = 0.9$.

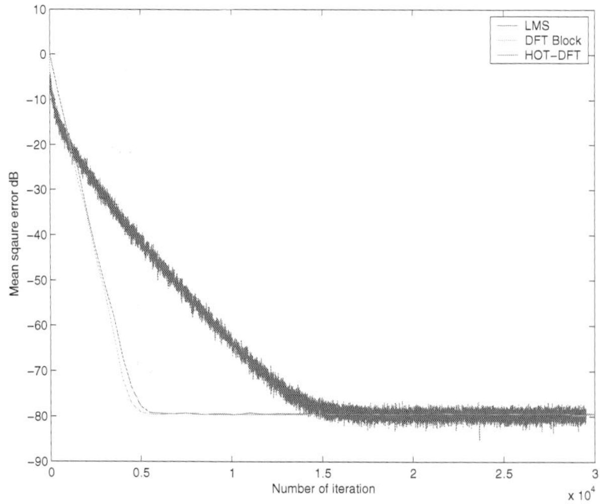

Fig. 5. Learning curves for the LMS, HOT DFT block LMS, and DFT block LMS algorithms. $N = 50$ and $K = 10$. $\rho = 0.9$.

Another coloring filter was also used to simulate the learning curves of the algorithms. The coloring filter was a bandpass filter with $H(z) = 0.1 - 0.2z^{-1} - 0.3z^{-2} + 0.4z^{-3} + 0.4z^{-4} - 0.2z^{-5} - 0.1z^{-6}$. The frequency response of the coloring filter is shown in Figure 7. The learning curves are shown in Figure 8. The simulations are again consistent with the theoretical predictions presented in this chapter.

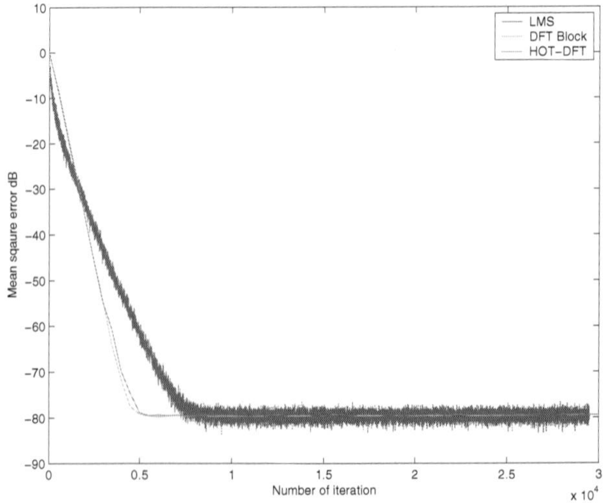

Fig. 6. Learning curves for the LMS, HOT DFT block LMS, and DFT block LMS algorithms. $N = 50$ and $K = 10$. $\rho = 0.8$.

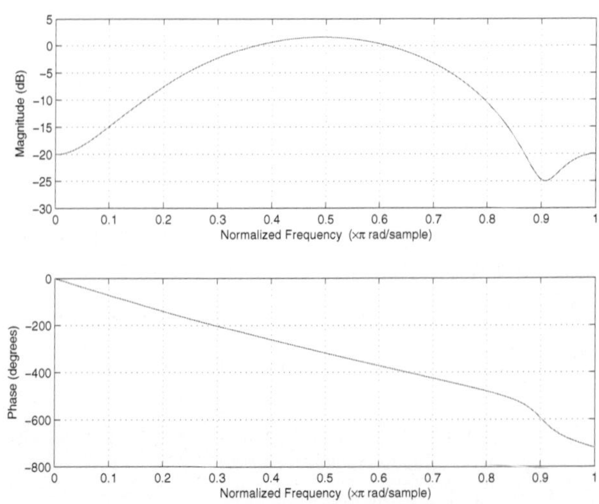

Fig. 7. Frequency response of the coloring filter.

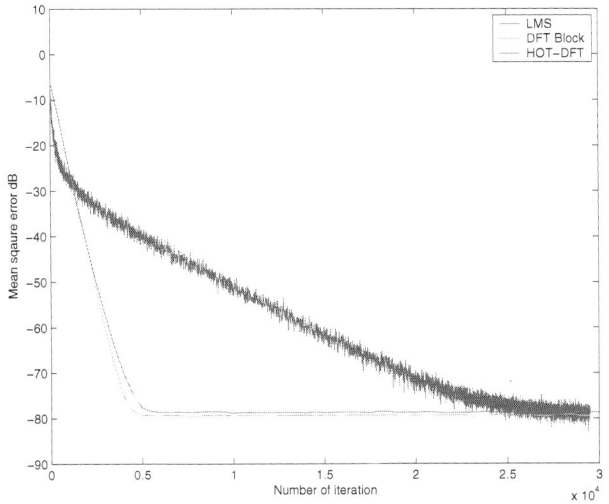

Fig. 8. Learning curves for the LMS, HOT DFT block LMS, and DFT block LMS algorithms. $N = 50$ and $K = 10$.

9. Conclusions

In this chapter a new computationally efficient block LMS algorithm was presented. This algorithm is called the HOT DFT block LMS algorithm. It is based on a newly developed transform called the HOT. The basis of the HOT has many zero-valued samples and resembles the DFT basis, which makes the HOT computationally attractive. The HOT DFT block LMS algorithm is very similar to the DFT block LMS algorithm and reduces it computational complexity by about 30% when the filter length is much smaller than the block length. The analytical predictions and simulations showed that the convergence characteristics of the HOT DFT block LMS algorithm are similar to that of the DFT block LMS algorithm.

10. References

Alkhouli, O.; DeBrunner, V.; Zhai, Y. & Yeary, M. (2005). "FIR Adaptive filters based on Hirschman optimal transform," IEEE/SP 13th Workshop on Statistical Signal Processing, 2005.

Alkhouli, O. & DeBrunner, V. (2007). "Convergence Analysis of Hirschman Optimal Transform (HOT) LMS adaptive filter," IEEE/SP 14th Workshop on Statistical Signal Processing, 2007.

Alkhouli, O. & DeBrunner, V. (2007). "Hirschman optimal transform block adaptive filter," International conference on Acoustics, Speech, and Signal Processing (ICASSP), 2007.

Clark, G.; Mitra S. & Parker, S. (1981). "Block implementation of adaptive digital filters," *IEEE Trans. ASSP*, pp. 744-752,ǎJun 1981.

DeBrunner, V.; Özaydin, M. & Przebinda T. (1999). "Resolution in time-frequency," *IEEE Trans. ASSP*, pp. 783-788, Mar 1999.

DeBrunner, V. & Matusiak, E. (2003). "An algorithm to reduce the complexity required to convolve finite length sequences using the Hirschman optimal transform (HOT)," *ICASSP 2003*, Hong Kong, China, pp. II-577-580, Apr 2003.

DeBrunner, V.; Havlicek, J.; Przebinda, T. & Özaydin M. (2005). "Entropy-based uncertainty measures for $L^2(R)^n$, $\ell^2(Z)$, and $\ell^2(Z/NZ)$ with a Hirschman optimal transform for $\ell^2(Z/NZ)$," *IEEE Trans. ASSP*, pp. 2690-2696, August 2005.

Farhang-Boroujeny, B. (2000). *Adaptive Filters Theory and Applications*. Wiley, 1999.

Farhang-Boroujeny, B. & Chan, K. (2000). "Analysis of the frequency-domain block LMS algorithm," *IEEE Trans. ASSP*, pp. 2332, Aug. 2000.

Ferrara, E. (1980). "Fast implementation of LMS adaptive filters," *IEEE Trans. ASSP*, vol. ASSP-28, NO. 4, Aug 1980.

Mitra, S. (2000). *Digital Signal Processing*. Mc Graw Hill, Second edition, 2000.

Haykin S. (2002). *Adaptive Filter Theory*. Prentice Hall information and system sciences series, Fourth edition, 2002.

Przebinda, H.; DeBrunner, V. & Özaydin M. (2001). "The optimal transform for the discrete Hirschman uncertainty principle," *IEEE Trans. Infor. Theory*, pp. 2086-2090, Jul 2001.

Widrow, B. & Hoff, Jr., M. (1980). "Adaptive switching circuit," *IRE WESCON Conv. Rec.*, pt. 4 pp. 96-104, 1980.

7

Real-Time Noise Cancelling Approach on Innovations-Based Whitening Application to Adaptive FIR RLS in Beamforming Structure

Jinsoo Jeong
Faculty of Biomedical Engineering and Health Science,
Universiti Teknologi Malaysia, Johor,
Malaysia

1. Introduction

The techniques for noise cancellation have been developed with applications in signal processing, such as homomorphic signal processing, sensor array signal processing and statistical signal processing. Some exemplar applications may be found from kepstrum (also known as complex ceptstrum) method, beamforming and ANC (adaptive noise cancelling) respectively as shown in Fig. 1.

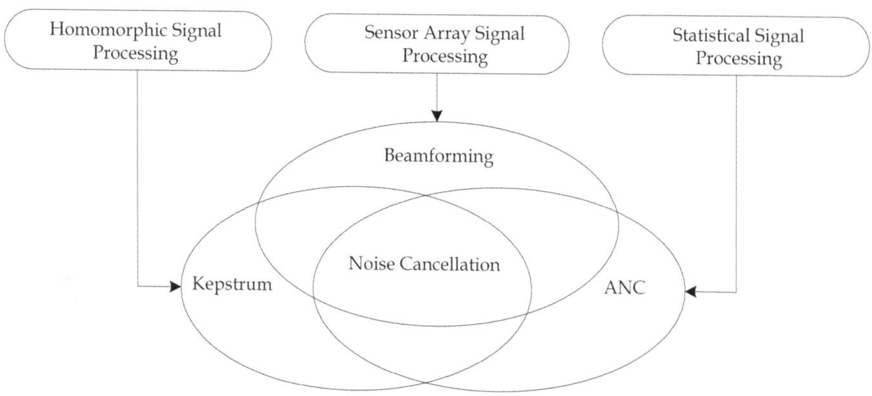

Fig. 1. Signal processing techniques and the application of methods for noise cancellation

Based on the two-microphone approach, the applications are characterized as three methods, which are based on identification of unknown system in acoustic channels, adaptive speech beamforming and adaptive noise cancellation. It can be described as generalized three sub-block diagram as shown in Fig. 2, where it is shown as three processing stages of (1) kepstrum (complex cepstrum), (2) beamforming and (3) ANC and also two structures of beamforming and ANC.

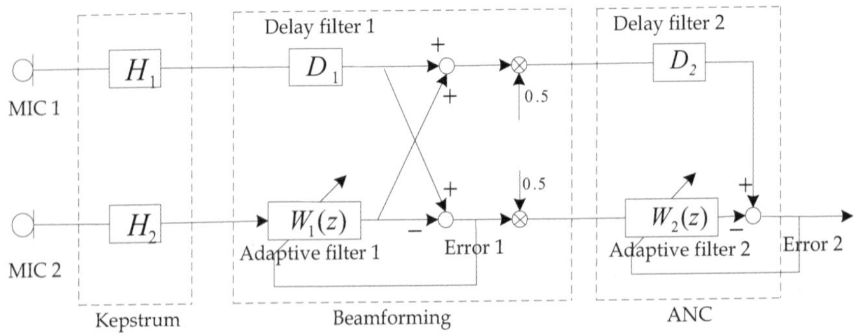

Fig. 2. Generalized diagram for the typical two-microphone approach

1. Kepstrum - estimation of acoustic path transfer functions (H_1 and H_2)

From the output of sensor array, the acoustic transfer functions (H_1 and H_2) are estimated from the acoustic channels as noise statistics during the noise period and it is applied to speech and noise period for noise cancellation. It can be applied as preprocessor to second processing stage, beamforming or directly to third processing stage, ANC. The application can be found from (Moir & Barrett, 2003; Jeong & Moir, 2008), where the unknown system has been estimated as the ratio (H_1 / H_2) of two acoustic transfer functions between each microphones and noise source. Kepstrum filter is used as estimate of unknown system and it is applied in front of SS (sum and subtract) functions in beamforming structure (Jeong & Moir, 2008).

2. Beamforming - adaptive filter (W_1), delay filter (D_1) and SS functions

The beamforming structure contains SS functions, where it is used as signal separator and enhancer by summing and subtracting the signals of the each microphones input (Griffiths & Jim, 1982). An adaptive filter 1 is placed in front of SS functions and used as speech beamforming filter (Compernolle, 1990). It is used as a beam steering input and hence DS (delay and sum) beamformer in primary input during speech period using VAD (voice activity detector) and its output is then applied to third stage, ANC as an enhanced primary input. Both output signals from the SS functions are divided by a number of microphones used (in the case of two microphone, it should be 0.5). Alternatively, adaptive filter 1 can be used as a first adaptive noise canceller. For this application, its output is a noise reference input to next cascading adaptive filter 2 during noise period in VAD (Wallace & Goubran, 1992). Based on a same structure, two-stage adaptive filtering scheme is introduced (Berghe and Wouters, 1998). As a speech directivity function, GCC (genenalized cross-correlation) based TDOA (time difference of arrival) function may alternatively be used instead of adaptive filter 1 in beamforming structure (Knapp & Carter, 1976).

3. ANC - adaptive filter (W_2) and delay filter (D_2)

The last part of block diagram shows ANC method (Widrow et al., 1975), where it consists of adaptive filter 2 and delay filter 2. The adaptive filter generally uses FIR (finite impulse response) LMS (least mean square) algorithm in signal processing or IIR (infinite impulse response) RLS (recursive least square) algorithm in adaptive control for the noise cancellation in MMSE (minimize mean square error) sense. According to the application, both algorithms show compromised effects between performance and computational complexity. It shows that RLS gives, on average, two-tenths of a decibel SNR (signal to noise ratio) improvement over the LMS algorithm (Harrison et al., 1986) but it requires a high demand of computational complexity for the processing. Delay filter 2 is used as noncausality filter to maintain a causality.

As desribed above, the techniques have been developed on the basis of above described methods and the structures. From the above analysis, kepstrum noise cancelling technique has been studied, where the kepstrum has been used for the identification of acoustic transfer functions between two microphones and the kepstrum coefficients from the ratio of two acoustic transfer functions have been applied in front of adaptive beamforming structure for noise cancellation and speech enhancement (Jeong & Moir, 2008). Furthermore, by using the fact that the random signal plus noise may be represented as output of normalized minimum phase spectral factor from the innovations white-noise input (Kalman & Bucy, 1961), the application of an innovations-based whitened form (here we call it as inverse kepstrum) has been investigated in a simulation test, where front-end inverse kepstrum has been analyzed with application of cascaded FIR LMS algorithm (Jeong, 2009) and also FIR RLS algorithm (Jeong, 2010a; 2010b), both in ANC structure for noise cancellation.

In this paper, for a practical real-time processing using RLS algorithm, analysis of innovations-based whitening filter (inverse kepstrum) has been extended to beamforming structure and it has been tested for the application in a realistic environment. From the simulation test, it will be shown that overall estimate from front-end inverse kepstrum processing with cascaded FIR RLS approximates with estimate of IIR RLS algorithm in ANC structure. This provides alternative solution from computational complexity on ANC application using pole-zero IIR RLS filter, which is mostly not acceptable to practical applications. For the application in realistic environment, it has been applied to beamforming structure for an effective noise cancelling application and it will be shown that the front-end kepstrum application with zero-model FIR RLS provides even better performance than pole-zero model IIR RLS algorithm in ANC structure.

2. Analysis of optimum IIR Wiener filtering and the application to two-microphone noise cancelling approach

For the IIR Wiener filtering approach, the z- transform of optimum LS (least squares) filter is constrained to be causal but is potentially of infinite duration, hence it has been defined by (Kailath, 1968) as

$$\mathrm{H}_{opt} = \frac{1}{\mathrm{H}^{+}(\mathrm{z})}\left[\frac{\Phi_{xd}(\mathrm{z})}{\mathrm{H}^{-}(\mathrm{z})}\right]_{+} = \mathrm{A}(\mathrm{z})\mathrm{B}(\mathrm{z}) \tag{1}$$

From the equation (1), it may be regarded as a cascaded form of transfer functions $A(z)$ and $B(z)$, where $\Phi_{xd}(z)$ is the double-sided z-transform of the cross-correlation function between the desired signal and the reference signal. $H^{+}(z)$ and $H^{-}(z)$ are the spectral factors of the double-sided z-transform, $\Phi_{xx}(z)$ from the auto-correlation of reference signal. These spectral factors have the property that the inverse z-transform of $H^{+}(z)$ is entirely causal and minimum phase, on the other hand, the inverse z- transform of $H^{-}(z)$ is non causal. The notation of + in outside bracket indicates that the z- transform of the causal part of the inverse z- transform of $B(z)$ is being taken.

From the optimum Wiener filtering structure, the innovations process ε_n can be obtained by the inverse of spectral factor $A(z)$ from the input signal of desired signal plus noise as shown in Fig. 3. Therefore, the optimal Wiener filter can be regarded as combination of two cascaded filters, a front-end whitening filter $A(z)$, which generates the white innovations process and a cascaded shaping filter $B(z)$, which provides a spectral shaping function for the input signal.

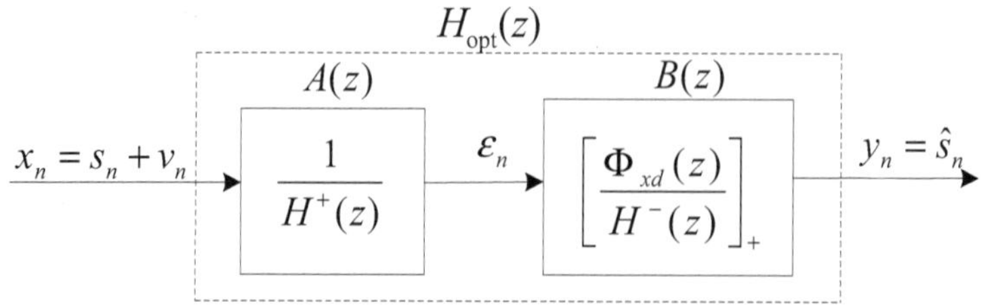

Fig. 3. Analysis of innovations-based optimal Wiener filter: $A(z)$: whitening filter and $B(z)$: spectral shaping filter

It can be applied to two-microphone noise cancelling structure as optimum IIR Wiener filtering approach as shown in Fig. 4.

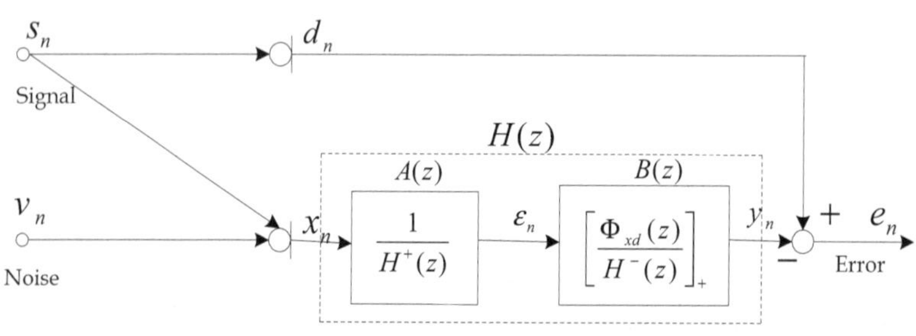

Fig. 4. Optimum IIR Wiener filtering application to two-microphone noise cancelling approach

3. Front-end whitening filter and cascaded adaptive FIR RLS filter

To obtain the innovations-based whitened sequence, inverse kepstrum filter is used as whitening filter. This section describes a whitening procedure by kepstrum processing as front-end application and overview of FIR RLS filter as rear-end application to beamforming structure (Jeong, 2010b).

3.1 The innovations-based whitening filter

Fig. 5 shows that the generating input model may be whitened as innovations white-noise by the inverse of minimum phase spectral factor from input signal of signal plus noise.

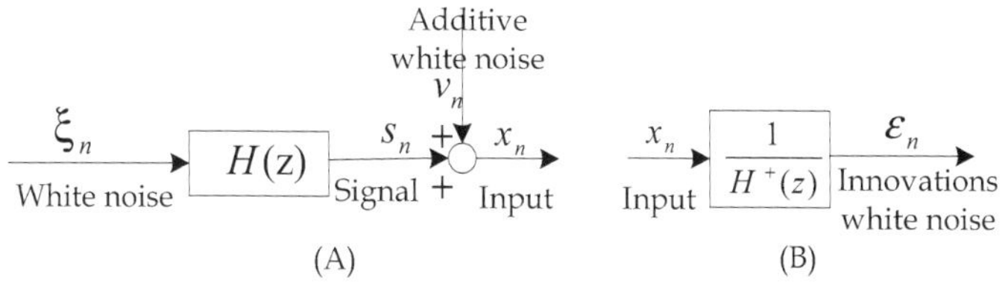

Fig. 5. (A): The generating input model for signal plus noise (x_n) (B): whitening model for innovations-based white noise input (ε_n)

To obtain the innovations white noise, the processing procedure is described as:

Step 1. Take periodogram (P) from FFTs (fast Fourier transforms) of the input signal $\mathrm{x_n}$.

$$\mathrm{P} = \frac{1}{\mathrm{N}}|\mathrm{X_i}|^2 \tag{2}$$

where N is frame size and $i = 0, 1, 2, \ldots, N\text{-}1$.

Step 2. Get the kepstrum coefficients from the inverse FFT (IFFT) of the logarithm of the periodogram.

$$\mathrm{k}_n = \{IFFT\ \ (\log P + \gamma)\} \tag{3}$$

where $\mathrm{K(z)} = \log P + \gamma$ (γ is Euler constant, 0.577215 is added to be unbiased).

Step 3. Negate it from the obtained kepstrum coefficients because the logarithmic function of inverse minimum phase transfer function can be obtained by a negated sign from the kepstrum coefficients.

$$\log\frac{1}{\mathrm{H^+(z)}} \leftrightarrow -\mathrm{K^+(z)} \tag{4}$$

Step 4. Normalize the negated kepstrum coefficients.

Step 5. Truncate it less than half frame size and then make first zeroth coefficient to half from their previous value.

Step 6. Convert it to impulse response by the recursive formula (Silvia & Robinson, 1978) as:

$$(n+1)h_{n+1} = \sum\nolimits_{m=0}^{n}(n+1-m)h_m(k_{n+1-m}), \quad 0 \le n \le l-1 \tag{5}$$

Step 7. Finally, convolve the impulse response (5) with input signal $\mathrm{x_n}$ to obtain the innovations whitened sequence.

3.2 The FIR RLS algorithm

The RLS algorithm is to estimate the inverse of the autocorrelation matrix of the input vector and it requires information from all the previous input data used (Haykins, 1996).

The recursive method of least squares is to minimize the residual sum of squares of the error signal (e_n) and find immediate search for the minimum of cost function, such as:

$$\nabla_h(J_n) = \nabla_h(\sum_{k=1}^{n} \beta^{n-k} e_k^2) = 0 \tag{6}$$

where $e_k = d_k - y_k$, β is exponentially weighted forgetting factor , $0 < \beta \leq 1$.
The resulting equation for the optimum filter weights at time n is described as normal equation:

$$w_n \mathbf{R}_n = \mathbf{p}_n \tag{7}$$

where autocorrelation matrix, $\mathbf{R}_n = \sum_{k=1}^{n} \beta^{n-k} \mathbf{x}_k \mathbf{x}_k^T = \mathbf{X}^{\mathrm{T}} \mathbf{\Lambda}\, \mathbf{X}$, cross-correlation vector,

$\mathbf{p}_n = \sum_{k=1}^{n} \beta^{n-k} d_k \mathbf{x}_k^T = \mathbf{X}^{\mathrm{T}} \mathbf{\Lambda}\, \mathbf{d}$ with $\mathbf{\Lambda} = \mathrm{diag}\,[\beta^{n-1}\ \beta^{n-2} ....1]$

Both $\mathbf{R}_n$ and $\mathbf{p}_n$ can be computed recursively:

$$\mathbf{R}_n = \beta\, \mathbf{R}_{n-1} + \mathbf{x}_n \mathbf{x}_n^H ,\ \mathbf{p}_n = \beta\, \mathbf{p}_{n-1} + d_n \mathbf{x}_n \tag{8}$$

To find the weight vector w_n from (7), we need the inverse matrix $\mathbf{R}_n^{-1}$ from $\mathbf{R}_n$. Using a matrix inversion lemma (Haykins, 1996), a recursive update equation for $\mathbf{R}_n^{-1}$ is found as:

$$\mathbf{R}_n^{-1} = \beta^{-1} \mathbf{R}_{n-1}^{-1} - \beta^{-1} \mu_n' \mathbf{x}_n^T \mathbf{R}_{n-1}^{-1} \tag{9}$$

where gain vector, $\mu_n' = \dfrac{\beta^{-1} \mathbf{R}_{n-1}^{-1} \mathbf{x}_n}{1 + \beta^{-1} \mathbf{x}_n^T \mathbf{R}_{n-1}^{-1} \mathbf{x}_n}$

The equation (9) is known as ordinary RLS algorithm and it is valid for FIR filters because no assumption is made about the input data $\mathbf{x}_n$. We can then find the weights update equation as:

$$\mathrm{w}_n = \mathrm{w}_{n-1} + \mu_n' (\mathrm{d}_n - \mathrm{x}_n \mathrm{w}_{n-1}) \tag{10}$$

4. Application to noise cancelling

Adaptive filter, such as FIR LMS filter (Widrow & Hoff, 1960) or IIR RLS filter (Ljung & Sodestrom, 1987) is used to estimate two acoustic path transfer functions ($\mathrm{H}_1(\mathrm{z})$ and $\mathrm{H}_2(\mathrm{z})$) between each mirophone input and noise source. It is represented as the ratio of $\mathrm{H}_1(\mathrm{z}) / \mathrm{H}_2(\mathrm{z})$ in the two-microphone ANC approach as shown in Fig. 6 (A). Front-end whitening application is used to estimate the inverse of acoustic path transfer function $\mathrm{H}_2(\mathrm{z})$ in the reference input shown in Fig. 6 (B), where the cascaded adaptive filter is used to estimate acoustic path transfer function, $\mathrm{H}_1(\mathrm{z})$ in the primary microphone input.
In this paper, the inverse kepstrum filter is used to estimate $1 / \mathrm{H}_2(\mathrm{z})$ as whitening filter in front of SS functions and FIR RLS algorithm is used as rear-end spectral shaping adaptive filter in two-microphone beamforming structure as shown in Fig. 7. As an alternative approach, the system identification based kepstrum method has been studied in beamforming structure (Jeong & Moir, 2008).

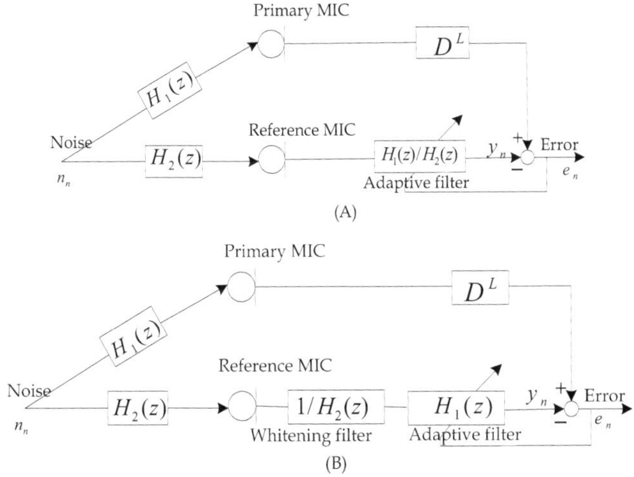

Fig. 6. (A) typical ANC method (B) front-end innovations based inverse kepstrum method, where both are applied to ANC structure

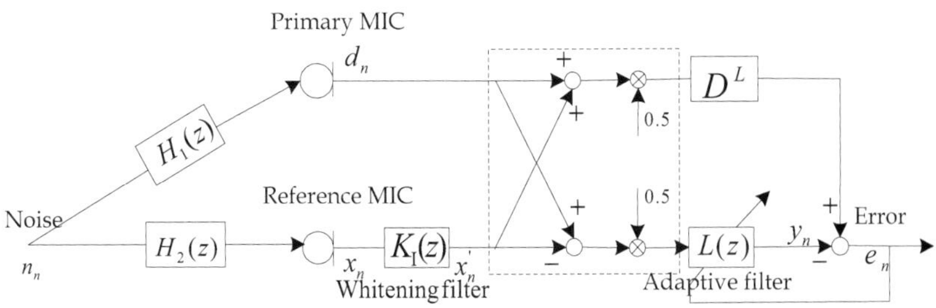

Fig. 7. Whitening application to beamforming structure: application of inverse kepstrum method

5. Experiment

The objective is to analyze the operation of the front-end innovations based whitening method and the rear-end FIR RLS filter between ANC and beamforming structure. For the simulation test, 2 kepsturm coefficients and first order of zero model RLS have been used, which will be compared with pole-zero model IIR RLS with first order of numerator polynomial and first order of denominator polynomial in ANC structure. Based on this, it will be tested in beamforming structrue for real-time processing in a realistic room environment, where noise cancelling performance will be compared with typical IIR RLS method in ANC structure. For the application of signal plus noise, a simple sine waveform (consisting of 500Hz, 550Hz and 700Hz) has been selected as a desired signal, which considered as a desired signal of speech signal with real data in noise signal. For the processing, two FFT points (2048 in simulation test and 4096 in real test) frame sizes have been used, and sampling frequency of 22050Hz and Nyquist frequency of around 11000Hz have been chosen. For the precise test, programmed operation is made to stop the estimate to freeze both kepstrum coefficients and adaptive (FIR and IIR RLS) filter weights when the signal is applied as desired speech signal (Jeong, 2010a; 2010b). The frozen coefficients and weights are then applied to desired signal and noise periods. For the test in a real environment, two unidirectional microphones (5cm distance apart) with broadside configuration have been set up and tested in a corner of room (3.8m(d)x3m(w)x2.8m(h)) with moderate reverberant status.

5.1 Simulation test in ANC structure

The noise characteristic between two microphones is estimated as the ratio of two acoustic path transfer functions, where the front-end innovations kepstrum estimates minimum phase term of a denominator polynomial and also zero-model FIR RLS algorithm of the cascaded adaptive filter estimates the remaining numerator polynomial as shown in Fig. 8. Both coefficients and weights are continously updated during the noise periods only and frozen during the signal plus noise periods.

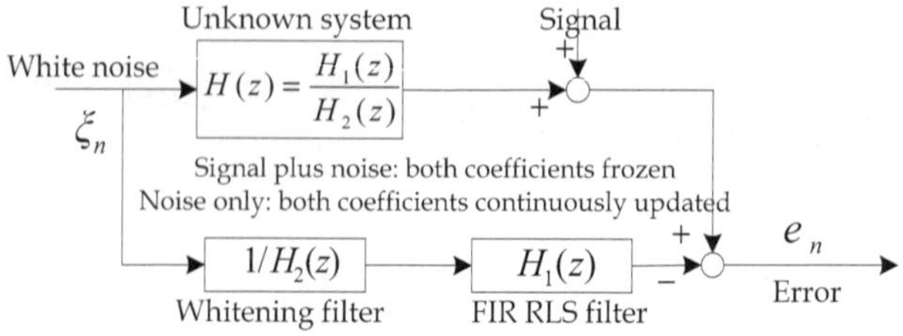

Fig. 8. Identification of unknown system in ANC structure based on estimates of innovations-based inverse kepstrum whitening filter and cascaded FIR RLS filter

5.2 Operation of innovations-based whitening filter and cascaded zero-model FIR RLS filter in ANC structure

To verify the operation of inverse kepstrum whitening filter with a nonminimum phase term from numerator polynomial and a minimum phase term from denominator polynomial, $H(z) = H_1(z) / H_2(z)$ has been used as a simple example of unknown system, where each acoustic transfer functions are

$$H_1(z) = 1 + 1.5z^{-1} \quad H_2(z) = 1 + 0.4z^{-1} \tag{11}$$

Hence $H(z) = (1 + 1.5z^{-1}) / (1 + 0.4z^{-1})$, which is illustrated as zero $(z = -1.5)$ and pole $(p = -0.4)$ in Fig. 9 (A).

Therefore, it can be described as a polynomial of:

$$H(z) = 1 + 1.1z^{-1} - 0.44z^{-2} + \ldots\ldots \tag{12}$$

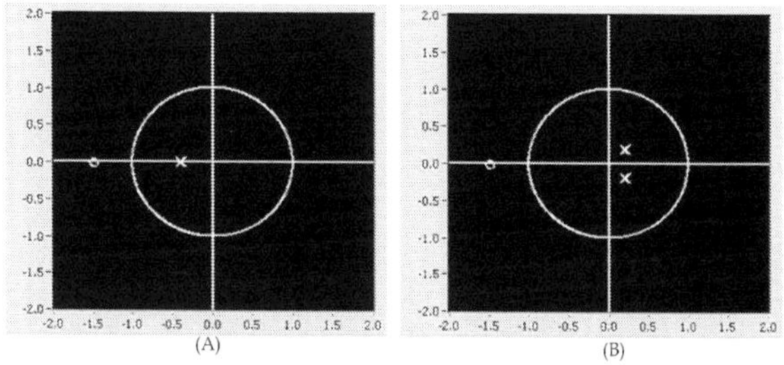

Fig. 9. Comparison of pole-zero placement: (A): ordinary IIR RLS (B): front-end inverse kepstrum method and cascaded FIR RLS

As shown in Fig. 9 (B), the front-end inverse kepstrum estimates minimum phase term (13) in denominator polynomial and cascaded zero-model RLS estimates remaining nonminimum phase term (14) in numerator polynomial,

$$K_I(z) = 1 / (1 + 0.4z^{-1}) \tag{13}$$

$$L(z) = (1 + 1.5z^{-1}) \tag{14}$$

It is also compared in terms of overall estimate, where overall estimate (III) from (C) is obtained from the convolution of estimate (I) and estimate (II). Table 1 shows that (A) is the ordinary IIR RLS with one pole $(p = -0.4)$ and one zero $(z = -1.5)$ model , (B) is its estimates, and (C) is estimates of front-end inverse kepstrum and cascaded FIR RLS as listed in Table 1. From the observation, it can be found that innovations based inverse kepstrum gives approximation to the ordinary IIR RLS, where it is also be verified in Fig. 9.

(A)	I: IIR RLS Numerator (weights)				
	1	1.5	-	-	-
	II: IIR RLS Denominator (weights)				
	1	0.4	-	-	-
	III: Overall estimate (weights)				
	1	1.1	− 0.44	0.176	− 0.070
(B)	I: IIR RLS Numerator (weights)				
	1	1.499	-	-	-
	II: IIR RLS Denominator (weights)				
	1	0.4	-	-	-
	III: Overall estimate (weights)				
	1	1.099	−0.439	0.175	− 0.070
(C)	I: Innovations kepstrum estimate of impulse response (coefficients)				
	1	-0.397	0.078	-	-
	II: Cascaded FIR RLS estimate (weights)				
	1	1.501	-	-	-
	III: Overall estimate (weights)				
	1	1.096	-0.525	0.122	0.000

Table 1. Comparison of overall estimate in vector weights: (A) IIR RLS in theory (B) IIR RLS in estimate (C) front-end innovations based inverse kepstrum and cascaded FIR RLS in estimate

5.3 Simulation test in beamforming structure

Based on the analysis in Fig. 2, whitening filter is applied to beamforming structure as front-end application as shown in Fig. 7, where it comprised of three parts, such as (1) whitening filter, (2) SS functions in beamforming structure and (3) adaptive filter in ANC structure as shown in Fig. 10.

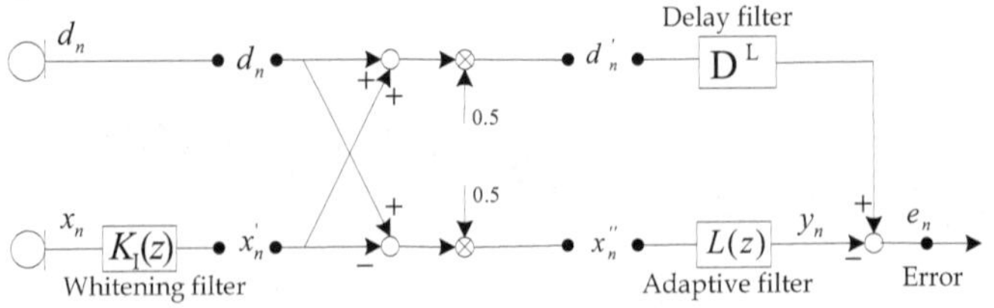

Fig. 10. Application of front-end whitening filter and rear-end adaptive filter to beamforming structure

Without application of whitening filter, acoustic path transfer function is estimated by adaptive filter $L(z)$ as the ratio of combined transfer functions, $\mathrm{H(z) = (H_1(z) + H_2(z)) / (H_1(z) - H_2(z))}$ in beamforming structure. With application of whitening filter $1/\mathrm{H_2(z)}$, the rear end adaptive filter estimates $\mathrm{L(z) = (H_1(z) + 1) / (H_1(z) - 1)}$ in beamforming structure as shown in Fig. 11 (A), where it is shown that adpative filter is only related with estimates of $\mathrm{H_1(z)}$. From the analysis on the last ANC structure, adaptive filter now estimates only numerator polynomial part $\mathrm{(H_1(z) + 1)}$ with one sample delay filter $\mathrm{D^{-1}}$ as shown in Fig. 11 (B). Both whitening coefficients and adaptive filter weights are continously updated during the noise period only, and then stopped and frozen during the signal plus noise period.

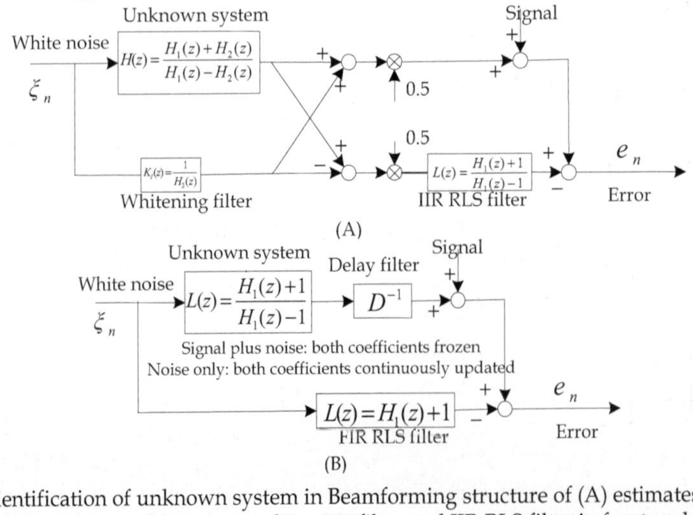

Fig. 11. Identification of unknown system in Beamforming structure of (A) estimates of innovations-based inverse kepstrum whitening filter and IIR RLS filter in front and rear of SS functions (B) estimate for adaptive FIR RLS filter with delay filter (one sample delayed) in the last ANC structure

5.4 Operation of front-end innovations-based whitening filter and rear-end zero-model FIR RLS filter in beamforming structure

With the use of same unknown system (11) as in ANC structure, the operation of inverse kepstrum whitening filter in front of SS functions in beamforming structure is same as one (13) in ANC structure.

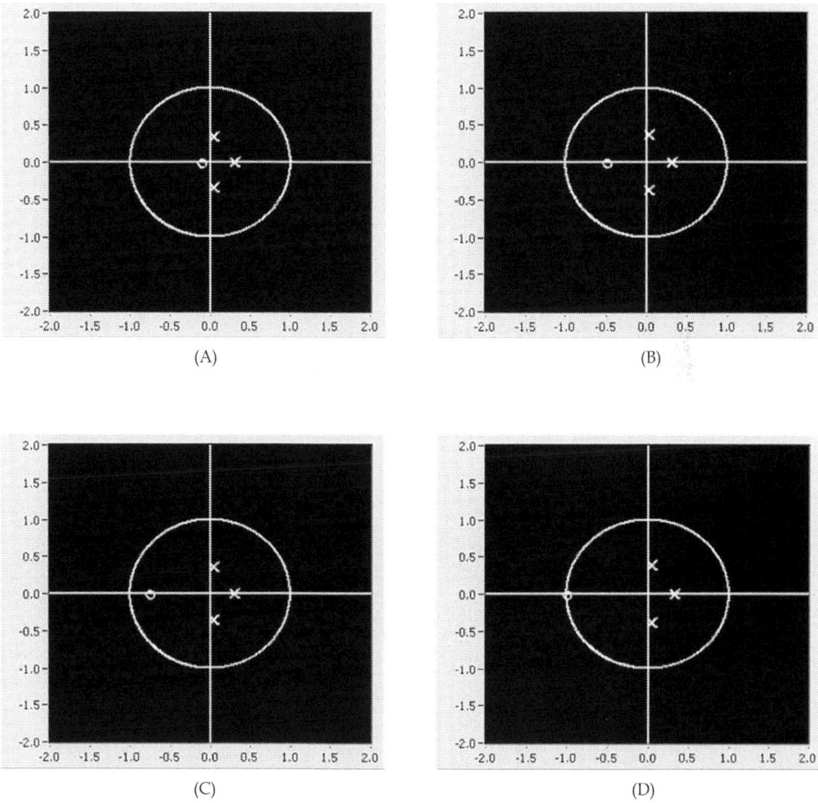

Fig. 12. Locations of pole-zero placement: (A) $H_1(z) = 1 + 0.2z^{-1}$ (B) $H_1(z) = 1 + 1z^{-1}$ (C) $H_1(z) = 1 + 1.5z^{-1}$ (D) $H_1(z) = 1 + 2z^{-1}$: $H_2(z)$ is commonly applied as $H_2(z) = 1 + 0.4z^{-1}$

The FIR RLS filter is then estimated on $(H_1(z) + 1)$, which gives that $L(z) = 1 + 0.75z^{-1}$, where a_0 =0.75. It shows that weight value is half in size from the orignal weight value, 1.5 in $H_1(z)$. Fig. 12 shows pole-zero locations according to different weight value in $H_1(z)$, where a_0 values are (A) 0.2 (B) 1 (C) 1.5 and (D) 2. With the use of three inverse kepstrum coefficients as shown in Fig. 12, it shows that adaptive FIR RLS is approximated to the half values, which are (A) 0.1 (B) 0.5 (C) 0.75 and (D) 1, respectively.

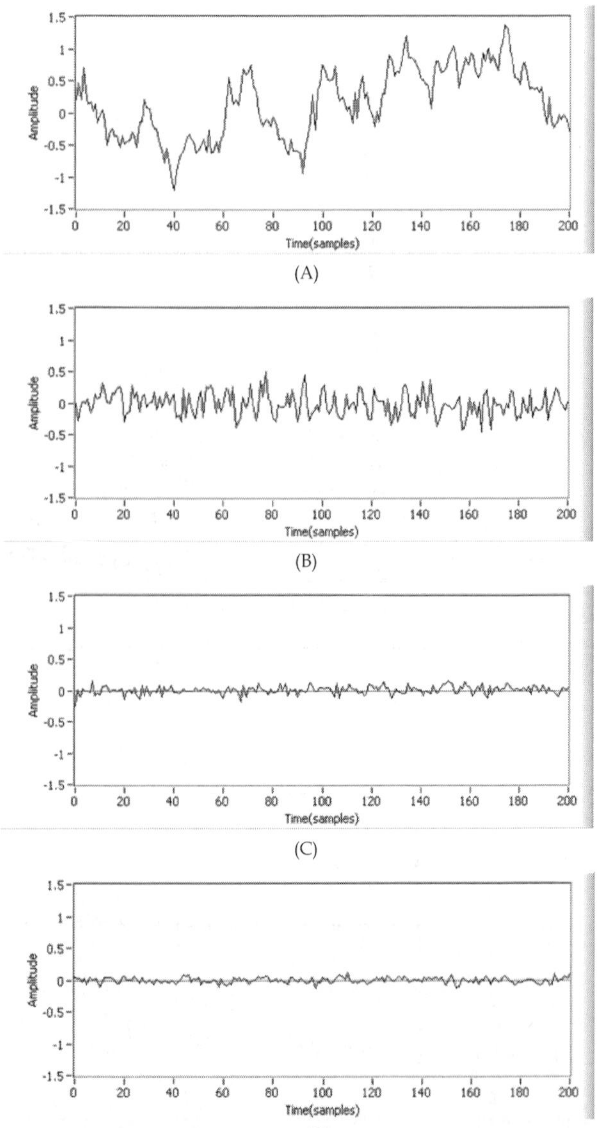

Fig. 13. Noise cancelling performance comparison in beamforming structure on (A) microphone ouput at x_n (B) whitening output x'_n (C) overall output e_n with inverse kepstrum filter only (wthout FIR RLS flter) and (D) overall output e_n with inverse kepstrum filter and FIR RLS filter

5.5 Test of noise cancellation on signal plus noise for real-time processing in a realistic environment

For real-time processing in a realistic room environment, it has been tested for the comparison of 1) the noise cancelling performance at each step in beamforming structure, and 2) the performance on front-end whitening application between ANC structure and beamforming structure, and finally 3) the noise cancelling performance in noise and signal plus noise between ordinary ANC approach using IIR RLS in ANC structure and front-end whitening approach with FIR RLS in beamforming structure.

Firstly, as shown in Fig. 13, the noise cancelling perfomance has been found from each processing stage, of 1) microphone output x_n, 2) inverse kepstrum filter output $x_n^{'}$ 3) overall output e_n with application of inverse kepstrum filter only and 4) overall output e_n with application of inverse kepstrum filter and FIR RLS filter from the each points in Fig. 10. For this test, 32 inverse kepstrum coefficients have been processed with FFT frame size 4096.

Based on this, it is found that inverse kepstrum filter works well in beamforming structrure.

Secondly, with the sole application by inverse kepstrum filter only, its noise cancelling performance has been tested in (A) ANC structure and it has been compared in (B) beamforming structure as shown in Fig. 14. From the test, it has been found that inverse kepsrum is more effective in beamforming structure than its application in ANC structure.

Thirdly, it has also been compared in average power spectrum between IIR RLS in ANC structure and inverse kepstrum filter in front with rear-end FIR RLS in beamforming structure. From the test result, it shows that inverse kepstrum provides better noise cancelling performance in frequency range over 1000 Hz for noise alone period as well as signal plus noise period as shown in Fig. 15.

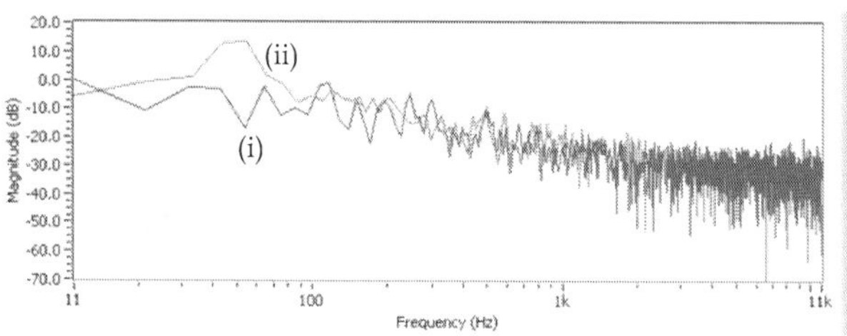

(A)

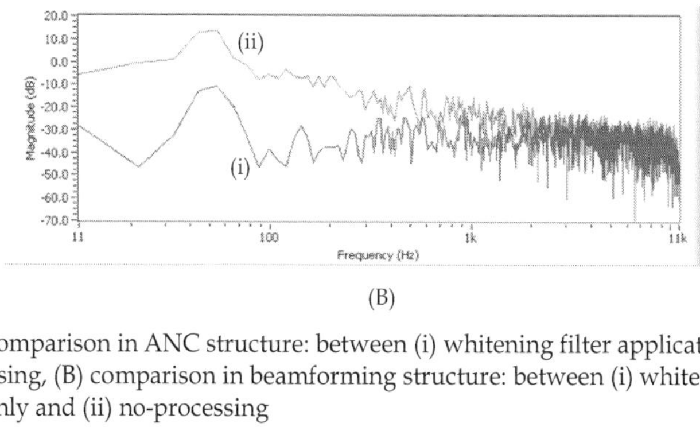

(B)

Fig. 14. (A) Comparison in ANC structure: between (i) whitening filter application only and (ii) no-processing, (B) comparison in beamforming structure: between (i) whitening filter application only and (ii) no-processing

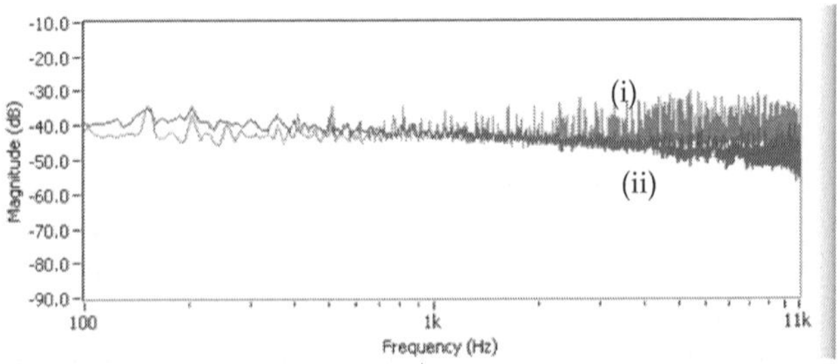

(A)

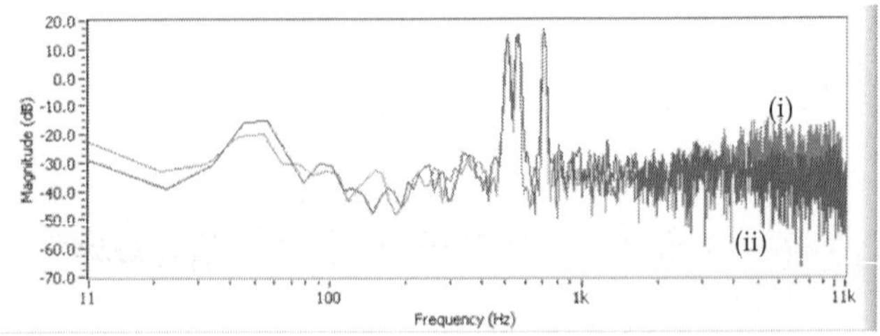

(B)

Fig. 15. Average power spectrum showing noise cancelling performance: comparison between (i) IIR RLS in ANC structure and (ii) whitening filter with FIR RLS in beamforming structure during the period of (A) noise and (B) signal and noise

6. Conclusion

It has been shown in simulation test that the application of front-end innovations-based whitening application (inverse kepstrum method) to cascaded zero model FIR RLS algorithm in ANC structure could perform almost same performance on convergence compared with pole-zero model IIR RLS in ANC structure. For the more effective performance in realistic environment, the front-end whitening application with rear-end FIR RLS to beamforming structure has shown better noise cancelling performance than the ordinary approach using pole-zero model IIR RLS in ANC structure. Therefore, when it is processed in real-time, it is claimed that the front-end whitening application could provide an effective solution due to a reduced computational complexity in inverse kepstrum processing using FFT/IFFT, which could be a benefit over sole application of IIR RLS algorithm.

7. Acknowledgment

This work was supported in part by the UTM Institutional Grant vote number 77523.

8. References

Berghe, J. V. & Wouters, J. (1998). An adaptive noise canceller for hearing aids using two nearby microphones, *Journal of the Acoustical Society of America*, 103 (6), pp. 3621-3626

Compernolle, D. V. (1990). Switching adaptive filters for enhancing noisy and reverberant speech from microphone array recordings, *International conference on acoustics, speech, and signal processing (ICASSP)*, pp. 833-836, Albuquerque,

Griffiths L. J. & Jim C. W. (1982). An alternative approach to linearly constrained adaptive beamforming, *IEEE transactions on antennas and propagation*, vol. AP-30, pp. 27-34

Haykin, S. (1996). *Adaptive filter theory*, third ed., Prentice-Hall Inc., Upper Saddle River, NJ,.

Jeong, J. & Moir, T. J. (2008). A real-time kepstrum approach to speech enhancement and noise cancellation, *Neurocomputing* 71(13-15), pp.2635-2649

Jeong, J. (2009). Analysis of inverse kepstrum and innovations-based applicaion to noise cancellation, *proceedings of the IEEE international symposium on industrial electronics (ISIE)*, pp. 890-896, July 5-8, 2009

Jeong, J. (2010a). Inverse kepstrum approach to FIR RLS algorithm and application to adaptive noise canceling, *proceedings of IEEE international conference on industrial technologies (ICIT)*, pp. 203-208, Vina del mar, Chile, March 14-17, 2010

Jeong, J. (2010b). Real-time acoustic noise canceling technique on innovations-based inverse kepstrum and FIR RLS, *proceedings of IEEE international symposium on intelligent control (ISIC)*, pp. 2444-2449, Yokohama, Japan, September 08-10, 2010

Kailath, T. (1968). An innovations approach to least-squares estimation-part I: linear filtering in additive white noise, *IEEE transactions on automatic control*, vol. 13, issue 6, pp. 646–655

Kalman, R.E. & Bucy, R. S. (1961). New results in linear filtering and prediction theory, *Transactions of the ASME – Journal of basic engineering*, 83: (1961): pp. 95-107

Knapp, C. & Carter, G. C. (1976). The generalized correlation method for estimation of time delay, *IEEE transaction on acoustics, speech and signal processing*, ASSP-24(4), pp. 320-327

Ljung, L. & Sodestrom, T. (1987). *Theory and practice of recursive estimation*: MIT Press

Moir, T. J. & Barrett, J. F. (2003). A kepstrum approach to filtering, smoothing and prediction with application to speech enhancement, *Proc. R. Soc. Lond. A* 2003(459): pp.2957-2976

Silvia, M. T. & Robinson, E. A. (1978). Use of the kepstrum in signal analysis, *Geoexploration*, 16(1978), pp. 55-73.

Wallace, R. B. & Goubran, R. A. (1992). Noise cancellation using parallel adaptive filters, *IEEE transaction on circuits and systems-II: Analog and digital signal processing*, 39 (4): pp. 239-243

Widrow, B., Glover, J. R. Jr., McCool, J. M., Kaunitz, J., Williams, C. S., Hearn, R. H., Zeidler, J. R., Dong, E. Jr., & Goodlin, R. C. (1975). Adaptive noise cancelling: principles and applications, *Proceedings of the IEEE*, 63 (12), pp.1692-1716

Widrow, B. & Hoff, M. E. (1960). Adaptive switching circuits, *IRE Wescon Convention Record*, pp. 96-104

8

Adaptive Fuzzy Neural Filtering for Decision Feedback Equalization and Multi-Antenna Systems

Yao-Jen Chang and Chia-Lu Ho
Department of Communication Engineering, National Central University, Taiwan (R. O. C.)

1. Introduction

1.1 Background

In ordinary channel equalizer and multi-antenna system, many types of detecting methods have been proposed to compensate the distorted signals or recover the original symbols of the desired user [1]-[3]. For channel equalization, transversal equalizers (TEs) and decision feedback equalizers (DFEs) are commonly used as a detector to compensate the distorted signals [2]. It is well-known that a DFE performs significantly better than a TE of equivalent complexity [2]. As to a multi-user-multi-antenna system, adaptive beamforming (BF) detectors have provided practical methods to recover the symbols of the desired user [3]. Many classical optimization algorithms, such as minimum mean-squared error (MMSE) [1]-[4], minimum bit-error rate (MBER) [5]-[9], adaptive MMSE/MBER training methods [6], [10]-[12] and the bagging (BAG) adaptive training method [13], are proposed to adjust the parameters of the above mentioned classical detectors (i.e., TE, DFE and BF).
Due to the optimal nonlinear classification characteristics in the observed space, Bayesian decision theory derived from maximum likelihood detection [15] has been extensively exploited to design the so-called Bayesian TE (BTE) [14]-[15], Bayesian DFE (BDFE) [16]-[17] and Bayesian BF (BBF) [18]-[19]. The bit-error rate (BER) or symbol-error rate (SER) results of Bayesian-based detectors are often referred to as the optimal solutions, and are extremely superior to those of MMSE, MBER, adaptive MMSE (such as least mean square algorithm [1]), adaptive MBER (such as linear-MBER algorithm [6]) or BAG-optimized detector. The BTE, BDFE and BBF can be realized by the radial basis functions (RBFs) [14], [17], [19]-[23]. Classically, the RBF TE, RBF DFE or RBF BF is trained with a clustering algorithm, such as k-means [14], [17], [24] and rival penalized competitive learning (RPCL) [25]-[31]. These clustering techniques can help RBF detectors find the center vectors (also called center units or centers) associated with radial Gaussian functions.

1.2 Motivation of FSCFNN equalization with decision feedback

The number of radial Gaussian functions of a RBF TE, i.e., the number of hidden nodes or the number of RBF nodes, can be obtained from a prior knowledge. The mathematical operation with respect to the equalizer order and the channel order can readily determine the number of hidden nodes [14, 16, 20]. However, if the channel order or equalizer order increases linearly, the number of hidden nodes in RBF TE grows exponentially, so do the computation and hardware complexity [20]. Trial-and-error method is an alternative way to determine the number of hidden nodes of RBF.

Except the clustering RBF detectors, there are other types of nonlinear detectors, such as multilayer perceptrons (MLPs) [32]-[38], adaptive neuro fuzzy inference system (ANFIS) [39]-[41] and self-constructing recurrent fuzzy neural networks (SCRFNNs) [42]-[44]. Traditionally, MLP and ANFIS detectors are trained by the back-propagation (BP) learning [32], [34], [35], [38], [40]. However, due to the improper initial parameters of MLP and ANFIS detectors, the BP learning often results in an occurrence of local minima which can lead to bad performance [38]. Recently, evolution strategy (ES) has been also used to train the parameters of MLP and ANFIS detectors [36], [41]. Although the ES inherently is a global and parallel optimization learning algorithm, tremendous computational costs in the training process make it impractical in modern communication environments. In addition, the structures (i.e., the numbers of hidden nodes) of MLP and ANFIS detectors must be fixed and assigned in advance and determined by trial-and-error method.

In 2005, the SCRFNN detector and its another version, i.e., self-constructing fuzzy neural network (SCFNN), have been applied to the channel equalization problem [43]-[44]. Specifically, the SCRFNN or SCFNN equalizers perform both self-constructing process and BP learning process simultaneously in the training procedure without the knowledge of channel characteristics. Initially, there are no hidden nodes (also called fuzzy rules hereinafter) in the SCRFNN or SCFNN structure. All of the nodes are flexibly generated online during the self-constructing process that not only helps automate structure modification (i.e., the number of hidden nodes is automatically determined by the self-constructing algorithm instead of the trial-and-error method) but also locates good initial parameters for the subsequent BP algorithm. The BER or SER of the SCRFNN TE and SCFNN TE thus is extremely superior to that of the classical BP-trained MLP and ANFIS TEs, and is close to the optimal Bayesian solution. Moreover, the self-constructing process of SCRFNN and SCFNN can construct a more compact structure due to setting conditions to restrict the generation of a new hidden node, and hence SCRFNN and SCFNN TEs results in lower computational costs compared to traditional RBF and ANFIS TEs.

Although the SCRFNN TE and SCFNN TE in [43-44] have provided a scheme to obtain satisfactory BER and SER performance with low computational complexity, it doesn't take advantage of decision feedback signals to improve the detecting capability. In Section 2, a novel DFE structure incorporated with a fast SCFNN learning algorithm is presented. We term it as fast SCFNN (FSCFNN) DFE [58]. FSCFNN DFE is composed of several FSCFNN TEs, each of which corresponding to one feedback input vector. Because the feedback input vector occurs independently, only one FSCFNN TE is activated to decide the estimated symbol at each time instant. Without knowledge of channel characteristics, the improvement over the classical SCRFNN or SCFNN TE can be achieved by FSCFNN DFE in terms of BER, computational cost and hardware complexity.

In modern communication channels, a time-varying fading caused by Doppler effect [33], [37], [49] and a frequency offset casued by Doppler effect and/or mismatch between the frequencies of the transmitter and receiver oscillators are usually unavoidable [45]. Moreover, a phase noise [45] also may exist due to distorted transmission environment and/or imperfect oscillators. Therefore, these distortions need to be compensated at the receiver to avoid a serious degradation. To the best of our knowledge, most of the work in the area of nonlinear TE or DFE over the past few decades focuses on the time-invariant channels. Therefore, the simulations of the FSCFNN DFE and the other nonlinear equalizing methods will be investigated in Section 2.3 under the linear and nonlinear channels with time-invariant or time-varying environment.

1.3 Motivation of adaptive RS-SCFNN beamformer

As mentioned in Section 1.1, for multi-antenna systems, classical adaptive BFs are designed based on the MMSE or MBER algorithm [1], [3], [6], [8], [11], [19]. This classical MMSE or MBER beamforming design requires that the number of users supported is no more than the number of receiving antenna elements [19], [46]. If this condition is not met, the multi-antenna system is referred to as overloaded or rank-deficient. Moreover, BER performance of MMSE and MBER beamformers in the rank-deficient system will be very poor. Due to the nonlinear classification ability as mentioned in Section 1.1, the BBF realized by a RBF detector has shown a significant improvement over the MMSE and MBER ones, especially in the rank-deficient multi-antenna system [19], [47], [48]. Recently, a symmetric property of BBF [8] is exploited to design a novel symmetric RBF (SRBF) BF [47]-[48]. This SRBF BF can obtain better BER performance and simpler training procedure than the classical RBF one. Differing from the clustering method, the MBER method [47] based on a stochastic approximation of Parzen window density estimation also can be used to train the parameters of RBF as demonstrated in [47]. Unfortunately, RBF BF trained by an enhanced *k*-means clustering [48] or the MBER algorithm still needs large amounts of hidden nodes and training data to achieve satisfactory BER performance.

To the best of our knowledge, all existing SCFNN detectors are designed for single-user single-antenna assisted systems. In Section 3, we thus propose to incorporate the SCFNN structure into multi-antenna assisted beamforming systems with the aid of a symmetric property of array input signal space. This novel BF is called symmetric SCFNN (S-SCFNN) BF. The training procedure of this S-SCFNN also contains self-constructing and parameter training phases. Although S-SCFNN BF has better BER performance and lower BF complexity than the standard SCFNN one, the BF complexity is still huge at low signal-to-noise (SNR) ratios. Thus, a simple inhibition criterion is added to the self-constructing training phase to greatly reduce the BF complexity, and this low-complexity S-SCFNN is called reduced S-SCFNN (RS-SCFNN). The simulation results have shown that the RS-SCFNN BF extremely outperforms the BFs incorporated with MMSE, MBER, SRBF and the classical SCFNN detectors in the rank-deficient multi-antenna assisted systems. Besides, the proposed SCFNN BF can flexibly and automatically determine different numbers of hidden nodes for various SNR environments, but, as discussed in Section 3.3, the RBF detector must assign hidden node's numbers as a fix constant for various SNR environments before training. Although the RBF BF can also assign the various numbers of hidden nodes for different SNRs, it needs huge manpower to achieve this goal.

2. Self-constructing fuzzy neural filtering for decision feedback equalizer

Classical equalizers, such as a transversal equalizer (TE) and a decision feedback equalizer (DFE), usually employ linear filters to equalize distorted signals. It has been shown that the mean square error (MSE) for a DFE is always smaller than that of a TE, especially when the channel has a deep spectral null in its bandwidth [2]. However, if the channel has severely nonlinear distortions, classical TE and DFE perform poorly. Generally speaking, the nonlinear equalization techniques proposed to address the nonlinear channel equalization problem are those presented in [14], [16], [17], [22], [32], [35], [39], [44], [54]. Chen *et al.* have derived a Bayesian DFE (BDFE) solution [16], which not only improves performance but also reduces computational cost compared to the Bayesian transversal equalizer (BTE). Based on the assumption that the channel order n_h has been known, i.e., the channel order n_h has been successfully estimated before detection process, a radial basis function (RBF) detection can realize the optimal BTE and BDFE solutions [14], [16]. However, as the channel order or/and the equalizer order increases, the computational cost and memory requirement will grow exponentially as mentioned in Section 1.2.

A powerful nonlinear detecting technique called fuzzy neural network (FNN) can make effective use of both easy interpretability of fuzzy logics and superior learning ability of neural networks, hence it has been adopted for equalization problems, e.g. an adaptive neuro fuzzy inference system (ANFIS)-based equalizer [39] and a self-constructing recurrent FNN (SCRFNN)-based equalizer [44]. Multilayer perceptron (MLP)-based equalizers [32], [35] are another kind of detection. Both FNN and MLP equalizers do not have to know the channel characteristics including the channel order and channel coefficients. For ANFIS and MLP nonlinear equalizers, the structure size must be fixed by trial-and-error method in advance, and all parameters are tuned by a gradient descent method. As to SCRFNN equalizer, it can simultaneously tune both the structure size and the parameters during its online learning procedure. Although the SCRFNN equalizer has provided a scheme to automatically tune the structure size, it doesn't derive an algorithm to improve the performance with the aid of decision feedback symbols. Thus, a novel adaptive filtering based on fast self-constructing neural network (FSCFNN) algorithm has been proposed with the aid of decision feedback symbols [58].

2.1 Equalization model with decision feedback

A general DFE model in a digital communication system is displayed in Figure 2.1 [2]. A sequence, $\{s(n)\}$, extracted from a source of information is transmitted and the transmitted symbols are then corrupted by channel distortion and buried in additive white Gaussian noise (AWGN). Then, the channel with nonlinear distortion is modeled as

$$r(n) = g(\hat{r}(n)) + v(n) = g\left(\sum_{i=0}^{n_h} h_i s(n-i)\right) + v(n), \tag{2.1}$$

where $g(\cdot)$ is a nonlinear distortion, h_i is the channel coefficient of the linear FIR channel $\hat{r}(n)$ with length $n_h + 1$ (n_h is also called channel order), $s(n)$ is the transmitted symbol at the time instant n, and $v(n)$ is the AWGN with zero mean and variance σ_v^2. The standard DFE is characterized by the three integers N_f, N_b and d known as the feedforward order, feedback order, and decision delay, respectively. We define the feedforward input vector at the time instant n as the sequence of the noisy received signals $\{r(n)\}$ inputting to the DFE, i.e.,

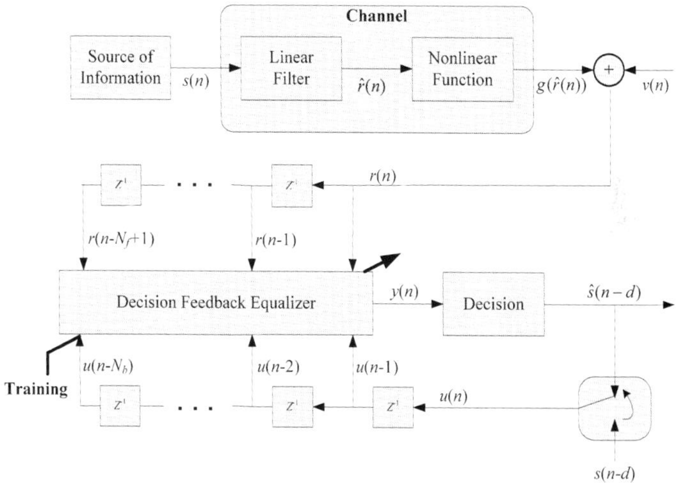

Fig. 2.1 General equalization model with decision feedback

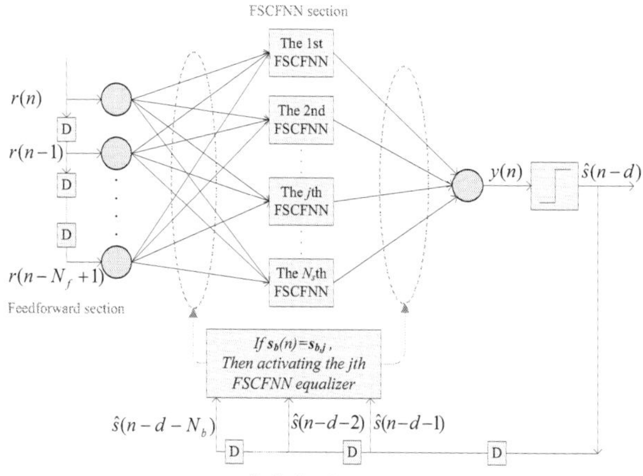

Fig. 2.2 FSCFNN DFE structure

$$\mathbf{s}_f(n) = [r(n), r(n-1), \ldots, r(n-N_f+1)]^T. \tag{2.2}$$

The feedback input vector that inputs into the DFE at the time instant n can be defined as the decision sequence, i.e.,

$$\mathbf{s}_b(n) = [u(n), u(n-1), \ldots, u(n-N_b+1)]^T = [\hat{s}(n-d-1), \hat{s}(n-d-2), \ldots, \hat{s}(n-d-N_b)]^T. \tag{2.3}$$

The output of the DFE is $y(n)$ and it is passed through a decision device to determine the estimated symbol $\hat{s}(n-d)$ of the desired symbol $s(n-d)$.

2.2 Adaptive FSCFNN decision feedback equalizer

A. Novel DFE design

The FSCFNN DFE structure shown in Figure 2.2 [58] consists of feedforward section, feedback section and FSCFNN section. The feedforward and feedback sections contain the signal vectors $\mathbf{s}_f(n)$ and $\mathbf{s}_b(n)$, where the notations N_f and N_b have been defined in Section 2.1. We assume that the FSCFNN section contains N_s FSCFNN equalizers. The transmitted sequence $\{s(n)\}$ is assumed to be an equiprobable and independent binary sequence taking +1 or –1 in this section. Thus, the estimated symbol can be easily determined by

$$\hat{s}(n-d) = \begin{cases} s_1 \equiv +1, if \ y(n) \geq 0 \\ s_2 \equiv -1, if \ y(n) < 0 \end{cases} \tag{2.4}$$

Usually, the feedback input vector $\mathbf{s}_b(n)$ in the training mode is formed by the known training symbols, i.e.,

$$\mathbf{s}_b(n) = [s(n\text{-}d\text{-}1), s(n\text{-}d\text{-}2), \ldots, s(n\text{-}d\text{-}N_b)]^T. \tag{2.5}$$

Without loss of generality, we can select $N_f = d + 1$, where d is chosen by a designer. Increasing d may improve performance, but reducing d reduces equalizer complexity. In this section, we set $d = 1$.

It is clear that the channel equalization process can be viewed as a classification problem, which seeks to classify observation vectors into one of the classes. Thus, we apply the principle of classification to designing the FSCFNN DFE. Suppose, at each time instant n, there are N_t transmitted symbols that will influence the decision output $y(n)$ of FSCFNN DFE:

$$\mathbf{s}_t(n) = [s(n), \ldots, s(n\text{-}d\text{-}1), \ldots, s(n\text{-}d\text{-}N_b), \ldots, s(n\text{-}N_t\text{+}1)]^T, \tag{2.6}$$

where the value $N_t \geq d + N_b + 1$ is determined by the channel order n_h. Since we assume that the FSCFNN DFE doesn't estimate the channel order n_h in advance, the value N_t will be unknown. Obviously, the sequence $\mathbf{s}_t(n)$ at the time instant n contains the correct feedback input vector $\mathbf{s}_b(n)$. Moreover, as $\mathbf{s}_t(n)$ sequentially going through a channel, the feedforward input vector $\mathbf{s}_f(n)$ is then generated. Clearly, the set of $\mathbf{s}_t(n)$ can be partitioned into 2^{N_b} subsets due to $\mathbf{s}_b(n)$ involving 2^{N_b} feedback states, denoted as $\mathbf{s}_{b,j}$, $j = 1 \sim 2^{N_b}$. Therefore, the set $R_d = \{\mathbf{s}_f(n)\}$ associated with feedforward input vectors can be also divided into 2^{N_b} subsets according to the feedback states:

$$R_d = \bigcup_{1 \leq j \leq 2^{N_b}} R_{d,j} \tag{2.7}$$

where $R_{d,j} = \{\mathbf{s}_f(n) \mid \mathbf{s}_b(n) = \mathbf{s}_{b,j}\}$, . Since each feedback state $\mathbf{s}_{b,j}$ occurs independently, the FSCFNN DFE uses $N_s = 2^{N_b}$ FSCFNN detectors to separately classify the N_s feedforward input subsets $R_{d,j}$ into 2 classes. Thus, for the feedforward input vectors belonging to $R_{d,j}$, the jth FSCFNN detector corresponding to $R_{d,j}$ will be exploited as shown in Figure 2.2 to further classify subset $R_{d,j}$ into 2 subsets according to the value of $s(n\text{-}d)$, i.e.,

$$R_{d,j} = \bigcup_{1 \leq i \leq 2} R_{d,j}^{(i)} \tag{2.8}$$

where $R_{d,j}^{(i)} = \{\mathbf{s}_f(n) | (\mathbf{s}_b(n) = \mathbf{s}_{b,j}) \wedge (s(n-d) = s_i)\}$, i = 1, 2. Thus, a feedfoward input vector with $\mathbf{s}_{b,j}$ being its feedback state can be equalized by solely observing subset $R_{d,j}$ corresponding to the jth FSCFNN detector.

B. Learning of the FSCFNN with decision feedback

If the FSCFNN DFE (Figure 2.2) receives a feedforward input vector $\mathbf{s}_f(n)$ with $\mathbf{s}_b(n)=\mathbf{s}_{b,j}$ at n, the j-th FSCFNN detection will be activated as mentioned above. The structure of this j-th FSCFNN detection is shown in Figure 2.3. The output of the j-th FSCFNN detector is defined as

$$O_j(n) = \sum_{k=1}^{K_j(n)} \omega_{k,j}(n) O_{k,j}^{(3)}(n) \tag{2.9}$$

with

$$O_{k,j}^{(3)}(n) = \prod_{p=1}^{N_f} \exp\left(-\frac{(O_p^{(1)}(n) - m_{kp,j}(n))^2}{2\sigma_{kp,j}^2(n)}\right) \tag{2.10}$$

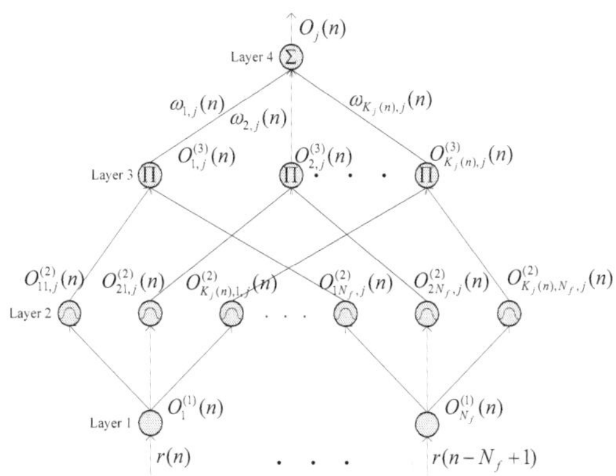

Fig. 2.3 Structure of the j-th FSCFNN

where $K_j(n)$ is the number of rule in the j-th FSCFNN detector, $w_{k,j}(n)$ is the consequent weight of the k-th rule in the j-th FSCFNN detector, and $m_{kp,j}(n)$ and $\sigma_{kp,j}(n)$ are the mean and standard deviation of the Gaussian membership function $O_{k,j}^{(3)}(n)$ corresponding to k-th rule in the j-th FSCFNN detector. Finally, the output value of FSCFNN DFE (Figure 2.2) at n is expressed as $y(n) = O_j(n)$.

Based on the self-constructing and parameter learning phases in SCRFNN structure [44], a fast learning version [58] has been proposed for FSCFNN DFE to further reduce the computational cost in the training period. Similarly, there are no fuzzy rules initially in each FSCFNN detector. As $\mathbf{s}_b(n)=\mathbf{s}_{b,j}$ at n, the proposed fast self-constructing and parameter learning phases are performed simultaneously in the j-th FSCFNN structure. In the self-constructing learning phase, we use two measures to judge whether to generate the hidden node or not. The first is the measure of the system error $\varepsilon = s(n-d) - \hat{s}(n-d)$ for considering the generalization performance of the overall network. The second is the measure of the maximum membership degree $\mu_{\max} = \max_k O_{k,j}^{(3)}(n)$. Consequently, for a feedforward input vector $s_f(n)$ with $s_b(n)=s_{b,j}$, the fast learning algorithm contains three possible scenarios to perform the self-constructing and parameter learning phases:

a. $\varepsilon \neq 0$ and $\mu_{\max} \leq \mu_{\min}$: It shows that the network obtains an incorrect estimated symbol and no fuzzy rule can geometrically accommodate the current feedforward input vector $s_f(n)$. Our strategy for this case is to try improving the entire performance of the current network by adding a fuzzy rule to cover the vector $s_f(n)$, i.e., $K_j(n+1) = K_j(n) + 1$. The parameters associated with the new fuzzy rule in the antecedent part of the j-th FSCFNN are initialized the same as those of SCRFNN:

$$\boldsymbol{m}_{new,j}(n) = \boldsymbol{s}_f(n), \quad \boldsymbol{\sigma}_{new,j}(n) = \sigma \cdot \boldsymbol{I} \tag{2.11}$$

where σ is set as 0.5 in this chapter.

b. $\varepsilon \neq 0$ and $\mu_{\max} > \mu_{\min}$: This means that the network obtains an incorrect estimated symbol but at least one fuzzy rule can accommodate the vector $s_f(n)$. Thus the parameter learning can be used here to improve the performance of the network and no fuzzy rule should be added.

c. $\varepsilon = 0$ This means that the network has obtained a correct estimated symbol. Thus, it is unnecessary to add a rule, but the parameter learning is still performed to optimize the parameters.

As to the parameter learning used in the above scenarios (a)-(c), any kind of gradient descent algorithms can be used to update the parameters.

2.3 Simulation results

The performance of the FSCFNN DFE will be examined in time-invariant and time-varying channels in this sub-section. Table 2.1 shows the transfer functions of the simulated time-invariant channels. For comparisons, SCRFNN [44], ANFIS DFE with 16 rules [39], RBF DFE [16] and BDFE [16], [17] are added in the experiments. The parameters N_f = 2 and N_b = 2 are chosen for the equalizers with decision feedback. The SCRFNN equalizer with 2 taps is performed without decision feedback as mentioned above. The RBF DFE with the k-means algorithm works under the assumption of the perfect knowledge of the channel order [16], [20]. The performance is determined by taking an average of 1000 individual runs, each of which involves a different random sequence for training and testing. The testing period for each individual run has a length of 1000. The size of training data will be discussed later.

Channel	Transfer function
Channel A [21]	$H(z) = 0.348z^0 + 0.870z^{-1} + 0.348z^{-2}$ $H_A(z) = H(z) + 0.2H^2(z)$
Channel B [14] [37]	$H_B(z) = 0.348z^0 + 0.870z^{-1} + 0.348z^{-2}$

Table 2.1 Transfer functions of the simulated channels

A. Time-invariant channel

Several comparisons are made with various methods for the nonlinear time-invariant channel A. Figure 2.4 shows the BER performance and average numbers of fuzzy rules needed in computation for FSCFNN DFE under various values $\mu_{\min}$ in a different length of training. Clearly, the results of BER performance are similar if $\mu_{\min} > 0.05$, but the numbers of rules are increased as $\mu_{\min}$ grows. Moreover, it shows that the needed training data size for FSCFNN DFE is about 300. Figure 2.5 demonstrates the BER performance and average numbers of rules for various methods. The SCRFNN with $\mu_{\min} = 0.00003$ is used in this plot. The FSCFNN DFEs with $\mu_{\min} = 0.5$ and $\mu_{\min} = 0.05$ are respectively denoted as FSCFNN DFE(A) and FSCFNN DFE(B) in this plot. Obviously, the FSCFNN DFEs are superior to the other methods. Because we want to obtain satisfactory BER performance, both 400 training data size for various methods and $\mu_{\min} = 0.05$ for FSCFNN DFE will be set in the following simulations.

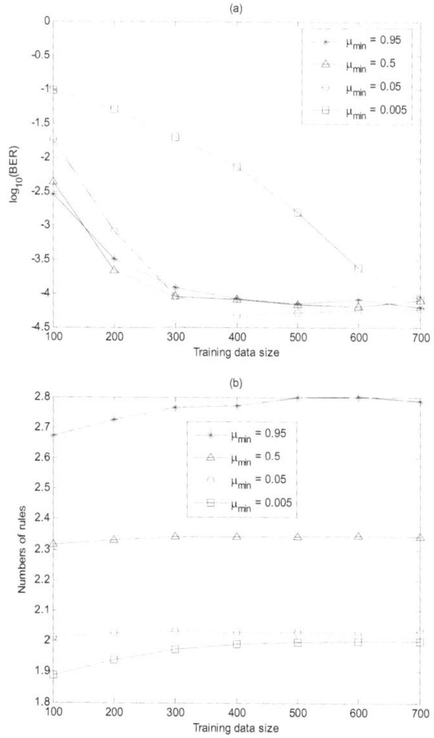

Fig. 2.4 Performance of FSCFNN DFE for various values $\mu_{\min}$ with a different length of training in the time-invariant channel A as SNR = 18 dB: (a) BER (b) Numbers of fuzzy rules

Figure 2.6 illustrates the performance of various methods at different SNRs. Note that the BERs in SNR = 20 dB are gained by averaging 10000 runs for accurate consideration.

Without knowledge of the channel, FSCFNN DFE improves the BER performance close to optimal BDFE solutions in satisfactory low numbers of rules.

Figures 2.7 & 2.8 show examples of the fuzzy rules generated by SCRFNN equalizer and FSCFNN DFE as SNR = 18 dB. The channel states and decision boundaries of the optimal solution are also plotted. The j-th FSCFNN detector can geometrically cluster the feedforward input vectors associated with $s_b(n)=s_{b,j}$, and in Figure 2.8, only 2 fuzzy rules in each FSCFNN are generated. Because the SCRFNN equalizer needs to cluster the whole input vectors, 4 fuzzy rules are created to attain this purpose (Figure 2.7). Therefore, FSCFNN DFE requires lower computational cost than SCRFNN in the learning or equalization period. In Figure 2.8, the optimal decision boundaries for four types of feedforward input vector subsets $R_{d,j}$ are almost linear, but the optimal decision boundary in SCRFNN is nonlinear. It also implies that classifying the distorted received signals into 2 classes in FSCFNN DFE is easier than that in SCRFNN equalizer. This is the main reason that the BER performance of FSCFNN DFE is superior to that of the classical SCRFNN equalizer.

B. Time-varying channel

The FSCFNN DFE is tested on time-varying channel environments. The following linear multipath time-varying channel model is used:

$$r(n) = h_1(n)s(n) + h_2(n)s(n-1) + h_3(n)s(n-2) + v(n) \tag{2.15}$$

where $h_i(n)$ represents the time-varying channel coefficients. We use a second-order low-pass digital Butterworth filter with cutoff frequency f_d to generate a time-varying channel [49], [55], where the value f_d determines the relative bandwidth (fade rate) of the channel time variation. The input to the Butterworth filter is a white Gaussian sequence with standard deviation $\xi = 0.1$. Then, a colored Gaussian output sequence is generated by this Butterworth filter, and is regarded as a time-varying channel coefficient. These time-varying coefficients can be further processed by centering the $h_1(n)$ at 0.348, $h_2(n)$ at 0.87 and $h_3(n)$ at 0.348. The linear time-varying channel B then is made.

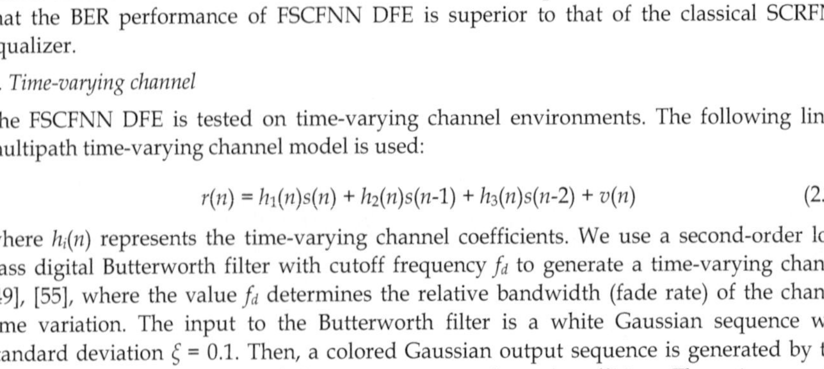

Fig. 2.5 Performance of various methods with a different length of training in the time-invariant channel A as SNR = 18 dB: (a) BER (b) Numbers of fuzzy rules

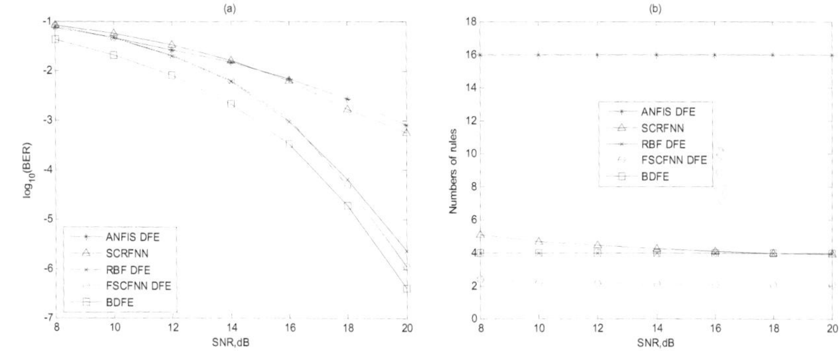

Fig. 2.6 Performance of various methods for different SNRs in the time-invariant channel A: (a) BER (b) Numbers of fuzzy rules

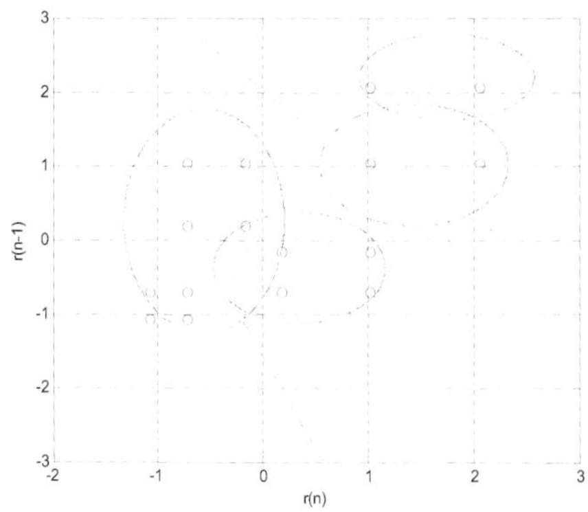

Fig. 2.7 Fuzzy rules generated by trained SCRFNN (ellipse), channel states (small circles) and optimal decision boundary (line) in the time-invariant channel A as SNR = 18dB

Figure 2.9 shows the performance of various methods for different f_d in time-varying channel B. Because the fade rate f_d in a real world is usually no larger than 0.1, thus we run the simulations from f_d = 0.02 (slowly time-varying) to f_d = 0.18 (fast time-varying). The FSCFNN DFEs with $\mu_{\min} = 0.95$ and $\mu_{\min} = 0.05$ are, respectively, denoted as FSCFNN DFE(A) and FSCFNN DFE(B) here. Besides, the values $\mu_{\min}$ in SCRFNN(A) and SCRFNN(B) are set as 0.00003 and 0.003, respectively. When the value of $\mu_{\min}$ is large enough, the BER performance of FSCFNN DFE for various time-varying environments may be satisfactory. Also, numbers of rules in FSCFNN DFE are increased as $\mu_{\min}$ grows. Because the FSCFNN DFE(B) has better performance in both time-varying channels B and C than the classical equalizers, the value $\mu_{\min} = 0.05$ is used in the following simulations of this paper.

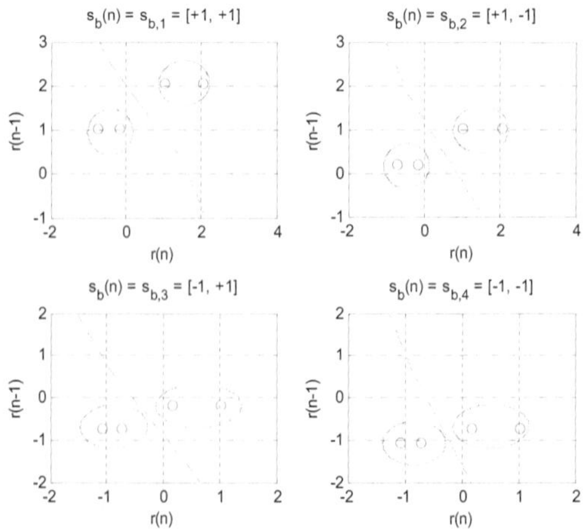

Fig. 2.8 Fuzzy rules generated by trained FSCFNN DFE (ellipse), channel states (small circles) and optimal decision boundaries (lines) for four feedback input vectors in the time-invariant channel A as SNR = 18dB

Figure 2.10 shows the performance of various methods for different SNRs in time-varying channel B. The SCRFNN equalizer with $\mu_{\min} = 0.003$ is used here for obtaining satisfactory performance. Note that the BER results as SNR = 18 dB in Figure 2.10(a) are gained by averaging 10000 runs for accurate consideration. The BER performance of FSCFNN DFE is slightly better than that of RBF DFE. However, the RBF DFE is assumed that the perfect knowledge of the channel order is acquired in advance for simulations. Similarly, numbers of rules needed in computation for FSCFNN DFE are the best.

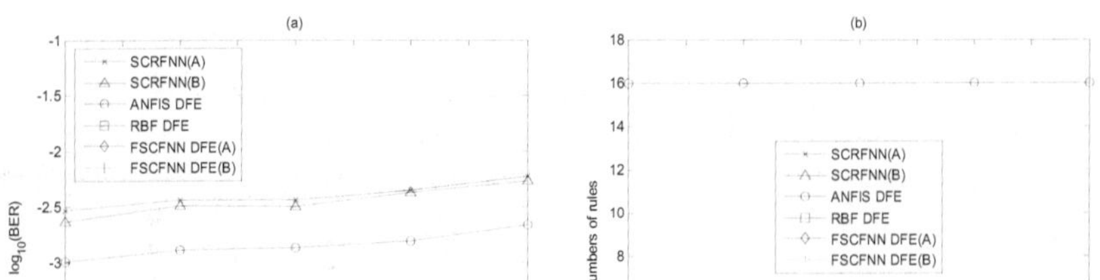

Fig. 2.9 Performance of various methods for different f_d in the time-varying channel B as SNR = 16 dB: (a) BER (b) Numbers of rules

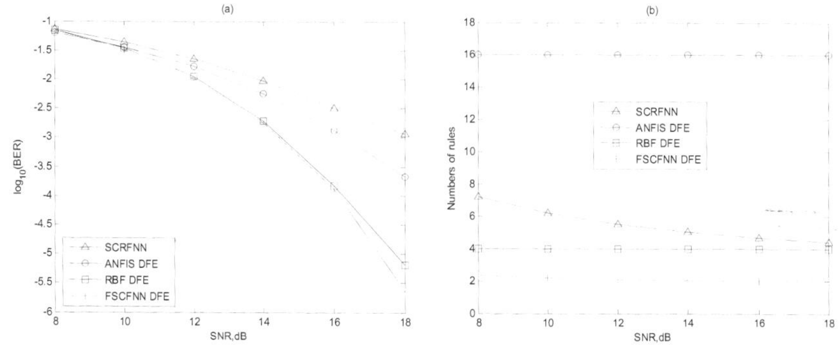

Fig. 2.10 Performance of various methods for different SNRs as $f_d = 0.1$ in the time-varying channel B (a) BER (b) Numbers of rules

3. Self-constructing fuzzy neural filtering for multi-antenna systems

Adaptive beamforming technology [3], [6], [8], [11], [18], [19], [46]-[48], [56] has been widely applied in smart antenna systems that can increase user's capacity and coverage in modern communication products. In this section, a powerful reduced symmetric self-constructing fuzzy neural network (RS-SCFNN) beamformer is presented for multi-antenna assisted systems. A novel training algorithm for the RS-SCFNN beamformer is proposed based on clustering of array input vectors and an adaptive minimum bit-error rate (MBER) method. An inherent symmetric property of the array input signal space is exploited to make training procedure of RS-SCFNN more efficient than that of standard SCFNN. In addition, the required amount of fuzzy rules can be greatly reduced in the RS-SCFNN structure. Simulation results demonstrate that RS-SCFNN beamformer provides superior performance to the classical linear ones and the other nonlinear ones, including symmetric radial basis function (SRBF), SCFNN and S-SCFNN, especially when supporting a large amount of users in the rank-deficient multi-antenna assisted system.

3.1 Multi-antenna array model

A uniformly spaced linear array is studied with L identical isotropic elements in this section, and the distance between the elements is represented by d. The plane waves impinge on the array in a θ angle in relation to the normal to the array and the difference of distance along one of the two adjacent ways is $d\sin\theta$. Note that the multi-antenna array model is completely the same as that in [6], [19], [46], [47], [57]. It is assumed that the system supports M users, and each user transmits a modulated signal on the same carrier frequency of $\omega = 2\pi f$. Then, the complex-valued signals received by the L-element antenna array are given by

$$x_l(n) = \sum_{i=1}^{M} A_i b_i(n) \exp(j\omega t_l(\theta_i)) + v_l(n) \tag{3.1}$$

where $1 \le l \le L$, $x_l(n) = x_l^R(n) + jx_l^I(n)$ is the complex-valued array input signal of the lth linear array element, n denotes the bit instance, the ith user's signal $b_i(n)$ is assumed to be a binary signal taking from the set {±1} with equal probability, A_i^2 denotes the signal power of user i, $t_l(\theta_i)=[(l-1)d\sin\theta_i]/c$ [57] is the relative time delay at element l for user i, θ_i is the direction of arrival (DOA) for user i, c is speed of light and $v_l(n)$ is the complex-valued white Gaussian noise having a zero mean and a variance of $2\sigma_v^2$. Without loss of generality, user 1 is assumed to be a desired user and the rest of the users are interfering users. The desired user's SNR is defined as $SNR = A_1^2/2\sigma_v^2$. We can rewrite (3.1) in a vector form:

$$\boldsymbol{x}(n) = \boldsymbol{P}\boldsymbol{b}(n) + \boldsymbol{v}(n), \tag{3.2}$$

Where $\boldsymbol{x}(n)=[x_1(n),\dots,x_L(n)]^T$, $\boldsymbol{v}(n)=[v_1(n),\dots,v_L(n)]^T$, the system matrix $\boldsymbol{P}$ is given by $[A_1\boldsymbol{s}_1, A_2\boldsymbol{s}_2,\dots,A_M\boldsymbol{s}_M]$ with the i-th user's steering vector $\boldsymbol{s}_i=[\exp(j\omega t_1(\theta_i)),\exp(j\omega t_2(\theta_i)),\dots,\exp(j\omega t_L(\theta_i))]^T$ (i.e., the spatial transfer function between the i-th emitting source and the array), and the transmitted bit vector is $\boldsymbol{b}(n)=[b_1(n),\dots,b_M(n)]^T$. The purpose of an adaptive beamformer is to reconstruct the desired user's signal $b_1(n)$ based on the array input vector $\boldsymbol{x}(n)$.

3.2 Adaptive beamformer based on SCFNN-related detection

A. Adaptive SCFNN beamformer

Because the detection process in any digital communication systems can be viewed as a classification problem, which seeks to classify the observed vectors into one of the classes. Thus, the SCFNN-based classifiers shown in Section 2 can also be applied to multi-antenna assisted beamforming systems, and the SCFNN beamformer can classify the array input signal space $\chi = \{\boldsymbol{x}(n)\}$ into two classes, i.e., $\chi^{(+)}=\{\boldsymbol{x}(n)\,|\,b_1(n)=+1\}$ and $\chi^{(-)}=\{\boldsymbol{x}(n)\,|\,b_1(n)=-1\}$. At the n-th time instant, the adaptive beamformer's output based on a standard SCFNN is then expressed by

$$y_s(\boldsymbol{x}(n)) = \sum_{k=1}^{K} w_k G_k(n), \tag{3.3}$$

where K is the number of fuzzy rules, w_k is the real-valued consequent weight of the k-th fuzzy rule, and $G_k(n)$ is the Gaussian membership function (GMF) of the k-th fuzzy rule, which is associated with the current array input vector $\boldsymbol{x}(n)$:

$$G_k(n) = \exp\left\{-\sum_{l=1}^{L}\left(\frac{(x_l^R(n)-c_{kl}^R)^2}{2(\sigma_{kl}^R)^2} + \frac{(x_l^I(n)-c_{kl}^I)^2}{2(\sigma_{kl}^I)^2}\right)\right\} \tag{3.4}$$

$$\equiv G(\boldsymbol{c}_k, \boldsymbol{\sigma}_k; \boldsymbol{x}(n))$$

where $c_{kl}=c_{kl}^R + jc_{kl}^I$ and $\sigma_{kl}=\sigma_{kl}^R + j\sigma_{kl}^I$, respectively, are the complex-valued center and complex-valued width of the k-th fuzzy rule for the l-th array input signal, and we define the center vector and width vector of the k-th fuzzy rule as $\boldsymbol{c}_k \equiv [c_{k1},\dots,c_{kL}]^T$ and $\boldsymbol{\sigma}_k \equiv [\sigma_{k1},\dots,\sigma_{kL}]^T$. The major difference between the equation (4.4) and a standard RBF [19] is that the ellipsoid GMFs are designed for the former, but the radial GMFs are used for the latter. To accommodate all geometric locations of $x(n)$ belonging to χ by little geometric clusters corresponding to GMFs (i.e., classify all observed vectors $x(n)$ with a small number K), the widths of the SCFNN classifier will be thus designed to be trainable to attain this purpose. The estimation of $b_1(n)$ is obtained by $\hat{b}_1(n) = \text{sgn}\{y_s(n)\}$.

As demonstrated in Section 2.2, the learning algorithm of a standard SCFNN detection involves two phases: self-constructing learning and parameter learning. Given a series of training data $(x(n), b_1(n))$, $n = 0, 1, 2, \ldots$, the SCFNN training algorithm is performed at each time instant n. Note that there are no fuzzy rules in adaptive SCFNN beamformer initially, too. In the self-constructing learning phase, the maximum membership degree $\mu_{\max} = \text{Max}_{1 \le k \le K} G_k(n)$ is also adopted to judge whether to generate a fuzzy rule or not, and the parameters of the fuzzy rule generated are then initialized properly. Consequently, the growth criterion that must be met before a new fuzzy rule is added is:

$$\mu_{\max} \le \mu_{\min} \tag{3.5}$$

where $\mu_{\min}$ is a pre-specified threshold ($0 < \mu_{\min} < 1$). This growth criterion implies that the geometric clusters corresponding to the existing fuzzy rules are far from the geometric location of the current array input vector $x(n)$. Hence, a new fuzzy rule should be generated to cover $x(n)$, i.e., $K \leftarrow K + 1$. Once a new fuzzy rule is added, its initial geometric cluster is assigned accordingly:

$$\boldsymbol{c}_{new} = \boldsymbol{x}(n) \text{ and } \sigma_{new,l} = \sigma,\ 1 \le l \le L, \tag{3.6}$$

where σ is an empirical pre-specified value and set as $1+j1$ in this section. By setting $\boldsymbol{c}_{new}$ as $x(n)$, the current vector $x(n)$ can be surely covered by this new fuzzy rule, and this design also satisfies the basic strategy of SCFNN, i.e., aiming to accommodate all geometric locations of the observed vectors. When the growth criterion defined in (3.5) doesn't be met at n, i.e., $\mu_{\max} > \mu_{\min}$, no fuzzy rule should be added and the parameter learning phase is performed to optimize the parameters of SCFNN beamformer, i.e., c_{kl}, σ_{kl} and w_k.

Traditionally, MMSE-based gradient descent methods are used for optimizing the parameters of a nonlinear detection [35], [38], [43], [44]. However, minimizing the MSE does not necessarily produce a low BER [5]-[9], [47] and hence an adaptive MBER-based gradient descent method recently has been proposed for a nonlinear structure [47]. In this chapter, we slightly modify the adaptive MBER method for the proposed SCFNN-related beamformers, which is summarized as follows. First, the decision variable $z(n) = b_1(n) \cdot y_S(\boldsymbol{x}(n))$ is defined [47] and the probability density function of $z(n)$ can be adaptively estimated by [47]

$$\tilde{p}(z,n) = \frac{1}{\sqrt{2\pi}\rho} \mathrm{e}^{-\frac{[z - b_1(n) y_S(\boldsymbol{x}(n))]^2}{2\rho^2}}, \tag{3.7}$$

where ρ is the chosen kernel width [47]. Then the estimated error probability of an SCFNN-related beamformer at the time instant n can be given by [47]

$$P_E(n) = \int_{-\infty}^{0} \tilde{p}(z,n) \mathrm{d}z. \tag{3.8}$$

The objective of the standard MBER method is to minimize $P_E(n)$ subject to the SCFNN-related beamformer's parameters. Namely, all of parameters of SCFNN are adapted by MBER-based gradient descent method. Because the criterion $\mu_{\max} > \mu_{\min}$ implies that the array input vector $\boldsymbol{x}(n)$ should be a member of the geometric cluster corresponding to $G_q(n)$, where $q = \arg \mathrm{Max}_{1\le k\le K} G_k(n)$, we propose to only optimize the parameters corresponding to the q-th fuzzy rule during MBER-based parameter training phase. By adopting this method, the time cost can be significantly reduced. Consequently, this modified MBER method (called C-MBER hereinafter for convenience) optimizes the parameters of the proposed SCFNN beamformer by the updating amount in (3.9)-(3.11):

$$\Delta w_q = -\gamma \frac{\partial P_E(n)}{\partial w_q} = \gamma \xi(n) G_q(n) \tag{3.9}$$

$$\Delta c_{ql}^Z = -\alpha \frac{\partial P_E(n)}{\partial c_{ql}^Z} = \alpha \xi(n) w_q G_q(n) \frac{x_l^Z(n) - c_{ql}^Z}{(\sigma_{ql}^Z)^2} \tag{3.10}$$

$$\Delta \sigma_{ql}^Z = -\beta \frac{\partial P_E(n)}{\partial \sigma_{ql}^Z} = \beta \xi(n) w_q G_q(n) \frac{(x_l^Z(n) - c_{ql}^Z)^2}{(\sigma_{ql}^Z)^3} \tag{3.11}$$

with

$$\xi(n) = \frac{\partial P_E(n)}{\partial y_S(\boldsymbol{x}(n))} = \frac{-1}{\sqrt{2\pi}\rho} \mathrm{e}^{-\frac{[y_S(\boldsymbol{x}(n))]^2}{2\rho^2}} \cdot b_1(n) \tag{3.12}$$

where $Z \in \{R, I\}$, α, β and γ are learning rates.

B. Adaptive S-SCFNN beamformer

In this sub-section, an inherent symmetry of the array input signal space is investigated and a novel S-SCFNN detection is designed based on this symmetry. First, let us denote $N_b = 2^{M-1}$ legitimate sequences of $\boldsymbol{b}(n)$ with $b_1(n) = +1$ as $\boldsymbol{b}_m^{(+)}$, $1 \le m \le N_b$, and denote 2^{M-1} legitimate sequences of $\boldsymbol{b}(n)$ with $b_1(n) = -1$ as $\boldsymbol{b}_m^{(-)} = -\boldsymbol{b}_m^{(+)}$, $1 \le m \le N_b$. Clearly, both of signal spaces $\chi^{(+)}$ and $\chi^{(-)}$ can be partitioned into N_b subspaces:

$$\chi^{(+)} = \cup_{1\le m\le N_b} \chi_m^{(+)} \text{ and } \chi^{(-)} = \cup_{1\le m\le N_b} \chi_m^{(-)}, \tag{3.13}$$

where $\chi_m^{(+)} = \{\boldsymbol{x}(n) | \boldsymbol{b}(n) = \boldsymbol{b}_m^{(+)}\}$ and $\chi_m^{(-)} = \{\boldsymbol{x}(n) | \boldsymbol{b}(n) = \boldsymbol{b}_m^{(-)}\}$. It can be easily seen that $\chi_m^{(+)} = \{\boldsymbol{x}(n) = \boldsymbol{P}\boldsymbol{b}_m^{(+)} + \boldsymbol{v}(n)\} \in \chi^{(+)}$ and $-\chi_m^{(+)} \equiv \left\{\boldsymbol{x}(n) = \boldsymbol{P}(-\boldsymbol{b}_m^{(+)}) - \boldsymbol{v}(n) = \boldsymbol{P}\boldsymbol{b}_m^{(-)} + \boldsymbol{v}(n)\right\} = \chi_m^{(-)} \in \chi^{(-)}$. Therefore, the two spaces $\chi^{(+)}$ and $\chi^{(-)}$ are distributed symmetrically, namely, for any subspace $\chi_m^{(-)} \in \chi^{(-)}$ the subspace $\chi_m^{(+)} \in \chi^{(+)}$ satisfies $\chi_m^{(-)} = -\chi_m^{(+)}$.

The basic idea of SCFNN learning is to accommodate all array input vectors $\boldsymbol{x}(n) \in \chi$ by adjusting the geometric clusters corresponding to $G_k(n)$, $k = 1, \ldots, K$. Since the signal spaces $\chi^{(+)}$ and $\chi^{(-)}$ are distributed symmetrically in the multi-antenna beamforming system, we propose to create symmetric geometric clusters to accommodate all of $\boldsymbol{x}(n) \in \chi$. Thus, the output of the proposed S-SCFNN beamformer is defined by

$$y_S(\boldsymbol{x}(n)) = \sum_{k=1}^{K} w_k (G_k^+(n) - G_k^-(n)) \tag{3.14}$$

with

$$G_k^+(n) = G(\boldsymbol{c}_k, \boldsymbol{\sigma}_k; \boldsymbol{x}(n)) \text{ and } G_k^-(n) = G(-\boldsymbol{c}_k, \boldsymbol{\sigma}_k; \boldsymbol{x}(n)), \tag{3.15}$$

where the geometric clusters corresponding to the two GMFs $G_k^+(n)$ and $G_k^-(n)$ are symmetric with each other. Moreover, all of geometric clusters corresponding to membership functions $G_k^+(n)$, $k = 1, \ldots, K$, are assumed to be capable of accommodating the vectors $\boldsymbol{x}(n) \in \chi^{(+)}$, and naturally all of geometric clusters corresponding to $G_k^-(n)$, $k = 1, \ldots, K$, can accommodate the vectors $\boldsymbol{x}(n) \in \chi^{(-)}$.

The learning procedure of SCFNN beamformer presented in the last section is modified here to make it suitable for the S-SCFNN beamformer. Similarly, there are no fuzzy rules initially in adaptive S-SCFNN beamformer. Because only the center vectors $\boldsymbol{c}_k \in \chi^{(+)}$, $k = 1 \sim K$, are needed in the S-SCFNN beamformer as defined in (3.14)-(3.15), we can focus on observing the array input vectors $\boldsymbol{x}(n) \in \chi^{(+)}$ during learning. Thus, the vector $\boldsymbol{x}(n) \in \chi^{(-)}$ with $b_1(n) = -1$ can be modified as $-\boldsymbol{x}(n) \in \chi^{(+)}$ before training:

$$\hat{\boldsymbol{x}}(n) = \begin{cases} \boldsymbol{x}(n), & if\ b_1(n) = 1 \\ -\boldsymbol{x}(n), & if\ b_1(n) = -1. \end{cases} \tag{3.16}$$

In the self-constructing learning phase, the maximum membership degree is also adopted. Because the k-th fuzzy rule of S-SCFNN detector is strongly related with the geometric clusters corresponding to both $G_k^+(n)$ and $G_k^-(n)$, the output value of $\{G_k^+(n) - G_k^-(n)\}$ is regarded as the membership degree that the current array input vector belongs to the k-th fuzzy rule. Thus the maximum membership degree is defined as

$$\mu_{\max} = \mathrm{Max}_{1 \le k \le K}\{G(c_k, \sigma_k; \hat{x}(n)) - G(-c_k, \sigma_k; \hat{x}(n))\}. \tag{3.17}$$

Consequently, the growth criterion that must be met before a new fuzzy rule is added is: $\mu_{\max} \le \mu_{\min}$, where $\mu_{\min}$ is as defined in (3.5). This criterion implies that the existing fuzzy rules cannot simultaneously satisfy the following two conditions:

(a) At least one of geometric clusters of $G_k^+(n)$ is close to the geometric location of $\hat{\mathrm{x}}(\mathrm{n})$.

(b) The geometric cluster of $G_k^-(n)$ should be relatively far from the geometric location of $\hat{\boldsymbol{x}}(n)$ compared to that of $G_k^+(n)$.

Hence, a new fuzzy rule should be generated to accommodate $\hat{\boldsymbol{x}}(n)$, i.e., $K \leftarrow K + 1$. Then, its initial symmetric clusters are assigned by

$$\boldsymbol{c}_{new} = \hat{\boldsymbol{x}}(n) \text{ and } \sigma_{new,l} = \sigma, 1 \le l \le L, \tag{3.18}$$

where σ is specified as in the last section.

When the growth criterion doesn't be met at n, no fuzzy rule should be added and the C-MBER method is performed to optimize the parameters of the S-SCFNN beamformer. The estimated error probability of S-SCFNN beamformer is the same as (3.8). Consequently, the updating amount of the S-SCFNN beamformer's parameters is derived as done in (3.9)- (3.12):

$$\Delta w_q = \gamma \xi(n)(G_q^+(n) + G_q^-(n)) \tag{3.19}$$

$$\Delta c_{ql}^Z = \alpha \xi(n) w_q (G_q^+(n) \frac{x_l^Z(n) - c_{ql}^Z}{(\sigma_{ql}^Z)^2} + G_q^-(n) \frac{x_l^Z(n) + c_{ql}^Z}{(\sigma_{ql}^Z)^2}) \tag{3.20}$$

$$\Delta \sigma_{ql}^Z = \beta \xi(n) w_q (G_q^+(n) \frac{(x_l^Z(n) - c_{ql}^Z)^2}{(\sigma_{ql}^Z)^3} - G_q^-(n) \frac{(x_l^Z(n) + c_{ql}^Z)^2}{(\sigma_{ql}^Z)^3}), \tag{3.21}$$

where

$$q = \arg \operatorname{Max}_{1 \le k \le K} \{ G(\boldsymbol{c}_k, \boldsymbol{\sigma}_k; \hat{\boldsymbol{x}}(n)) - G(-\boldsymbol{c}_k, \boldsymbol{\sigma}_k; \hat{\boldsymbol{x}}(n)) \}. \tag{3.22}$$

C. Adaptive RS-SCFNN beamformer

Because SCFNN or S-SCFNN learning procedure would generate too many fuzzy rules at low SNRs in applications, we further propose a reduced S-SCFNN (RS-SCFNN) beamformer here. The RS-SCFNN beamformer's output is completely the same as the S-SCFNN one, i.e., (3.14)-(3.15).

Like the S-SCFNN learning procedure, there are no fuzzy rules initially in the RS-SCFNN beamformer, and we focus on observing the vectors $\boldsymbol{x}(n) \in \chi^{(+)}$ during learning. The learning procedure also contains the self-constructing and parameter learning phases. It can be easily seen from (3.13) that the reasonable number of the Gaussian clusters inside the subspace $\chi^{(+)}$ is $N_b = 2^{M-1}$, so, actually, it is enough to accommodate all the geometric locations of $\boldsymbol{x}(n) \in \chi^{(+)}$ by creating N_b geometric Gaussian clusters, i.e., the maximum number of K should be 2^{M-1}. In the application of multi-antenna assisted systems, the user's number M supported usually is regarded as a known number [20]-[21]. Therefore, a simple inhibition criterion $K \le N_b$ can be added in the self-constructing learning phase. Then, the criteria that must be met before a new fuzzy rule is added are:

$$\mu_{\max} \le \mu_{\min} \text{ and } K \le N \tag{3.23}$$

where $\mu_{\max}$ and $\mu_{\min}$ are as defined in the SCFNN or S-SCFNN learning, and the integer N is pre-assigned to be no larger than N_b. With the aid of the latter criterion in (3.23), the number of fuzzy rules generated during learning can be greatly reduced at low SNRs compared with that of the S-SCFNN beamformer. The initial cluster setting of a new fuzzy rule and the parameter learning phase are the same as described in (3.18)-(3.22).

The center vectors $\boldsymbol{c}_k$ of the adaptive SRBF beamformer in the literature have been trained by several algorithms, such as classical k-means clustering, improved enchanced k-means clustering [48] and MBER method [47]. However, a serious slow convergence easily occurs in these classical clustering due to the improper initialization. Moreover, if the number of the center vectors is really huge, the classical algorithms will even need a longer training sequence to achieve convergence. Compared to the adaptive SRBF beamformer, the proposed RS-SCFNN beamformer has a faster convergence capability. By using the criterion $\mu_{\max} < \mu_{\min}$ during the self-constructing learning phase, the initial location of the new center vector $\boldsymbol{c}_{new} = \hat{\boldsymbol{x}}(n)$ can be far from the locations of the other existing center vectors $\boldsymbol{c}_k$. This feature avoids two or more center vectors initially located around the same ideal center.

Although in this section we design the adaptive RS-SCFNN beamformer under the BPSK beamforming system, its extension to high-order quadrature amplitude modulation (QAM) schemes is also achievable. For example, for the 4-QAM modulation, the array input signal space χ can be partitioned into the four subsets $\chi^{(\pm 1 \pm j)}$ depending on the value of $b_1(n)$ as the above derivation. Besides, for the four subspaces $\chi^{(\pm 1 \pm j)}$, the following symmetric relationship can be easily verified by using the same derivation in S-SCFNN learning: $\chi^{(-1+j)} = +j \cdot \chi^{(+1+j)}$, $\chi^{(-1-j)} = -1 \cdot \chi^{(+1+j)}$ and $\chi^{(+1-j)} = -j \cdot \chi^{(+1+j)}$. Then, the idea of creating symmetric geometric clusters to accommodate all $\boldsymbol{x}(n) \in \chi$ can be exploited to modify the 4-QAM FNN detector in [41] [44]. The derivation for the high-order QAM RS-SCFNN beamformer is much more complex and is beyond the scope of this work.

3.3 Simulation results

In this sub-section, a rank-deficient multi-antenna assisted beamforming systems is used to demonstrate the efficiency of the proposed adaptive RS-SCFNN beamformer. The beamforming systems considered is summarized in Table 3.1. As done in [1], [6], [11], [18], [19], [47], [48], DOAs for each user are fixed, and the distance between linear array elements is $d = \lambda/2$. The simulated narrowband channels are $A_i = 1 + j0$ as done in [19], [47]. The threshold $\mu_{\min}$ for various SCFNN related beamformers is set as 0.06 in the three systems. For comparisons, the linear MMSE [1], linear adaptive MBER [8], adaptive SRBF [47] and optimal Bayesian solution [19] are added in the simulations. The MBER learning rates for different nonlinear adaptive beamformers are listed in Table 3.2, and are used in the following simulations. These MBER learning rates were found on conditions of 1000 training data and 8-dB SNR, and are the best choices satisfying the three systems for each nonlinear adaptive beamformer. Note that SCFNN, S-SCFNN and RS-SCFNN are trained by the C-MBER method during parameter learning phase, and SRBF is trained by the MBER method [10]. The RS-SCFNN-M in Table 3.2 denotes RS-SCFNN trained with the standard MBER method. The MBER learning rate for linear beamformer [6] is set as 0.1 in the simulations. The simulation results are obtained by averaging 10^4 individual runs, each of which involves a different random sequence for training and testing. The testing data size is 10^3, and the training data size will be given later.

Simulated system	User i	1	2	3	4	5	6
$M = 6$, $L = 4$	DOA θ_i	0°	10°	-17°	15°	20°	-15°

Table 3.1 Multi-antenna assisted beamforming system simulated in Section 3.3

Beamformers	α	β	γ	ρ
SCFNN	0.25	0.01	0.005	0.7
S-SCFNN	2.5	0.55	0.5	0.25
RS-SCFNN	2.5	0.55	0.5	0.25
RS-SCFNN-M	0.3	0.25	0.05	0.2
SRBF	0.3	0.3	0.3	0.2

Table 3.2 MBER learning rates for different nonlinear adaptive beamformers used in Section 3.3

Due to the fact of $N \leq N_b = 2^{6-1} = 32$, we choose $N = 23$ and $N = 28$ for RS-SCFNN beamformers in the simulations. The chosen training data size for all adaptive beamformers is 400 in the simulated System A. Figure 3.1 depicts the BER performance for adaptive SCFNN related beamformers. Figure 3.2 shows the average numbers of fuzzy rules for adaptive SCFNN related beamformers. Since adaptive S-SCFNN beamformer only observes half the array input signal space χ during training, S-SCFNN can generate half as many fuzzy rules as SCFNN. Namely, the S-SCFNN beamformer only needs to train half as many parameters ($\boldsymbol{c}_k$, $\boldsymbol{\sigma}_k$ and $\boldsymbol{w}_k$) as the SCFNN one. As a result, the parameters of S-SCFNN beamformer can quickly converge, and thus the SCFNN exploiting symmetry has better BER performance than the standard SCFNN. When SNR is larger than 2 dB, the average numbers of fuzzy rules for S-SCFNN and RS-SCFNN beamformers are almost the same. Thus they also have similar BER performance at SNR = 4 ~ 8 dB. However, the numbers of fuzzy rules for S-SCFNN beamformer are sharply increased at low SNRs. With tiny sacrifice for BER performance, the numbers of fuzzy rules for RS-SCFNN can be effectively limited within the number N as mentioned in Section 3.2. In order to check the performance of C-MBER and MBER methods, the RS-SCFNN-M beamformer is also plotted. The results indicate that the RS-SCFNN with C-MBER has the similar performance to the RS-SCFNN with MBER (RS-SCFNN-M). Note that the C-MBER method only needs to train parameters associated with one of fuzzy rules as mentioned in Section 3.2, but the standard MBER method [47] have to train parameters associated with all of fuzzy rules.

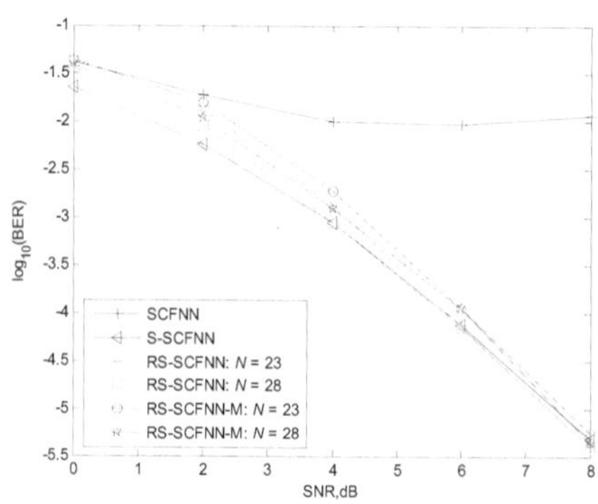

Fig. 3.1 BER performance for adaptive SCFNN related beamformers

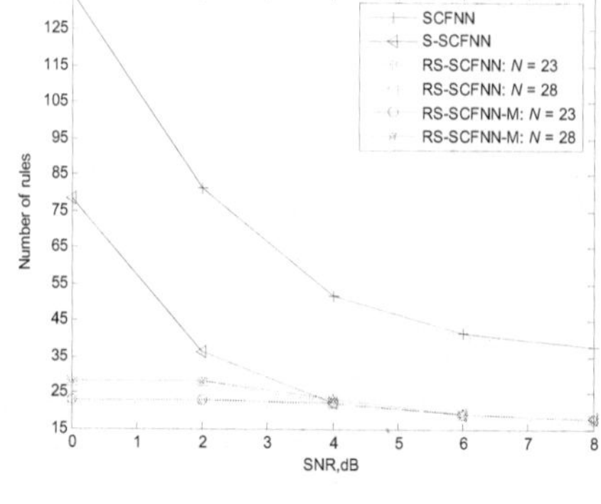

Fig. 3.2 Numbers of hidden nodes for adaptive SCFNN related beamformers

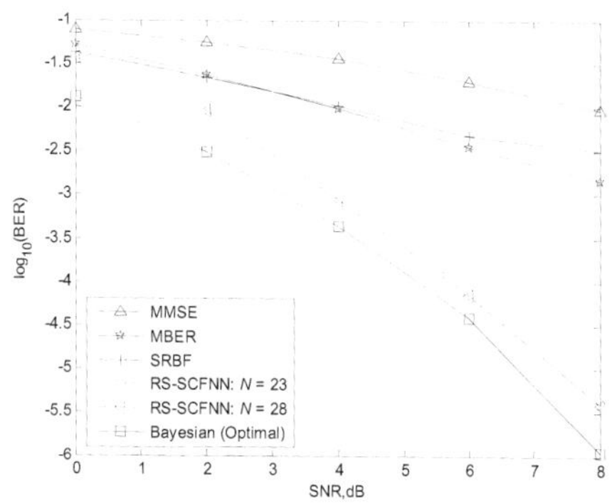

Fig. 3.3 BER performance for various adaptive beamformers

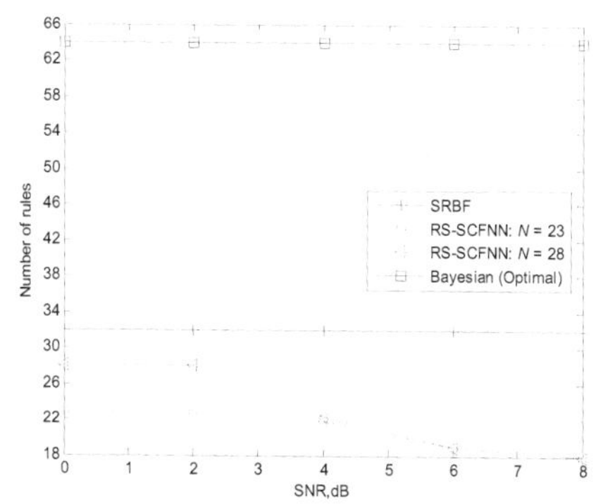

Fig. 3.4 Numbers of hidden nodes for adaptive SRBF and RS-SCFNN beamformers

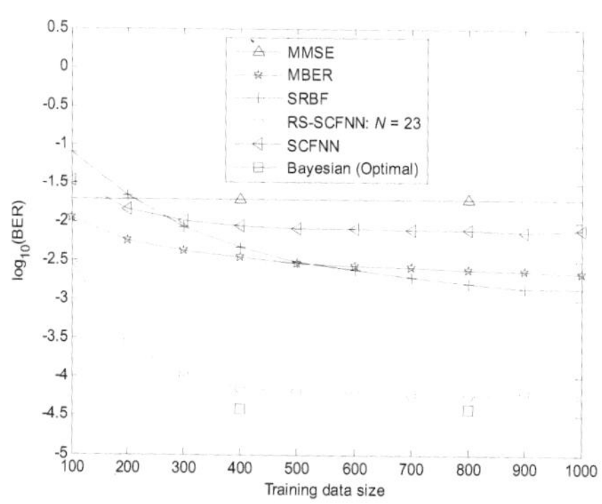

Fig. 3.5 Convergence rates for different adaptive beamformers at SNR = 6 dB

The number of rules for SRBF beamformer is fixed before training and specified by $2^{M-1} = 32$ as done in [47]. Then the BER performance for various kinds of adaptive beamformers is illustrated in Figure 3.3, and the average numbers of rules for various nonlinear adaptive beamformers are plotted in Fig. 3.4. In such rank-deficient system and low amount of training data, the proposed RS-SCFNN beamformers can provide excellent BER performance compared to the classical linear and nonlinear ones. As shown in Figure 3.4, the numbers of rules for adaptive RS-SCFNN beamformer can be determined flexibly at different SNRs, but those for adaptive SRBF one must be fixed to a constant at every SNR. Of course, the SRBF beamformer also can assign different numbers of hidden nodes for various SNRs, but it will need huge manpower to achieve this purpose. The relatively large numbers of rules and bad initial parameters for SRBF easily lead to a slow convergence or poor BER results. However, the proposed RS-SCFNN beamformer can set good initial parameters as specified in Section 3.2 with little fuzzy rules, so the RS-SCFNN has the BER results close to Bayesian solutions. The BER convergence rates for different beamformers are demonstrated in Figure 3.5. We can see that the proposed RS-SCFNN beamformer can obtain satisfactory performance close to Bayesian solutions if the training data size up to 300.

4. Conclusion

This chapter provides different versions of SCFNN-based detectors for various system models to improve the performance of classical nonlinear detectors. For improving the classical RBF, FNN and SCRFNN equalizers in both time-invariant and time-varying channels, a novel FSCFNN DFE has been demonstrated in Section 2. Specifically, FSCFNN DFE is composed of several FSCFNN detectors, each of which corresponds to one feedback input vectors. The fast learning processes, i.e., self-constructing and parameter learning, are adopted in FSCFNN DFE to make it suitable in time-varying environments. The fast learning algorithm of FSCFNN DFE has set conditions on the increase demand of fuzzy rules during the self-constructing algorithm and FSCFNN DFE only activates only one FSCFNN detector at each time instant. Therefore, the computational complexity of FSCFNN DFE is less than that of traditional equalizers. In multi-antenna systems, adaptive beamformers based on SCFNN detectors are also presented in Section 3. By adopting the symmetric property of array input signal space, the RS-SCFNN learning algorithm can be easier than the standard SCFNN one. From the simulations, we can see that the SCFNN-based adaptive beamformers can flexibly and automatically determine structure size themselves for various SNRs. Therefore, we conclude that the adaptive RS-SCFNN beamformer is potentially a better scheme than the SRBF and SCFNN ones. Because the competitors of SCFNN-based detectors, such as RBF and FNN, have been successfully applied to the space-time equalization, turbo equalization, DOA estimation, high-level QAM systems, OOK optical communications and CDMA or OFDM communication systems in the literature (IEEE/IET Journals etc.), the future work for SCFNN detectors could be the extension to the above mentioned systems or the improvement of SCFNN-based detectors based on the issues of determination of threshold $\mu_{\min}$ and the method for simplifying the complexity.

5. References

[1] S. Haykin, Adaptive filter theory (4th Edition), Prentice Hall, 2002.

[2] T.S. Rappaport, Wireless communications: principles and practice (2nd Edition), Prentice Hall, 2002.

[3] J. Litva, T.K.Y. Lo, Digital beamforming in wireless communications, Artech House, 1996.
[4] Y. Gong, X. Hong, "OFDM joint data detection and phase noise cancellation based on minimum mean square prediction error," Signal Process., vol. 89, pp. 502-509, 2009.
[5] M.Y. Alias, A.K. Samingan, S. Chen, L. Hanzo, "Multiple antenna aided OFDM employing minimum bit error rate multiuser detection," Electron. Lett., vol. 39, no. 24, pp. 1769-1770, 2003.
[6] S. Chen, N.N. Ahmad, L. Hanzo, "Adaptive minimum bit error rate beamforming," IEEE Trans. Wirel. Commun., vol. 4, no.2, pp. 341-348, 2005.
[7] J. Li, G. Wei, F. Chen, "On minimum-BER linear multiuser detection for DS-CDMA channels," IEEE Trans. Signal Process., vol. 55, no.3, pp. 1093-1103, 2007.
[8] T.A. Samir, S. Elnoubi, A. Elnashar, "Block-Shannon minimum bit error rate beamforming," IEEE Trans. Veh. Technol., vol. 57, no.5, pp. 2981-2990, 2008.
[9] W. Yao, S. Chen, S. Tan, L. Hanzo, "Minimum bit error rate multiuser Transmission designs using particle swarm optimisation," IEEE Trans. Wirel. Commun., vol. 8, no.10, pp. 5012-5017, 2009.
[10] S. Gollamudi, S. Nagaraj, S. Kapoor, Y.F. Huang, "Set-membership filtering and a set-membership normalized LMS algorithm with an adaptive step size," IEEE Signal Process. Lett., vol. 5, no. 5, pp. 111-114, 1998.
[11] Y.C. Liang, F.P.C. Chin, "Coherent LMS algorithms," IEEE Commun. Lett., vol. 4, no. 3, pp. 92-94, 2000.
[12] S. Choi, T.W. Lee, D. Hong, "Adaptive error-constrained method for LMS algorithms and applications," Signal Process., vol. 85, pp. 1875-1897, 2005.
[13] E.F. Harrington, "A BPSK decision-feedback equalization method robust to phase and timing errors," IEEE Signal Process. Lett., vol. 12, pp. 313-316, 2005.
[14] S. Chen, B. Mulgrew, P.M. Grant, "A clustering technique for digital communications channel equalization using radial basis function networks," IEEE Trans. Neural Netw., vol. 4, no. 4, pp. 570-579, 1993.
[15] J. Montalvão, B. Dorizzi, J. Cesar M. Mota, "Why use Bayesian equalization based on finite data blocks," Signal Process., vol. 81, pp. 137-147, 2001.
[16] S. Chen, B. Mulgrew, S. McLaughlin, "Adaptive Bayesian equalizer with decision feedback," IEEE Trans. Signal Process., vol. 41, no. 9, pp. 2918-2927, 1993.
[17] S. Chen, S. McLaughlin, B. Mulgrew, P.M. Grant, "Bayesian decision feedback equalizer for overcoming co-channel interference," IEE Proc.-Commun., vol. 143, no. 4, pp. 219-225, 1996.
[18] S. Chen, L. Hanzo, A. Wolfgang, "Kernel-based nonlinear beamforming construction using orthogonal forward selection with the fisher ratio class separability measure," IEEE Signal Process. Lett., vol. 11, no. 5, pp. 478-481, 2004.
[19] S. Chen, L. Hanzo, A. Wolfgang, "Nonlinear multiantenna detection methods," EURASIP J Appl. Signal Process., vol. 9, pp. 1225-1237, 2004.
[20] J. Lee, C. Beach, N. Tepedelenlioglu, "A practical radial basis function equalizer," IEEE Trans. Neural Netw., vol. 10, pp. 450-455, 1999.

[21] P.C. Kumar, P. Saratchandran, N. Sundararajan, "Minimal radial basis function neural networks for nonlinear channel equalization," IEE Proc.-Vis. Image Signal Process., vol. 147, no. 5, pp. 428-435, 2000.

[22] M.S. Yee, B.L. Yeap, L. Hanzo, "Radial basis function-assisted turbo equalization," IEEE Trans. Commun., vol. 51, pp. 664-675, 2003.

[23] Wolfgang, S. Chen, L. Hanzo, "Radial basis function network assisted space-time equalisation for dispersive fading environments," Electron. Lett., vol. 40, no. 16, pp. 1006-1007, 2004.

[24] J.B. MacQueen, "Some methods for classification and analysis of multivariate observations," Proceedings of the 5th Berkeley Symposium on Mathematics Statistics and Probability, Berkeley, U.S.A., pp. 281-297, 1967.

[25] R. Assaf, S.E. Assad, Y. Harkouss, "Adaptive equalization for digital channels RBF neural network," Proceedings of the European Conference on Wireless Technology, Paris, France, pp. 347-350, 2005.

[26] R. Assaf, S.E. Assad, Y. Harkouss, "Adaptive equalization of nonlinear time varying-channel using radial basis network," Proceedings of the 2006 International Conference on Information and Communication Technologies, Damascus, Syria, pp. 1866-1871, 2006.

[27] L. Xu, A. Krzyzak, E. Oja, "Rival penalized competitive learning for clustering analysis, RBF net, and curve detection," IEEE Trans. Neural Netw., vol. 4, no. 4, pp. 636-649, 1993.

[28] Y.M. Cheung, "On rival penalization controlled competitive learning for clustering with automatic cluster *number* selection," IEEE Trans. Knowl. Data Eng., vol. 17, no. 11, pp. 1583-1588, 2005.

[29] J. Ma, T. Wang, "A cost-function approach to rival penalized competitive learning (RPCL)," IEEE Trans. Syst. Man Cybern. Part B-Cybern., vol. 36, no. 4, pp. 722-737, 2006.

[30] S. Chen, T. Mei, M. Luo, H. Liang, "Study on a new RPCCL clustering algorithm," Proceedings of the 2007 IEEE International Conference on Mechatronics and Automation, Harbin, China, pp. 299-303, 2007.

[31] X. Qiao, G. Ji, H. Zheng, "An improved rival penalized competitive learning algorithm based on fractal dimension of algae image," Proceedings of the 2008 IEEE Control and Decision Conference, Yantai, China, pp. 199-202, 2008.

[32] S. Siu, G.J. Gibson, C.F.N. Cowan, "Decision feedback equalization using neural network structures and performance comparison with standard architecture," IEE Proc.-Commun., vol. 137, pp. 221-225, 1990.

[33] J. Coloma, R.A. Carrasco, "MLP equaliser for frequency selective time-varying channels," Electron. Lett., vol. 30, pp. 503-504, 1994.

[34] C.H. Chang, S. Siu, C.H. Wei, "Decision feedback equalization using complex backpropagation algorithm," Proceedings of 1997 IEEE International Symposium on Circuits and Systems, Hong Kong, China, pp. 589-592, 1997.

[35] S.S. Yang, C.L. Ho, C.M. Lee, "HBP: improvement in BP algorithm for an adaptive MLP decision feedback equalizer," IEEE Trans. Circuits Syst. II-Express Briefs, vol. 53, no. 3, pp. 240-244, 2006.

[36] S. Siu, S.S. Yang, C.M. Lee, C.L. Ho, "Improving the Back-propagation algorithm using evolutionary strategy," IEEE Trans. Circuits Syst. II-Express Briefs, vol. 54, no. 2, pp. 171-175, 2007.
[37] K. Mahmood, A. Zidouri, A. Zerquine, "Performance analysis of a RLS-based MLP-DFE in time-invariant and time-varying channels," Digit. Signal Prog., vol. 18, no. 3, pp. 307-320, 2008.
[38] S.S. Yang, S. Siu, C.L. Ho, "Analysis of the initial values in split-complex backpropagation algorithm," IEEE Trans. Neural Netw., vol. 19, pp. 1564-1573, 2008.
[39] J.S.R. Jang, C.T. Sun, E. Mizutani, Neuro-fuzzy and soft computing - a computational approach to learning and machine intelligence, Prentice Hall, 1997.
[40] C.H. Lee, Y.C. Lin, "An adaptive neuro-fuzzy filter design via periodic fuzzy neural network," Signal Process., vol. 85, pp. 401-411, 2005.
[41] S. Siu, C.L. Ho, C.M. Lee, "TSK-based decision feedback equalizer using an evolutionary algorithm applied to QAM communication systems," IEEE Trans. Circuits Syst. II-Express Briefs,vol. 52, pp. 596-600, 2005.
[42] F.J. Lin, C.H. Lin, P.H. Shen, "Self-constructing fuzzy neural network speed controller for permanent-magnet synchronous motor drive," IEEE Trans. Fuzzy Syst., vol. 9, no. 5, pp. 751-759, 2001.
[43] W.D. Weng, R.C. Lin, C.T. Hsueh, "The design of an SCFNN based nonlinear channel equalizer," J. Inf. Sci. Eng., vol. 21, pp. 695-709, 2005.
[44] R.C. Lin, W.D. Weng, C.T. Hsueh, "Design of an SCRFNN-based nonlinear channel equaliser," IEE Proc.-Commun., vol. 152, no. 6, pp. 771-779, 2005.
[45] A. Bateman, A. Bateman, Digital communications: design for the real world, Addison Wesley, 1999.
[46] M. Martínez-Ramón, J.L. Rojo-Álvarez, G. Camps-Valls, C.G. Christodoulou, "Kernel antenna array processing," IEEE Trans. Antennas Propag., vol. 55, no. 3, pp. 642-650, 2007.
[47] S. Chen, A. Wolfgang, C.J. Harris, L. Hanzo, "Adaptive nonlinear least bit error-rate detection for symmetrical RBF beamforming," Neural Netw., vol. 21, pp. 358-367, 2008.
[48] S. Chen, A. Wolfgang, C.J. Harris, L. Hanzo, "Symmetric complex-valued RBF receiver for multiple-antenna-aided wireless systems," IEEE Trans. Neural Netw., vol. 19, no. 9, pp. 1657-1663, 2008.
[49] Q. Liang, J.M. Mendel, "Overcoming time-varying co-channel interference using type-2 fuzzy adaptive filter," IEEE Trans. Circuits Syst. II-Express Briefs, vol. 47, pp. 1419-1428, 2000.
[50] Q. Liang, J.M. Mendel, "Equalization of nonlinear time-varying channels using type-2 fuzzy adaptive filters," IEEE Trans. Fuzzy Syst., vol. 8, no. 5, pp. 551-563, 2000.
[51] Y.J. Chang, C.L. Ho, "Improving the BP algorithm using RPCL for FNN-based adaptive equalizers," Proceedings of 2008 National Symposium on Telecommunications, Yunlin, Taiwan, pp. 1385-1388, 2008.
[52] Y.J. Chang, C.L. Ho, "SOFNN-based equalization using rival penalized controlled competitive learning for time-varying environments," Proceedings of 2009

International Conference on Wireless Communication and Signal Processing, Nanjian, China, 2009.

[53] S. Han, I. Lee, W. Pedrycz, "Modified fuzzy c-means and Bayesian equalizer for nonlinear blind channel," Appl. Soft. Comput., vol. 9, pp. 1090-1096, 2009.

[54] J. Choi, A.C. de C. Lima, S. Haykin, "Kalman filter-trained recurrent neural equalizers for time-varying channels," IEEE Trans. Commun., vol. 53, no. 3, pp. 472-480, 2005.

[55] C.F.N. Cowan, S. Semnani, "Time-variant equalization using a novel nonlinear adaptive structure," Int. J. Adapt. Control Signal Process., vol. 12, no. 2, pp. 195-206, 1998.

[56] R. Kohno, "Spatial and temporal communication theory using adaptive antenna array," IEEE Pers. Commun., vol. 5, no. 1, pp. 28-35, 1998.

[57] Ju´nior, A.D.D. Neto, W. Mata, "Determination of multiple direction of arrival in antennas arrays with radial basis functions," Neurocomputing, vol. 70, pp. 55-61, 2006.

[58] Y.J. Chang, S.S. Yang, C.L. Ho, " Fast Self-constructing Fuzzy Neural Network-based Decision Feedback Equaliser in Time-invariant and Time-varying Channels," IET Commun., vol. 4, no. 4, pp. 463-471, 2010.

9

A Stereo Acoustic Echo Canceller Using Cross-Channel Correlation

Shigenobu Minami
Toshiba Corporation
Japan

1. Introduction

Stereo acoustic echo canceller is becoming more and more important as an echo canceller is applied to consumer products like a conversational DTV. However it is well known that if there is strong cross-channel correlation between right and left sounds, it cannot converge well and results in echo path estimation misalignment. This is a serious problem in a conversational DTV because the speaker output sound is combination of a far-end conversational sound, which is essentially monaural, and TV program sound, which has wide variety of sound characteristics, monaural sound, stereo sound or mixture of them. To cope with this problem, many stereo echo cancellation algorithms have been proposed. The methods can be categorized into two approaches. The first one is to de-correlate the stereo sound by introducing independent noise or non-linear post-processing to right and left speaker outputs. This approach is very effective for single source stereo sound case, which covers most of conversational sounds, because the de-correlation prevents rank drop to solve a normal equation in a multi-channel adaptive filtering algorithm. Moreover, it is simple since many traditional adaptation algorithms can be used without any modification. Although the approach has many advantages and therefore widely accepted, it still has an essential problem caused by the de-correlation which results in sound quality change due to insertion of the artificial distortion. Even though the inserted distortion is minimized so as to prevent sound quality degradation, from an entertainment audio equipment view point, such as a conversational DTV, many users do not accept any distortion to the speaker output sound. The second approach is desirable for the entertainment types of equipments because no modification to the speaker outputs is required. In this approach, the algorithms utilize cross-channel correlation change in a stereo sound. This approach is also divided into two approaches, depending on how to utilize the cross-channel correlation change. One widely used approach is affine projection method. If there are small variations in the cross-channel correlation even in a single sound source stereo sound, small un-correlated component appears in each channel. The affine projection method can produce the best direction by excluding the auto-correlation bad effect in each channel and by utilizing the small un-correlated components. This approach has a great advantage since it does not require any modification to the stereo sound, however if the variation in the cross-channel correlation is very small, improvement of the adaptive filter convergence is very small. Since the rank drop problem of the stereo adaptive filter is essentially not solved, we may need slight inserted distortion which reduces merit of this method. Another headache is that the method requires P by P inverse matrix calculation in an each sample. The inverse matrix operation can be relaxed by choosing P as small number, however small P sometimes cannot attain sufficient convergence speed improvement. To attain better performance even by small P, the affine projection method sometimes realized together with sub-band method. Another method categorized in the second approach is "WARP" method. Unlike to affine projection method which utilizes small change in the cross-channel correlation, the method utilizes large change in the cross-channel correlation. This approach is based on the nature of usual conversations. Even though using stereo sound for conversations, most parts of conversations are single talk monaural sound. The cross-channel correlation is usually very high and it remains almost stable during a single talking. A large change happens when talker change or talker's face movement happens. Therefore, the method applies a monaural adaptive filter to single sound source stereo sound and multi-channel (stereo) adaptive filter to non-single sound source stereo sound. Important feature of the method is two monaural adaptive filter estimation results and one stereo adaptive filter estimation result is transformed to each other by using projection matrixes, called WARP matrixes. Since a monaural adaptive filter is applied when a sound is single source stereo sound, we do not need to suffer from the rank problem.

In this chapter, stereo acoustic echo canceller methods, multi-channel least mean square, affine projection and WARP methods, all of them do not need any modification to the speaker output sounds, are surveyed targeting conversational DTV applications. Then WARP method is explained in detail.

2. Stereo acoustic echo canceller problem

2.1 Conversational DTV

Since conversational DTV should keep smooth speech communication even when it is receiving a regular TV program, it requires following functionalities together with traditional DTV systems as shown in Fig. 1.

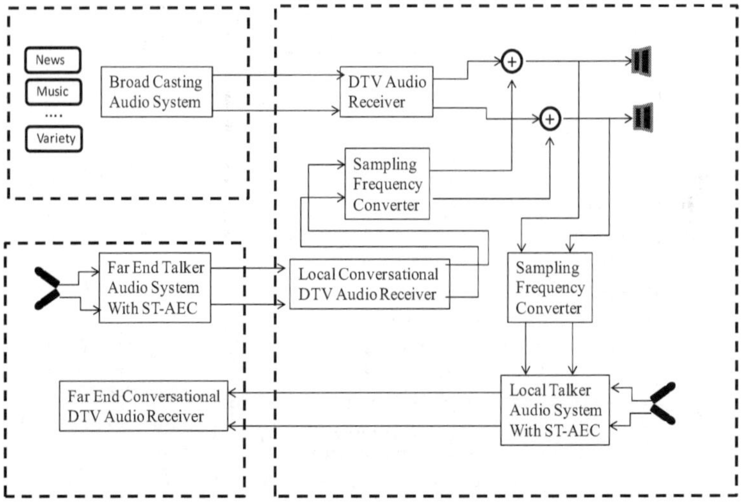

Fig. 1. Audio System Example in a Conversational DTV

1. Mixing of broadcasting sound and communication speech: Two stereo sounds from the DTV audio receiver and local conversational speech decoder are mixed and sent to the stereo speaker system.
2. Sampling frequency conversion: Sampling frequency of DTV sound is usually wider than that of conversational service, such as $f_{SH} = 48kHz$ for DTV sound and $f_S = 16kHz$ for conversational service sound, we need sampling frequency conversion between DTV and conversational service audio parts
3. Stereo acoustic canceller: A stereo acoustic echo canceller is required to prevent howling and speech quality degradation due to acoustic coupling between stereo speaker and microphone.

Among the above special functionalities, the echo canceller for the conversational DTV is technically very challenging because the echo canceller should cancel wide variety of stereo echoes for TV programs as well as stereo speech communications.

2.2 Stereo sound generation model

A stereo acoustic echo canceller system is shown in Fig. 2 with typical stereo sound generation model, where all signals are assumed to be discrete time signals at the kth sampling timing by f_S sampling frequency and the sound generation model is assumed to be linier finite impulse response (FIR) systems which has a sound source signal $x_{Si}(k)$ as an input and stereo sound $x_{Ri}(k)$ and $x_{Li}(k)$ as outputs with additional uncorrelated noises $x'_{URi}(k)$ and $x'_{ULi}(k)$. By using matrix and array notations of the signals as

$$
\begin{aligned}
\mathbf{X}_{Si}(k) &= [\mathbf{x}_{Si}(k), \mathbf{x}_{Si}(k-1), \cdots \mathbf{x}_{Si}(k-P+1)] \\
\mathbf{x}_{Si}(k) &= [x_{Si}(k), x_{Si}(k-1), \cdots x_{Si}(k-N+1)]^T \\
\mathbf{x}_{Ri}(k) &= [x_{Ri}(k), x_{Ri}(k-1), \cdots x_{Ri}(k-N+1)]^T \\
\mathbf{x}_{Li}(k) &= [x_{Li}(k), x_{Li}(k-1), \cdots x_{Li}(k-N+1)]^T \\
\mathbf{x}'_{URi}(k) &= [x'_{URi}(k), x'_{URi}(k-1), \cdots x'_{URi}(k-N+1)]^T \\
\mathbf{x}'_{ULi}(k) &= [x'_{ULi}(k), x'_{ULi}(k-1), \cdots x'_{ULi}(k-N+1)]^T
\end{aligned} \tag{1}
$$

where P and N are impulse response length of the FIR system and tap length of the adaptive filter for each channel, respectively.

Then the FIR system output $\mathbf{x}_i(k)$ is 2N sample array and is expressed as

$$
\mathbf{x}_i(k) = \begin{bmatrix} \mathbf{x}_{Ri}(k) \\ \mathbf{x}_{Li}(k) \end{bmatrix} = \begin{bmatrix} \mathbf{X}_{Si}(k)\mathbf{g}_{Ri}(k) + \mathbf{x}'_{URi}(k) \\ \mathbf{X}_{Si}(k)\mathbf{g}_{Li}(k) + \mathbf{x}'_{ULi}(k) \end{bmatrix}. \tag{2}
$$

where $\mathbf{g}_{Ri}(k)$ and $\mathbf{g}_{Li}(k)$ are P sample impulse responses of the FIR system defined as

$$
\begin{aligned}
\mathbf{g}_{Ri}(k) &= [g_{Ri,0}(k), g_{Ri1}(k), \cdots, g_{Ri,v}(k),, \cdots, g_{Ri,P-1}(k)]^T \\
\mathbf{g}_{Li}(k) &= [g_{Li,0}(k), g_{Li1}(k), \cdots, g_{Li,v}(k),, \cdots, g_{Li,P-1}(k)]^T
\end{aligned}. \tag{3}
$$

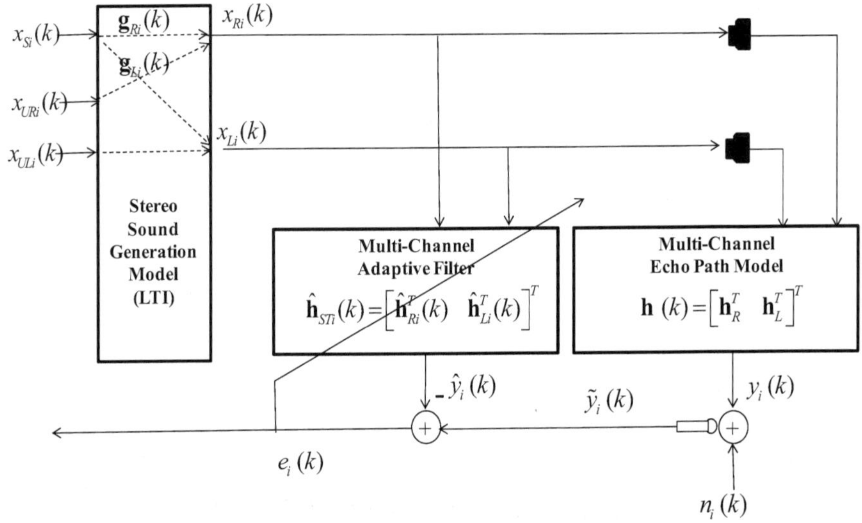

Fig. 2. Traditional Stereo Acoustic Echo Canceller System Configuration with Typical Stereo Sound Generation Model.

In(2), if $\mathbf{g}_{Ri}(k)$ and $\mathbf{g}_{Li}(k)$ are composed of constant array, $\mathbf{g}_{Ri}$ and $\mathbf{g}_{Li}$ during the *ith* period, and small time variant arrays, $\Delta\mathbf{g}_{Ri}(k)$ and $\Delta\mathbf{g}_{Li}(k)$ which are defined as

$$\begin{aligned}
\mathbf{g}_{Ri} &= [g_{Ri,0}, g_{Ri1}, \cdots, g_{Ri,\nu}, \cdots, g_{Ri,P-1}]^T \\
\mathbf{g}_{Li} &= [g_{Li,0}, g_{Li1}, \cdots, g_{Li,\nu}, \cdots, g_{Li,P-1}]^T \\
\Delta\mathbf{g}_{Ri}(k) &= [\Delta g_{Ri,0}(k), \Delta g_{Ri1}(k), \cdots, \Delta g_{Ri,\nu}(k), \cdots, \Delta g_{Ri,P-1}(k)]^T \\
\Delta\mathbf{g}_{Li}(k) &= [\Delta g_{Li,0}(k), \Delta g_{Li1}(k), \cdots, \Delta g_{Li,\nu}(k), \cdots, \Delta g_{Li,P-1}(k)]^T
\end{aligned} \quad (4)$$

(2) is re-written as

$$\begin{bmatrix} \mathbf{x}_{Ri}(k) \\ \mathbf{x}_{Li}(k) \end{bmatrix} = \begin{bmatrix} \mathbf{X}_{Si}(k)\mathbf{g}_{Ri} + \mathbf{X}_{Si}(k)\Delta\mathbf{g}_{Ri}(k) + \mathbf{x}'_{URi}(k) \\ \mathbf{X}_{Si}(k)\mathbf{g}_{Li} + \mathbf{X}_{Si}(k)\Delta\mathbf{g}_{Li}(k) + \mathbf{x}'_{ULi}(k) \end{bmatrix}. \quad (5)$$

This situation is usual in the case of far-end single talking because transfer functions between talker and right and left microphones vary slightly due to talker's small movement. By assuming the components are also un-correlated noise, (5) can be regarded as a linear time invariant system with independent noise components, $x_{URi}(k)$ and $x_{ULi}(k)$, as

$$\begin{bmatrix} \mathbf{x}_{Ri}(k) \\ \mathbf{x}_{Li}(k) \end{bmatrix} = \begin{bmatrix} \mathbf{X}_{Si}(k)\mathbf{g}_{Ri} + \mathbf{x}_{URi}(k) \\ \mathbf{X}_{Si}(k)\mathbf{g}_{Li} + \mathbf{x}_{ULi}(k) \end{bmatrix}. \quad (6)$$

where

$$\mathbf{x}_{URi}(k) = \mathbf{X}_{Si}(k)\Delta\mathbf{g}_{Ri}(k) + \mathbf{x}'_{URi}(k)$$
$$\mathbf{x}_{ULi}(k) = \mathbf{X}_{Si}(k)\Delta\mathbf{g}_{Li}(k) + \mathbf{x}'_{ULi}(k) \quad (7)$$

In (6), if there are no un-correlated noises, we call the situation as strict single talking.
In this chapter, sound source signal($x_{Si}(k)$), uncorrelated noises ($x'_{URi}(k)$ and $x'_{ULi}(k)$) are assumed as independent white Gaussian noise with variance σ_{xi} and σ_{Ni} , respectively.

2.3 Stereo acoustic echo canceller problem

For simplification, only one stereo audio echo canceller for the right side microphone's output signal $\tilde{y}_i(k)$, is explained. This is because the echo canceller for left microphone output is apparently treated as the same way as the right microphone case. As shown in Fig.2, the echo canceller cancels the acoustic echo $y_i(k)$ as

$$e_i(k) = y_i(k) - \hat{y}_i(k) + n_i(k) \quad (8)$$

where $e_i(k)$ is acoustic echo canceller's residual error, $n_i(k)$ is a independent background noise, $\hat{y}_i(k)$ is an FIR adaptive filter output in the stereo echo canceller, which is given by

$$\hat{y}_i(k) = \hat{\mathbf{h}}^T_{Ri}(k)\mathbf{x}_{Ri}(k) + \hat{\mathbf{h}}^T_{Li}(k)\mathbf{x}_{Li}(k) \quad (9)$$

where $\hat{\mathbf{h}}_{Ri}(k)$ and $\hat{\mathbf{h}}_{Li}(k)$ are N tap FIR adaptive filter coefficient arrays.

Error power of the echo canceller for the right channel microphone output, $\sigma^2_{ei}(k)$, is given as:

$$\sigma^2_{ei}(k) = (y_{Ri}(k) - \hat{\mathbf{h}}^T_{STi}(k)\mathbf{x}_i(k) + n_i(k))^2 \quad (10)$$

where $\hat{\mathbf{h}}_{STi}(k)$ is a stereo echo path model defined as

$$\hat{\mathbf{h}}_{STi}(k) = \left[\hat{\mathbf{h}}^T_{Ri}(k) \quad \hat{\mathbf{h}}^T_{Li}(k)\right]^T . \quad (11)$$

Optimum echo path estimation $\hat{\mathbf{h}}_{OPT}$ which minimizes the error power $\sigma^2_e(k)$ is given by solving the linier programming problem as

$$Minimize\left[\sum_{k=0}^{N_{LS}-1} \sigma^2_{ei}(k)\right] \quad (12)$$

where N_{LS} is a number of samples used for optimization. Then the optimum echo path estimation for the *ith* LTI period $\hat{\mathbf{h}}_{OPTi}$ is easily obtained by well known normal equation as

$$\hat{\mathbf{h}}_{OPTi} = \left(\sum_{k=0}^{N_{LS}-1} (\tilde{y}_i(k)\mathbf{x}_i(k))\right)\mathbf{X}^{-1}_{NLSi} \quad (13)$$

where $\mathbf{X}_{NLSi}$ is an auto-correlation matrix of the adaptive filter input signal and is given by

$$\mathbf{X}_{NLSi} = \sum_{k=0}^{N_{LS}-1}(\mathbf{x}_i(k)\mathbf{x}_i^T(k)) = \begin{bmatrix} \mathbf{A}_i & \mathbf{B}_i \\ \mathbf{C}_i & \mathbf{D}_i \end{bmatrix} = \begin{bmatrix} \sum_{k=0}^{N_{LS}-1}(\mathbf{x}_{Ri}(\mathrm{k})\mathbf{x}_{Ri}^T(\mathrm{k})) & \sum_{k=0}^{N_{LS}-1}(\mathbf{x}_{Ri}(\mathrm{k})\mathbf{x}_{Li}^T(\mathrm{k})) \\ \sum_{k=0}^{N_{LS}-1}(\mathbf{x}_{Li}(\mathrm{k})\mathbf{x}_{Ri}^T(\mathrm{k})) & \sum_{k=0}^{N_{LS}-1}(\mathbf{x}_{Li}(\mathrm{k})\mathbf{x}_{Li}^T(\mathrm{k})) \end{bmatrix}. \tag{14}$$

By (14), determinant of $\mathbf{X}_{NLSi}$ is given by

$$\left|\mathbf{X}_{NLSi}\right| = \left|\mathbf{A}_i\right|\left|\mathbf{D}_i - \mathbf{C}_i\mathbf{A}_i^{-1}\mathbf{B}_i\right| . \tag{15}$$

In the case of the stereo generation model which is defined by(2), the sub-matrixes in (14) are given by

$$\begin{aligned}
\mathbf{A}_i &= \sum_{k=0}^{N_{LS}-1}(\mathbf{X}_{Si}(k)\mathbf{G}_{RRi}\mathbf{X}_{Si}^T(k) + 2\mathbf{x}_{URi}(k)(\mathbf{X}_{Si}(k)\mathbf{g}_{Ri})^T + \mathbf{x}_{URi}(k)\mathbf{x}_{URi}^T(k)) \\
\mathbf{B}_i &= \sum_{k=0}^{N_{LS}-1}(\mathbf{X}_{Si}(k)\mathbf{G}_{RLi}\mathbf{X}_{Si}^T(k) + \mathbf{x}_{URi}(k)(\mathbf{X}_{Si}(k)\mathbf{g}_{Ri})^T + \mathbf{x}_{ULi}(k)(\mathbf{X}_{Si}(k)\mathbf{g}_{Ri})^T + \mathbf{x}_{URi}(k)\mathbf{x}_{ULi}^T(k)) \\
\mathbf{C}_i &= \sum_{k=0}^{N_{LS}-1}(\mathbf{X}_{Si}(k)\mathbf{G}_{LRi}\mathbf{X}_{Si}^T(k) + \mathbf{x}_{ULi}(k)(\mathbf{X}_{Si}(k)\mathbf{g}_{Ri})^T + \mathbf{x}_{URi}(k)(\mathbf{X}_{Si}(k)\mathbf{g}_{Li})^T + \mathbf{x}_{ULi}(k)\mathbf{x}_{URi}^T(k)) \\
\mathbf{D}_i &= \sum_{k=0}^{N_{LS}-1}(\mathbf{X}_{Si}(k)\mathbf{G}_{LLi}\mathbf{X}_{Si}^T(k) + 2\mathbf{x}_{ULi}(k)(\mathbf{X}_{Si}(k)\mathbf{g}_{Li})^T + \mathbf{x}_{ULi}(k)\mathbf{x}_{ULi}^T(k))
\end{aligned} .\tag{16}$$

where

$$\mathbf{G}_{RRi} = \mathbf{g}_{Ri}\mathbf{g}_{Ri}^T, \mathbf{G}_{RLi} = \mathbf{g}_{Ri}\mathbf{g}_{Li}^T, \mathbf{G}_{LRi} = \mathbf{g}_{Li}\mathbf{g}_{Ri}^T, \mathbf{G}_{LLi} = \mathbf{g}_{Li}\mathbf{g}_{Li}^T . \tag{17}$$

In the cease of strict single talking where $\mathbf{x}_{URi}(k)$ and $\mathbf{x}_{ULi}(k)$ do not exist, (16) becomes very simple as

$$\begin{aligned}
\mathbf{A}_i &= \sum_{k=0}^{N_{LS}-1}(\mathbf{X}_{Si}(k)\mathbf{G}_{RRi}\mathbf{X}_{Si}^T(k)) \\
\mathbf{B}_i &= \sum_{k=0}^{N_{LS}-1}(\mathbf{X}_{Si}(k)\mathbf{G}_{RLi}\mathbf{X}_{Si}^T(k)) \\
\mathbf{C}_i &= \sum_{k=0}^{N_{LS}-1}(\mathbf{X}_{Si}(k)\mathbf{G}_{LRi}\mathbf{X}_{Si}^T(k)) \\
\mathbf{D}_i &= \sum_{k=0}^{N_{LS}-1}(\mathbf{X}_{Si}(k)\mathbf{G}_{LLi}\mathbf{X}_{Si}^T(k))
\end{aligned} . \tag{18}$$

To check the determinant $\left|\mathbf{X}_{NLSi}\right|$, we calculate $\left|\mathbf{X}_{NLSi}\right|\left|\mathbf{C}_i\right|$ considering $\mathbf{B}_i = \mathbf{C}_i^T$ as

$$\begin{aligned} |\mathbf{X}_{NLSi}||\mathbf{C}_i| &= |\mathbf{A}_i||(\mathbf{D}_i\mathbf{C}_i - \mathbf{C}_i\mathbf{A}_i^{-1}\mathbf{B}_i\mathbf{C}_i| \\ &= |\mathbf{A}_i||(\mathbf{D}_i\mathbf{C}_i - \mathbf{C}_i\mathbf{B}_i\mathbf{C}_i\mathbf{A}_i^{-1}| \end{aligned} \quad . \tag{19}$$

Then $|\mathbf{D}_i\mathbf{C}_i - \mathbf{C}_i\mathbf{B}_i\mathbf{C}_i\mathbf{A}_i^{-1}|$ becomes zero as

$$\begin{aligned} &|\mathbf{D}_i\mathbf{C}_i - \mathbf{C}_i\mathbf{A}_i^{-1}\mathbf{B}_i\mathbf{C}_i| \\ &= \left|\sum_{k=0}^{N_{LS}-1} (\mathbf{X}_{Si}(k)(\mathbf{G}_{LLi} - \mathbf{G}_{LRi}\mathbf{G}^{-1}{}_{RRi}\mathbf{G}_{RLi})\mathbf{X}_{Si}^T(k))\mathbf{X}_{Si}(k)\mathbf{G}_{LRi}\mathbf{X}_{Si}^T(k))\right| \\ &= N\sigma_{xi}^2 \left|\sum_{k=0}^{N_{LS}-1} (\mathbf{X}_{Si}(k)(\mathbf{g}_{Li}^T\mathbf{g}_{Li}(\mathbf{g}_{Li}\mathbf{g}_{Ri}^T - \mathbf{g}_{Li}\mathbf{g}_{Ri}^T(\mathbf{g}_{Ri}\mathbf{g}_{Ri}^T)^{-1}\mathbf{g}_{Ri}\mathbf{g}_{Ri}^T)\mathbf{X}_{Si}^T(k))\right| \\ &= 0 \end{aligned} \quad . \tag{20}$$

Hence no unique solution can be found by solving the normal equation in the case of strict single talking where un-correlated components do not exist. This is a well known stereo adaptive filter cross-channel correlation problem.

3. Stereo acoustic echo canceller methods

To improve problems addressed above, many approaches have been proposed. One widely accepted approach is de-correlation of stereo sound. To avoid the rank drop of the normal equation(13), small distortion such as non-linear processing or modification of phase is added to stereo sound. This approach is simple and effective to endorse convergence of the multi-channel adaptive filter, however it may degrade the stereo sound by the distortion. In the case of entertainment applications, such as conversational DTV, the problem may be serious because customer's requirement for sound quality is usually very high and therefore even small modification to the speaker output sound cannot be accepted. From this view point, approaches which do not need to add any modification or artifacts to the speaker output sound are desirable for the entertainment use. In this section, least square (LS), stereo affine projection (AP), stereo normalized least mean square (NLMS) and WARP methods are reviewed as methods which do not need to change stereo sound itself.

3.1 Gradient method

Gradient method is widely used for solving the quadratic problem iteratively. As a generalized gradient method, let denote M sample orthogonalized error array $\boldsymbol{\varepsilon}_{Mi}(\mathrm{k})$ based on original error array $\mathbf{e}_{Mi}(\mathrm{k})$ as

$$\boldsymbol{\varepsilon}_{Mi}(\mathrm{k}) = \mathbf{R}_i(k)\mathbf{e}_{Mi}(\mathrm{k}) \tag{21}$$

where $\mathbf{e}_{Mi}(\mathrm{k})$ is an M sample error array which is defined as

$$\mathbf{e}_{Mi}(\mathrm{k}) = [e_i(k), e_i(k-1), \cdots e_i(k-M+1)]^T \tag{22}$$

and $\mathbf{R}_i(k)$ is a $M \times M$ matrix which orthogonalizes the auto-correlation matrix $\mathbf{e}_{Mi}(\mathrm{k})\mathbf{e}_{Mi}^T(\mathrm{k})$. The orthogonalized error array is expressed using difference between adaptive filter coefficient array $\hat{\mathbf{h}}_{STi}(\mathrm{k})$ and target stereo echo path $2N$ sample response $\mathbf{h}_{ST}$ as

$$\boldsymbol{\varepsilon}_{Mi}(\mathrm{k}) = \mathbf{R}_i(k)\mathbf{X}_{M2Ni}^T(k)(\mathbf{h}_{ST} - \hat{\mathbf{h}}_{STi}(\mathrm{k})) \tag{23}$$

where $\mathbf{X}_{M2Ni}(k)$ is a Mx2N matrix which is composed of adaptive filter stereo input array as defined by

$$\mathbf{X}_{M2Ni}(k) = [\mathbf{x}_i(k), \mathbf{x}_i(k-1), \cdots \mathbf{x}_i(k-M+1)]. \tag{24}$$

By defining an echo path estimation error array $\mathbf{d}_{STi}(k)$ which is defined as

$$\mathbf{d}_{STi}(k) = \mathbf{h}_{ST} - \hat{\mathbf{h}}_{STi}(\mathrm{k}) \tag{25}$$

estimation error power $\sigma_{\varepsilon i}^2(\mathrm{k})$ is obtained by

$$\sigma_{\varepsilon i}^2(\mathrm{k}) = \boldsymbol{\varepsilon}_{Mi}^T(\mathrm{k})\boldsymbol{\varepsilon}_{Mi}(\mathrm{k}) = \mathbf{d}_{STi}^T(\mathrm{k})\mathbf{Q}_{2N2Ni}(k)\mathbf{d}_{STi}(\mathrm{k}) \tag{26}$$

where

$$\mathbf{Q}_{2N2Ni}(k) = \mathbf{X}_{M2Ni}(k)\mathbf{R}_i^T(k)\mathbf{R}_i(k)\mathbf{X}_{M2Ni}^T(k). \tag{27}$$

Then, (26) is regarded as a quadratic function of $\hat{\mathbf{h}}_{STi}(k)$ as

$$f(\hat{\mathbf{h}}_{STi}(k)) = \frac{1}{2}\hat{\mathbf{h}}_{STi}^T(\mathrm{k})\mathbf{Q}_{2N2Ni}(k)\hat{\mathbf{h}}_{STi}^T(\mathrm{k}) - \hat{\mathbf{h}}_{STi}^T(\mathrm{k})\mathbf{Q}_{2N2Ni}\mathbf{h}_{ST}. \tag{28}$$

For the quadratic function, gradient $\boldsymbol{\Delta}_i(k)$ is given by

$$\boldsymbol{\Delta}_i(k) = -\mathbf{Q}_{2N2Ni}(k)\mathbf{d}_{STi}(\mathrm{k}). \tag{29}$$

Iteration of $\hat{\mathbf{h}}_{STi}(k)$ which minimizes $\sigma_{\varepsilon i}^2(\mathrm{k})$ is given by

$$\begin{aligned} \hat{\mathbf{h}}_{STi}(k+1) &= \hat{\mathbf{h}}_{STi}(k) - \alpha\boldsymbol{\Delta}_i(k) \\ &= \hat{\mathbf{h}}_{STi}(k) + \alpha\mathbf{Q}_{2N2Ni}(k)\mathbf{d}_{STi}(\mathrm{k}) \\ &= \hat{\mathbf{h}}_{STi}(k) + \alpha\mathbf{X}_{M2Ni}(k)\mathbf{R}_i^T(k)\mathbf{R}_i(k)\mathbf{e}_{Mi}(\mathrm{k}) \end{aligned} \tag{30}$$

where α is a constant to determine step size.
Above equation is very generic expression of the gradient method and following approaches are regarded as deviations of this iteration.

3.2 Least Square (LS) method (M=2N)

From(30), the estimation error power between estimated adaptive filter coefficients and stereo echo path response, $\mathbf{d}_i^T(k)\mathbf{d}_i(k)$ is given by

$$\mathbf{d}_i^T(k+1)\mathbf{d}_i(k+1)=\mathbf{d}_i^T(k)(\mathbf{I}_{2N}-\alpha\mathbf{Q}_{2N2Ni}(k))(\mathbf{I}_{2N}-\alpha\mathbf{Q}_{2N2Ni}(k))^T\mathbf{d}_i(k) \quad (31)$$

where $\mathbf{I}_{2N}$ is a $2N\times 2N$ identity matrix. Then the fastest convergence is obtained by finding $\mathbf{R}_i(k)$ which orthogonalizes and minimizes eigenvalue variance in $\mathbf{Q}_{2N2Ni}(k)$.
If M=2N, $\mathbf{X}_{2M2Ni}(k)$ is symmetric square matrix as

$$\mathbf{X}_{M2Ni}(k)=\mathbf{X}_{M2Ni}^T(k) \quad (32)$$

and if $\mathbf{X}_{M2Ni}(k)\cdot\mathbf{X}_{M2Ni}^T(k)(=\mathbf{X}_{M2Ni}^T(k)\cdot\mathbf{X}_{M2Ni}(k))$ is a regular matrix so that inverse matrix exists, $\mathbf{R}_i^T(k)\mathbf{R}_i(k)$ which orthogonalizes $\mathbf{Q}_{2N2Ni}(k)$ is given by

$$\mathbf{R}_i^T(k)\mathbf{R}_i(k)=(\mathbf{X}_{2N2Ni}^T(k)\mathbf{X}_{2N2Ni}(k))^{-1} \quad (33)$$

By substituting (33) for (30)

$$\hat{\mathbf{h}}_{STi}(k+1)=\hat{\mathbf{h}}_{STi}(k)+\alpha\mathbf{X}_{2N2Ni}(k)(\mathbf{X}_{2N2Ni}^T(k)\mathbf{X}_{2N2Ni}(k))^{-1}\mathbf{e}_{Ni}(\mathrm{k}) \quad (34)$$

Assuming initial tap coefficient array as zero vector and $\alpha=0$ during 0 to 2N-1th samples and $\alpha=1$ at 2Nth sample , (34) can be re-written as

$$\hat{\mathbf{h}}_{STi}(2N)=\mathbf{X}_{2N2Ni}(2\mathrm{N}\text{-}1)(\mathbf{X}_{2N2Ni}^T(2\mathrm{N}\text{-}1)\mathbf{X}_{2N2Ni}(2\mathrm{N}\text{-}1))^{-1}\mathbf{y}_i(2\mathrm{N}\text{-}1) \quad (35)$$

where $\mathbf{y}_i(\mathrm{k})$ is $2N$ sample echo path output array and is defined as

$$\mathbf{y}_i(\mathrm{k})=[y_i(k),y_i(k-1),\cdots y_i(k-2N+1)]^T \quad (36)$$

This iteration is done only once at $2N-1th$ sample. If $N_{LS}=2N$, inverse matrix term in (35) is written as

$$\mathbf{X}_{2N2Ni}^T(k)\mathbf{X}_{2N2Ni}(k)=\sum_{k=0}^{N_{LS}-1}(\mathbf{x}_i(k)\mathbf{x}_i^T(k))=\mathbf{X}_{NLSi} \quad (37)$$

Comparing (13) and (35) with (37), it is found that LS method is a special case of gradient method when M equals to 2N.

3.3 Stereo Affine Projection (AP) method (M=P$\leq$N)

Stereo affine projection method is assumed as a case when M is chosen as FIR response length P in the LTI system. This approach is very effective to reduce 2Nx2N inverse matrix operations in LS method to PxP operations when the stereo generation model is assumed to be LTI system outputs from single WGN signal source with right and left channel independent noises as shown in Fig.2. For the sake of explanation, we define stereo sound signal matrix $\mathbf{X}_{P2Ni}(k)$ which is composed of right and left signal matrix $\mathbf{X}_{Ri}(k)$ and $\mathbf{X}_{Li}(k)$ for P samples as

$$\mathbf{X}_{P2Ni}(k)=\begin{bmatrix}\mathbf{X}_{Ri}^T(k) & \mathbf{X}_{Li}^T(k)\end{bmatrix}^T=\begin{bmatrix}\mathbf{X}_{2Si}(k)\mathbf{G}_{Ri}^T+\mathbf{X}_{URi}(k)\\ \mathbf{X}_{2Si}(k)\mathbf{G}_{Li}^T+\mathbf{X}_{ULi}(k)\end{bmatrix} \quad (38)$$

where

$$\mathbf{X}_{2Si}(k)=[\mathbf{x}_{Si}(k),\mathbf{x}_{Si}(k-1),\cdots\mathbf{x}_{Si}(k-2P+2)] \tag{39}$$

$\mathbf{X}_{URi}(k)$ and $\mathbf{X}_{ULi}(k)$ are un-correlated signal matrix defined as

$$\begin{aligned}\mathbf{X}_{URi}(k)&=[\mathbf{x}_{URi}(k),\mathbf{x}_{URi}(k-1),\cdots\mathbf{x}_{URi}(k-P+1)]\\ \mathbf{X}_{ULi}(k)&=[\mathbf{x}_{ULi}(k),\mathbf{x}_{ULi}(k-1),\cdots\mathbf{x}_{ULi}(k-P+1)]\end{aligned} \tag{40}$$

$\mathbf{G}_{Ri}$ and $\mathbf{G}_{Li}$ are source to microphones response (2P-1)xP matrixes and are defined as

$$\mathbf{G}_{Ri}=\begin{bmatrix}\mathbf{g}_{2R,0,i}^{T}\\ \mathbf{g}_{2R,1,i}^{T}\\ \cdots\\ \mathbf{g}_{2R,P-1,i}^{T}\end{bmatrix}=\begin{bmatrix}\mathbf{g}_{Ri}^{T} & 0 & \cdots & 0\\ 0 & \mathbf{g}_{Ri}^{T} & \ddots & 0\\ 0 & 0 & \cdots & 0\\ 0 & 0 & \cdots & \mathbf{g}_{Ri}^{T}\end{bmatrix},\mathbf{G}_{Li}=\begin{bmatrix}\mathbf{g}_{2RL,0,i}^{T}\\ \mathbf{g}_{2L,1,i}^{T}\\ \cdots\\ \mathbf{g}_{2L,P-1,i}^{T}\end{bmatrix}=\begin{bmatrix}\mathbf{g}_{Li}^{T} & 0 & \cdots & 0\\ 0 & \mathbf{g}_{Li}^{T} & \ddots & 0\\ 0 & 0 & \cdots & 0\\ 0 & 0 & \cdots & \mathbf{g}_{Li}^{T}\end{bmatrix}. \tag{41}$$

As explained by(31), $\mathbf{Q}_{2N2Ni}(k)$ determines convergence speed of the gradient method. In this section, we derive affine projection method by minimizing the max-min eigenvalue variance in $\mathbf{Q}_{2N2Ni}(k)$. Firstly, the auto-correlation matrix is expressed by sub-matrixes for each stereo channel as

$$\mathbf{Q}_{N2Ni}(k)=\begin{bmatrix}\mathbf{Q}_{ANNi}(k) & \mathbf{Q}_{BNNi}(k)\\ \mathbf{Q}_{CNNi}(k) & \mathbf{Q}_{DNNi}(k)\end{bmatrix} \tag{42}$$

where $\mathbf{Q}_{ANNi}(k)$ and $\mathbf{Q}_{DNNi}(k)$ are right and left channel auto-correlation matrixes, $\mathbf{Q}_{BNNi}(k)$ and $\mathbf{Q}_{CNNi}(k)$ are cross channel-correlation matrixes. These sub-matrixes are given by

$$\begin{aligned}&\mathbf{Q}_{ANNi}(k)=\mathbf{X}_{2Si}(k)\mathbf{G}_{Ri}^{T}\mathbf{R}_{i}^{T}(k)\mathbf{R}_{i}(k)\mathbf{G}_{Ri}\mathbf{X}_{2Si}^{T}(k)+\mathbf{X}_{URi}(k)\mathbf{R}_{i}^{T}(k)\mathbf{R}_{i}(k)\mathbf{X}_{URi}^{T}(k)\\ &+2\mathbf{X}_{2Si}(k)\mathbf{R}_{i}^{T}(k)\mathbf{R}_{i}(k)\mathbf{X}_{URi}^{T}(k)\\ &\mathbf{Q}_{BNNi}(k)=\mathbf{X}_{2Si}(k)\mathbf{G}_{Ri}^{T}\mathbf{R}_{i}^{T}(k)\mathbf{R}_{i}(k)\mathbf{G}_{Li}\mathbf{X}_{2Si}^{T}(k)+\mathbf{X}_{URi}(k)\mathbf{R}_{i}^{T}(k)\mathbf{R}_{i}(k)\mathbf{X}_{ULi}^{T}(k)\\ &+2\mathbf{X}_{URi}(k)\mathbf{R}_{i}^{T}(k)\mathbf{R}_{i}(k)\mathbf{X}_{ULi}^{T}(k)\\ &\mathbf{Q}_{CNNi}(k)=\mathbf{X}_{2Si}(k)\mathbf{G}_{Li}^{T}\mathbf{R}_{i}^{T}(k)\mathbf{R}_{i}(k)\mathbf{G}_{Ri}\mathbf{X}_{2Si}^{T}(k)+\mathbf{X}_{ULi}(k)\mathbf{R}_{i}^{T}(k)\mathbf{R}_{i}(k)\mathbf{X}_{URi}^{T}(k)\\ &+2\mathbf{X}_{ULi}(k)\mathbf{R}_{i}^{T}(k)\mathbf{R}_{i}(k)\mathbf{X}_{UTi}^{T}(k)\\ &\mathbf{Q}_{DNNi}(k)=\mathbf{X}_{2Si}(k)\mathbf{G}_{Li}^{T}\mathbf{R}_{i}^{T}(k)\mathbf{R}_{i}(k)\mathbf{G}_{Li}\mathbf{X}_{2Si}^{T}(k)+\mathbf{X}_{ULi}(k)\mathbf{R}_{i}^{T}(k)\mathbf{R}_{i}(k)\mathbf{X}_{ULi}^{T}(k)\\ &+2\mathbf{X}_{2Si}(k)\mathbf{R}_{i}^{T}(k)\mathbf{R}_{i}(k)\mathbf{X}_{ULi}^{T}(k)\end{aligned} \tag{43}$$

Since the iteration process in (30) is an averaging process, the auto-correlation matrix $\mathbf{Q}_{2N2Ni}(k)$ is approximated by using expectation value of it, $\tilde{\mathbf{Q}}_{2N2Ni}(k)=\langle\mathbf{Q}_{2N2Ni}(k)\rangle$. Then expectation values for sub-matrixes in (42) are simplified applying statistical independency between sound source signal and noises and *Tlz* function defined in Appendix as

$$\begin{aligned}
\tilde{\mathbf{Q}}_{ANNi} &= Tlz(\langle \tilde{\mathbf{X}}_{2Si}(k)\mathbf{G}_{Ri}^T\mathbf{R}_i^T(k)\mathbf{R}_i(k)\mathbf{G}_{Ri}\tilde{\mathbf{X}}_{2Si}^T(k)\rangle) + Tlz(\langle \tilde{\mathbf{X}}_{URi}(k)\mathbf{R}_i^T(k)\mathbf{R}_i(k)\tilde{\mathbf{X}}_{URi}(k)\rangle) \\
\tilde{\mathbf{Q}}_{BNNi} &= Tlz(\langle \tilde{\mathbf{X}}_{2Si}(k)\mathbf{G}_{Ri}^T\mathbf{R}_i^T(k)\mathbf{R}_i(k)\mathbf{G}_{Li}\tilde{\mathbf{X}}_{2Si}^T(k)\rangle) \\
\tilde{\mathbf{Q}}_{CNNi} &= Tlz(\langle \tilde{\mathbf{X}}_{2Si}(k)\mathbf{G}_{Li}^T\mathbf{R}_i^T(k)\mathbf{R}_i(k)\mathbf{G}_{Ri}\tilde{\mathbf{X}}_{2Si}^T(k)\rangle) \\
\tilde{\mathbf{Q}}_{DNNi} &= Tlz(\langle \tilde{\mathbf{X}}_{2Si}(k)\mathbf{G}_{Li}^T\mathbf{R}_i^T(k)\mathbf{R}_i(k)\mathbf{G}_{Li}\tilde{\mathbf{X}}_{2Si}(k)\rangle) + Tlz(\langle \tilde{\mathbf{X}}_{ULi}(k)\mathbf{R}_i^T(k)\mathbf{R}_i(k)\tilde{\mathbf{X}}_{ULi}(k)\rangle)
\end{aligned} \tag{44}$$

where

$$\begin{aligned}
\tilde{\mathbf{X}}_{2Si}(k) &= [\tilde{\mathbf{x}}_{2Si}(k), \tilde{\mathbf{x}}_{2Si}(k-1), \cdots \tilde{\mathbf{x}}_{2Si}(k-P+1)]^T \\
\tilde{\mathbf{X}}_{URi}(k) &= [\tilde{\mathbf{x}}_{URi}(k), \tilde{\mathbf{x}}_{URi}(k-1), \cdots \tilde{\mathbf{x}}_{URi}(k-P+1)] \\
\tilde{\mathbf{X}}_{ULi}(k) &= [\tilde{\mathbf{x}}_{ULi}(k), \tilde{\mathbf{x}}_{ULi}(k-1), \cdots \tilde{\mathbf{x}}_{ULi}(k-P+1)]
\end{aligned} \tag{45}$$

with

$$\begin{aligned}
\tilde{\mathbf{x}}_{2Si}(k) &= [x_{Si}(k), x_{Si}(k-1), \cdots x_{Si}(k-2p+2)]^T \\
\tilde{\mathbf{x}}_{URi}(k) &= [x_{URi}(k), x_{URi}(k-1), \cdots x_{URi}(k-p+1)]^T \\
\tilde{\mathbf{x}}_{ULi}(k) &= [x_{ULi}(k), x_{ULi}(k-1), \cdots x_{ULi}(k-p+1)]^T
\end{aligned} . \tag{46}$$

Applying matrix operations to $\mathbf{Q}_{2N2Ni}$, a new matrix $\mathbf{Q}'_{2N2Ni}$ which has same determinant as $\mathbf{Q}_{2N2Ni}$ is given by

$$\mathbf{Q}'_{2N2Ni}(k) = \begin{bmatrix} \mathbf{Q}'_{ANNi}(k) & 0 \\ 0 & \mathbf{Q}'_{DNNi}(k) \end{bmatrix} \tag{47}$$

where

$$\mathbf{Q}'_{ANNi} = Tlz(\mathbf{Q}''_{ANNi}), \mathbf{Q}'_{DNNi} = Tlz(\mathbf{Q}''_{DNNi}) . \tag{48}$$

Since both $\tilde{\mathbf{X}}_{2Si}(k)\mathbf{G}_{Ri}^T$ and $\tilde{\mathbf{X}}_{2Si}(k)\mathbf{G}_{Li}^T$ are symmetric PxP square matrixes, $\mathbf{Q}''_{ANNi}$ and $\mathbf{Q}''_{BNNi}$ are re-written as

$$\begin{aligned}
\mathbf{Q}''_{ANNi} &= \langle \tilde{\mathbf{X}}_{2Si}(k)\mathbf{G}_{Ri}^T\mathbf{R}_i^T(k)\mathbf{R}_i(k)\mathbf{G}_{Ri}\tilde{\mathbf{X}}_{2Si}^T(k) + \tilde{\mathbf{X}}_{2Si}(k)\mathbf{G}_{Li}^T\mathbf{R}_i^T(k)\mathbf{R}_i(k)\mathbf{G}_{Li}\tilde{\mathbf{X}}_{2Si}^T(k)\rangle \\
&+ \langle \tilde{\mathbf{X}}_{URi}(k)\mathbf{R}_i^T(k)\mathbf{R}_i(k)\tilde{\mathbf{X}}_{URi}^T(k)\rangle \\
&= \langle \tilde{\mathbf{X}}_{2Si}(k)(\mathbf{G}_{Ri}^T\mathbf{G}_{Ri} + \mathbf{G}_{Li}^T\mathbf{G}_{Li})\tilde{\mathbf{X}}_{2Si}^T(k)\rangle \mathbf{R}_i^T(k)\mathbf{R}_i(k) + \langle \tilde{\mathbf{X}}_{URi}(k)\tilde{\mathbf{X}}_{URi}^T(k)\rangle \mathbf{R}_i^T(k)\mathbf{R}_i(k) . \\
&= (N\sigma_{Xi}^2(\mathbf{G}_{Ri}\mathbf{G}_{Ri}^T + \mathbf{G}_{Li}\mathbf{G}_{Li}^T) + N\sigma_{Ni}^2\mathbf{I}_P)\mathbf{R}_i^T(k)\mathbf{R}_i(k) \\
\mathbf{Q}''_{DNNi} &= N\sigma_{Ni}^2\mathbf{I}_P\mathbf{R}_i^T(k)\mathbf{R}_i(k)
\end{aligned} \tag{49}$$

As evident by(47), (48) and(49), $\mathbf{Q}'_{2N2Ni}(k)$ is composed of major matrix $\mathbf{Q}'_{ANNi}(k)$ and noise matrix $\mathbf{Q}'_{DNNi}(k)$. In the case of single talking where sound source signal power σ_X^2 is much larger than un-correlated signal power σ_{Ni}^2, $\mathbf{R}_i^T(k)\mathbf{R}_i(k)$ which minimizes eigenvalue spread in $\mathbf{Q}_{2N2Ni}(k)$ so as to attain the fastest convergence is given by making $\mathbf{Q}''_{ANNi}$ as a identity matrix by setting $\mathbf{R}_i^T(k)\mathbf{R}_i(k)$ as

$$\mathbf{R}_i^T(k)\mathbf{R}_i(k) \simeq (N\sigma_{Xi}^2(\mathbf{G}_{Ri}\mathbf{G}_{Ri}^T + \mathbf{G}_{Li}\mathbf{G}_{Li}^T))^{-1} \tag{50}$$

In other cases such as double talking or no talk situations, where we assume σ_X^2 is almost zero, $\mathbf{R}_i^T(k)\mathbf{R}_i(k)$ which orthogonalizes $\mathbf{Q}''_{ANNi}$ is given by

$$\mathbf{R}_i^T(k)\mathbf{R}_i(k) \simeq (N\sigma_{Ni}^2\mathbf{I}_P)^{-1} \tag{51}$$

Summarizing the above discussions, the fastest convergence is attained by setting $\mathbf{R}_i^T(k)\mathbf{R}_i(k)$ as

$$\mathbf{R}_i^T(k)\mathbf{R}_i(k) = \left(\mathbf{X}_{P2Ni}^T(k)\mathbf{X}_{P2Ni}(k)\right)^{-1}. \tag{52}$$

Since

$$\begin{aligned}
&\left\langle \mathbf{X}_{P2Ni}^T(k)\mathbf{X}_{P2Ni}(k)\right\rangle = \\
&\left\langle \begin{bmatrix} \mathbf{G}_{Ri}\mathbf{X}_{2Si}^T(k) + \mathbf{X}_{URi}^T(k) & \mathbf{G}_{Li}\mathbf{X}_{2Si}^T(k) + \mathbf{X}_{ULi}^T(k)\end{bmatrix} \begin{bmatrix} \mathbf{X}_{2Si}(k)\mathbf{G}_{Ri}^T + \mathbf{X}_{URi}(k) \\ \mathbf{X}_{2Si}(k)\mathbf{G}_{Li}^T + \mathbf{X}_{ULi}(k)\end{bmatrix}\right\rangle \\
&= \left\langle \mathbf{G}_{Ri}\mathbf{X}_{2Si}^T(k)\mathbf{X}_{2Si}(k)\mathbf{G}_{Ri}^T + \mathbf{G}_{Li}\mathbf{X}_{2Si}^T(k)\mathbf{X}_{2Si}(k)\mathbf{G}_{Li}^T + \mathbf{X}_{URi}^T(k)\mathbf{X}_{URi}(k) + \mathbf{X}_{ULi}^T(k)\mathbf{X}_{ULi}(k)\right\rangle \\
&\simeq N\sigma_{Xi}^2(\mathbf{G}_{Ri}\mathbf{G}_{Ri}^T + \mathbf{G}_{Li}\mathbf{G}_{Li}^T) + 2N\sigma_{Ni}^2\mathbf{I}_P
\end{aligned} \tag{53}$$

By substituting (52) for (30), we obtain following affine projection iteration :

$$\hat{\mathbf{h}}_{STi}(k+1) = \hat{\mathbf{h}}_{STi}(k) + \alpha\mathbf{X}_i(k)(\mathbf{X}_{P2Ni}^T(k)\mathbf{X}_{P2Ni}(k))^{-1}\mathbf{e}_{Pi}(\mathrm{k}). \tag{54}$$

In an actual implementation α is replaced by $\boldsymbol{\mu}$ for forgetting factor and $\delta\mathrm{I}$ is added to the inverse matrix to avoid zero division as shown bellow.

$$\hat{\mathbf{h}}_{ST}(k+1) = \hat{\mathbf{h}}_{ST}(k) + \alpha\mathbf{X}_{P2Ni}(\mathrm{k})[\mathbf{X}_{P2Ni}^T(\mathrm{k})\mathbf{X}_{P2Ni}(\mathrm{k}) + \delta\mathrm{I}]^{-1}\boldsymbol{\mu}\mathbf{e}_{Pi}(k) \tag{55}$$

where $\delta(\ll 1)$ is very small positive value and

$$\boldsymbol{\mu} = diag[1,(1-\mu),\cdots,(1-\mu)^{p-1}]. \tag{56}$$

The method can be intuitively understood using geometrical explanation in Fig. 3. As seen here, from a estimated coefficients in a k-1th plane a new direction is created by finding the nearest point on the i th plane in the case of traditional NLMS approach. On the other hand, affine projection creates the best direction which targets a location included in the both i-1 and i th plane.

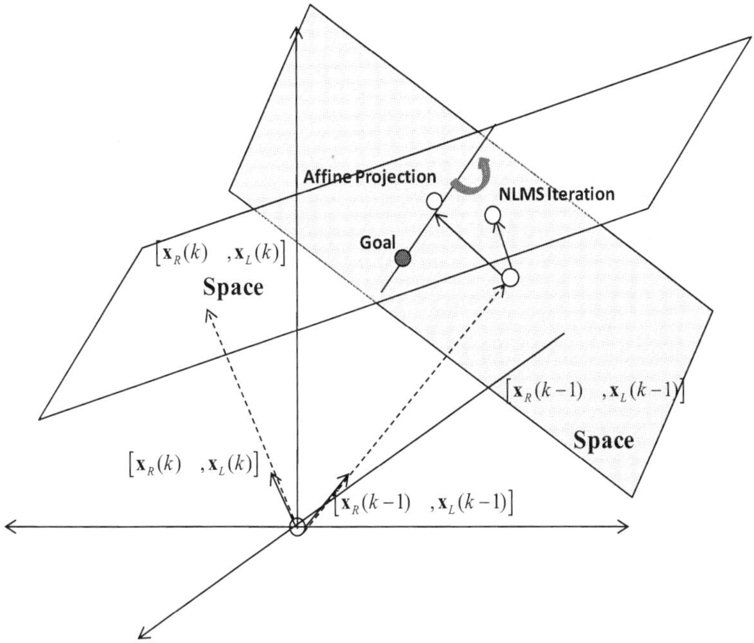

Fig. 3. Very Simple Example for Affine Method

3.4 Stereo Normalized Least Mean Square (NLMS) method (M=1)

Stereo NLMS method is a case when M=1 of the gradient method.
Equation (54) is re-written when M =1 as

$$\hat{\mathbf{h}}_{STi}(k+1)=\hat{\mathbf{h}}_{STi}(k)+\alpha\mathbf{x}_i(k)(\mathbf{x}_{Ri}^T(k)\mathbf{x}_{Ri}(k)+\mathbf{x}_{Li}^T(k)\mathbf{x}_{Li}(k))^{-1}e_i(\mathrm{k}) \tag{57}$$

It is well known that convergence speed of (57) depends on the smallest and largest eigenvalue of the matrix $\mathbf{Q}_{2N2Ni}$. In the case of the stereo generation model in Fig.2 for single talking with small right and left noises, we obtain following determinant of $\mathbf{Q}_{2N2Ni}$ for M=1 as

$$\begin{aligned}\left|\mathbf{Q}_{2N2Ni}(k)\right| &= \left|\mathbf{x}_i(k)(\mathbf{x}_i^T(k)\mathbf{x}_i(k))^{-1}\mathbf{x}_i^T(k)\right| \\ &\simeq (\mathbf{g}_{Ri}^T\mathbf{g}_{Ri}+\mathbf{g}_{Li}^T\mathbf{g}_{Li})^{-1}\left|(\mathbf{g}_{Ri}\mathbf{g}_{Ri}^T+\mathbf{g}_{Li}\mathbf{g}_{Li}^T)\right|\left|\sigma_N^2\mathbf{I}_N\right|\end{aligned} \tag{58}$$

If eigenvalue of $\mathbf{g}_{Ri}\mathbf{g}_{Ri}^T+\mathbf{g}_{Li}\mathbf{g}_{Li}^T$ are given as

$$\left|(\mathbf{g}_{Ri}\mathbf{g}_{Ri}^T+\mathbf{g}_{Li}\mathbf{g}_{Li}^T)\right| = \lambda_{\min i}^2\cdots\lambda_{\max i}^2 \tag{59}$$

where $\lambda_{\min i}^2$ and $\lambda_{\max i}^2$ are the smallest and largest eigenvalues, respectively.

$\left|\mathbf{Q}_{2N2Ni}(k)\right|$ is given by assuming un-correlated noise power σ_{Ni}^2 is very small ($\sigma_{Ni}^2 \ll \lambda_{\min i}^2$) as

$$\left|\mathbf{Q}_{2N2Ni}(k)\right| = (\mathbf{g}_{Ri}^T\mathbf{g}_{Ri} + \mathbf{g}_{Li}^T\mathbf{g}_{Li})^{-1} \cdot \sigma_{Ni}^2 \cdots \sigma_{Ni}^2 \cdot \lambda_{\min i}^2 \cdots \lambda_{\max i}^2 \tag{60}$$

Hence, it is shown that stereo NLMS echo-canceller's convergence speed is largely affected by the ratio between the largest eigenvalue of $\mathbf{g}_{Ri}\mathbf{g}_{Ri}^T + \mathbf{g}_{Li}\mathbf{g}_{Li}^T$ and non-correlated signal power σ_{Ni}^2. If the un-correlated sound power is very small in single talking, the stereo NLMS echo canceller's convergence speed becomes very slow.

3.5 Double adaptive filters for Rapid Projection (WARP) method

Naming of the WARP is that this algorithm projects the optimum solution between monaural space and stereo space. Since this algorithm dynamically changes the types of adaptive filters between monaural and stereo observing sound source characteristics, we do not need to suffer from rank drop problem caused by strong cross-channel correlation in stereo sound. The algorithm was originally developed for the acoustic echo canceller in a pseudo-stereo system which creates artificial stereo effect by adding delay and/or loss to a monaural sound. The algorithm has been extended to real stereo sound by introducing residual signal after removing the cross-channel correlation.

In this section, it is shown that WARP method is derived as an extension of affine projection which has been shown in 3.3.

By introducing error matrix $\mathbf{E}_i(k)$ which is defined by

$$\mathbf{E}_i(k) = \left[\mathbf{e}_{Pi}(k) \quad \mathbf{e}_{Pi}(k-1) \quad \cdots \quad \mathbf{e}_{Pi}(k-p+1)\right] \tag{61}$$

iteration of the stereo affine projection method in (54) is re-written as

$$\hat{\mathbf{H}}_{STi}(k+1) = \hat{\mathbf{H}}_{STi}(k) + \alpha\mathbf{X}_{P2Ni}(k)(\mathbf{X}_{P2Ni}^T(k)\mathbf{X}_{P2Ni}(k))^{-1}\mathbf{E}_i(k) \tag{62}$$

where

$$\hat{\mathbf{H}}_{STi}(k) = \left[\hat{\mathbf{h}}_{STi}(k) \quad \hat{\mathbf{h}}_{STi}(k-1) \quad \cdots \quad \hat{\mathbf{h}}_{STi}(k-p+1)\right] \tag{63}$$

In the case of strict single talking, following assumption is possible in the *ith* LTI period by (53)

$$\left\langle \mathbf{X}_{PNi}^T(k)\mathbf{X}_{PNi}(k) \right\rangle \cong \mathbf{G}_{RRLLi} \tag{64}$$

where $\mathbf{G}_{RRLLi}$ is a PxP symmetric matrix as

$$\mathbf{G}_{RRLLi} = N\sigma_{Xi}^2(\mathbf{G}_{Ri}\mathbf{G}_{Ri}^T + \mathbf{G}_{Li}\mathbf{G}_{Li}^T) \tag{65}$$

By assuming $\mathbf{G}_{RRLLi}$ as a regular matrix, (62) can be re-written as

$$\hat{\mathbf{H}}_{STi}(k+1)\mathbf{G}_{RRLLi} = \hat{\mathbf{H}}_{STi}(k)\mathbf{G}_{RRLLi} + \alpha\mathbf{X}_{P2Ni}(k)\mathbf{E}_i(k) \tag{66}$$

Re-defining echo path estimation matrix $\hat{\mathbf{H}}_{STi}(k)$ by a new matrix $\hat{\mathbf{H}}'_{STi}(k)$ which is defined by

$$\hat{\mathbf{H}}'_{STi}(k)=\hat{\mathbf{H}}_{STi}(k)\mathbf{G}_{RRLLi} \tag{67}$$

(66) is re-written as

$$\hat{\mathbf{H}}'_{STi}(k+1)=\hat{\mathbf{H}}'_{STi}(k)+\alpha\dot{\mathbf{X}}_{P2Ni}(k)\mathbf{E}_i(k) \tag{68}$$

Then the iteration is expressed using signal matrix $\mathbf{X}_{2Si}(k)$ as

$$\hat{\mathbf{H}}'_{STi}(k+1)=\hat{\mathbf{H}}'_{STi}(k)+\alpha\begin{bmatrix}\mathbf{X}_{2Si}(k)\mathbf{G}_{Ri}^T+\mathbf{X}_{URi}(k)\\ \mathbf{X}_{2Si}(k)\mathbf{G}_{Li}^T+\mathbf{X}_{ULi}(k)\end{bmatrix}\mathbf{E}_i(k) \tag{69}$$

In the case of strict single talking where no un-correlated signals exist, and if we can assume $\mathbf{G}_{Li}$ is assumed to be an output of a LTI system $\mathbf{G}_{RLi}$ which is PxP symmetric regular matrix with input $\mathbf{G}_{Ri}$, then (69) is given by

$$\begin{gathered}\begin{bmatrix}\hat{\mathbf{H}}'_{STRi}(k+1)\\ \hat{\mathbf{H}}'_{STLi}(k+1)\end{bmatrix}=\begin{bmatrix}\hat{\mathbf{H}}'_{STRi}(k)\\ \hat{\mathbf{H}}'_{STLi}(k)\end{bmatrix}+\alpha\begin{bmatrix}\mathbf{X}_{2Si}(k)\mathbf{G}_{Ri}\mathbf{E}_i(k)\\ \mathbf{X}_{2Si}(k)\mathbf{G}_{Ri}\mathbf{G}_i\mathbf{E}_i(k)\end{bmatrix}\\ \begin{bmatrix}\hat{\mathbf{H}}'_{STRi}(k+1)\\ \hat{\mathbf{H}}'_{STLi}(k+1)\mathbf{G}_{RLi}^{-1}\end{bmatrix}=\begin{bmatrix}\hat{\mathbf{H}}'_{STRi}(k)\\ \hat{\mathbf{H}}'_{STLi}(k)\mathbf{G}_{RLi}^{-1}\end{bmatrix}+\alpha\begin{bmatrix}\mathbf{X}_{2Si}(k)\mathbf{G}_{Ri}\mathbf{E}_i(k)\\ \mathbf{X}_{2Si}(k)\mathbf{G}_{Ri}\mathbf{E}_i(k)\end{bmatrix}\end{gathered} \tag{70}$$

It is evident that rank of the equation in (70) is N not 2N, therefore the equation becomes monaural one by subtracting the first law after multiplying $(\mathbf{G}_{RLi})^{-1}$ from the second low as

$$\hat{\mathbf{H}}_{MONRLi}(k+1)=\hat{\mathbf{H}}_{MONRLi}(k)+2\alpha\mathbf{X}_{Ri}(k)\mathbf{E}_i(k) \tag{71}$$

where

$$\hat{\mathbf{H}}_{MONRLi}(k)=\hat{\mathbf{H}}'_{STRi}(k)+\hat{\mathbf{H}}'_{STLi}(k)\mathbf{G}_{RLi}^{-1} \tag{72}$$

or assuming $\mathbf{G}_{Ri}=\mathbf{G}_{Li}\mathbf{G}_{LRi}$

$$\hat{\mathbf{H}}_{MONLRi}(k+1)=\hat{\mathbf{H}}_{MONLRi}(k)+2\alpha\mathbf{X}_{Li}(k)\mathbf{E}_i(k) \tag{73}$$

where

$$\hat{\mathbf{H}}_{MONRLi}(k)=\hat{\mathbf{H}}'_{STLi}(k)+\hat{\mathbf{H}}'_{STRi}(k)\mathbf{G}_{LRi}^{-1} \tag{74}$$

Selection of the iteration depends on existence of the inverse matrix $\mathbf{G}_{RLi}^{-1}$ or $\mathbf{G}_{LRi}^{-1}$ and the detail is explained in the next section.
By substituting (67) to (72) and (74), we obtain following equations;

$$\hat{\mathbf{H}}_{MONRLi}(k)=\hat{\mathbf{H}}_{STRi}(k)\mathbf{G}_{RRLLi}+\hat{\mathbf{H}}_{STLi}(k)\mathbf{G}_{RRLLi}\mathbf{G}_{RLi}^{-1} \tag{75}$$

or

$$\hat{\mathbf{H}}_{MONLRi}(k) = \hat{\mathbf{H}}_{STRi}(k)\mathbf{G}_{RRLLi}\mathbf{G}_{LRi}^{-1} + \hat{\mathbf{H}}_{STLi}(k)\mathbf{G}_{RRLLi} \tag{76}$$

From the stereo echo path estimation view point, we can obtain $\hat{\mathbf{H}}_{MONRLi}(k)$ or $\hat{\mathbf{H}}_{MONLRi}(k)$, however we can't identify right and left echo path estimation from the monaural one. To cope with this problem, we use two LTI periods for separating the right and left estimation results as

$$\begin{aligned}
&\begin{bmatrix} \hat{\mathbf{H}}_{MONLRi}^T \\ \hat{\mathbf{H}}_{MONLRi-1}^T \end{bmatrix} = \begin{bmatrix} \mathbf{G}_{RRLLi}^T & \mathbf{G}_{RRLLi}\mathbf{G}_{RLi}^{-1} \\ \mathbf{G}_{RRLLii-1}^T & \mathbf{G}_{RRLLi-1}\mathbf{G}_{RLi-1}^{-1} \end{bmatrix} \begin{bmatrix} \hat{\mathbf{H}}_{STRi}^T \\ \hat{\mathbf{H}}_{STLi} \end{bmatrix} \cdots \mathbf{G}_{RLi} \text{ and } \mathbf{G}_{RLi-1} \\
&\qquad\qquad\qquad\qquad\qquad\qquad\qquad\qquad \text{are regular matrix} \\
&\begin{bmatrix} \hat{\mathbf{H}}_{MONLRi}^T \\ \hat{\mathbf{H}}_{MONLRi-1}^T \end{bmatrix} = \begin{bmatrix} \mathbf{G}_{RLRLi}^T\mathbf{G}_{LRi}^{-1} & \mathbf{G}_{RRLLi} \\ \mathbf{G}_{RRLLi-1}^T\mathbf{G}_{LRi-1}^{-1} & \mathbf{G}_{RRLLi-1} \end{bmatrix} \begin{bmatrix} \hat{\mathbf{H}}_{STRi}^T \\ \hat{\mathbf{H}}_{STLi} \end{bmatrix} \cdots \mathbf{G}_{LRi} \text{ and } \mathbf{G}_{LRi-1} \\
&\qquad\qquad\qquad\qquad\qquad\qquad\qquad\qquad \text{are regular matrix} \\
&\begin{bmatrix} \hat{\mathbf{H}}_{MONLRi}^T \\ \hat{\mathbf{H}}_{MONLRi-1}^T \end{bmatrix} = \begin{bmatrix} \mathbf{G}_{RRLLi}^T & \mathbf{G}_{RRLLi}\mathbf{G}_{RLi}^{-1} \\ \mathbf{G}_{RRLLi-1}^T\mathbf{G}_{LRi-1}^{-1} & \mathbf{G}_{RRLLi-1} \end{bmatrix} \begin{bmatrix} \hat{\mathbf{H}}_{STRi}^T \\ \hat{\mathbf{H}}_{STLi} \end{bmatrix} \cdots \mathbf{G}_{RLi} \text{ and } \mathbf{G}_{LRi-1} \\
&\qquad\qquad\qquad\qquad\qquad\qquad\qquad\qquad \text{are regular matrix} \\
&\begin{bmatrix} \hat{\mathbf{H}}_{MONLRi}^T \\ \hat{\mathbf{H}}_{MONLRi-1}^T \end{bmatrix} = \begin{bmatrix} \mathbf{G}_{RRLLi}^T\mathbf{G}_{LRi}^{-1} & \mathbf{G}_{RRLLi} \\ \mathbf{G}_{RRLLi-1}^T & \mathbf{G}_{RRLLi-1}\mathbf{G}_{RLi-1}^{-1} \end{bmatrix} \begin{bmatrix} \hat{\mathbf{H}}_{STRi}^T \\ \hat{\mathbf{H}}_{STLi} \end{bmatrix} \cdots \mathbf{G}_{LRi} \text{ and } \mathbf{G}_{RLi-1} \\
&\qquad\qquad\qquad\qquad\qquad\qquad\qquad\qquad \text{are regular matrix}
\end{aligned} \quad .(77)$$

where $\hat{\mathbf{H}}_{MONLRi}$ and $\hat{\mathbf{H}}_{MONLRi-1}$ are monaural echo canceller estimation results at the end of each LTI period, $\hat{\mathbf{H}}_{STRi}$ and $\hat{\mathbf{H}}_{STLi}$ are right and left estimated stereo echo paths based on the $i-1th$ and ith LTI period's estimation results.
Equation (77) is written simply as

$$\hat{\mathbf{H}}_{MONi,i-1} = \mathbf{W}_i^{-1}\hat{\mathbf{H}}_{STi} \tag{78}$$

where $\hat{\mathbf{H}}_{MONRLij}^T$ is estimation result matrix for the $i-1th$ and ith LTI period's as

$$\hat{\mathbf{H}}_{MONi,i-1} = \begin{bmatrix} \hat{\mathbf{H}}_{MONRLi}^T \\ \hat{\mathbf{H}}_{MONRLi-1}^T \end{bmatrix} \tag{79}$$

$\hat{\mathbf{H}}_{STi}^T$ is stereo echo path estimation result as

$$\hat{\mathbf{H}}_{STi} = \begin{bmatrix} \hat{\mathbf{H}}_{STRi}^T \\ \hat{\mathbf{H}}_{STLi}^T \end{bmatrix} \tag{80}$$

$\mathbf{W}_i^{-1}$ is a matrix which projects stereo estimation results to two monaural estimation results and is defined by

$$\mathbf{W}_i^{-1} = \begin{cases} \begin{bmatrix} \mathbf{G}_{RRLLi}^T & \mathbf{G}_{RRLLi}\mathbf{G}_{RLi}^{-1} \\ \mathbf{G}_{RRLLi-1}^T & \mathbf{G}_{RRLLi-1}\mathbf{G}_{RLi-1}^{-1} \end{bmatrix} \cdots \mathbf{G}_{RLi} \text{ and } \mathbf{G}_{RLi-1} \text{ are regular matrix} \\ \begin{bmatrix} \mathbf{G}_{RRLLi}^T\mathbf{G}_{LRi}^{-1} & \mathbf{G}_{RRLLi} \\ \mathbf{G}_{RRLLi-1}^T\mathbf{G}_{RLRi-1}^{-1} & \mathbf{G}_{RRLLi-1} \end{bmatrix} \cdots \mathbf{G}_{LRi} \text{ and } \mathbf{G}_{LRi-1} \text{ are regular matrix} \\ \begin{bmatrix} \mathbf{G}_{RRLLi}^T & \mathbf{G}_{RRLLi}\mathbf{G}_{RLi}^{-1} \\ \mathbf{G}_{RLi-1}^T\mathbf{G}_{LRi-1}^{-1} & \mathbf{G}_{RRLLi-1} \end{bmatrix} \cdots \mathbf{G}_{RLi} \text{ and } \mathbf{G}_{LRi-1} \text{ are regular matrix} \\ \begin{bmatrix} \mathbf{G}_{RRLLi}^T\mathbf{G}_{LRi}^{-1} & \mathbf{G}_{RRLLi} \\ \mathbf{G}_{RRLLi-1}^T & \mathbf{G}_{RRLLi-1}\mathbf{G}_{RLi-1}^{-1} \end{bmatrix} \cdots \mathbf{G}_{LRi} \text{ and } \mathbf{G}_{RLi-1} \text{ are regular matrix} \end{cases} \quad (81)$$

By swapping right side hand and left side hand in(78), we obtain right and left stereo echo path estimation using two monaural echo path estimation results as

$$\hat{\mathbf{H}}_{STi} = \mathbf{W}_i \hat{\mathbf{H}}_{MONi,i-1}. \quad (82)$$

Since $\mathbf{W}_i^{-1}$ and $\mathbf{W}_i$ are used to project optimum solutions in two monaural spaces to corresponding optimum solution in a stereo space and vice-versa, we call the matrixes as WARP functions. Above procedure is depicted in Fig. 4. As shown here, the WARP system is regarded as an acoustic echo canceller which transforms stereo signal to correlated component and un-correlated component and monaural acoustic echo canceller is applied to the correlated signal. To re-construct stereo signal, cross-channel correlation recovery matrix is inserted to echo path side. Therefore, WARP operation is needed at a LTI system change.

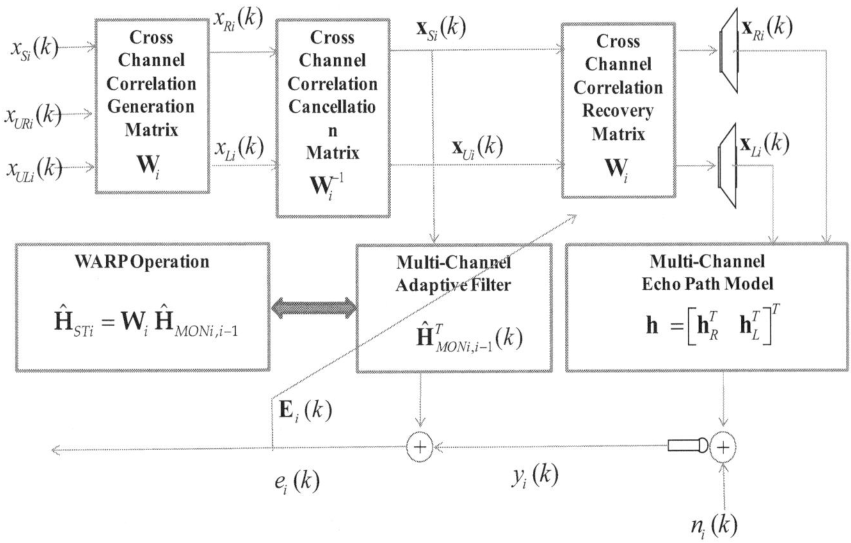

Fig. 4. Basic Principle for WARP method

In an actual application such as speech communication, the auto-correlation characteristics $\mathbf{G}_{RRLLi}$ varies frequently corresponding speech characteristics change, on the other hand the cross-channel characteristics $\mathbf{G}_{RLi}$ or $\mathbf{G}_{LRi}$ changes mainly at a far-end talker change. So, in the following discussions, we apply NLMS method as the simplest affine projection (P=1).
The mechanism is also intuitively understood by using simple vector planes depicted in Fig. 5.

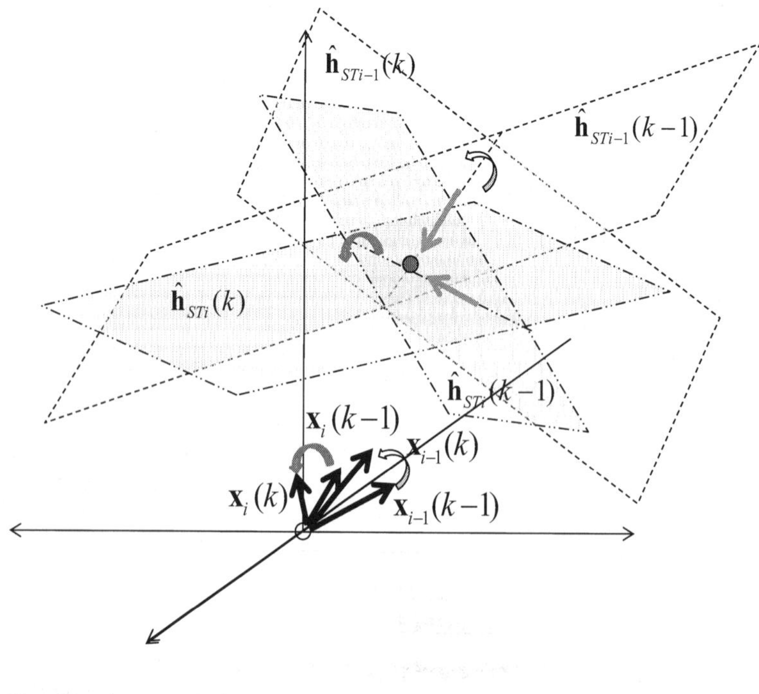

Fig. 5. Very Simple Example for WARP method

As shown here, using two optimum solutions in monaural spaces (in this case on the lines) the optimum solution located in the two dimensional (stereo) space is calculated directly.

4. Realization of WARP

4.1 Simplification by assuming direct-wave stereo sound

Both stereo affine projection and WARP methods require P x P inverse matrix operation which needs to consider its high computation load and stability problem. Even though the WARP operation is required only when the LTI system changes such as far-end talker change and it is much smaller computation than inverse matrix operations for affine projection which requires calculations in each sample, simplification of the WARP operation is still important. This is possible by assuming that target stereo sound is composed of only direct wave sound from a talker (single talker) as shown in Fig. 6.

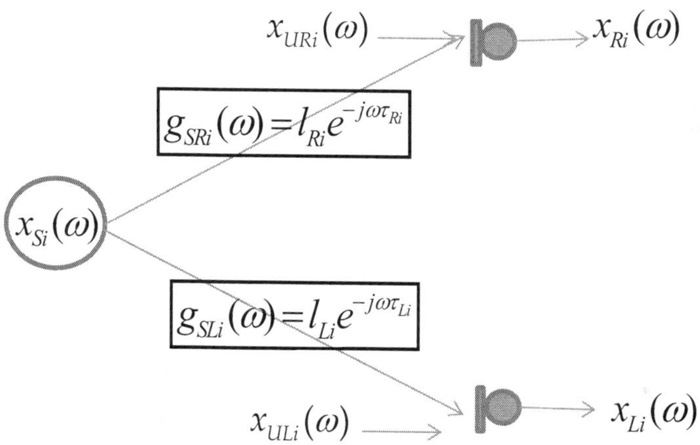

Fig. 6. Stereo Sound Generation System for Single Talking

In figure 6, a single sound source signal at an angular frequency ω in the *ith* LTI period, $x_{Si}(\omega)$, becomes a stereo sound composed of right and left signals, $x_{Ri}(\omega)$ and $x_{Li}(\omega)$, through out right and left LTI systems, $g_{SRi}(\omega)$ and $g_{SLi}(\omega)$ with additional un-correlated noise $x_{URi}(\omega)$ and $x_{ULi}(\omega)$ as

$$\begin{aligned} x_{Ri}(\omega) &= g_{SRi}(\omega)x_{Si}(\omega) + x_{URi}(\omega) \\ x_{Li}(\omega) &= g_{SLi}(\omega)x_{Si}(\omega) + x_{ULi}(\omega) \end{aligned}. \tag{83}$$

In the case of simple direct-wave systems, (83) can be re-written as

$$\begin{aligned} x_{Ri}(\omega) &= l_{Ri}e^{-j\omega\tau_{Ri}}x_{Si}(\omega) + x_{URi}(\omega) \\ x_{Li}(\omega) &= l_{Li}e^{-j\omega\tau_{Li}}x_{Si}(\omega) + x_{ULi}(\omega) \end{aligned} \tag{84}$$

where l_{Ri} and l_{Li} are attenuation of the transfer functions and τ_{Ri} and τ_{Li} are analog delay values.

Since the right and left sounds are sampled by $f_S(=\omega_S/2\pi)$ Hz and treated as digital signals, we use z- domain notation instead of ω-domain as

$$z = \exp[2\pi\omega j/\omega_s]. \tag{85}$$

In z-domain, the system in Fig.4 is expressed as shown in Fig. 7.

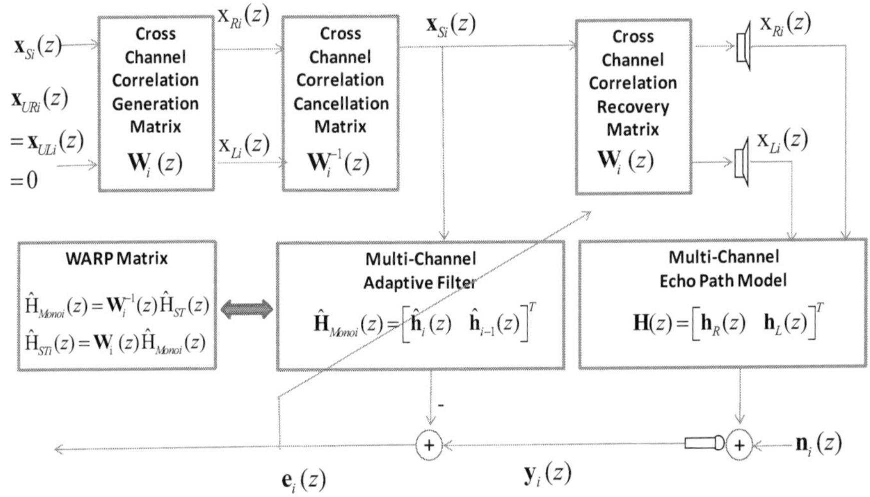

Fig. 7. WARP Method using Z-Function

As shown in Fig.7, the stereo sound generation model for $\mathbf{x}_i(z)$ is expressed as

$$\mathbf{x}_i(z) = \begin{bmatrix} \mathbf{x}_{Ri}(z) \\ \mathbf{x}_{Li}(z) \end{bmatrix} = \begin{bmatrix} \mathbf{g}_{SRi}(z)\mathbf{x}_{Si}(z) + \mathbf{x}_{URi}(z) \\ \mathbf{g}_{SLi}(z)\mathbf{x}_{Si}(z) + \mathbf{x}_{ULi}(z) \end{bmatrix} \tag{86}$$

where $\mathbf{x}_{Ri}(z)$, $\mathbf{x}_{Li}(z)$, $\mathbf{g}_{SRi}(z)$, $\mathbf{g}_{SLi}(z)$, $\mathbf{x}_{Si}(z)$, $\mathbf{x}_{URi}(z)$ and $\mathbf{x}_{ULi}(z)$ are z-domain expression of the band-limited sampled signals corresponding to $x_{Ri}(\omega)$, $x_{Li}(\omega)$, $g_{SRi}(\omega)$, $g_{SLi}(\omega)$, $x_{URi}(\omega)$ and $x_{ULi}(\omega)$, respectively. Adaptive filer output $\hat{\mathbf{y}}_i(z)$ and microphone output $\mathbf{y}_i(z)$ at the end of *ith* LTI period is defined as

$$\begin{aligned} \hat{\mathbf{y}}_i(z) &= \hat{\mathbf{h}}_i^T(z)\mathbf{x}_i(z) \\ \mathbf{y}_i(z) &= \mathbf{h}^T(z)\mathbf{x}_i(z) + \mathbf{n}_i(z) \end{aligned} \tag{87}$$

where $\mathbf{n}_i(z)$ is a room noise, $\hat{\mathbf{h}}_i(z)$ and $\hat{\mathbf{h}}_i(z)$ are stereo adaptive filter and stereo echo path characteristics at the end of *ith* LTI period respectively and which are defined as

$$\hat{\mathbf{H}}_{STi}(z) = \begin{bmatrix} \hat{\mathbf{h}}_{Ri}(z) \\ \hat{\mathbf{h}}_{Li}(z) \end{bmatrix}, \mathbf{H}_{ST}(z) = \begin{bmatrix} \mathbf{h}_R(z) \\ \mathbf{h}_L(z) \end{bmatrix}. \tag{88}$$

Then cancellation error is given neglecting near end noise by

$$\mathbf{e}_i(z) = \mathbf{y}_i(z) - \hat{\mathbf{H}}_{STi}^T(z)\mathbf{x}_i(z) \tag{89}$$

In the case of single talking, we can assume both $\mathbf{x}_{URi}(z)$ and $\mathbf{x}_{ULi}(z)$ are almost zero, and (89) can be re-written as

$$\mathbf{e}_i(z) = \mathbf{y}_i(z) - (\mathbf{g}_{SRi}(z)\hat{\mathbf{h}}_{Ri}(z) + \mathbf{g}_{SLi}(z)\hat{\mathbf{h}}_{Li}(z))\mathbf{x}_{Si}(z) \tag{90}$$

Since the acoustic echo can also be assumed to be driven by single sound source $\mathbf{x}_{Si}(z)$, we can assume a monaural echo path $\mathbf{h}_{Monoi}(z)$ as

$$\mathbf{h}_{Monoi}(z) = \mathbf{g}_{SRi}(z)\mathbf{h}_R(z) + \mathbf{g}_{SLi}(z)\mathbf{h}_L(z)\,. \tag{91}$$

Then (90) is re-written as

$$\mathbf{e}_i(z) = (\mathbf{h}_{Monoi}(z) - (\mathbf{g}_{SRi}(z)\hat{\mathbf{h}}_{Ri}(z) + \mathbf{g}_{SLi}(z)\hat{\mathbf{h}}_{Li}(z)))\mathbf{x}_{Si}(z)\,. \tag{92}$$

This equation implies we can adopt monaural adaptive filter by using a new monaural quasi-echo path $\hat{\mathbf{h}}_{Monoi}(z)$ as

$$\hat{\mathbf{h}}_{Monoi}(z) = \mathbf{g}_{SRi}(z)\hat{\mathbf{h}}_{Ri}(z) + \mathbf{g}_{SLi}(z)\hat{\mathbf{h}}_{Li}(z)\,. \tag{93}$$

However, it is also evident that if LTI system changes both echo and quasi-echo paths should be up-dated to meet new LTI system. This is the same reason for the stereo echo canceller in the case of pure single talk stereo sound input. If we can assume the acoustic echo paths is time invariant for two adjacent LTI periods, this problem is easily solved by satisfying require rank for solving the equation as

$$\begin{bmatrix} \hat{\mathbf{h}}_{Monoi}(z) \\ \hat{\mathbf{h}}_{Monoi-1}(z) \end{bmatrix} = \mathbf{W}_i^{-1}(z) \begin{bmatrix} \hat{\mathbf{h}}_{Ri}(z) \\ \hat{\mathbf{h}}_{Li}(z) \end{bmatrix}. \tag{94}$$

where

$$\mathbf{W}_i^{-1}(z) = \begin{bmatrix} \mathbf{g}_{SRi}(z) & \mathbf{g}_{SLi}(z) \\ \mathbf{g}_{SRi-1}(z) & \mathbf{g}_{SLi-1}(z) \end{bmatrix} \tag{95}$$

In other words, using two echo path estimation results for corresponding two LTI periods, we can project monaural domain quasi-echo path to stereo domain quasi echo path or vice - versa using WARP operations as

$$\begin{aligned} \hat{\mathbf{H}}_{STi}(z) &= \mathbf{W}_i(z)\hat{\mathbf{H}}_{Monoi}(z) \\ \hat{\mathbf{H}}_{Monoi}(z) &= \mathbf{W}_i^{-1}(z)\hat{\mathbf{H}}_{STi}(z) \end{aligned}. \tag{96}$$

where

$$\hat{\mathbf{H}}_{Monoi}(z) = \begin{bmatrix} \hat{\mathbf{h}}_{Monoi}(z) \\ \hat{\mathbf{h}}_{Monoi-1}(z) \end{bmatrix}, \hat{\mathbf{H}}_{STi}(z) = \begin{bmatrix} \hat{\mathbf{h}}_{Ri}(z) \\ \hat{\mathbf{h}}_{Li}(z) \end{bmatrix}. \tag{97}$$

In actual implementation, it is impossible to obtain real $\mathrm{W}_i(z)$, which is composed of unknown transfer functions between a sound source and right and left microphones, so use one of the stereo sounds as a single talk sound source instead of a sound source. Usually, higher level sound is chosen as a pseudo-sound source because higher level sound is usually closer to one of the microphones. Then, the approximated WARP function $\tilde{\mathbf{W}}_i(z)$ is defined as

$$\tilde{\mathbf{W}}_i(z) = \begin{cases} \begin{bmatrix} 1 & \mathbf{g}_{\mathbf{RLi}}(z) \\ 1 & \mathbf{g}_{\mathbf{RLi\text{-}1}}(z) \end{bmatrix} \cdots RR-Transition \\ \begin{bmatrix} 1 & \mathbf{g}_{\mathbf{RLi}}(z) \\ \mathbf{g}_{\mathbf{LRi\text{-}1}}(z) & 1 \end{bmatrix} \cdots RL-Transition \\ \begin{bmatrix} \mathbf{g}_{\mathbf{LRi}}(z) & 1 \\ 1 & \mathbf{g}_{\mathbf{RLi\text{-}1}}(z) \end{bmatrix} \cdots LR-Transition \\ \begin{bmatrix} \mathbf{g}_{\mathbf{LRi}}(z) & 1 \\ \mathbf{g}_{\mathbf{LRi\text{-}1}}(z) & 1 \end{bmatrix} \cdots LL-Transition \end{cases} \tag{98}$$

where $\mathbf{g}_{RLi}(z)$ and $\mathbf{g}_{LRi}(z)$ are cross-channel transfer functions between right and left stereo sounds and are defined as

$$\mathbf{g}_{RLi}(z) = \mathbf{g}_{SLi}(z) / \mathbf{g}_{SRi}(z), \mathbf{g}_{LRi}(z) = \mathbf{g}_{SRi}(z) / \mathbf{g}_{SLi}(z). \tag{99}$$

The RR, RL, LR and LL transitions in (98) mean a single talker's location changes. If a talker' location change is within right microphone side (right microphone is the closest microphone) we call RR-transition and if it is within left-microphone side (left microphone is the closest microphone) we call LL-transition. If the location change is from right-microphone side to left microphone side, we call RL-transition and if the change is opposite we call LR-transition. Let's assume ideal direct-wave single talk case. Then the ω domain transfer functions, $g_{RLi}(\omega)$ and $g_{LRi}(\omega)$ are expressed in z-domain as

$$\mathbf{g}_{RLi}(z) = l_{RLi}\varphi(\delta_{RLi,}z)z^{-d_{RLi}}, \mathbf{g}_{LRi}(z) = l_{LRi}\varphi(\delta_{LRi,}z)z^{-d_{LRi}} \tag{100}$$

where $\delta_{RLi,}$, and $\delta_{LRi,}$ are fractional delays and d_{RLi} and d_{LRi} are integer delays for the direct-wave to realize analog delays τ_{RLi} and τ_{LRi} , these parameters are defined as

$$\begin{aligned} d_{RLi} &= INT[\tau_{RLi} f_S].d_{LRi} = INT[\tau_{LRi} f_S], \\ \delta_{RLi,} &= Mod[\tau_{RLi} f_S], \delta_{LRi,} = Mod[\tau_{LRi} f_S] \end{aligned} \tag{101}$$

$\varphi(\delta, z)$ is a "Sinc Interpolation" function to interpolate a value at a timing between adjacent two samples and is given by

$$\boldsymbol{\varphi}(\delta, z) = \sum_{\nu=-\infty}^{\infty} \frac{\sin(\pi\nu - \delta)}{(\pi\nu - \delta)} z^{-\nu}. \tag{102}$$

4.2 Digital filter realization of WARP functions

Since LL-transition and LR transition are symmetrical to RR-transition and RL-transition respectively, Only RR and RL transition cases are explained in the following discussions. By solving (96) applying WARP function in(98), we obtain right and left stereo echo path estimation functions as

$$\begin{aligned}\hat{\mathbf{h}}_{Ri}(z) &= \frac{\hat{\mathbf{h}}_{Monoi}(z) - \hat{\mathbf{h}}_{Monoi-1}(z)}{\mathbf{g}_{RLi-1}(z) - \mathbf{g}_{RLi}(z)} \\ \hat{\mathbf{h}}_{Li}(z) &= \frac{\mathbf{g}_{RLi-1}(z)\hat{\mathbf{h}}_{Monoi}(z) - \mathbf{g}_{RLi}(z)\hat{\mathbf{h}}_{Monoi-1}(z)}{\mathbf{g}_{RLi-1}(z) - \mathbf{g}_{RLi}(z)}\end{aligned} \quad \cdots RR-Transition \qquad (103)$$

or

$$\begin{aligned}\hat{\mathbf{h}}_{Ri}(z) &= \frac{\hat{\mathbf{h}}_{Monoi}(z) - \mathbf{g}_{RLi-1}(z)\hat{\mathbf{h}}_{Monoi-1}(z)}{1 - \mathbf{g}_{LRi}(z)\mathbf{g}_{RLi-1}(z)} \\ \hat{\mathbf{h}}_{Li}(z) &= \frac{\hat{\mathbf{h}}_{Monoi-1}(z) - \mathbf{g}_{LRi}(z)\hat{\mathbf{h}}_{Monoi}(z)}{1 - \mathbf{g}_{LRi}(z)\mathbf{g}_{RLi-1}(z)}\end{aligned} \quad \cdots RL-Transition \qquad (104)$$

By substituting (100) for (104), we obtain

$$\begin{aligned}\hat{\mathbf{h}}_{Ri}(z) &= \frac{\hat{\mathbf{h}}_{Monoi}(z) - \hat{\mathbf{h}}_{Monoi-1}(z)}{l_{RLi-1}\boldsymbol{\varphi}(\delta_{RLi-1},z)z^{-d_{RLi-1}} - l_{RLi}\boldsymbol{\varphi}(\delta_{RLi},z)z^{-d_{RLi}}} \\ \hat{\mathbf{h}}_{Li}(z) &= \frac{l_{RLi-1}\boldsymbol{\varphi}(\delta_{RLi-1},z)z^{-d_{RLi-1}}\hat{\mathbf{h}}_{Monoi}(z) - l_{RLi}\boldsymbol{\varphi}(\delta_{RLi},z)z^{-d_{RLi}}\hat{\mathbf{h}}_{Monoi-1}(z)}{l_{RLi-1}\boldsymbol{\varphi}(\delta_{RLi-1},z)z^{-d_{RLi-1}} - l_{RLi}\boldsymbol{\varphi}(\delta_{RLi},z)z^{-d_{RLi}}}\end{aligned} \quad \cdots RR-Transition \quad (105)$$

and

$$\begin{aligned}\hat{\mathbf{h}}_{Ri}(z) &= \frac{\hat{\mathbf{h}}_{Monoi}(z) - l_{RLi-1}\varphi(\delta_{RLi-1},z)z^{-d_{RLi-1}}\hat{\mathbf{h}}_{Monoi-1}(z)}{1 - l_{LRi}\varphi(\delta_{LRi},z)l_{RLi-1}\varphi(\delta_{RLi-1},z)z^{-(d_{RLi-1}+d_{LRi})}} \\ \hat{\mathbf{h}}_{Li}(z) &= \frac{\hat{\mathbf{h}}_{Monoi-1}(z) - l_{LRi}\varphi(\delta_{LRi},z)z^{-d_{LRi}}\hat{\mathbf{h}}_{Monoi}(z)}{1 - l_{LRi}\varphi(\delta_{LRi},z)l_{RLi-1}\varphi(\delta_{RLi-1},z)z^{-(d_{RLi-1}+d_{LRi})}}\end{aligned} \quad \cdots RL-Transition \qquad (106)$$

Since $\boldsymbol{\varphi}(\delta,z)$ is an interpolation function for a delay δ, the delay is compensated by $\boldsymbol{\varphi}(-\delta,z)$ as

$$\boldsymbol{\varphi}(-\delta,z) \cdot \boldsymbol{\varphi}(\delta,z) = 1. \qquad (107)$$

From(107), (105) is re-written as

$$\begin{aligned}\hat{\mathbf{h}}_{Ri}(z) &= \frac{(\hat{\mathbf{h}}_{Monoi}(z) - \hat{\mathbf{h}}_{Monoi-1}(z))l_{RLi-1}^{-1}\boldsymbol{\varphi}(-\delta_{RLi-1},z)z^{d_{RLi-1}}}{1 - (l_{RLi}l_{RLi-1}^{-1})\boldsymbol{\varphi}(-\delta_{RLi-1},z)\boldsymbol{\varphi}(\delta_{RLi},z)z^{-(d_{RLi}-d_{RLi-1})}} \\ \hat{\mathbf{h}}_{Li}(z) &= \frac{\hat{\mathbf{h}}_{Monoi}(z) - l_{RLi}l_{RLi-1}^{-1}\boldsymbol{\varphi}(\delta_{RLi},z)\boldsymbol{\varphi}(-\delta_{RLi-1},z)z^{-d_{RLi}+d_{RLi-1}}\hat{\mathbf{h}}_{Monoi-1}(z)}{1 - (l_{RLi}l_{RLi-1}^{-1})\boldsymbol{\varphi}(-\delta_{RLi-1},z)\boldsymbol{\varphi}(\delta_{RLi},z)z^{-(d_{RLi}-d_{RLi-1})}}\end{aligned} \quad \cdots RR-Transition \quad (108)$$

These functions are assumed to be digital filters for the echo path estimation results as shown in Fig.8.

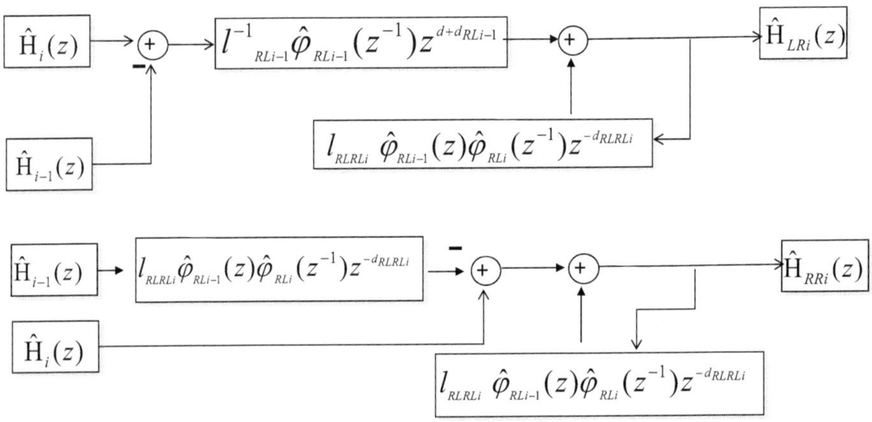

Fig. 8. Digital Filter Realization for WARP Functions

4.3 Causality and stability of WARP functions

Stability conditions are obtained by checking denominator of (108) and(106) $\mathbf{D}_{RRi}(z)$ and $\mathbf{D}_{RLi}(z)$ which are defined as

$$\begin{aligned} &|\mathbf{D}_{RRi}(z)| < 1 \cdots RR - Transition \\ &|\mathbf{D}_{RLi}(z)| < 1 \cdots RL - Transition \end{aligned} \tag{109}$$

where

$$\begin{aligned} &\mathbf{D}_{RRi}(z) = l_{RLi} l_{RLi-1}^{-1} \boldsymbol{\varphi}(-\delta_{RLi-1}, z)\boldsymbol{\varphi}(\delta_{RLi}, z) z^{-(d_{RLi}-d_{RLi-1})} \ldots RR - Transition \\ &\mathbf{D}_{RLi}(z) = l_{LRi} l_{RLi-1} \boldsymbol{\varphi}(\delta_{LRi}, z)\boldsymbol{\varphi}(\delta_{RLi-1}, z) z^{-(d_{RLi-1}+d_{LRi})} \ldots RL - Transition \end{aligned} \tag{110}$$

From(109),

$$\begin{aligned} &|\boldsymbol{\varphi}(-\delta_{RLi-1}, z)\boldsymbol{\varphi}(\delta_{RLi}, z)| \le |\boldsymbol{\varphi}(-\delta_{RLi-1}, z)||\boldsymbol{\varphi}(\delta_{RLi}, z)| \cdots RR - Transition \\ &|\boldsymbol{\varphi}(\delta_{LRi}, z)\boldsymbol{\varphi}(\delta_{RLi-1}, z)| \le |\boldsymbol{\varphi}(\delta_{LRi}, z)||\boldsymbol{\varphi}(\delta_{RLi-1}, z)| \cdots RR - Transition \end{aligned} \tag{111}$$

By using numerical calculations,

$$|\boldsymbol{\varphi}(\delta, z)| < 1.2 \tag{112}$$

Substituting (112) for (109),

$$\begin{aligned} &l_{RLi} l_{RLi-1}^{-1} < 1/1.44 \cdots RR - Transition \\ &l_{LRi} l_{RLi-1} < 1/1.44 \cdots RL - Transition \end{aligned} \tag{113}$$

Secondly, conditions for causality are given by checking the delay of the feedback component of the denominators $\mathbf{D}_{RRi}(z)$ and $\mathbf{D}_{RLi}(z)$. Since convolution of a "Sinc Interpolation" function is also a "Sinc Interpolation" function as

$$\boldsymbol{\varphi}(\delta_{A,}z)\cdot\boldsymbol{\varphi}(\delta_{B,}z)=\boldsymbol{\varphi}(\delta_{A}+\delta_{B,}z). \tag{114}$$

Equation (110) is re-written as

$$\begin{aligned}\mathbf{D}_{RRi}(z)&=l_{RLi}l_{RLi-1}^{-1}\boldsymbol{\varphi}(\delta_{RLi,}-\delta_{RLi-1,}z)z^{-(d_{RLi}-d_{RLi-1})}\cdots RR-Transition\\ \mathbf{D}_{RLi}(z)&=l_{LRi}l_{RLi-1}\boldsymbol{\varphi}(\delta_{LRi}+\delta_{RLi-1,}z)z^{-(d_{RLi-1}+d_{LRi})}\cdots RL-Transition\end{aligned} \tag{115}$$

The "Sinc Interpolation" function is an infinite sum toward both positive and negative delays. Therefore it is essentially impossible to endorse causality. However, by permitting some errors, we can find conditions to maintain causality with errors. To do so, we use a "Quasi-Sinc Interpolation" function which is defined as

$$\tilde{\boldsymbol{\varphi}}(\delta,z)=\sum_{\nu=-N_F+1}^{N_F}\frac{\sin(\pi\nu-\delta)}{(\pi\nu-\delta)}z^{-\nu}. \tag{116}$$

where $2N_F$ is a finite impulse response range of the "Quasi-Sinc Interpolation" $\tilde{\varphi}(\delta,z)$. Then the error power by the approximation is given as

$$\oint\tilde{\boldsymbol{\varphi}}(\delta,z)\tilde{\boldsymbol{\varphi}}^{*}(\delta,z)dz=\sum_{\nu=-\infty}^{-N_F}\frac{\sin^2(\pi\nu-\delta)}{(\pi\nu-\delta)^2}z^{-\nu}+\sum_{\nu=N_F+1}^{\infty}\frac{\sin^2(\pi\nu-\delta)}{(\pi\nu-\delta)^2}z^{-\nu}. \tag{117}$$

Equation (116) is re-written as

$$\tilde{\boldsymbol{\varphi}}(\delta,z)=\sum_{\nu=0}^{2N_F-1}\frac{\sin(\pi\nu-\delta)}{(\pi\nu-\delta)}z^{-\nu-N_F+1}. \tag{118}$$

By substituting (118) for (115),

$$\begin{aligned}\mathbf{D}_{RRi}(z)&\simeq l_{RLi}l_{RLi-1}^{-1}\tilde{\boldsymbol{\varphi}}(\delta_{RLi,}-\delta_{RLi-1,}z)z^{-(d_{RLi}-d_{RLi-1}-N_F+1)}\cdots RR-Transition\\ \mathbf{D}_{RLi}(z)&\simeq l_{LRi}l_{RLi-1}\tilde{\boldsymbol{\varphi}}(\delta_{LRi}+\delta_{RLi-1,}z)z^{-(d_{RLi-1}+d_{LRi}-N_F+1)}\cdots RL-Transition\end{aligned} \tag{119}$$

Then conditions for causality are

$$\begin{aligned}d_{RLi}-d_{RLi-1}&\geq N_F-1\cdots RR-Transition\\ d_{RLi-1}+d_{LRi}&\geq N_F-1\cdots RL-Transition\end{aligned} \tag{120}$$

The physical meaning of the conditions are the delay difference due to talker's location change should be equal or less than cover range of the "Quasi-Sinc Interpolation" $\tilde{\boldsymbol{\varphi}}(\delta,z)$ in the case of staying in the same microphone zone and the delay sun due to talker's location change should be equal or less than cover range of the "Quasi-Sinc Interpolation" $\tilde{\boldsymbol{\varphi}}(\delta,z)$ in the case of changing the microphone zone.

4.4 Stereo echo canceller using WARP

Total system using WARP method is presented in Fig. 9, where the system composed of five components, far-end stereo sound generation model, cross-channel transfer function (CCTF) estimation block, stereo echo path model, monaural acoustic echo canceller (AEC-I) block, stereo acoustic echo canceller (AEC-II) block and WARP block.

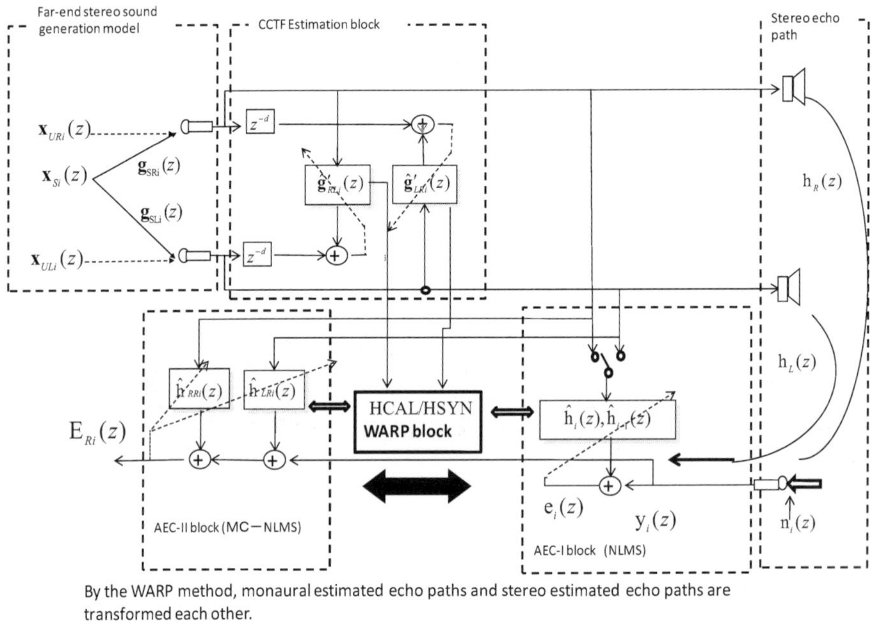

Fig. 9. System Configuration for WARP based Stereo Acoustic Echo Canceller

As shown in Fig.9, actual echo cancellation is done by stereo acoustic echo canceller (AEC-II), however, a monaural acoustic echo canceller (AEC-I) is used for the far-end single talking. The WARP block is active only when the cross-channel transfer function changes and it projects monaural echo chancellor echo path estimation results for two LTI periods to one stereo echo path estimation or vice-versa.

5. Computer simulations

5.1 Stereo sound generation model

Computer simulations are carried out using the stereo generation model shown in Fig.10 for both white Gaussian noise (WGN) and an actual voice. The system is composed of cross-channel transfer function estimation blocks (CCTF), where all signals are assumed to be sampled at $f_S = 8KHz$ after 3.4kHz cut-off low-pass filtering. Frame length is set to 100 samples. Since the stereo sound generation model is essentially a continuous time signal system, over-sampling (x6, $f_A = 48KHz$) is applied to simulate it. In the stereo sound generation model, three far-end talker's locations, A Loc(1)=(-0.8,1.0), B Loc(2)=(-0.8,0.5), C Loc(3)=(-0.8,0.0), D Loc(4)=(-0.8,-0.5) and D Loc(5)=(-0.8,-1.0) are used and R/L microphone locations are set to R-Mic=(0,0.5) and L-Mic=(0,-0.5), respectively. Delay is calculated assuming voice wave speed as 300m/sec. In this set-up, talker's position change for WGN is assumed to be from location A to location B and finally to location D, in which each talker stable period is set to 80 frames. The position change for voice is from C->A and the period is set to 133 frames. Both room noise and reverberation components in the far-end terminals is assumed, the S/N is set to 20dB ~ 40dB.

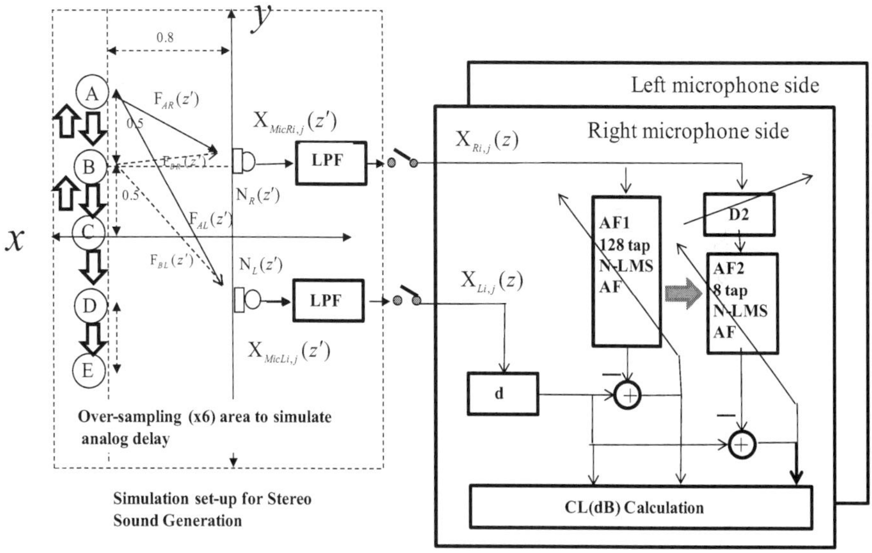

Fig. 10. Stereo Sound Generation Model and Cross-Channel Transfer Function Detector

5.2 Cross-channel transfer function estimation

In WARP method, it is easily imagine that the estimation performance of the cross-channel transfer function largely affects the echo canceller cancellation performances. To clarify the transfer function estimation performance, simulations are carried out using the cross-channel transfer function estimators (CCTF). The estimators are prepared for right microphone side sound source case and left microphone side sound source case, respectively. Each estimator has two NLMS adaptive filters, longer (128) tap one and shorter (8) tap one. The longer tap adaptive filter (AF1) is used to find a main tap and shorter one (AF2) is used to estimate the transfer function precisely as an impulse response.

Figure 11 shows CCTF estimation results as the AF1 tap coefficients after convergence setting single male voice sound source to the locations C, B and A in Fig. 11. Detail responses obtained by AF2 are shown in Fig. 12.As shown the results, the CCTF estimation works correctly in the simulations.

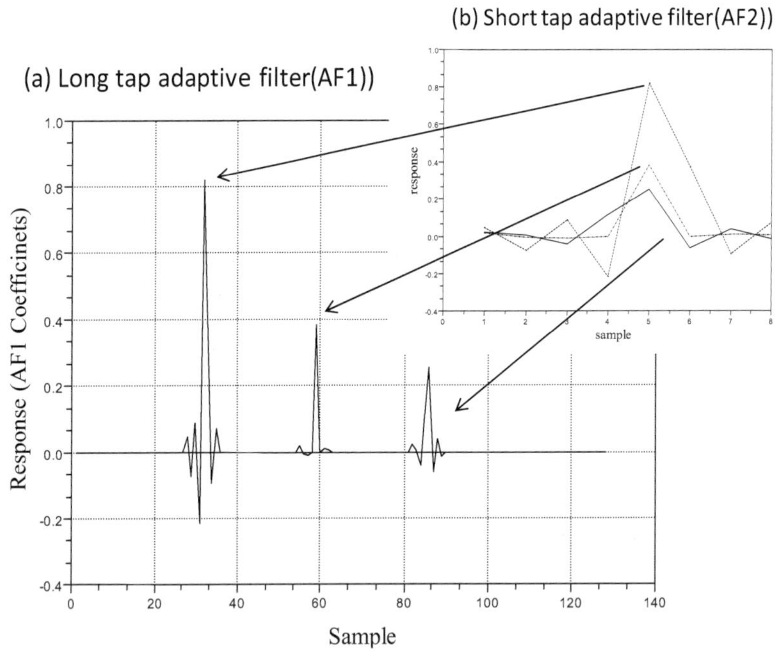

Fig. 11. Impulse Response Estimation Results in CCTF Block

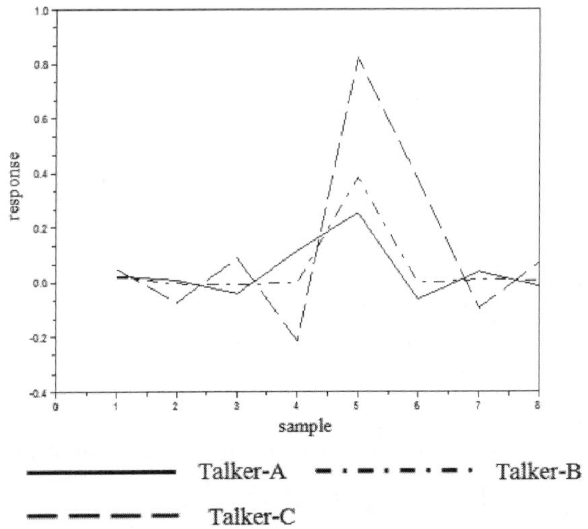

Fig. 12. Estimated Tap Coefficients by Short Tap Adaptive Filter in CCTF Estimation Block

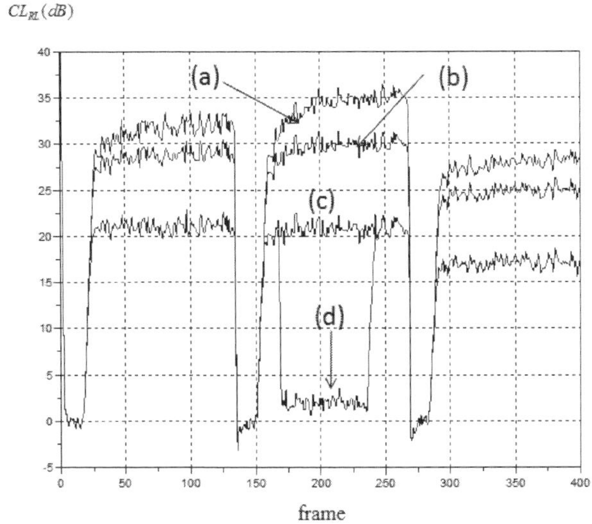

(a)Room Noise S/N=40dB Direct / Reverberation Ratio=40dB

(b)Room Noise S/N=30dB Direct / Reverberation Ratio=30dB

(c)Room Noise S/N=20dB Direct / Reverberation Ratio=20dB

(d)Room Noise S/N=30dB Direct / Reverberation Ratio=20dB F-DT ON

Fig. 13. Cross-Channel Correlation Cancellation Performances

Cancellation performances of the cross-channel correlation under room noise (WGN) are obtained using the adaptive filter (AF2) and are shown is Fig. 13, where S/N is assumed to be 20dB, 30dB and 40dB. In the figure $CL_{RL}(dB)$ is power reduction in dB which is observed by the signal power before and after cancellation of the cross-channel correlation by AF2. As shown here, more than 17dB cross-channel correlation cancellation is attained.

5.3 Echo canceller performances

To evaluate echo cancellation performances of the WARP acoustic echo canceller which system is shown in Fig. 10, computer simulations are carried out assuming 1000tap NLMS adaptive filters for both stereo and monaural echo cancellers. The performances of the acoustic echo canceller are evaluated by two measurements. The first one is the echo return loss enhancement $ERLE_{ij}(dB)$, which is applied to the WGN source case and is defined as

$$\mathrm{ERLE}_{L\cdot(i-1)+j-1} = \begin{cases} 10\log_{10}\left(\sum_{k=0}^{N_F-1} y^2_{i,j,k} \Big/ \sum_{k=0}^{N_F-1} e^2_{MONi,j,k}\right)\cdots MonauralEchoCanceller \\ 10\log_{10}\left(\sum_{k=0}^{N_F-1} y^2_{i,j,k} \Big/ \sum_{k=0}^{N_F-1} e^2_{STi,j,k}\right)\cdots StereoEchoCanceller \end{cases} \tag{121}$$

where $e_{MONi,j,k}$ and $e_{MONi,j,k}$ are residual echo for the monaural echo canceller (AEC-I) and stereo echo canceller (AEC-II) for the kth sample in the jth frame in the ith LTI period, respectively. The second measurement is normalized misalignment of the estimated echo paths and are defined as

$$NORM_{L\cdot(i-1)+j-1} = 10\log_{10}\left(\frac{(\mathbf{h}_R)^T(\mathbf{h}_R)+(\mathbf{h}_L)^T(\mathbf{h}_L)}{(\mathbf{h}_R-\hat{\mathbf{h}}_{Ri,j})^T(\mathbf{h}_L-\hat{\mathbf{h}}_{Li,j})}\right) \tag{122}$$

where $\hat{h}_{Ri,j}$ and $\hat{h}_{Li,j}$ are stereo echo canceller estimated coefficient arrays at the end of $(i,j)th$ frame, respectively. h_R and h_L are target stereo echo path impulse response arrays, respectively.

5.3.1 WARP echo canceller basic performances for WGN

The simulation results for WARP echo canceller in the case of WGN sound source, no far-end double talking and no local noise, are shown in Fig. 14. In the simulations, talker is assumed to move from A to E every 80 frames (1sec). In Fig.14, the results (a) and (b) show ERLEs for monaural and stereo acoustic echo cancellers (AEC-I and AEC-II), respectively.

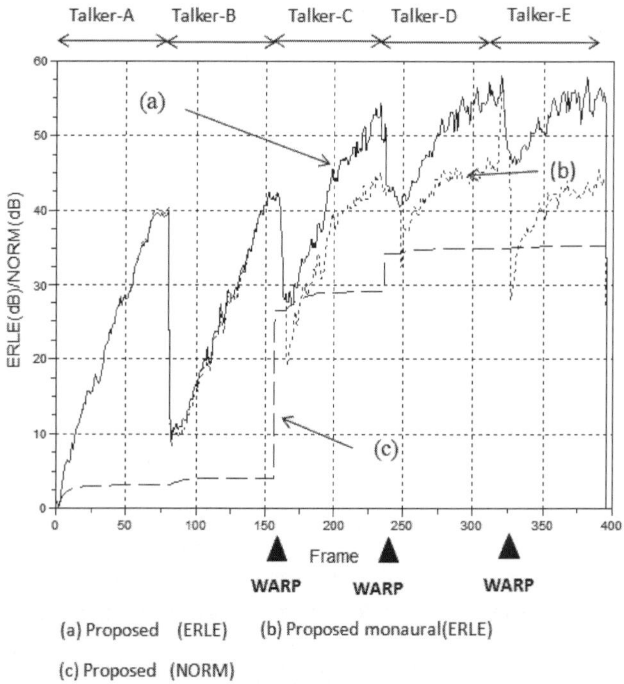

Fig. 14. WARP Echo Cancellation Performances for WGN Source

The WARP operations are applied at the boundaries of the three LTI periods for the talkers C, D and E. NORM for the stereo echo canceller (AEC-II). As shown here, after two LTI periods (A, B periods), NORM and ERLE improves quickly by WARP projection at WARP timings in the Fig. 16. As for ERLE, stereo acoustic echo canceller shows better performance than monaural echo canceller. This is because the monaural echo canceller estimates an echo path model which is combination of CCTF and real stereo echo path and therefore the performance is affected by the CCTF estimation error. On the other hand, the echo path model for the stereo echo canceller is purely the stereo echo path model which does not include CCTF.

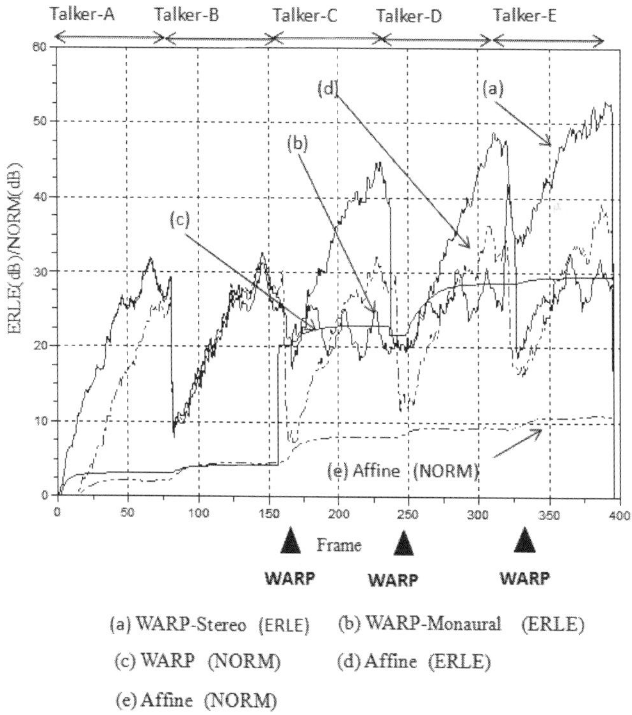

Fig. 15. Echo Cancellation Performance Comparison for WGN Source

Secondary, the WARP acoustic echo canceller is compared with a stereo echo canceller based on an affine projection method. In this case, the right and left sounds at kth sample in the $(i,j)th$ frame, x'_{Rijk} and x'_{Lijk}, are assumed to have independent level shift to the original right and left sounds, x_{Rijk} and x_{Lijk}, for simulating small movement of talker's face as

$$\begin{aligned} x'_{Rijk} &= (1 + \alpha_{Level} \cdot \sin(2\pi k / (f_s \cdot T_X))) x_{Rijk} \\ x'_{Lijk} &= (1 + \alpha_{Level} \cdot \cos(2\pi k / (f_s \cdot T_X))) x_{Lijk} \end{aligned} \tag{123}$$

where α_{Level} and T_X are constants which determine the level shift ratio and cycle. Figure 15 shows the cancellation performances when α_{Level} and T_X are 10% and 500msec, respectively.

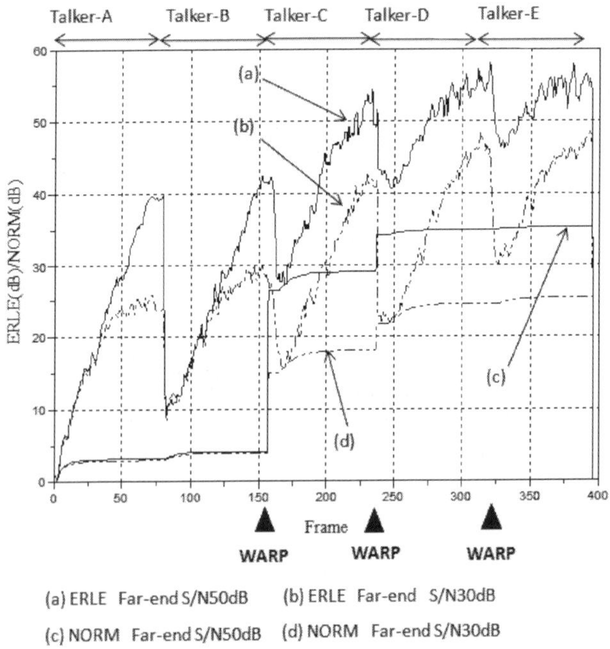

Fig. 16. WARP Echo Canceller Performances Affected by Far-End Back Ground Noise

In Fig. 15, the WARP method shows more than 10dB better stereo echo path estimation performance, NORM, than that of affine projection (P=3). ERLE by stereo echo canceller base on WARP method is also better than affine projection (P=3). ERLE by monaural acoustic echo canceller based on WARP method is somehow similar cancellation performance as affine method (P=3), however ERLE improvement after two LTI periods by the WARP based monaural echo canceller is better than affine based stereo echo canceller.

Figure 16 shows the echo canceller performances in the case of CCTF estimation is degraded by room noise in the far-end terminal. S/N in the far-end terminal is assumed to be 30dB or 50dB. Although the results clearly show that lower S/N degrade ERLR or NORM, more than 15dB ERLE or NORM is attained after two LTI periods.

Figure 17 shows the echo canceller performances in the case of echo path change happens. In this simulation, echo path change is inserted at 100frame. The echo path change is chosen 20dB, 30dB and 40dB. It is observed that echo path change affects the WARP calculation and therefore WARP effect degrades at 2nd and third LTI period boundary.

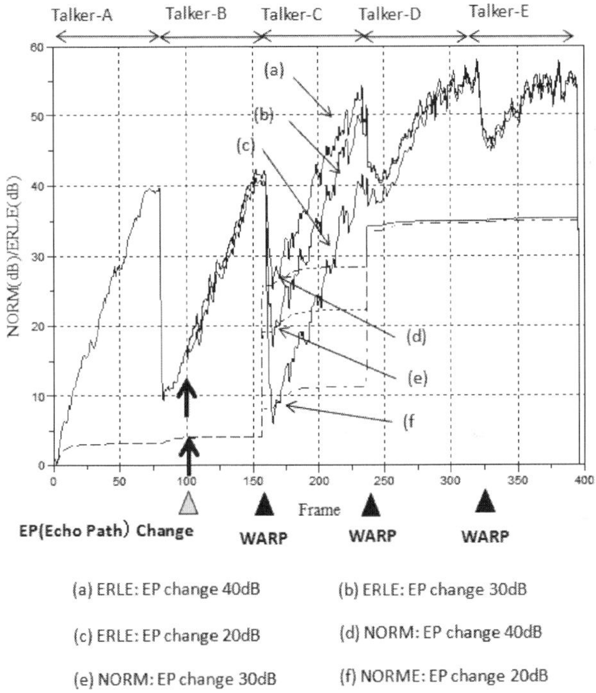

Fig. 17. WARP Echo Canceller Cancellation Performance Drops Due to Echo Path Chance

Figure 18 summarizes NORM results for stereo NLMS method, affine projection method as WARP method. In this simulation, as a non-linear function for affine projection, independent absolute values of the right and left sounds are added by

$$\begin{aligned} x'_{Rijk} &= x_{Rijk} + 0.5 \cdot \alpha_{ABS} \cdot (x_{Rijk} + |x_{Rijk}|) \\ x'_{Lijk} &= x_{Lijk} + 0.5 \cdot \alpha_{ABS} \cdot (x_{Lijk} - |x_{Lijk}|) \end{aligned} \tag{124}$$

where α_{ABS} is a constant to determine non-liner level of the stereo sound and is set to 10%. In this simulation, an experiment is carried out assuming far-end double talking, where WGN which power is same as far-end single talking is added between 100 and 130 frames.

As evident from the results in Fig. 18, WARP method shows better performances for the stereo echo path estimation regardless far-end double talking existence. Even in the case 10% far end signal level shit, WARP method attains more than 20% NORM comparing affine method (P=3) with 10% absolute non-linear result.

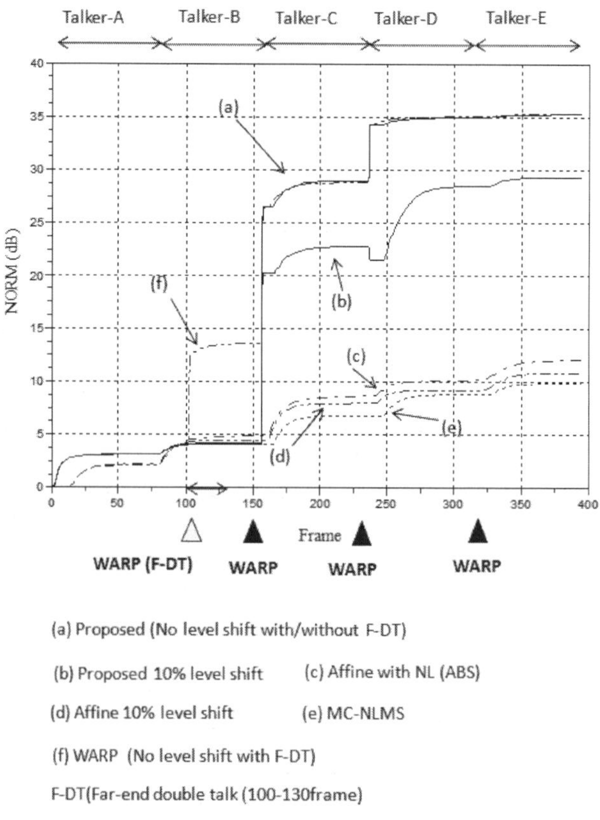

Fig. 18. Echo Path Estimation Performance Comparison for NLMS, Affine and WARP Methods

5.3.2 WARP echo canceller basic performances for voice

Figure 19 shows NORM and residual echo level (Lres) for actual male voice sound source. Since voice sound level changes frequently, we calculate residual echo level Lres (dB) instead of ERLE(dB) for white Gaussian noise case. Although slower NORM and Lres convergence than white Gaussian is observed, quick improvement for the both metrics is observed at the talker B and A border. In this simulation, we applied 500 tap NLMS adaptive filter. Affine projection may give better convergence speed by eliminating auto-correlation in the voice, however it is independent effect from WARP effect. WARP and affine projection can be used together and may contribute to convergence speed up independently.

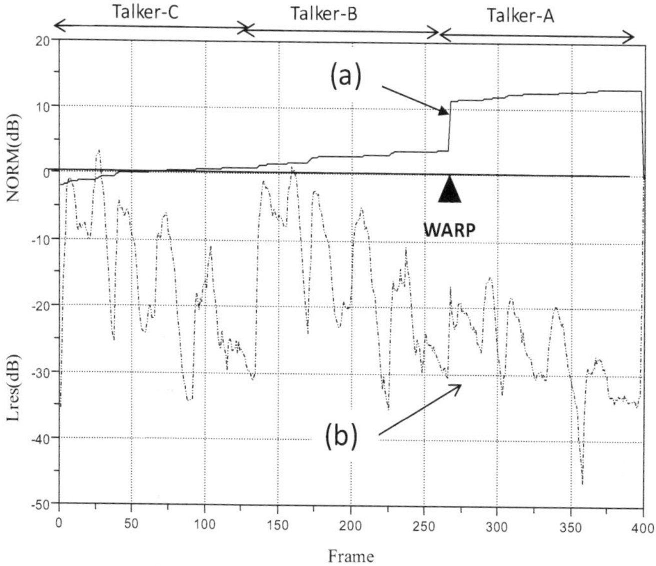

(a) NORM Far-end S/N30dB

(b) Lres Far-end S/N30dB

Fig. 19. Residual Echo (Lres (dB) Level and Normalized Estimated Echo Misalignment. (NORM) for the voice Source at Far-end Terminal S/N=30dB.
(Level shift 0, 500tap Step gain=1.0)

6. Conclusions

In this chapter stereo acoustic echo canceller methods are studied from cross-channel correlation view point aiming at conversational DTV use. Among many stereo acoustic echo cancellers, we focused on AP (including LS and stereo NLMS methods) and WARP methods, since these approaches do not cause any modification nor artifacts to speaker output stereo sound which is not desirable consumer audio-visual products such as DTV. In this study, stereo sound generation system is modeled by using right and left Pth order LTI systems with independent noises. Stereo LS method (M=2P) and stereo NLMS method (M=P=1) are two extreme cases of general AP method which requires MxM inverse matrix operation in each sample. Stereo AP method (M=P) can produce the best iteration direction fully adopting un-correlated component produced by small fluctuation in the stereo cross-channel correlation by calculating PxP inverse matrix operations in each sample. Major problem of the method is that it cannot cope with strict single talking where no un-correlated signals exist in right and left channels and therefore rank drop problem happens. Contrary to AP method, WARP method creates a stereo echo path estimation model applying a monaural adaptive filter for two LTI periods at a chance of far-end talker change. Since it creates stereo echo path estimation using two monaural echo path models for two

LTI periods, we do not suffer from any rank drop problem even in a strict single talking. Moreover, using WARP method, computational complexity can be reduced drastically because WARP method requires PxP inverse matrix operations only at LTI characteristics change such as far-end talker change. However, contrary to AP method, it is clear that performance of WARP method may drop if fluctuation in cross-channel correlation becomes high. Considering above pros-cons in affine projection and WARP methods, it looks desirable to apply affine method and WARP method dynamically depending on the nature of stereo sound. In this chapter, an acoustic echo canceller based on WARP method which equips both monaural and stereo adaptive filters is discussed together with other gradient base stereo adaptive filter methods. The WARP method observes cross-channel correlation characteristics in stereo sound using short tap pre-adaptive filters. Pre-adaptive filter coefficients are used to calculate WARP functions which project monaural adaptive filter estimation results to stereo adaptive filter initial coefficients or vice-versa.

To clarify effectiveness WARP method, simple computer simulations are carried out using white Gaussian noise source and male voice, using 128tap NLMS cross-channel correlation estimator, 1000tap monaural NLMS adaptive filter for monaural echo canceller and 2x1000tap (2x500tap for voice) multi-channel NLMS adaptive filter for stereo echo canceller. Followings are summary of the results:

1. Considering sampling effect for analog delay, x6 over sampling system is assumed for stereo generation model. 5 far-end talker positions are assumed and direct wave sound from each talker is assumed to be picked up by far-end stereo microphone with far-end room background noise. The simulation results show we can attain good cross-channel transfer function estimation rapidly using 128tap adaptive filter if far-end noise S/N is reasonable (such as 20-40dB).
2. Using the far-end stereo generation model and cross-channel correlation estimation results, 1000tap NLMS monaural NLMS adaptive filter and 2-1000 tap stereo NLMS adaptive filters are used to clarify effectiveness of WARP method. In the simulation far-end talker changes are assumed to happen at every 80frames (1frame=100sample). Echo return loss Enhancement (ERLE) MORMalized estimation error power (NORM) are used as measurements. It is clarified that both ERLE and NORM are drastically improved at the far-end talker change by applying WARP operation.
3. Far-end S/N affects WARP performance, however, we can still attain around SN-5dB ERLE or NORM.
4. We find slight convergence improvement in the case of AP method (P=3) with non-linear operation. However, the improvement is much smaller than WARP at the far-end talker change. This is because sound source is white Gaussian noise in this simulation and therefore merit of AP method is not archived well.
5. Since WARP method assumes stereo echo path characteristics remain stable, stereo echo path characteristics change degrade WARP effectiveness. The simulation results show the degradation depends on how much stereo echo path moved and the degradation appears just after WARP projection.
6. WARP method works correctly actual voice sound too. Collaboration with AP method may improve total convergence speed further more because AP method improves convergence speed for voice independent from WARP effect.

As for further studies, more experiments in actual environments are necessary. The author would like to continue further researches to realize smooth and natural conversations in the future conversational DTV.

7. Appendix

If $N \times N$ matrix $\mathbf{Q}$ is defined as

$$\mathbf{Q} = \mathbf{X}_{2S}^{T}(k)\mathbf{G}^{T}\mathbf{G}\ \mathbf{X}_{2S}(k) \quad \text{(A-1)}$$

where $\mathbf{X}_{2S}(k)$ is a $(2P-1)$ sample array composed of white Gaussian noise sample $x\ (k)$ as

$$\begin{aligned} \mathbf{X}_{2S}(k) &= [\mathbf{x}\ (k), \mathbf{x}\ (k-1), \cdots \mathbf{x}\ (k-N+1)] \\ \mathbf{x}\ (k) &= [x\ (k), x\ (k-1), \cdots x\ (k-2p+2)]^{T} \end{aligned} \quad \text{(A-2)}$$

$\mathbf{G}$ is defined as a $(2P-1) \times P$ matrix as

$$\mathbf{G} = \begin{bmatrix} \mathbf{g}^{T} & 0 & \cdots & 0 \\ 0 & \mathbf{g}^{T} & \ddots & 0 \\ 0 & 0 & \cdots & 0 \\ 0 & 0 & \cdots & \mathbf{g}^{T} \end{bmatrix} \quad \text{(A-3)}$$

where $\mathbf{g}$ is P sample array defined as

$$\mathbf{g} = [g_0, g_1, \cdots, g_v \cdots g_{P-1}]^{T}. \quad \text{(A-4)}$$

Then $\langle \mathbf{Q} \rangle$ is a Toepliz matrix and is expressed using $P \times P$ ($P \le N$) Toepliz matrix $\langle \mathbf{Q}' \rangle$ as

$$\langle \mathbf{Q} \rangle = Tlz(\langle \mathbf{Q}' \rangle) \quad \text{(A-5)}$$

This is because $(u,v)th$ element of the matrix $\langle \mathbf{Q} \rangle$, $a_{TlZ}(u,v)$ is defined as

$$a_{TlZ}(u,v) = \left\langle \mathbf{x}^{T}(k-u)\mathbf{G}^{T}\mathbf{G}\ \mathbf{x}(k-v) \right\rangle. \quad \text{(A-6)}$$

Considering

$$\left\langle \mathbf{x}^{T}(k-u)\mathbf{G}^{T}\mathbf{G}\mathbf{x}\ (k-v) \right\rangle = 0 \cdots \text{for all } |u-v| \ge P \quad \text{(A-7)}$$

the element $a_{TlZ}(u,v)$ is given as

$$a_{TlZ}(u,v) = \begin{cases} a(u-v,0) \cdots P-1 \ge u-v \ge 0 \\ a(0,v-u) \cdots P-1 \ge v-u > 0 \\ 0 \cdots |u-v| \ge P \end{cases}. \quad \text{(A-8)}$$

By setting the (u,v) th element of $P \times P$ ($P \le N$) Toepliz matrix $\langle \mathbf{Q}' \rangle$ as $a_{TlZ}(u,v)$ ($(0 \le u < P, 0 \le v < P)$), we define a function $Tlz(\langle \mathbf{Q}' \rangle)$ which determines $N \times N$ Toepliz matrix $\mathbf{Q}$.

It is noted that if $\mathbf{Q}'$ is a identity matrix $\mathbf{Q}$ is also identity matrix.

8. References

J. Nagumo, "A Learning Identification Method for System Identification", IEEE Trans. AC. 12 No.3 Jun 1967 p282

M.M.Sondhi et.al. "Acoustic Echo Cancellation for Stereophonic Teleconferencing", Workshop on Applications of Signal Processing to Audio and Acoustics, May 1991.

Benesty. J, Amand. F, Gillorie A, Grenier Y, "adaptive filtering algorithm for a stereophonic echo cancellation" Proc. Of ICASSP-96, Vol.5, May 1996, 3099-3012..

J. Benesty, D.R. Morgan and M.M. Sondhi, "A better understanding and an improved solution to the specific problems of stereophonic acoustic echo canceller", IEEE Trans. Speech Audio Processing, vol. 6, No. 2 pp156-165, Mar 1998.

Bershad NJ, "Behavior of the ε -normalized LMS algorithm with Gaussian inputs", IEEE Transaction on Acoustic, Speech and Signal Processing 1987, ASSP-35(5): 636-644.

T. Fujii and S.Shimada, "A Note on Multi-Cannel Echo Cancelers," technical report of ICICE on CS, pp 7-14, Jan. 1984

A. Sugiyama, Y. Joncour and A. Hirano, "A stereo echo canceller with correct echo-path identification based on an input-sliding technique", IEEE Trans. On Signal Processing, vol. 49, No. 11, pp2577-2587 2001.

Jun-Mei Yang;Sakai,"Stereo acoustic echo cancellation using independent component analysis" IEEE, Proceedings of 2007

International Symposium on Intelligent Signal Processing and Communication Systems (USA) P.P.121-4

Jacob Benesty, R.Morgan, M. M. Sondhi, "A hybrid Momo/Stereo Acoustic Echo Canceller", IEEE Transactions on Speech and Audio Processing, Vol. 6. No. 5, September 1998.

S. Shimauchi, S.;Makino, S., "Stereo projection echo canceller with true echo path estimation", IEEE Proc. of ICASSP95, vol. 3662 P.P.3059-62 vol.5 PD:1995

S. Makino, K. Strauss, S. Shimauchi, Y. Haneda, and A.Nakagawa,"Subband Stereo Echo Canceller using the projection algorithm with fast convergence to the true echo path", IEEE Proc. of ICASSP 97, pp299-302, 1997

S. Shimauchi, S. Makino, Y. Haneda, and Y.Kaneda, "New configuration for a stereo echo canceller with nonlinier pre-processing", IEEE Proc. of ICASSP 98, pp3685-3688, 1998

S. Shimauchi, S. Makino, Y. Haneda, A. Nakagawa, S. Sakauchi, "A stereo echo canceller implemented using a stereo shaker and a duo-filter control system", IEEE ICASSP99 Vo. 2 pp857-60, 1999

Akira Nakagawa and Youichi Haneda, " A study of an adaptive algorithm for stereo signals with a power difference", IEEE ICASSP2002,Vol. 2, II-1913-16, 2002

S. Minami, "An Echo Canceller with Comp. & Decomposition of Estimated Echo Path Characteristics for TV Conference & Multi-Media Terminals", The 6th Karuizawa Workshop on Circuits and Sytstems, April 19-20 1993 pp 333-337

S.Minami,"An Acoustic Echo Canceler for Pseudo Stereophonic Voice", IEEE GLOBCOM'87 35.1 Nov. 1987

S.Minami, " A stereophonic Voice Coding Method for teleconferencing", IEEE ICCC. 86, 46.6, June 1986

Multi-Channel Acoustic Echo Canceller with Microphone/Speaker Array ITC-CSCC'09 pp 397-400 (2009)

WARP-AEC: A Stereo Acoustic Echo Canceller based on W-Adaptive filters for Rapid Projection IEEE ISPACS'09

10

EEG-fMRI Fusion: Adaptations of the Kalman Filter for Solving a High-Dimensional Spatio-Temporal Inverse Problem

Thomas Deneux[1,2]
[1]*Centre National de Recherche Scientifique, Institut de Neurosciences Cognitives de la Méditerranée, Marseille,*
[2]*Institut National de la Recherche en Informatique et Automatique, Sophia-Antipolis, France*

1. Introduction

Recording the dynamics of human brain activity is a key topic for both neuroscience fundamental research and medicine. The two main techniques used, Electro- and Magneto-encephalography (EEG/MEG) on the one hand, functional Magnetic Resonance Imaging (fMRI) on the other hand, measure different aspects of this activity, and have dramatically different temporal and spatial resolutions. There is an important literature dedicated to the analysis of EEG/MEG (REF) and fMRI data (REF). Indeed, the both techniques provide partial and noisy measures of the hidden neural activity, and sophisticated methods are needed to reconstruct this activity as precisely as possible. Adaptive filtering algorithms seem well-adapted to this reconstruction, since the problem can easily be formulated as a dynamic system, but it is only recently that such formulations have been proposed for EEG analysis (Jun et al., 2005), fMRI analysis (Johnston et al., 2008; Murray & Storkey, 2008; Riera et al., 2004), or EEG-fMRI fusion (Deneux & Faugeras, 2006b; Plis et al., 2010).

In this chapter, we focus on the so-called "EEG-fMRI fusion", i.e. the joint analysis of EEG/MEG and fMRI data obtained on the same experiment. For more than a decade, EEG-fMRI fusion has become a hot topic, because it is believed that both techniques used together should provide higher levels of information on brain activity, by taking advantage of the high temporal resolution of EEG, and spatial resolution of fMRI. However, the two modalities and their underlying principles are so different from each other that the proposed solutions were often *ad hoc*, and lacked a common formalism. We show here how the use of dynamic system formulation and adaptive filter algorithms appears to be a natural way to achieve the EEG-fMRI fusion.

However, not only do adaptive filtering techniques offer new possibilities for the EEG-fMRI fusion, but also this specific problem brings new challenges and fosters the development of new filtering algorithms. These challenges are mostly a very high dimensionality, due to the entanglement between the temporal and spatial dimensions, and high levels of non-linearity, due to the complexity of the physiological processes involved. Thus, we will present some new developments that we issued, in particular, the design of a variation of the Kalman filter and smoother which performs a bi-directional sweep, first backward and second forward. And we will show directions for the development of new algorithms.

The results presented in this chapter have already been published in (Deneux and Faugeras, 2010). Therefore, we focus more here on explaining in detail our comprehension of the EEG-fMRI fusion problem, and of its solution through the design of new algorithms. In this introduction, we pose the problem, its specific difficulties, and advocate the use of adaptive filters to solve it. In a second part, we will tackle a simplified, linear, problem: we present our Kalman-based fusion algorithm, discuss its characteristics and prove that it is more suitable to estimate smooth activities, while the estimation of sparse activities would rather necessitate the development of new algorithms based on the minimization of a L^1-norm. In a third part, we will address the problem of strong nonlinearities: we present a modification of the Kalman-based algorithm, and also call for the development of new, more flexible, methods based for example on particle filters.

1.1 Physiological basis of EEG/MEG and fMRI

Figure 1(A) briefly explains how the cerebral activity gives raise to the EEG/MEG and fMRI signals. EEG and MEG measure directly the electrical activity in the brain. In the case of EEG, a set of electrodes (up to 300 in the most advanced EEG helmets) are positioned on the head of the subject, in electric contact with the skin, and measure an electric potential. In the case of MEG, a set of coils are positioned around the head but without touching it, and measure the magnetic field generated by the currents circulating inside the head. These currents themselves are the consequence of the electric activity of a large number of neurons which are activated together. EEG and MEG have an excellent temporal resolution, since the propagation of currents is instantaneous at this temporal scale. They also provide some spatial information, since it is possible to model the current propagation and then solve an inverse problem to localize the activity which generated the specific pattern observed over the different sensors (Hämäläinen et al., 1993). The spatial resolution of this localization however is poor (error range of ~1cm); even, this inverse problem is ill-posed since some sources configurations can generate no signal on the sensors.

fMRI measures secondary effects of the electrical activity, called the hemodynamic response. Indeed, the increased energy consumption in an activated brain region leads to a chain of events, in particular a higher O_2 extraction from the blood, followed by an increase in the blood flow. This impacts the magnetic resonance signals recorded by the MRI scanner, because of the changes in the concentration of the deoxyhemoglobine molecule. Indeed, the magnetic properties of the hemoglobin molecule change after it delivered the oxygen molecule it was carrying, which induces higher decays of the magnetic resonance signals. All in one, a cerebral activity leads to a smooth increase in the MRI signal, also called blood-oxygen level dependent (BOLD) signal; this increase lasts for a few (3~4) seconds, and is usually followed by a small undershoot (Ogawa et al., 1993). This BOLD signal is localized with a millimeter or sub-millimeter precision but, obviously, lacks temporal resolution.

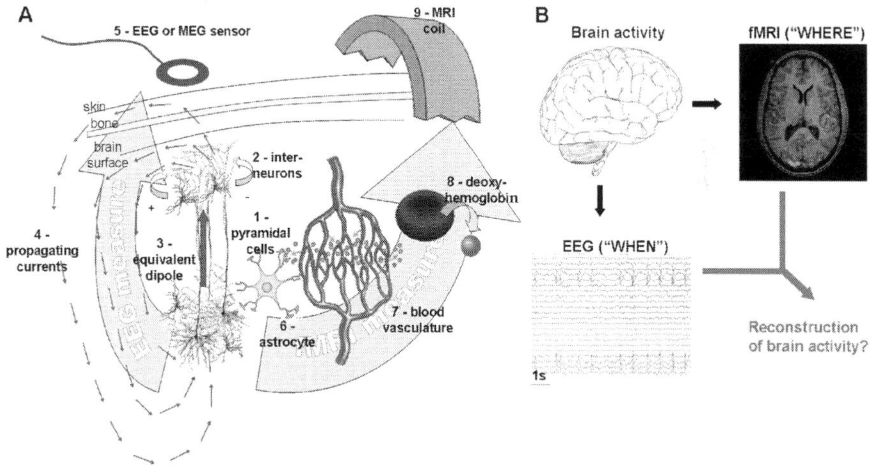

Fig. 1. (A) Physiological basis: this figure briefly summarizes the main effects giving rise to the measured signals. For the EEG/MEG: the brain gray matter is organized in cortical columns where large number of cells work synchronously; in particular, the large pyramidal cells (1), which have a characteristic parallel vertical organization, but also other cellular types such as the smaller interneurons (2); when synchrony is sufficiently large, the electrical activities of the neurons sum up together, and can be represented by an equivalent dipole (3), which generate circulating currents (4) through the brain and even outside of it; EEG sensors touching the skin, or MEG sensors placed close to it (5) can detect voltage differences, or currents, generated by the neural activity. For the functional MRI: neuronal activity (1,2) consumes energy, which is provided by the astrocytes (6), which themselves extract glucose and oxygen from the blood, and regulate the blood flow in the cerebral vasculature; this affects the concentration of deoxyhemoglobin, i.e. hemoglobin which delivered its oxygen molecule; deoxyhemoglobin itself, due to its paramagnetic properties, perturbs the local magnetic field and modifies the magnetic resonance signals recorded by the MRI coil (9). (B) EEG-fMRI fusion: EEG or MEG capture mostly temporal information about the unknown brain activity: the electric signals measured by the sensors on the scalp. On the contrary, fMRI captures mostly spatial information, which leads to precise maps showing which brain regions are active. Ideally, EEG-fMRI fusion should produce an estimation of the activity which takes into account these complimentary information.

It thus appears that EEG/MEG and fMRI recordings are complimentary (Figure 1(B)), the first providing more information on the timing of the studied activity, the second, on its localization. Therefore, many experimental studies combine acquisitions using the two modalities. Such acquisitions can be performed separately, by repeating the same experimental paradigm under both modalities: in such case, averaging over multiple repetitions will be necessary to reduce the trial-to-trial variability. Also, simultaneous acquisition of EEG and fMRI is possible and found specific application in the study of epilepsy (Bénar et al., 2003; Gotman et al., 2004; Lemieux, et al., 2001; Waites et al., 2005) and resting states (Goldman et al., 2002; Laufs et al., 2003) (note that, since on the contrary MEG cannot be acquired simultaneously with fMRI, we focus here on EEG-fMRI fusion; however, our results will remain true for MEG-fMRI fusion in the context of separate average acquisitions). Apart from a few trivial cases, the joint analysis of the two dataset in order to best reconstruct the observed neural activity presents several specific challenges

1.2 Challenges of EEG-fMRI fusion

1.2.1 Concepts

Many different approaches and strategies have been proposed for EEG-fMRI fusion. Reviews such as (Daunizeau et al., 2010; Rosa et al., 2010) propose different criteria to classify them, two important ones being (i) whether the method is symmetric or not, and (ii) what information do EEG and fMRI share: spatial information, temporal information, or both?

Here, we use schematic examples to help explaining about these different methods. Figure 2(A) shows a very simple example where brain activity only consists of a unique event, which occurs at a specific location and with a specific dynamic. Then, this activity can be fully reconstructed as the cross-product of the spatial information provided by fMRI and the temporal information provided by EEG. On the contrary, in figure 2(B), several events occur at distinct instants and distinct locations, and then more information is needed to determine which part of the signals corresponds to which event. For example, if only spatial information is extracted from fMRI (find 2 regions which are activated), then the weak spatial resolution of the EEG must be used to determine which of the signals it records are likely to originate from the first region or from the second: this is the principle of non-symmetric fMRI-guided EEG reconstructions (Ahlfors et al., 2004). Conversely, one could only extract dynamics from the EEG data, and then use the weak temporal resolution of fMRI to determine which regions in the brain match those dynamics: this is the principle of non-symmetric fMRI analysis based on EEG regressors used in epilepsy, for example (Grova et al., 2008) and rest studies (Laufs et al., 2003). In fact, these two examples are very useful to help understand any EEG-fMRI method, even when additional levels of complexity are added, for example in region-based algorithms which rely on a known parcellation of the cortex (Daunizeau et al., 2007; Ou et al. 2010). And they rather call for the use of symmetric methods, which extract both spatial and temporal information from both the EEG and fMRI.

Figure 2(C) sketches a more complex pattern of activity, and the corresponding EEG and fMRI measures. EEG has the same temporal resolution as the neural activity, but its spatial dimension is smaller, indicating loss of information; and the opposite is true for fMRI. Then, each modality could be used alone to estimate the original activity, while obviously the best estimate should be obtained when using the two datasets.

1.2.2 High dimensionality

Figure 2(C) also introduces a Bayesian formalism to describe EEG-fMRI fusion. If we note u the neural activity, y^{EEG} and y^{fMRI} the EEG and fMRI measures, the aim of fusion is to estimate u given y^{EEG} and y^{fMRI}, or even better, its a posteriori distribution $p(u \mid y^{EEG}, y^{fMRI})$. It would then be also possible to compute a posteriori distribution when considering only one of the modalities, $p(u \mid y^{EEG})$ and $p(u \mid y^{fMRI})$.

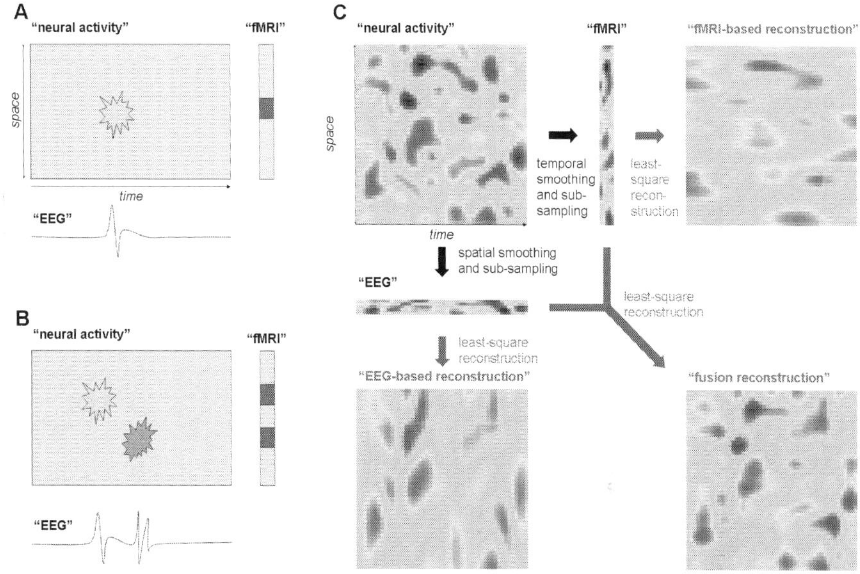

Fig. 2. Schematic representations of EEG-fMRI fusion. (A) The neural activity dynamics are represented by a 2-dimensional array (x-axis is time, y-axis is space). A yellow pattern inside this array marks a single event; the location of this event can be identified precisely by fMRI (red mark), and its exact dynamic can be recorded by the EEG (time courses). In such case, these only information, i.e. spatial information from the fMRI and temporal information from the EEG are sufficient to fully describe the event. (B) The same schematics are used, but two events occur now, at two different locations and with different dynamics (see the yellow and orange patterns). In such case, the sole spatial information from fMRI and temporal information from EEG is not sufficient to fully describe the events since it is not possible to determine which part of these information correspond to which event. (C) Now, a similar spatio-temporal array features a complex activity. Both the temporal and spatial dimensions of EEG and fMRI are considered: the fMRI [EEG, resp.] measure is represented by a narrow vertical [horizontal] array to indicate a reduced temporal [spatial] resolution; more precisely, these measures were obtained by low-pass filtering and sub-sampling the neural activity along the appropriate dimension. The "EEG-fMRI fusion" problem consists in estimating the neural activity given the two measures, and should result in a better reconstruction than when using only the EEG or the fMRI measures (it is indeed the case here, since fMRI-only reconstruction lacks spatial precision, and EEG-only reconstruction lacks temporal resolution).

As we noticed above, the temporal dimension and spatial dimension are highly entangled in the EEG-fMRI fusion problem. Indeed, one EEG measure at time t on a specific sensor is influenced by neural activity at time t in a large part of the cortex if not all; and conversely, one fMRI measure at time t and at a specific spatial location x is influenced by neural activity during the last ~10 seconds before t at location x. Therefore, traditional approaches estimate $p(u \mid y^{EEG})$ independently for each time point, and $p(u \mid y^{fMRI})$ independently for each spatial location. But it is not possible to "cut the problem in smaller pieces" in order to estimate p(u | y^{EEG}, y^{fMRI}). This results in an inverse problem of very high dimensionality: the dimension of u, which surely depends on the temporal and spatial resolution used. If we choose for u the spatial resolution of fMRI, and the temporal resolution of EEG, then its dimension is the product of several thousands of spatial locations (number of cortical sources) by up to one thousand of time instants per second of experiment (for an EEG sampling rate at 1kHz).

If the experimental data is averaged over repetitions of a specific paradigm, then its total temporal length can be limited to a few seconds, such that the temporal and spatial sizes of u are in the same range. On the contrary, if the interest is in estimating the neural activity without any averaging, the length can be of several minutes or more, and the temporal size of u becomes extremely large. It is in this case that adaptive filter techniques are particularly interesting. Also, it is obvious that, although fMRI measures depend on activity which occurred in the last ~10s, they are independent from earlier activities; therefore, the adaptive filter will need to keep in memory some information in order to link the delayed detections of the activity by EEG and fMRI, but this memory does not need either to cover the full extent of the experiment.

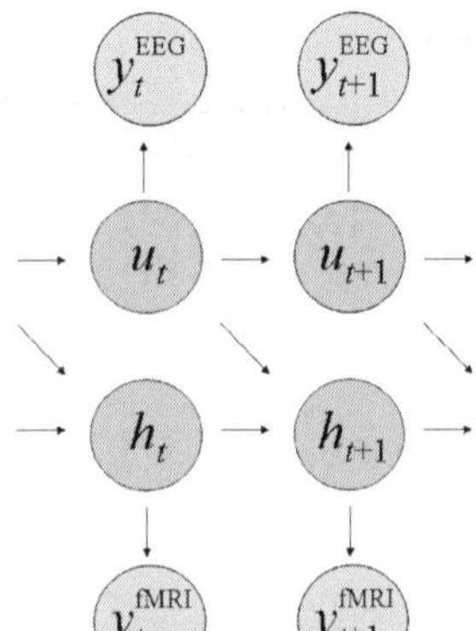

Fig. 3. Graphical representation of the forward model. This model features the evolution of the neural activity u, and of the hemodynamic activity h (driven by the neural activity), the EEG measure y^{EEG} (which depends only on the neural activity), and the fMRI measure (which depends directly only on the hemodynamic state, and hence depends indirectly on the neural activity). Blue background indicate measures, which are known, while orange background indicate hidden states, which have to be estimated from the measures.

The graph in figure 3 represents the forward model which will guide us in designing algorithms for EEG-fMRI fusion. The neural activity at time t, u_t, has its own evolution, and is driving the evolution of metabolic and hemodynamic variables, such as oxygen and glucose consumption, blood flow, volume and oxygenation, represented altogether by the variable h_t. At time t, the EEG measure is a function only of neural activity at the same time, while the fMRI measure is a function of the hemodynamic state. Note that the acquisition rate of fMRI is in fact much lower than that of EEG, but it can be useful for the sake of simplicity to re-interpolate it at the rate of EEG, without loss in the algorithm capabilities (Plis et al., 2010).

1.2.3 Nonlinearity

The second challenge of EEG-fMRI fusion is the high level of nonlinearity which can exist in the forward model depicted in figure 3. To make it clear, let us first show how this graph corresponds to the physiological models depicted in figure 1. Clearly, EEG measure y_t^{EEG} is the signal recorded by the set of EEG sensors (5) and fMRI measure y_t^{fMRI} is the MRI image reconstructed after resonance signals have been recorded by the MRI coil (9). The metabolic/hemodynamic state h_t is the state of all elements involved in the hemodynamic response (6,7,8). The case of the so-called "neural activity" u_t is more delicate, since it can be either a complex description of the actual activities of different types of neurons (1,2), or simply the electric dipole that averages electrical activities in a small region (3).

And here resides the main source of nonlinearity. Indeed, different types of neuronal activities can lead to the same energy consumption and hence to similar fMRI signals, and yet, average into very different equivalent dipoles of current. For example, some activity can result in a dipole with an opposite orientation, or even can be invisible to the EEG. This explains in particular that some activity can bee seen only by fMRI (when electrical activities do not have a preferred current orientation), or only by EEG (when a large area has a low-amplitude but massively parallel activity).

Besides, authors have also often emphasized the nonlinearity of the hemodynamic process (transition $h_t \rightarrow h_{t+!}$), but in fact these nonlinearities, for example those found in the "Balloon Model" modeling (Buxton et al., 2004), are less important, and linear approximations can be used as long as the error they introduce does not exceed the level of noise in the data (Deneux et al., 2006a). Note also that the spatial extent of the hemodynamic response to a local activity can be larger than that of the activity itself, since changes can be elicited in neighboring vessels; however, such distant hemodynamic effects can still be a linear function of the local activity. In any case, such small discrepancies in the spatial domain are usually ignored, mostly because of a lack of knowledge.

As a summary, EEG-fMRI fusion is a difficult problem, because of its high dimensionality, where space and time are intrinsically entangled, and because of nonlinear relations - and surely a lack of robust knowledge - at the level of the underlying link between electric and hemodynamic activities. Therefore, different approaches are proposed to tackle these difficulties. The aforementioned non-symmetric methods are efficient in specific experimental situations. Region-based methods decrease the dimensionality by clustering the source space according to physiologically-based. Here, we do not attempt to decrease the dimensionality, or simplify the inverse problem, but we propose the use of adaptive filters to solve it.

2. Kalman-based estimation under the linear assumption

We first prove the feasibility of EEG-fMRI fusion using adaptive filters under the linear assumption, i.e. we ignore the last comments about nonlinearity and rather assume a straight, linear, relation between the electric activity (modeled as the amplitude of a current dipole directed outward the brain surface) and the energy consumption and hemodynamic changes. The inverse problem can then be solved using the Kalman filter and smoother. We show estimation results on simulated dataset using a neural activity spread on 2000 cortical sources, sampled at 200Hz, during one minute. Since we observe that the method performs better when the activity is smooth rather than sparse, we use schematic examples to prove that indeed, this is the consequence of the minimization of a L^2-norm by the Kalman algorithm, while new algorithms which would minimize a L^1-norm would be more adapted to the estimation of sparse activities.

2.1 Methods

2.1.1 Kalman filter and smoother

The forward model summarized in figure 3 can be simply described in the dynamic model formalism:

$$\begin{cases} \dot{x}(t) = F(x(t)) + \xi(t) \\ y(t) = G(x(t)) + \eta(t) \end{cases}, \tag{1}$$

where the $x(t)$, the *hidden state*, is the combination of the neural activity $u(t)$ and the hemodynamic state $h(t)$, and $y(t)$, the *measure*, is the combination of $y^{EEG}(t)$ and $y^{fMRI}(t)$, $\xi(t)$ is a white noise process, and $\eta(t)$ a Gaussian noise. Once time is discretized and the evolution and measure equations are linearized, it yields:

$$\begin{cases} x_1 = x^0 + \xi^0, & \xi^0 \sim N(0,Q^0) \\ x_{k+1} = Ax_k + \xi_k, & \xi_k \sim N(0,Q) \\ y_k = Dx_x + \eta_k, & \eta_k \sim N(0,R) \end{cases}, \tag{2}$$

where A and D are the evolution and measure matrices, obtained by linearization of F and G, $N(0,Q^0)$ is the Gaussian initial a priori distribution of the hidden state, and $N(0,Q)$ and $N(0,R)$ are the Gaussian distributions of the evolution and measure noises.

Estimating the hidden state given the measures is performed with the 2 steps of the Kalman filter and smoother (Kalman, 1960; Welch & Bishop, 2006; Welling, n.d.). The first step runs forward and successively estimates the distributions $p(x_k \mid y_1,\ldots,y_k)$ for increasing values of k. The second runs backward and estimates $p(x_k \mid y_1,\ldots,y_n)$ for decreasing values of k (n being the total number of measure points).

We recall here the equations for this estimation, for which we introduce the following notation (note that all distributions are Gaussian, therefore they are fully described by their mean and variance):

$$\begin{aligned} \hat{x}_k^l &= E(x_k \mid y_1,\ldots,y_l) \\ P_k^l &= V(x_k \mid y_1,\ldots,y_l) \end{aligned}. \tag{3}$$

First, the Kalman filters starts with the a priori distribution of x_1:

$$\begin{aligned} \hat{x}_1^0 &= x^0 \\ P_1^0 &= Q^0 \end{aligned}, \tag{4}$$

then repeats for $k = 1, 2, \ldots, n$ the "measurement update":

$$\begin{aligned} K &= P_k^{k-1} D^T (D P_k^{k-1} D^T + R)^{-1} \\ \hat{x}_k^k &= \hat{x}_k^{k-1} + K(y_k - D\hat{x}_k^{k-1}) \\ P_k^k &= (I - KD) P_k^{k-1} \end{aligned}, \tag{5}$$

and the "time update":

$$\begin{aligned} \hat{x}_{k+1}^{k} &= A\hat{x}_{k}^{k} \\ P_{k+1}^{k} &= AP_{k}^{k}A^{T} + Q \end{aligned} . \tag{6}$$

Second, the Kalman smoother repeats for $k = n\text{-}1, n\text{-}2, \ldots, 1$:

$$\begin{aligned} J &= P_{k}^{k}A^{T}(P_{k+1}^{k})^{-1} \\ \hat{x}_{k}^{n} &= \hat{x}_{k}^{k} + J(\hat{x}_{k+1}^{n} - \hat{x}_{k+1}^{k}) \\ P_{k}^{n} &= P_{k}^{k} + J(P_{k+1}^{n} - P_{k+1}^{k})J^{T} \end{aligned} . \tag{7}$$

Specific details about the implementation of the algorithm will be mentioned in the discussion sub-section below.

2.1.2 Physiological models

Now, we give detail on the evolution and measure functions and noises, by modeling explicitly each transition in figure 3.
The neural evolution is modeled by an auto-regressive Ornstein-Uhlenbeck process:

$$\dot{u}(t) = -\lambda u(t) + \xi_{u}(t), \tag{8}$$

where λ is a positive parameter which controls the temporal autocorrelation of sources time courses ($\langle u(t)u(t+\Delta t)\rangle / \langle u(t)u(t)\rangle = \exp(-\lambda\,\Delta t)$), and ξ_u is a Gaussian innovation noise. This noise is white in time, but can be made smooth in space and thus make u itself smooth in space, by setting its variance matrix such that it penalizes the sum of square differences between neighboring locations.
Since u represents here the amplitudes of equivalent dipoles of current at the sources locations, the EEG measure is a linear function of it:

$$y^{EEG}(t) = Bu(t) + \eta^{EEG}(t), \tag{9}$$

where B is the matrix of the EEG forward problem, constructed according to the Maxwell equations for the propagation of currents through the different tissues and through the skull (Hamalainen et al. 1993). The measure noise $\eta^{EEG}(t)$ is Gaussian and independent in time and space.
Finally, the hemodynamic state evolution and the fMRI measure are modeled using the Balloon Model introduced by R. Buxton (Buxton et al., 2004):

$$\begin{cases} \ddot{f}(t) &= \varepsilon u - \kappa_{s}\dot{f}(t) - \kappa_{f}(f(t)-1) \\ \dot{v}(t) &= \dfrac{1}{\tau}(f(t) - v(t)^{1/\alpha}) \\ \dot{q}(t) &= \dfrac{1}{\tau}(f(t)\dfrac{1-(1-E_{0})^{1/f(t)}}{E_{0}} - v(t)^{1/\alpha}\dfrac{q(t)}{v(t)}) \\ y^{fMRI}(t) &= V_{0}(a_{1}(v(t)-1) + a_{2}(q(t)-1)) + \eta^{fMRI}(t) \end{cases}, \tag{10}$$

where the hemodynamic state $h(t)$ is represented by four variables: the blood flow $f(t)$, its time derivative, the blood flow $v(t)$ and the blood oxygenation $q(t)$. ε, κ_s, κ_f, τ, α, E_0, V_0, a_1 and a_2 are physiological parameters. The measure noise $\eta^{fMRI}(t)$ is Gaussian and independent in time and space.

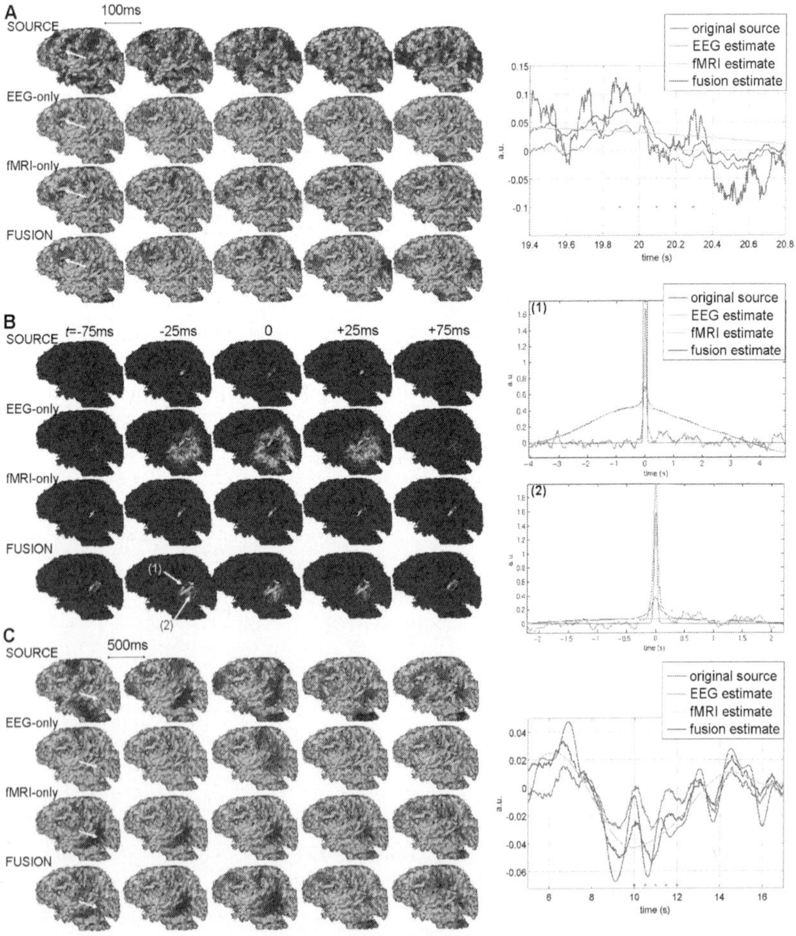

Fig. 4. EEG-fMRI fusion using the linear Kalman filter and smoother. (A) A neural activity has been generated on 2,000 sources spread on the cortical surface according to the model, then EEG and fMRI measures of this activity were generated. 5 snapshots of the activity at intervals of 100ms are shown (row 'SOURCE'). Below are shown the Kalman reconstruction using only EEG measures ('EEG-only'), only fMRI measures ('fMRI-only'), or both together ('FUSION'). Noticeable, EEG estimate is very smooth in space, fMRI estimate is varies very slowly in time, and the fusion estimate is the closest to the true activity. The white arrows indicate one particular source location, and the graph on the right compares the time courses of the true activity of this source with its three estimations. We can also observe that the fMRI estimate is much smoother than the EEG estimate, and that the fusion estimate is the closest to the true signal. (B) In a second simulation, neural activity was chosen to represent a brief (50ms) activation of a few neighboring sources. Similar displays show that EEG finds a brief but spread activity, fMRI find a precisely localized but slow activity, and the fusion estimates finds

a trade-off between the two of them. Two locations are shown with arrows: the center of the true activity, and the center of the activity found by EEG alone: again, the two graphs on the right show how the fusion algorithm finds a trade-off between the two previous estimates.
(C) In a third simulation, the generated activity is smooth in both time and space. The results are similar to (A), and it appears even more clearly that the fusion algorithm efficiently combines information provided by EEG and fMRI.

Note that the above physiological parameters, as well as the variances of the different evolution and measure noise, are fixed to some physiologically-meaningful values (Friston et al., 2000) for both simulation and estimation.

2.2 Results

We used the forward model (equation (8)) to generate a random neural activity at 2000 source locations spread on the cortical surface, for a time duration of 1 min, at a 200Hz sampling rate (Figure 4(A), first row). And to generate EEG (equation (9)) and fMRI measures (equation (10)) of this activity. Then, the Kalman filter and smoother (equations (4)-(7)) were used to estimate the initial activity, based either on the EEG measure alone, fMRI measure, or both together. Figure 4 shows these estimation results and compares them to the true initial activity: the left part compares snapshots of the activity map (both true and estimated) at different time instants, and the right part compares the true and estimated time courses of one selected source.

Specific characteristics of the estimation results can be observed: the EEG-alone estimations are very smooth spatially, but change fast in time; inversely, the fMRI-alone estimations have more spatial details, but vary very slowly in time; finally, the fusion estimations are the most similar to the true activity. All this is in accordance with the idea that EEG-fMRI should combine the good temporal resolution of EEG and good spatial resolution of fMRI. More quantitatively, table 1 (first column) shows indeed that the fusion estimate is the one which best correlates the true activity. Even, the part of variance explained by the fusion estimate is almost equal to the sum of the parts of variance explained by the EEG and fMRI estimates, indicating that the two modalities capture complimentary rather than redundant information, and that the fusion algorithm efficiently combines these information.

% correlation (and % of variance explained)	*Activity generated by the forward model*	*Sparse activity*	*Smooth activity*
EEG estimate	29.7 (8.8)	7.2 (-14.3)	54.5 (27.6)
fMRI estimate	33.9 (11.5)	7.7 (0.4)	63.6 (40.4)
Fusion estimate	43.1 (18.6)	11.0 (1.1)	74.1 (54.6)

Table 1. **Quantification of estimation accuracies in the case of three different simulations.** We use two different measurements of how good an estimate $\hat{u}$ fits the real signal u, both expressed in percentages. The first is the correlation $< u,\hat{u} > / \| u \|_2 \| \hat{u} \|_2$; it is important to note that correlation does not inform whether signals were estimated with the correct amplitude (the correlation is 1 if the signals are only proportionals). Thus we also use the percentage of variance of source u explained by estimate $\hat{u}$, defined as $1 - \| u - \hat{u} \|_2^2 / \| u \|_2^2$; note that it can be negative even if the correlation if positive, in the case where subtracting $\hat{u}$ to u does not decrease the variance of u (i.e. when the part of the variance of $\hat{u}$ which really accounts for some variance present in u is less than the part of pure estimation error).

This is shown with even more details in figure 5, where true and estimated activities have been decomposed as sums of activities in specific temporal and spatial bandwidths. Thus, the goodness of fit could be computed independently for different temporal and spatial frequencies. We can observe then that fMRI estimates accurately activities with low temporal frequencies (blue surface), while EEG best estimates activities with low spatial frequencies (green surface). And the EEG-fMRI fusion (yellow surface) efficiently combines information provided by both measures, since it provides a better fit than both measures in any frequency domain.

As a result, it appears that EEG-fMRI fusion gives the best performances on activities which are smooth both in time and space, as opposed to fast-varying activities. We illustrated this result by producing two additional simulations. First, we generated a very sparse and focused activity, by activating only a small number of neighboring sources during a short period of time (50ms). Second, we generated a smooth activity, by performing a temporal and a spatial low-pass filtering of activity generated by the model. In both cases, we used the model to generate corresponding EEG and fMRI measures, and then estimated the activity: results are shown in figure 4, parts B and C, and the goodness of fit are displayed in table 1, two rightmost columns. In both cases EEG and fMRI succeed in collaborating to produce a fusion estimation better than they do alone. As expected from the previous considerations, the fusion is very satisfying on the smooth dataset, and more than 50% of the variance of the true sources activity is explained. On the contrary, its result on the sparse activity is disappointing: it seems to give an average of the EEG and fMRI estimates rather than recovering the focused activity.

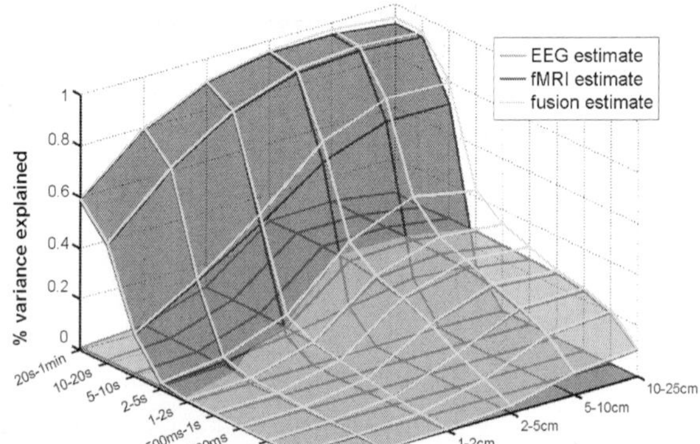

Fig. 5. Spectral analysis of EEG-fMRI fusion efficiency. The correspondence between the true activity and estimated activity are quantified independently in separate temporal and spatial frequency domains, using the percentage of variance explained as in table 1. We observe that fMRI estimation is accurate at low time frequencies, while EEG estimation is accurate at low spatial frequencies. The fusion estimation is efficient, in the sense that its accuracy is superior to both EEG and fMRI estimations in all frequency domains, and in some specific domains where EEG and fMRI do bring complementary information (at temporal scale of 1~10s and spatial scale >2cm), it yields even higher values by combining these information.

2.3 Discussion

2.3.1 Computational cost

Our simulations prove the feasibility of EEG-fMRI fusion at a realistic scale despite its high dimensionality, at least in the case of a linear forward model, using the Kalman filter and smoother algorithms. We would like to stress here the specific aspects of their implementation which made it possible, and further improvements which are desirable.

First of all, it is important to note that the fact that we used a linear model was critical for keeping a reasonable computational cost, because the Kalman filter and smoother exhibit some particular properties which would have been lost if we had used the extended Kalman filter to run estimations using the exact nonlinear equations (in particular, equation (10)). Indeed, the most costly operations are the matrix computations in equations (5)-(7). The P_k^{k-1} and P_k^k variance matrices describe the degree of certitude about the hidden state estimation just before and after the measure update; they obviously depend on the characteristics of the noise (matrices Q^0, Q and R), but, in the case of the linear Kalman filter, they do not depend on the values of the measurements y_k. Moreover, they converge to some limits (Welling, n.d.), which we note $\overline{P}$ and $\hat{P}$, when $k \to +\infty$; these limits are the solutions of the system:

$$\begin{cases} K = \overline{P}D^T(D\overline{P}D^T + R)^{-1} \\ \hat{P} = (I - KD)\overline{P} \\ \overline{P} = A\hat{P}A^T + Q \end{cases} . \tag{11}$$

Therefore, the variance matrices can be pre-computed, and for values of k sufficiently large, it is possible to use $\overline{P}$ and $\hat{P}$ instead, which in the case of long experiments decreases dramatically the number of times that the matrix operations in (5) and (6) must be performed. We can even go one step further by choosing $Q^0 = \overline{P}$: then, for all k we have $P_k^{k-1} = \overline{P}$ and $P_k^k = \hat{P}$. This choice for Q^0 is equivalent to saying that at time 0 the system has been running for a long time already according to its natural evolution equations, and that we have an information on its state from previous measures; since in fact such previous measures do not exist, this a priori variance is too small, which could have the consequence that the beginning of the estimated sequence underfits the measures; however we did not observe important estimation errors in the beginning of our simulations; on the other hand this choice is particularly convenient in terms of computational and memory cost.

The EEG-fMRI fusion algorithm can then be performed the following way:

- Apply iteratively the matrix computations in (5) and (6) until P_k^{k-1} and P_k^k converge to their limits $\overline{P}$ and $\hat{P}$, starting with $P_1^0 = Q$ and stopping after a number of iterations determined heuristically
- Compute $K = \overline{P}D^T(D\overline{P}D^T + R)^{-1}$ and $J = \hat{P}A\overline{P}^{-1}$
- Apply the vector operations in equations (5), (6) and (7) to compute the estimation of the hidden states, using for all k $P_k^{k-1} = \overline{P}$ and $P_k^k = \hat{P}$. Note that it is not necessary to compute the values of the P_k^n variance matrices.

The total computational cost is determined by the cost of the first step, the matrix convergence. The time complexity of this convergence is $O(n^3 f_s)$, where n is the number of cortical sources, and f_s the sampling frequency: indeed, the limiting factor is the

multiplication of matrices of size O(n), repeated O(f_s) times to reach the convergence. Since memory limitation can also occur for large values of n, it is also important to know the space complexity: it is equal to O(n^2), the number of elements of the variance matrices. For our simulations, the convergence of the variance matrices (300 iterations) took 24 hours on an AMD Opteron 285, 2.6GHz, and occupied 5Gb RAM. Since we used n = 2,000 sources, and since the size of the hidden state $x(t) = \{u(t),h(t)\}$ is $5n$, it involved multiplications and inversion of square matrices of size 10,000.
One should note that such size is in fact quite small, compared to the total size of the neural activity to be estimated. For example, in our simulation the number of elements of u is $n*f_s*T$ = 2,000*200*60 = 24,000,000. As mentioned in the introduction, decreasing this dimensionality was made possible by the use of adaptive filtering.

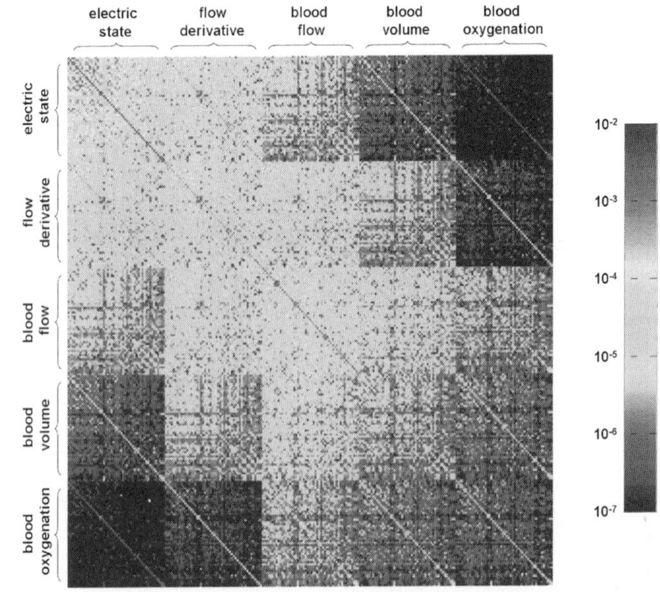

Fig. 6. Structure of the Kalman covariance matrices, displayed at a logarithmic scale. An example variance matrix is shown: the $\hat{P}$ matrix obtained after convergence of the P_k^k, in the case of a low-dimension simulation with 50 sources. Since the hidden state $x(t)$ is the concatenation of the electric state $u(t)$ and the four hemodynamic variables in $h(t)$, this matrix, which expresses the a posteriori variance of $x(t)$ given all measures at $t'<t$ is organized by blocks: the first block is the a posteriori variance of $u(t)$, the next diagonal blocks are the variances of the hemodynamic states, and the other blocks are covariances between different states. Within one block, the diagonal contains the variances for individual sources, while the other elements are covariance between different sources. Although the matrix is dense, it is highly structured, and a large number of values are very small (note the logarithmic scale: 6 orders of magnitudes are displayed): we suggest that future work will study this structure and the convergence process, and look for ways to decrease its computational cost.

A promising direction for decreasing the computational cost would be to describe the variance matrices in a more compact way than full symmetric matrices. Indeed, although the matrices are not sparse, they exhibit some specific structure, as shown in figure 6, and studying carefully this structure should enable the description of the matrices using a lower dimension representation. Maybe even these matrices can be only approximated: indeed, they contain covariance information between all pairs of hidden states, for example between the electric state at a first location and the hemodynamic state at second distant location, which is not necessarily critical for the estimation. However, it must be ensured that approximations do not affect the numerical stability of the algorithm.
Another approach would be to use specialized numerical methods in order to reach faster the convergences of matrices $\overline{P}$ and $\hat{P}$, unless an analytic expression as a function of Q and R can be derived!

2.3.2 Algorithm

Our simulations showed that using the Kalman filter and smoother to perform EEG-fMRI fusion is efficient when estimating an activity which is smooth in space and time. In such case indeed, the effects of the disparity between the resolutions of both modalities are attenuated, therefore the information they provide on the underlying neural activity can be combined together in an efficient way.
On the contrary, when estimating a sparse and focused activity as in figure 4(B), results are more disappointing. The EEG-only estimation is focused in time, but spread and imprecise in space, while the fMRI-only estimation is focused in space, but spread in time. Thus, an ideal fusion algorithm should be able to reconstruct an activity focalized both in time and space. But instead, our fusion estimate looks more like an average between the EEG-only and fMRI-only estimates.
In fact, this is a direct consequence of using the Kalman filter; even, this is a consequence of using Bayesian methods which assume Gaussian distributions! Indeed, when using the Kalman filter or any such method, the a priori distribution of the neural activity u is a Gaussian (fully described in our case by the initial distribution $p(u_1)$ and the Markov chain relation $p(u_{k+1} \mid u_k)$), and estimating u will rely on a term which minimizes a L^2-norm of u (i.e. a weighted sum of square differences). We show using schematic examples that the minimization of a L^2-norm results in solutions which are smooth rather than sparse, and in the case of two measures of the same activity u which have very different temporal and spatial resolution, estimation results show similar pattern as observed above with two components, one smooth in time, the other smooth in space.
These examples are as in figure 2(C): a 2-dimensional array represents u, one dimension standing for time and the second for space. We use a simple forward model: "EEG" and "fMRI" measures are obtained by low-pass filtering and subsampling u in the spatial and temporal dimension, respectively, resulting in lower resolution versions of u. The corresponding inverse problem - estimate u given the two measures - is then strongly under-determined, as is the real EEG-fMRI fusion inverse problem, and some constraint can be imposed on the estimated $\hat{u}$ in order to decide between an infinity of solutions. We compared minimizing the L^2-norm of $\hat{u}$, i.e. its mean square, and minimizing the L^1-norm, i.e. its mean absolute value. Figure 7 shows several different estimations, using various patterns for the true activity u.

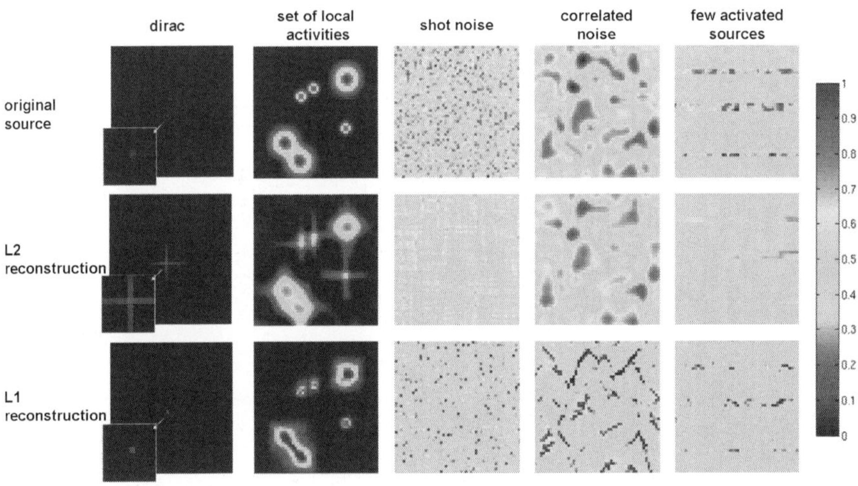

Fig. 7. Schematic reconstructions illustrate the different behavior of L^2-norm based and L^1-norm based algorithms. Different patterns of activity are generated, one per column, to produce 2-dimensional array as in figure 2(C), representing the neural activity. Schematic EEG and fMRI measures are generated, again as in figure 2(C). The first row displays these activity. The second and third row display reconstructions of the activity from the 2 measures, based either on the minimization of the L^2-norm or the L^1-norm of the source. We can notice that L^1-norm method produces sparse estimates (which is preferable in the case of a Dirac, a set of local activities, or when only a few sources are activated). The L^2-norm method produces smoother estimates, more precisely, the sum of two components, one smooth in time, the second smooth is space; it is more appropriate to the case of a smooth activity (the 'correlated noise' column).

It happens that, very clearly, the L^1-norm leads to sparse estimates, while the L^2-norm leads to smooth estimates, which even more precisely show two component, one smooth in time, the second smooth in spread. For example, a Dirac is perfectly estimated by the L^1-norm algorithm, and very poorly by the L^2-norm algorithm. A set of focal activities is also better estimated using the L^1-norm. On the contrary, a smooth activity is better estimated using the L^2-norm.

In fact, all this is quite well-known in the image processing domain (Aubert and Kornprobst 2006; Morel and Solimini 1995). However, the consequences are important: algorithms based on L^2-norm such as the Kalman filter and smoother are appropriate for EEG-fMRI fusion whenever the neural activity to be estimated is known to be smooth in time and space (one can think for example about spreading waves of activity). Inversely, if the activity is known to be sparse, the inverse problem should be solved through the minimization of other norms, such as the L^1-norm, which means that any Bayesian method relying on Gaussian distribution would not be appropriate. Rather this calls for the development of new algorithms, if possible still performing a temporal filtering, which would be based for example on the L^1-norm.

3. Handling nonlinear electric-metabolic relation

As we explained in the introduction, assuming a linear relation between the electric activities that yield the EEG measure and the metabolic and hemodynamic activities that yield the fMRI BOLD signal is a coarse approximation, and can even be a non-sense for a wide range of activities. For example, applied on oscillating activities, where the orientation of the equivalent dipole is repeatedly inverted, a linear model would generate no hemodynamic activity (since temporal averaging of the oscillations would be null). It is thus necessary to use a nonlinear modeling: for example, one would think to consider energy consumption not any more proportional to the electric activity, but to its absolute value, and regardless of his sign.
However, in the case of a nonlinear model, the EEG-fMRI fusion inverse problem becomes much harder to solve. Though we still advocate the use of adaptive filter techniques, the choice of the Kalman filter, or here its nonlinear version, the extended Kalman filter (EKF), becomes more problematic. First, the computational cost advantage of pre-computing the variance matrices cannot apply any more.

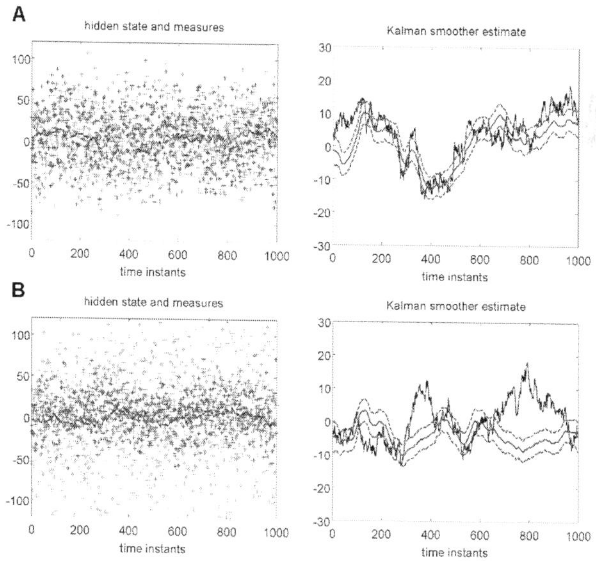

Fig. 8. Limits of the extended Kalman filter and smoother. (A) Left: the time course of a scalar hidden state is generated as a Brownian motion (solid line), and a 2-elements noisy measure is generated, the first measure being obtained by the linear identity function (dark gray crosses), and the second, by the non-linear absolute value function (light gray crosses). Right: reconstruction of the hidden state by the Kalman filter and smoother; black solid line: true time courses; gray solid line: estimated time courses; gray dashed lines: representation of the a posteriori variance, the true time courses indeed lies within this variance. (B) More weight is given to the nonlinear measure (the linear measure is noisier, while the nonlinear measure is less noisy). The estimation now fails is gets trapped in local minima where the sign of the hidden state is misestimated.

Second, EKF can handle only small nonlinearities, and not strong ones such as the use of an absolute value. Simulations in figure 8 demonstrate this fact: we use a simple dynamical model, the hidden state is a one-dimensional Brownian motion, and the measure consists of two scalars, the first equal to the hidden state plus noise, the second equal to the absolute value of hidden state plus noise (left part of the figure). In figure 8(A), the noise in the first measure is sufficiently low so that the estimation using the Kalman filter and smoother is successful. On the contrary, in figure 8(B), the noise in the first measure is higher, so that information on the sign of the hidden state is weaker: then the estimation diverges strongly from the true value. More precisely, the estimation gets trapped in a local minimum, and the local linearizations and approximations with a Gaussian performed by the EKF become totally erroneous compared to the real a posteriori distribution.

As a consequence, we would like to encourage the development of new adaptive filter algorithms, based for example on particle filtering. However, we will show in this section on low-dimensionality examples that it is still possible to use the extended Kalman filter, thanks to (i) a modeling of electric-metabolic relations which minimizes nonlinearities and can handle the strong disparity between the fast temporal variations of the EEG signals and slow variations of the fMRI signals, and (ii) a new backward-forward estimation scheme that minimizes estimation errors.

3.1 Methods

3.1.1 Physiological model

Several studies attest that fMRI signals correlate particularly well oscillating EEG activities in specific frequency domains (Kilner et al., 2005; Laufs et al., 2003; Martinez-Montes et al., 2004; Riera et al., 2010). In such cases, the hemodynamic activity depends linearly, not on the current intensities themselves, but rather on the power of the currents in these specific frequencies. We propose here a simple model for the current intensity that favors oscillating patterns and makes it easy to link hemodynamics to the oscillation amplitude. It consists in describing the current intensity at a given source location as:

$$u(t) = \chi(t)\cos(2\pi f_c t + \varphi(t)) , \tag{16}$$

where $\chi(t)$ is the envelope of the signal, f_c is the preferred frequency, and $\varphi(t)$ a phase shift. $\cos(2\pi f_c t)$ reflects the intrinsic dynamic of the region, while $\chi(t)$ reflects a modulation of this activity in amplitude, and $\varphi(t)$ a modulation in frequency (if $\dot{\varphi}(t) > 0$, the frequency is higher, and if $\dot{\varphi}(t) < 0$, the frequency is lower) . Note that although $u(t)$ varies fast, $\chi(t)$ and $\varphi(t)$ can change at a slower pace (figure 9).

The evolution of χ and φ is modeled as follows:

$$\begin{cases} \dot{\chi}(t) = -\lambda_\chi \chi(t) + \xi_\chi(t), & \xi_\chi \sim N(0,Q_\chi) \\ \dot{\varphi}(t) = -\lambda_\varphi(\varphi(t) - \tilde{\varphi}^{\sigma\varphi}(t)) + \xi\varphi(t), & \xi_\varphi \sim N(0,Q_\varphi) \end{cases} . \tag{17}$$

χ is driven by the same Ornstein-Uhlenbeck process as in our earlier model (8), except that we did not allow χ to become negative (at each iteration of the generation of the simulated data, whenever it would become negative, it was reset to zero). φ is driven by a similar innovative process, but the phase shift at a given source location, instead of being pulled back towards zero, is pulled back towards the average phase shift over neighboring locations, $\tilde{\varphi}^{\sigma\varphi}$: this ensures a spatial coherence between sources, controlled by the model parameter σ_φ.

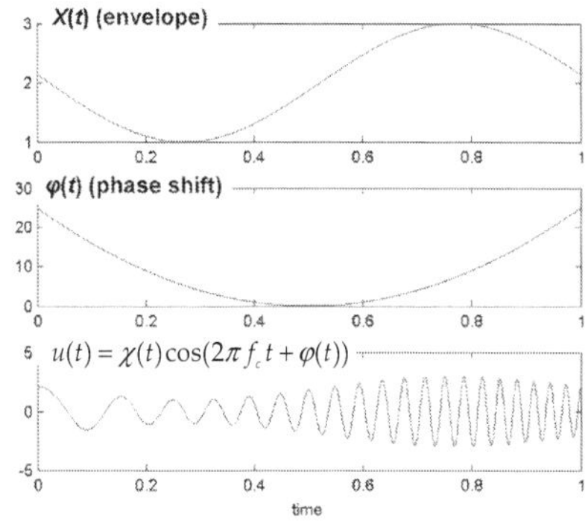

Fig. 9. Hidden states of the nonlinear model for neural activity. The signal u is defined by two hidden states χ and φ which can vary much slower than u itself.

Then we model the EEG measure as in equation (9), i.e. it is a linear function of $u(t)$. Note however that, since now u itself is represented by χ and φ, the EEG measure has become a nonlinear function of the hidden state: in fact, the transition $u_t \rightarrow y_t^{EEG}$ is now nonlinear. Besides, fMRI measure now depends linearly on the signal envelope $\chi(t)$: the first equation in (10) is replaced by

$$\ddot{f}(t) = \varepsilon\chi(t) - \kappa_s \dot{f}(t) - \kappa_f (f(t) - 1)\,. \tag{18}$$

3.1.2 Backward-forward scheme for the extended Kalman filter

We now have a nonlinear dynamical system:

$$\begin{cases} x_1 = x^0 + \xi^0, & \xi^0 \sim N(0,Q^0) \\ x_{k+1} = F(x_k) + \xi_k, & \xi_k \sim N(0,Q) \\ y_k = G(x_x) + \eta_k, & \eta_k \sim N(0,R) \end{cases}, \tag{19}$$

where F and G are nonlinear evolution and measure functions. Whereas it would be possible to linearize again F without major harm, the measure function G on the contrary is highly nonlinear because of the $\cos(2\pi f_c t + \varphi(t))$ in the EEG measure.

We would like to use the extended Kalman filter and smoother (Arulampalam et al., 2002; Welch & Bishop, 2006) to estimate the hidden state. However, as observed in figure 9, small errors of the estimation can lead to erroneous linearizations, and therefore to increased errors in the next filtering steps, causing divergence. Also, as explained earlier, the classical Kalman filter estimates $p(x_k \mid y_1,...,y_k)$ for k = 1…n, and the Kalman smoother estimates $p(x_k \mid y_1,...,y_n)$ for k = n-1…1. The problem is that $p(x_k \mid y_1,...,y_k)$ does not use any fMRI information to estimate x_k, since the fMRI measure occurs only several seconds later. Therefore, we propose to first run a backward sweep during which we estimate $p(x_k \mid y_k,...,y_n)$ for k = n…1, and only after a forward sweep, to estimate $p(x_k \mid y_1,...,y_n)$ for k = 2…n. Indeed, $p(x_k \mid y_k,...,y_n)$ will make less estimation error since $\{y_k,...,y_n\}$ contains both EEG and fMRI information about activity x_k.

We introduce the new notation:

$$\begin{aligned}\breve{x}_k^l &= E(x_k \mid y_l,\dots,y_n)\\ \breve{P}_k^l &= V(x_k \mid y_l,\dots,y_n)\end{aligned}. \tag{19}$$

First, it is important to point out that, in the absence of any measurement, all states x_k have the same a priori distribution $N(x^0,P^0)$, where P^0 can be obtained by repeating the Kalman filter time update step until convergence:

$$P^{(0)} = 0, \quad P^{(k+1)} = AP^{(k)}A^T + Q, \quad P^0 = \lim_{k\to\infty} P^{(k)}. \tag{20}$$

First, the backward step starts with the a priori distribution of x_n:

$$\begin{aligned}\breve{x}_n^{n+1} &= x^0\\ \breve{P}_n^{n+1} &= P^0\end{aligned}, \tag{21}$$

then, for $k = n, n\text{-}1, \dots, 1$, repeats the "measurement update":

$$\begin{aligned}K &= \breve{P}_k^{k+1}D^T(D\breve{P}_k^{k+1}D^T + R)^{-1}\\ \breve{x}_k^k &= \breve{x}_k^{k+1} + K(y_k - G(\breve{x}_k^{k+1}))\\ \breve{P}_k^k &= (I - KD)\breve{P}_k^{k+1}\end{aligned}, \tag{22}$$

where D is the derivative of the measure function at $\breve{x}_k^{k+1}$: $G(x) \approx G(\breve{x}_k^{k+1}) + D(x - \breve{x}_k^{k+1})$, and the "backward time update":

$$\begin{aligned}J &= P^0A^T(AP^0A^T + Q)^{-1}\\ \breve{x}_k^{k+1} &= x^0 + J(\breve{x}_{k+1}^{k+1} - x^0)\\ \breve{P}_k^{k+1} &= J\breve{P}_{k+1}^{k+1}J^T + (I - JA)P^0\end{aligned}, \tag{23}$$

where A is the derivative of the evolution function at $\breve{x}_k^{k+1}$: $F(x) \approx F(\breve{x}_k^{k+1}) + A(x - \breve{x}_k^{k+1})$.
Second, the forward smoothing steps repeats for $k = 2, 3, \dots, n$:

$$\begin{aligned}L &= (Q^{-1} + (P_{k+1}^{k+1})^{-1})^{-1}Q^{-1}\\ \breve{x}_{k+1}^1 &= \breve{x}_{k+1}^{k+1} + L(F(\breve{x}_k^1) - \breve{x}_{k+1}^{k+1})\\ \breve{P}_{k+1}^1 &= (Q^{-1} + (P_{k+1}^{k+1})^{-1})^{-1} + LA\breve{P}_k^1(LA)^T\end{aligned}. \tag{24}$$

We derived these equations in a similar way to how the measure update step is derived in (Welling, n.d.):

- Our measure update is the same as for the Kalman filter.
- The backward time update is obtained by first proving that $p(x_k \mid x_{k+1}) = N(x^0 + J(x_{k+1} - x^0), (I - JA)P^0)$, and then by calculating $p(x_k \mid y_{k+1},\dots,y_n) = \int_{xk+1} p(x_k \mid x_{k+1})p(x_{k+1} \mid y_{k+1},\dots,y_n)dx_{k+1}$.
- The forward smoothing step is obtained by first proving that $p(x_{k+1} \mid x_k, y_1,\dots,y_n) = N(\breve{x}_{k+1}^{k+1} + L(F(\breve{x}_k^1) - \breve{x}_{k+1}^{k+1}), (Q^{-1} + (P_{k+1}^{k+1})^{-1})^{-1})$, and then by calculating $p(x_{k+1} \mid y_1,\dots,y_n) = \int_{xk+1} p(x_{k+1} \mid x_k, y_1,\dots,y_n)p(x_k \mid y_1,\dots,y_n)dx_{k+1})$.

Since we observed some divergences when applying this second smoothing step due to accumulating errors in the estimation of the phase, we applied it only on the estimation of the envelope (and kept the result from the first step only for the phase estimate).

3.2 Results

We have run this algorithm on a highly reduced dataset where the cortical surface was downsampled to 10 cortical patches, and only 3 EEG electrodes were considered (so as to preserve the underdetermination of the EEG backward problem). We generated 1min long patterns of activity, sampled at 200Hz, with an average frequency of the oscillations f_c=10Hz. First we generated a cortical activity and measures according to the model (17); then we estimated the activity from these measures: figure 10(A) shows estimation results, which are quantified in table 2, first two columns. We compare estimations obtained by applying the filtering technique to either the EEG alone, fMRI alone, or both together (in the case of fMRI alone, since there is no information on the phase φ, only the estimated envelope is displayed): we see that the envelope of the signals is best estimated using fMRI alone, whereas the EEG-fMRI fusion estimates the signals better than EEG-only. We also generated a one-second width pulse of activity and noisy fMRI and EEG measures, and the estimation results (figure 10(B) and two last columns in table 2) are even more significant: the fusion estimate clearly provides the best estimate of the signals and of their envelopes.

% correlation	*Activity generated by the forward model*		*Sparse activity*	
	Original source	Envelope of source	Original source	Envelope of source
EEG estimate	29.0	17.6	42.2	36.2
fMRI estimate		50.7		49.6
Fusion estimate	24.	34.1	23.2	68.5

Table 2. Quantification of estimation accuracies for the nonlinear model in the case of two different simulations using 10 sources. For every estimation, we quantify using correlation the fit between the estimated sources and the original simulated sources ($u = \chi \cos \varphi$), as well as between the envelopes (hidden state χ). Note that in the case of fMRI-only estimation, there is no information on φ, so no number is given for the fit to original source and for the fit to EEG.

3.3 Discussion

3.3.1 Algorithm

We briefly discuss here the specific ideas presented in this section. First, the way we proposed to describe the electric activity in term of envelope and phase is very specific, and should be used only in the analysis of experiments where it is well-founded (i.e. experiments where the fMRI signals are known to correlate with EEG activity in a given frequency range). However, the key idea of this modeling could still be used in different models: it is to set apart the information which is accessible to fMRI, in our case χ, the envelope of the activity, which somehow measures "how much the source is active" in total, but is ignorant of the exact dynamics of the currents u. In such a way, EEG and fMRI measures collaborate in estimating χ, but the phase shift φ is estimated only by the EEG (at least at a first approximation, since in fact in the fusion algorithm, all the different states are linked through their covariance). Furthermore, χ is easier to estimate for the fMRI since it can evolve slower that u, which corresponds more to its weak temporal resolution; and similarly, φ can be easier to estimate for the EEG if there is a high phase coherence among the sources of a same region, because then less spatial resolution is needed.

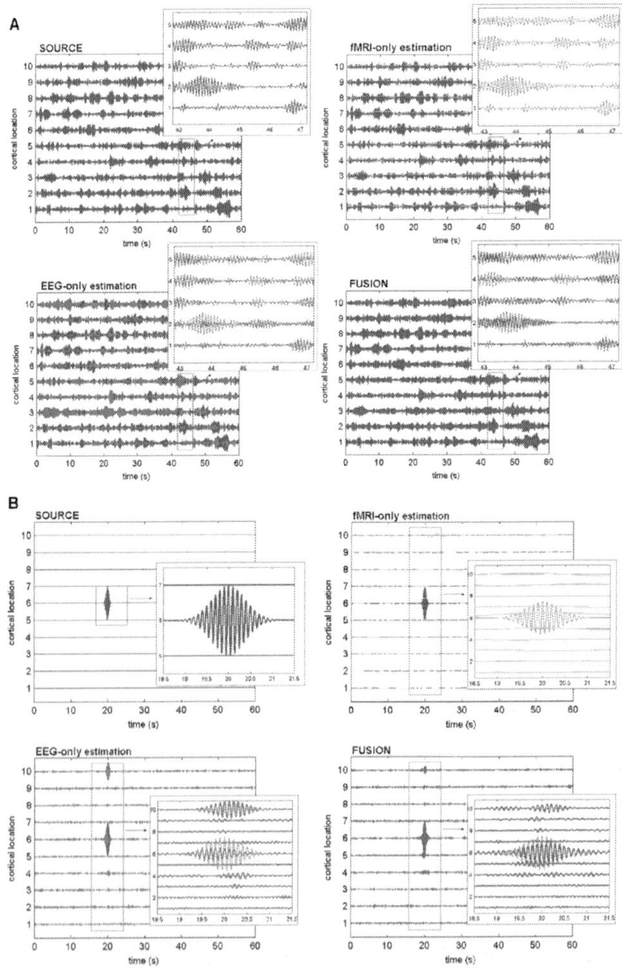

Fig. 10. EEG-fMRI fusion using the nonlinear Kalman algorithm. (A) A neural activity has been generated on 10 sources according to the nonlinear model, then EEG and fMRI measures of this activity were generated (panel 'SOURCE'). We can observe in the structure of this activity the modulations of χ, the envelope of the signals, the intrinsic oscillatory activity at frequency f_{c}, and in the magnified area, the dephasing between different sources due to the variations of the state φ. EEG and fMRI measures were generated according to the model, and estimations were performed on either EEG, fMRI or both (the 3 next panels). Note that the fMRI estimate is not oscillating since φ is not estimated. We can observe the improved estimation in the fusion case compared to the EEG case. (B) In a second simulation, a single pulse of activity was generated. We can observe very well that the EEG estimate finds the accurate dynamics, the fMRI estimate finds the accurate localization, and the fusion produces a very satisfying estimate, with the correct dynamic and localization.

Indeed, we could run estimation for ten (as shown here) to a few hundred sources, as shown in (Deneux & Faugeras, 2010) spread on the cortical surface, but to estimate the activity of several thousands sources would be too demanding, because the simplifications which apply in the linear case (section 2.3.1) do not any more. However, there is a large room for further improvements.

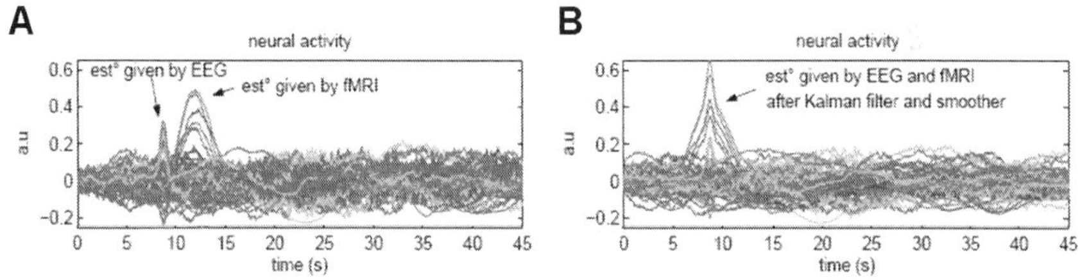

Fig. 11. Details of the Kalman filter and smoother steps. Estimation obtained using the linear model on a dataset with 1,000 sources with a focused activity. (A) After only the Kalman filter has been applied, the neural activity estimate is not accurate, and one can recognize two peaks, which 'imprint' the information given by the EEG and fMRI measure (the second could not be placed correctly in time since the filter encounters the fMRI measures too late). (B) After the Kalman smoother has been applied, this 'fMRI-informed peak' has been put back at the correct time location.

Second, we want to stress that the adaptation we propose for the extended Kalman filter, where the backward sweep is performed before the forward sweep, might be well-adapted for many other situations where adaptive filters are used on a nonlinear forward model, but where the measure of the phenomenon of interest are delayed in time. We already explained above that the order between these two sweeps matters because accumulating errors cause divergence, therefore it is preferable that the first sweep will be as exact as possible. Note that this is due exclusively to the errors made in the local linearizations performed by the extended Klaman filter; on the contrary, the order of the sweeps does not matter in the case of a linear model, and all the derivations for the means and variances of $p(x_k \mid y_1,\dots,y_l)$ are exact. To illustrate this fact, we show in figure 11 the neural activity estimated in the previous part by the linear Kalman filter and smoother: although the Kalman filter estimate is not accurate, it somehow "memorizes" the information brought late by fMRI data (figure 10(A)); therefore, this information is later available to the Kalman smoother, which can then "bring it back to the good place" (figure 10(B)).

3.3.2 Future improvements

In the previous part of this chapter we had proven that adaptive filters can be used to solve the EEG-fMRI fusion inverse problem on a dataset of a realistic size, but we had to assume a linear forward model of the measures. Here we have shown that this linear assumption can be overcome, and that more physiologically accurate nonlinear models can be used and new algorithms designed that handle these nonlinearities, although at a significantly increased computational cost.

First, Kalman methods can probably be improved to reduce the computational cost, as we already mentioned above (for example, by using low-dimensional descriptions of the variance matrices). But it is probably even preferable to develop novel algorithms that can specifically deal with the strong nonlinearities of the model. For example, (Plis et al., 2010) proposed a particle filter algorithm (Arulampalam et al., 2002) to estimate the dynamics of a given region of interest based on EEG and fMRI measures. Unfortunately, the fact that they reduced the spatial dimension to a single ROI reduced the interest of their method, since the fMRI could not bring any additional information compared to the EEG, and they admit that increasing the spatial dimension would pose important computational cost problems, as the number of particles used for the estimation should increase exponentially with the number of regions. However, particle filters seem to be a good direction of research, all the more since they do not assume specific Gaussian distributions, and hence - as we saw in the previous part - could be more efficient in estimating sparse and focused activities.

Besides, there are interesting questions to ask about the dimension of the hidden neural activity. On the one hand, we would like it to have a temporal resolution as good as that of the EEG, and a spatial resolution as good as that of the fMRI. On the other hand, this leads to a very high total dimension for u, which is the main cause of high computational cost, and it is tempting to rather decrease this dimension. Several works have proposed approaches based on regions of interests (Daunizeau et al., 2007; Ou et al., 2010), where the spatial dimension is reduced by clustering the sources according to anatomical or physiological considerations. It is possible however that new approaches will be able in the same time to keep high temporal and spatial resolution, and decrease the total dimension of the source space, by using multi-level, or any other complex description of the neural activity relying on a reduced number of parameters.

4. Conclusion

We have proposed two algorithms to perform EEG-fMRI fusion, both based on the Kalman filter and smoother. Both algorithms aim at estimating the spatio-temporal patterns of a hidden neural activity u responsible for both EEG and fMRI measurements, the relation between them being described by a physiological forward model. The first algorithm assumes a linear model and in such case, fusion appeared to be feasible on data of a realistic size (namely, activity of 2,000 sources spread on the cortical surface, sampled at 200Hz during several minutes). The second algorithm relies on a more accurate nonlinear model, and though its increased computational cost led to estimations on only 100 sources, it gives a proof of principle for using adaptive filters to perform EEG-fMRI fusion based on realistic nonlinear models.

We would like to stress however that these progresses on the methodological front should not hide the fundamental physiological questions regarding whether EEG and fMRI measure the same phenomena at all, as we discussed in our introduction, and as recent reviews (Rosa et al., 2010) pinpoint to still be a problematic question. Nevertheless, if the question should be answered negatively *in general*, it remains that many simultaneous EEG-fMRI studies proved to be successful in specific contexts such as epilepsy or α-rythms activity. In such case, the development of new fusion algorithms which target the estimation of the neural activity spatio-temporal patterns should focus on such specific applications and on the specific links which exist between the two measures in theses contexts. This is what we plan to do in our future works with real data: in fact, our nonlinear algorithm, where we assumed a very specific oscillatory activity and a linear relation between the fMRI BOLD signals and the envelope of this activity is a preliminary for such development.

As we mentioned in the introduction, this work is not only a contribution to the human brain imaging field, but also to the algorithmic field, since a new modification of the Kalman filter was proposed that filters first backward, and second forward, and since it fosters the development of new algorithms and filters. In particular, we call for new methods that can handle nonlinear models and non-Gaussian distributions. We advocate in particular the minization of L^1-norm rather than L^2-norm in order to estimate accurately sparse and focused activities, and the reduction of the computational cost of either Kalman methods or particle filter methods through the use of low-dimensional representations of high-dimensional distributions.

5. References

Ahlfors SP, Simpson GV. (2004). Geometrical interpretation of fMRI-guided MEG/EEG inverse estimates, *Neuroimage* 1:323–332

Arulampalam, M. Sanjeev; Maskell, Simon; Neil Gordon & Clapp, Tim. (2002). A Tutorial on Particle Filters for Online Nonlinear/Non-Gaussian Bayesian Tracking *IEEE transactions on signal processing*, 50, 174-188

Bénar, C.; Aghakhani, Y.; Wang, Y.; Izenberg, A.; Al-Asmi, A.; Dubeau, F. & Gotman, J. (2003). Quality of EEG in simultaneous EEG-fMRI for epilepsy *Clin Neurophysiol*, 114, 569-580T

Buxton, R. B.; UludaNg, K.; Dubowitz, D. J. & Liu, T. (2004). Modelling the hemodynamic response to brain activation *NeuroImage*, 23, 220 - 233

Daunizeau, J.; Grova, C.; Marrelec, G.; Mattout, J.; Jbabdi, S.; Pélégrini-Issac, M.; Lina, J. M. & Benali, H. (2007). Symmetrical event-related EEG/fMRI information fusion in a variational Bayesian framework *Neuroimage.*, 36, 69 - 87

Daunizeau J, Laufs H, Friston KJ. (2010). EEG-fMRI information fusion: Biophysics and data analysis, In: *EEG-fMRI-Physiology, Technique and Applications*, Mulert L (eds.) Springer DE

Deneux, T. & Faugeras, O. (2006a). Using nonlinear models in fMRI data analysis: model selection and activation detection *Neuroimage*, 32, 1669-1689

Deneux, T. & Faugeras, O. (2006b). EEG-fMRI fusion of non-triggered data using Kalman filtering *International Symposium on Biomedical Imaging*, 2006, 1068-1071

Deneux, T. & Faugeras, O. (2010). EEG-fMRI Fusion of Paradigm-Free Activity Using Kalman Filtering *Neural Comput.*, 22, 906 - 948

Friston, K. J.; Mechelli, A.; Turner, R. & Price, C. J. (2000). Nonlinear Responses in fMRI : the Balloon Model, Volterra Kernels, and Other Hemodynamics, *NeuroImage*, 12, 466-477

Goldman, R. I.; Stern, J. M.; Engel, J. J. & Cohen, M. S. (2002). Simultaneous EEG and fMRI of the alpha rhythm, *Neuroreport*, 13, 2487-2492

Gotman, J.; Bénar, C. & Dubeau, F. (2004). Combining EEG and fMRI in epilepsy: Methodological challenges and clinical results, *Journal of Clinical Neurophysiology*, 21

Grova C, Daunizeau J et al. (2008). Assessing the concordance between distributed EEG source localization and simultaneous EEG-fMRI studies of epileptic spikes, *Neuroimage* 39:755–774

Hämäläinen, M.; Hari, R.; Ilmoniemi, R. J.; Kunuutila, J. & Lounasmaa, O. V. (1993). Magnetoencephalography: Theory, instrumentation, and applications to noninvasive studies of the working human brain, *Rev. Modern Phys.*, 65, 413-497

Johnston, L. A., Duff, E., Mareels, I., and Egan, G. F. (2008). Nonlinear estimation of the bold signal. *Neuroimage* 40, 504–514.

Jun, S.-C., George, J. S., Pare-Blagoev, J., Plis, S. M., Ranken, D. M., Schmidt, D. M., and Wood, C. C. (2005). Spatiotemporal Bayesian inference dipole analysis for MEG neuroimaging data. *Neuroimage* 28, 84–98.

Kalman, R. E. (1960). A New Approach to Linear Filtering and Prediction Problems, *Transactions of the ASME--Journal of Basic Engineering*, 82, 35-45

Kilner, J. M.; Mattout, J.; Henson, R. & Friston, K. J. (2005). Hemodynamic correlates of EEG: a heuristic, *Neuroimage*, 28, 280-286

Laufs, H.; Kleinschmidt, A.; Beyerle, A.; Eger, E.; Salek-Haddadi, A.; Preibisch, C. & Krakow, K. (2003). EEG-correlated fMRI of human alpha activity, *Neuroimage*, 19, 1463-76

Lemieux, L.; Krakow, K. & Fish, D. R. (2001). Comparison of spike-triggered functional MRI BOLD activation and EEG dipole model localization, *Neuroimage*, 14, 1097-1104

Martinez-Montes, E.; Valdes-Sosa, P. A.; Miwakeichi, F.; Goldman, R. I. & Cohen, M. S. (2004). Concurrent EEG/fMRI analysis by multiway Partial Least Squares, *Neuroimage*, 22, 1023-1034

Murray, L., and Storkey, A. (2008). Continuous time particle filtering for fMRI, In: *Advances in Neural Information Processing Systems*, Vol. 20, eds J. C. Platt, D. Koller, Y. Singer, and S. Roweis (Cambridge, MA: MIT Press), 1049–1056.

Ogawa, S.; Menon, R. S.; Tank, D. W.; Kim, S.; Merkle, H.; Ellerman, J. M. & Ugurbil, K. (1993). Function brain mapping by blood oxygenation level-dependent contrast magnetic resonance imaging: a comparison of signal characteristics with a biophysical model, *Biophys. J.*, 64, 803-812

Ou, W.; Nummenmaa, A.; Ahveninen, J. & Belliveau, J. W. (2010). Multimodal functional imaging using fMRI-informed regional EEG/MEG source estimation *Neuroimage.*, 52, 97-108

Plis, S. M., Ranken, D. M., Schmidt, D. M., and Wood, C. C. (2005). Spatiotemporal Bayesian inference dipole analysis for MEG neuroimaging data. *Neuroimage* 28, 84–98.

Riera, J.; Watanabe, J.; Kazuki, I.; Naoki, M.; Aubert, E.; Ozaki, T. & Kawashima, R. (2004). A state-space model of the hemodynamic approach: nonlinear filtering of BOLD signals, *NeuroImage*, 21, 547-567

Riera J, Sumiyoshi A. (2010). Brain oscillations: Ideal scenery to understand the neurovascular coupling, *Curr Op Neurobiol* 23:374–381, 2010.

Rosa, M. J.; Daunizeau, J. & Friston, K. J. (2010). EEG-fMRI integration: A critical review of biophysical modeling and data analysis approaches, *J Integr Neurosci.*, 2010, 9, 453 - 476

Waites, A. B., Shaw, M. E., Briellmann, R. S., Labate, A., Abbott, D. F., & Jackson, G. D. (2005). How reliable are fMRI-EEG studies of epilepsy? A nonparametric approach to analysis validation and optimization. *Neuroimage*, 24(1), 192–199.

Welch, G. & Bishop, G. (2006). *An Introduction to the Kalman Filter*

Welling, M., Max Welling's classnotes in machine learning. (N.d.). Available online at http://www.cs.toronto.edu/~welling/classnotes/papers_class/KF.ps.gz.

11

Adaptive-FRESH Filtering

Omar A. Yeste Ojeda and Jesús Grajal
Universidad Politécnica de Madrid
Spain

1. Introduction

Adaptive filters are self-designing systems for information extraction which rely for their operation on a recursive algorithm (Haykin, 2001). They find application in environments where the optimum filter cannot be applied because of lack of knowledge about the signal characteristics and/or the data to be processed. This a priori knowledge required for the design of the optimum filter is commonly based on stochastic signal models, which traditionally are stationary. However, the parameters of many signals found in communication, radar, telemetry and many other fields can be represented as periodic functions of time (Gardner, 1991). When this occurs, stationary signal models cannot exploit the signal periodicities, while cyclostationary models become more suitable since they represent more reliably the statistical signal properties.[1]

Firstly, let us review some of the key points of cyclostationary signals, while introducing some definitions that will be used throughout this chapter. We have said that most of signals used in many fields such as communication, radar, or telemetry exhibit statistical parameters which vary periodically with time. The periodicities of these parameters are related to the parameters of the signal modulation, such as the carrier frequency or the chip rate among others (Gardner, 1986; 1994). Let the second-order[2] auto-correlation function of a zero-mean stochastic signal be defined as:

$$R_{xx}(t,\lambda) \triangleq \mathrm{E}\left\{x(t)\, x^*(\lambda)\right\} \tag{1}$$

A signal is said to be (second-order) cyclostationary if, and only if, its (second-order) auto-correlation function is a periodic function of time, namely with period T. Therefore, it can be expanded in a Fourier series (Giannakis, 1998):

$$R_{xx}(t,\lambda) = \sum_{p=-\infty}^{\infty} R_{xx}^{\alpha_p}(t-\lambda)\, e^{j2\pi\alpha_p\lambda} \tag{2}$$

where $\alpha_p = p/T$ are called the *cycle frequencies* of $x(t)$, and the set of all the cycle frequencies is referred to as the *cyclic spectrum*. The Fourier coefficients of the expansion in (2) are named

---

[1] Cyclostationary signal models are a more general class of stochastic processes which comprise the stationary ones. Therefore, they always represent the statistical properties of the signal at least as well as the stationary ones.

[2] Since the optimality criterion used in this chapter is based on the Mean Squared Error (MSE), only the second-order statistical moments are of interest to us. The first-order statistical moment (i.e. the mean) is zero by assumption. Throughout this chapter, the second-order cyclostationarity is exploited. For brevity, hereinafter the cyclostationarity and correlation functions are assumed to be of second order, even without explicit mention.

cyclic auto-correlation functions and are computed as:

$$R_{xx}^{\alpha_p}(\tau) \triangleq \frac{1}{T} \int_0^T R_{xx}(t+\tau,t)\, e^{-j\frac{2\pi}{T}pt}\, dt \tag{3}$$

In practice, the signal periodicities are often incommensurable with each other, which yields that the auto-correlation function in (1) is not periodic, but an almost-periodic function of time. In this general case (in the sense that periodic functions are a particular case of almost-periodic ones), the signal is said to be almost-cyclostationary, and its auto-correlation function allows its expansion as a generalized Fourier series:

$$R_{xx}(t,\lambda) = \sum_{\alpha_p \in \mathrm{A}_{xx}} R_{xx}^{\alpha_p}(t-\lambda)\, e^{j2\pi\alpha_p\lambda} \tag{4}$$

where the set A_{xx} stands for the cyclic spectrum of $x(t)$, and is generally composed of the sum and difference of integer multiples of the signal periodicities (Gardner, 1987; Gardner et al., 1987; Napolitano & Spooner, 2001). Additionally, the definition of the cyclic auto-correlation functions must be changed accordingly:

$$R_{xx}^{\alpha}(\tau) \triangleq \lim_{T\to\infty} \frac{1}{2T} \int_{-T}^{T} R_{xx}(t+\tau,t)\, e^{-j2\pi\alpha t}\, dt \tag{5}$$

One of the most important properties of almost-cyclostationary signals concerns the existence of correlation between their spectral components. The periodicity of the auto-correlation function turns into spectral correlation when it is transformed to the frequency domain. As a result, almost-cyclostationarity and spectral correlation are related in such a way that a signal exhibits almost-cyclostationary properties if, and only if, it exhibits spectral correlation too. Let $X_{\Delta f}(t,f)$ be the spectral component of $x(t)$, around time t and frequency f, and with spectral bandwidth Δf:

$$X_{\Delta f}(t,f) = \int_{t-\frac{1}{2\Delta f}}^{t+\frac{1}{2\Delta f}} x(u)\, e^{-j2\pi f u}\, du \tag{6}$$

The spectral correlation function of the signal $x(t)$ is defined as:

$$S_{xx}^{\alpha}(f) \triangleq \lim_{\Delta f\to 0} \Delta f \lim_{T\to\infty} \frac{1}{2T} \int_{-T}^{T} \mathrm{E}\left\{ X_{\Delta f}(t,f)\, X_{\Delta f}^{*}(t,f-\alpha) \right\} dt \tag{7}$$

which represents the time-averaged correlation between two spectral components centered at frequencies f and $f-\alpha$, as their bandwidth tends to zero. It can be demonstrated that the spectral correlation function matches de Fourier transform of the cyclic correlation functions (Gardner, 1986), that is:

$$S_{xx}^{\alpha}(f) = \int_{-\infty}^{\infty} R_{xx}^{\alpha}(\tau)\, e^{-j2\pi f\tau}\, d\tau \tag{8}$$

where the inherent relationship between almost-cyclostationarity and spectral correlation is fully revealed. Intuitively, Eq. (8) means that the spectral components of almost-cyclostationary signals are correlated with other spectral components which are spectrally separated at the periodicities of their correlation function, i.e. their cyclic spectrum. For this reason the cycle frequency is also known as spectral separation (Gardner, 1991). Note that, at cycle frequency zero, the cyclic auto-correlation function in (5) represents the stationary (or time-averaged) part of the nonstationary auto-correlation function in (3). Therefore, it is straightforward from (8) that the spectral correlation function matches the Power Spectral Density (PSD) at $\alpha = 0$, and also represents the auto-correlation of the signal spectral components, which is indicated by (7).

The key result from the above is that, since almost-cyclostationary signals exhibit spectral correlation, a single spectral component can be restored not only from itself, but also from other components which are spectrally separated from it as indicated by the cyclic spectrum of the signal. It is clear that a simple Linear Time-Invariant (LTI) filter cannot achieve this spectral restoration, but intuition says that a kind of filter which incorporates frequency shifts within its structure could. Contrary to optimal linear filtering of stationary signals, which results in time-invariant filters, the optimal linear filters of almost-cyclostationary signals are Linear Almost-Periodically Time-Variant (LAPTV) filters (also known as *poly-periodic* filters (Chevalier & Maurice, 1997)). This optimality can be understood in the sense of Signal-to-Noise Ratio (SNR) maximisation or in the sense of Minimum Mean Squared Error (MMSE, the one used in this chapter), where the optimal LAPTV filter may differ depending on the criterion used. Therefore, LAPTV filters find application in many signal processing areas such as signal estimation, interference rejection, channel equalization, STAP (Space-Time Adaptive Processing), or watermarking, among others (see (Gardner, 1994) and references therein, or more recently in (Adlard et al., 1999; Chen & Liang, 2010; Chevalier & Blin, 2007; Chevalier & Maurice, 1997; Chevalier & Pipon, 2006; Gameiro, 2000; Gelli & Verde, 2000; Gonçalves & Gameiro, 2002; Hu et al., 2007; Li & Ouyang, 2009; Martin et al., 2007; Mirbagheri et al., 2006; Ngan et al., 2004; Petrus & Reed, 1995; Whitehead & Takawira, 2004; 2005; Wong & Chambers, 1996; Yeste-Ojeda & Grajal, 2008; Zhang et al., 2006; 1999)).

This chapter is devoted to the study of LAPTV filters for adaptive filtering. In the next sections, the fundamentals of LAPTV filters are briefly described. With the aim of incorporating adaptive strategies, the theoretical development is focused on the FRESH (FREquency SHift) implementation of LAPTV filters. FRESH filters are composed of a set of frequency shifters followed by an LTI filter, which notably simplifies the analysis and design of adaptive algorithms. After reviewing the theoretical background of adaptive FRESH filters, an important property of adaptive FRESH filters is analyzed: Their capability to operate in the presence of errors in the LAPTV periodicities. This property is important because small errors in these periodicities, which are quite common in practice due to non-ideal effects, can make the use of LAPTV filters unfeasible.

Finally, an application example of adaptive FRESH filters is used at the end of this chapter to illustrate their benefit in real applications. In that example, an adaptive FRESH filter constitutes an interference rejection subsystem which forms part of a signal interception system. The goal is to use adaptive FRESH filtering for removing the unwanted signals so that a subsequent subsystem can detect any other signal present in the environment. Therefore, the interference rejection and signal detection problems can be dealt with independently, allowing the use of high sensitivity detectors with poor interference rejection properties.

2. Optimum linear estimators for almost cyclostationary processes

This section is devoted to establishing the optimality of LAPTV filters for filtering almost-cyclostationary signals. The theory of LAPTV filters can be seen as a generalization of the classical Wiener theory for optimal LTI filters, where the signals involved are no longer stationary, but almost-cyclostationary. Therefore, optimal LTI filters become a particularization of LAPTV ones, as stationary signals can be seen as a particularization of almost-cyclostationary ones.

The Wiener theory defines the optimal (under MMSE criterion) LTI filter for the estimation of a desired signal, $d(t)$, given the input (or observed) signal $x(t)$, when both $d(t)$ and $x(t)$ are jointly stationary. In this case, their auto- and cross-correlation functions do not depend on the time, but only on the lag, and the estimation error results constant too. Otherwise, the estimation error becomes a function of time. The Wiener filter is still the optimal LTI filter if, and only if, $d(t)$ and $x(t)$ are jointly stationarizable processes (those which can be made jointly stationary by random time shifting) (Gardner, 1978). In this case, the Wiener filter is optimal in the sense of Minimum Time-Averaged MSE (MTAMSE). For instance, jointly almost-cyclostationary processes (those whose auto- and cross-correlation functions are almost-periodic functions of time) are always stationarizable. Nonetheless, if $x(t)$ and $d(t)$ are jointly almost-cyclostationary, it is possible to find an optimal filter which minimizes the MSE at all instants, which becomes a Linear Almost-Periodically Time-Variant (LAPTV) filter (Gardner, 1994). This result arises from the orthogonality principle of optimal linear estimators (Gardner, 1986), which is developed next.

Let $\widehat{d}(t)$ be the estimate of $d(t)$ from $x(t)$, obtained through the linear filter $h(t,\lambda)$:

$$\widehat{d}(t) = \int_{-\infty}^{\infty} h(t,u)\, x(u)\, du \tag{9}$$

The orthogonality principle establishes that, if $h(t,\lambda)$ is optimum, then input signal $x(t)$ and the estimation error ($\varepsilon(t) = d(t) - \widehat{d}(t)$) are orthogonal with each other: [3]

$$\mathrm{E}\left\{\varepsilon(t)\, x^*(\lambda)\right\} = 0\,, \quad \forall \lambda, t \in \mathbb{R} \tag{10}$$

$$R_{dx}(t,\lambda) = \int_{-\infty}^{\infty} h_\Gamma(t,u)\, R_{xx}(u,\lambda)\, du\,, \quad \forall \lambda, t \in \mathbb{R} \tag{11}$$

where

$$R_{uv}(t,\lambda) \triangleq \mathrm{E}\left\{u(t)\, v^*(\lambda)\right\} \tag{12}$$

stands for the cross-correlation function between $u(t)$ and $v(t)$, and $h_\Gamma(t,\lambda)$ stands for the optimal LAPTV filter (where the meaning of the subindex Γ will be clarified in the next paragraphs). Since $d(t)$ and $x(t)$ are jointly almost-cyclostationary by assumption, their auto- and cross-correlation functions are almost-periodic functions of time, and therefore they can be expanded as a generalized Fourier series (Corduneanu, 1968; Gardner, 1986):

$$R_{dx}(t,\lambda) = \sum_{\alpha_k \in \mathrm{A}_{dx}} R_{dx}^{\alpha_k}(t-\lambda)\, e^{j2\pi\alpha_k\lambda} \tag{13}$$

$$R_{xx}(t,\lambda) = \sum_{\beta_p \in \mathrm{B}_{xx}} R_{xx}^{\beta_p}(t-\lambda)\, e^{j2\pi\beta_p\lambda} \tag{14}$$

where A_{dx} and B_{xx} are countable sets consisting of the cycle frequencies of $R_{dx}(t,\lambda)$ and $R_{xx}(t,\lambda)$, respectively. In addition, the cyclic cross- and auto-correlation functions $R_{dx}^{\alpha}(\tau)$

[3] Up to this point, the signals considered are real valued and therefore the complex-conjugation operator can be ignored. However, it is incorporated in the formulation for compatibility with complex signals, which will be considered in following sections.

and $R^{\alpha}_{xx}(\tau)$ are computed as generalized Fourier coefficients (Gardner, 1986):

$$R^{\alpha}_{dx}(\tau) \triangleq \lim_{T\to\infty} \frac{1}{2T} \int_{-T}^{T} R_{dx}(t+\tau,t)\; e^{-j2\pi\alpha t}\, dt \tag{15}$$

$$R^{\alpha}_{xx}(\tau) \triangleq \lim_{T\to\infty} \frac{1}{2T} \int_{-T}^{T} R_{xx}(t+\tau,t)\; e^{-j2\pi\alpha t}\, dt \tag{16}$$

Substitution of (13) and (14) in (11) yields the condition:

$$\sum_{\alpha_k \in A_{dx}} R^{\alpha_k}_{dx}(t-\lambda)\; e^{j2\pi\alpha_k\lambda} = \sum_{\beta_p \in B_{xx}} \int_{-\infty}^{\infty} h_\Gamma(t,u)\; R^{\beta_p}_{xx}(u-\lambda)\; e^{j2\pi\beta_p\lambda}\, du \tag{17}$$

This condition can be satisfied for all $t, \lambda \in \mathbb{R}$ if $h_\Gamma(t,\lambda)$ is also an almost-periodic function of time, and therefore, can be expanded as a generalized Fourier series (Gardner, 1993; Gardner & Franks, 1975):

$$h_\Gamma(t,\lambda) \triangleq \sum_{\gamma_q \in \Gamma} h^{\gamma_q}_\Gamma(t-\lambda)\; e^{j2\pi\gamma_q\lambda} \tag{18}$$

where Γ is the minimum set containing A_{dx} and B_{xx} which is closed in the addition and subtraction operations (Franks, 1994). The Fourier coefficients in (18), $h^{\gamma_q}_\Gamma(\tau)$, can be computed analogously to Eq. (15) and (16). Then, the condition in (17) is developed by using the definition in (18), taking the Fourier transform, and augmenting the sets A_{dx} and B_{xx} to the set Γ, which they belong to, yielding the following condition:

$$\sum_{\alpha_k \in \Gamma} S^{\alpha_k}_{dx}(f)\; e^{j2\pi\alpha_k\lambda} = \sum_{\beta_p,\gamma_q \in \Gamma} H^{\gamma_q}_\Gamma(f)\; S^{\beta_p}_{xx}(f-\gamma_q)\; e^{j2\pi(\beta_p+\gamma_q)\lambda} \tag{19}$$

which must be satisfied for all $f, \lambda \in \mathbb{R}$, and where the Fourier transform of the cyclic cross- and auto-correlation functions,

$$S^{\alpha}_{uv}(f) = \int_{-\infty}^{\infty} R^{\alpha}_{uv}(\tau)\; e^{-j2\pi f\tau}\, d\tau \tag{20}$$

stands for the spectral cross- and auto-correlation function, respectively (Gardner, 1986). Finally, we use the fact that two almost-periodic functions are equal if and only if their generalized Fourier coefficients match (Corduneanu, 1968), which allows to reformulate (19) as the design formula of optimal LAPTV filters:

$$S^{\alpha_k}_{dx}(f) = \sum_{\gamma_q \in \Gamma} H^{\gamma_q}_\Gamma(f)\; S^{\alpha_k-\gamma_q}_{xx}(f-\gamma_q)\,, \quad \forall \alpha_k \in \Gamma,\ \forall f \in \mathbb{R} \tag{21}$$

Note that the sets of cycle frequencies A_{dx} and B_{xx} are, in general, subsets of Γ. Consequently, the condition in (21) makes sense under the consideration that $S^{\alpha}_{dx}(f) = 0$ if $\alpha \notin A_{dx}$, and $S^{\alpha}_{xx}(f) = 0$ if $\alpha \notin B_{xx}$, which is coherent with the definitions in (15) and (16). Furthermore, (21) is also coherent with the classical Wiener theory. When $d(t)$ and $x(t)$ are jointly stationary, then the sets of cycle frequencies A_{dx}, B_{xx}, and Γ consist only of cycle frequency zero, which yields that the optimal linear estimator is LTI and follows the well known expression of Wiener filter:

$$S^{0}_{dx}(f) = H^{0}_\Gamma(f)\; S^{0}_{xx}(f) \tag{22}$$

Let us use a simple graphical example to provide an overview of the implications of the design formula in (21). Consider the case where the signal to be estimated, $s(t)$, is corrupted

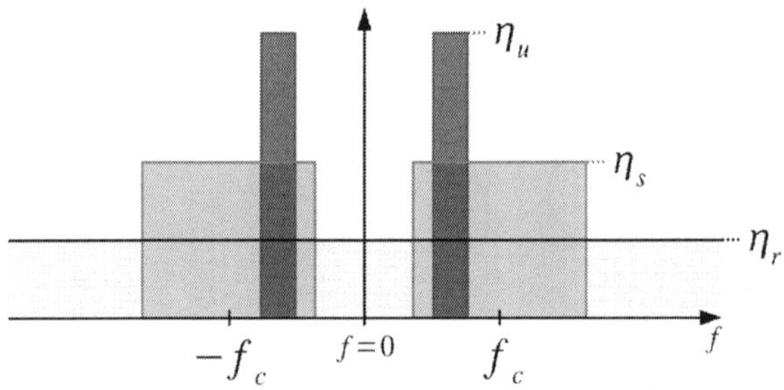

Fig. 1. Power spectral densities of the signal, the noise and interference in the application example.

by additive stationary white noise, $r(t)$, along with an interfering signal, $u(t)$, to form the observed signal, that is:

$$x(t) = s(t) + r(t) + u(t) \tag{23}$$

$$d(t) = s(t) \tag{24}$$

Assuming that $s(t)$, $r(t)$, and $u(t)$ are statistically independent processes, the design formula becomes:

$$S_{ss}^{\alpha_k}(f) = \sum_{\gamma_q \in \Gamma} H_\Gamma^{\gamma_q}(f) \left[S_{ss}^{\alpha_k - \gamma_q}(f - \gamma_q) + S_{rr}^{\alpha_k - \gamma_q}(f - \gamma_q) + S_{uu}^{\alpha_k - \gamma_q}(f - \gamma_q) \right] \tag{25}$$

In the following, let us consider the PSDs plotted in Fig. 1 for the signal, the noise and the interference, all of which are flat in their spectral bands, with PSD levels η_s, η_r and η_u, respectively. Let us further simplify the example by assuming that the signal is received with a high Signal-to-Noise Ratio (SNR), but low Signal-to-Interference Ratio (SIR), so that $\eta_u \gg \eta_s \gg \eta_r$. The Wiener filter can be obtained directly from Fig. 1, and becomes:

$$H_w(f) = \begin{cases} \frac{\eta_s}{\eta_s + \eta_r + \eta_u} \approx 0 & f \in B_u \\ \frac{\eta_s}{\eta_s + \eta_r} \approx 1 & f \notin B_u,\ f \in B_s \\ 0 & f \notin B_s \end{cases} \tag{26}$$

where B_u and B_s represent the frequency intervals comprised in the spectral bands of the interference and the signal, respectively. Thus, the Wiener filter is not capable of restoring the signal spectral components which are highly corrupted by the interference, since they are almost cancelled at its output.

On the contrary, an LAPTV filter could restore the spectral components cancelled by the Wiener filter depending on the spectral auto-correlation function of the signal and the availability at the input of correlated spectral components of the signal which are not perturbed by the interference. In our example, consider that the signal $s(t)$ is Amplitude Modulated (AM). Then, the signal exhibits spectral correlation at cycle frequencies $\alpha = \pm 2f_c$, in addition to cycle frequency zero, which means that the signal spectral components at positive frequencies are correlated with those components at negative frequencies (Gardner, 1987). [4] The spectral correlation function of the AM signal is represented in Fig. 2.

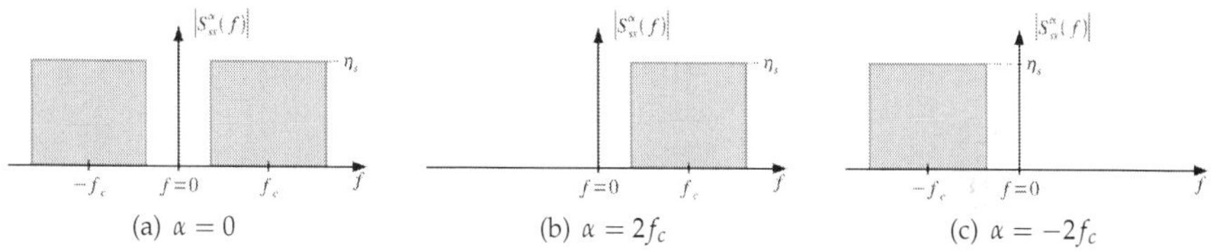

Fig. 2. Spectral correlation function of the signal with AM modulation.

The design formula in (25) states that the Fourier coefficients of the optimal LAPTV filter represent the coefficients of a linear combination in which frequency shifted version of $S_{xx}^{\alpha}(f)$ are combined in order to obtain $S_{dx}^{\alpha}(f)$. For simplicity, let us suppose that the set of cycle frequencies Γ only consists of the signal cyclic spectrum, that is $\Gamma = \{-2f_c,\, 0,\, 2f_c\}$, so that the design formula must be solved only for these values of α_k. Suppose also that the cycle frequencies $\pm 2f_c$ are exclusive of $s(t)$, so that $S_{xx}^{\pm 2f_c}(f) = S_{ss}^{\pm 2f_c}(f)$. This is coherent with the assumption that noise is stationary and with Fig. 1, where the bandwidth of the interference is narrower than $2f_c$, and therefore none of its spectral components is separated $2f_c$ in frequency. Fig. 3 graphically represents the conditions imposed by the design formula (25) on the Fourier coefficients of the optimal LAPTV filter, where each column stands for the different equations as α_k takes different values from Γ. The plots in the first three rows stand for the amplitude of the frequency shifted versions of the spectral auto-correlation function of the signal, the noise and the interference, while the plots in the last row represent the spectral cross-correlation between the input and the desired signals. The problem to be solved is to find the filter Fourier coefficients, $\{H_{\Gamma}^{-2f_c}(f),\, H_{\Gamma}^{0}(f),\, H_{\Gamma}^{2f_c}(f)\}$, which multiplied by the spectral correlation functions represented in the first three rows, and added together, yield the spectral cross-correlation function in the last row.

Firstly, let us pay attention to the spectral band of the interference at positive frequencies. From Fig. 3, the following equation system apply:

$$\left\{\begin{array}{l} S_{xx}^{0}(f)\; H_{\Gamma}^{0}(f) + S_{xx}^{-2f_c}\,(f-2f_c)\; H_{\Gamma}^{2f_c}(f) = S_{ss}^{0}(f) \\ S_{xx}^{2f_c}(f)\; H_{\Gamma}^{0}(f) + S_{xx}^{0}\,(f-2f_c)\; H_{\Gamma}^{2f_c}(f) = S_{ss}^{2f_c}(f) \qquad ,\ f \in B_u^{+} \\ S_{xx}^{0}(f+2f_c)\; H_{\Gamma}^{-2f_c}(f) = 0 \end{array}\right. \tag{27}$$

[4] The definition of the spectral correlation function used herein (see Eq. (7)) differs in the meaning of frequency from the definition used by other authors, as in (Gardner, 1987). Therein, the frequency stands for the mean frequency of the two spectral components whose correlation is computed. Both definitions are related with each other by a simple change of variables, that is $S_{xx}^{\alpha}(f) = S'^{\alpha}_{xx}(f-\alpha/2)$, where $S'^{\alpha}_{xx}(f)$ corresponds to spectral correlation function according to the definition used in (Gardner, 1987).

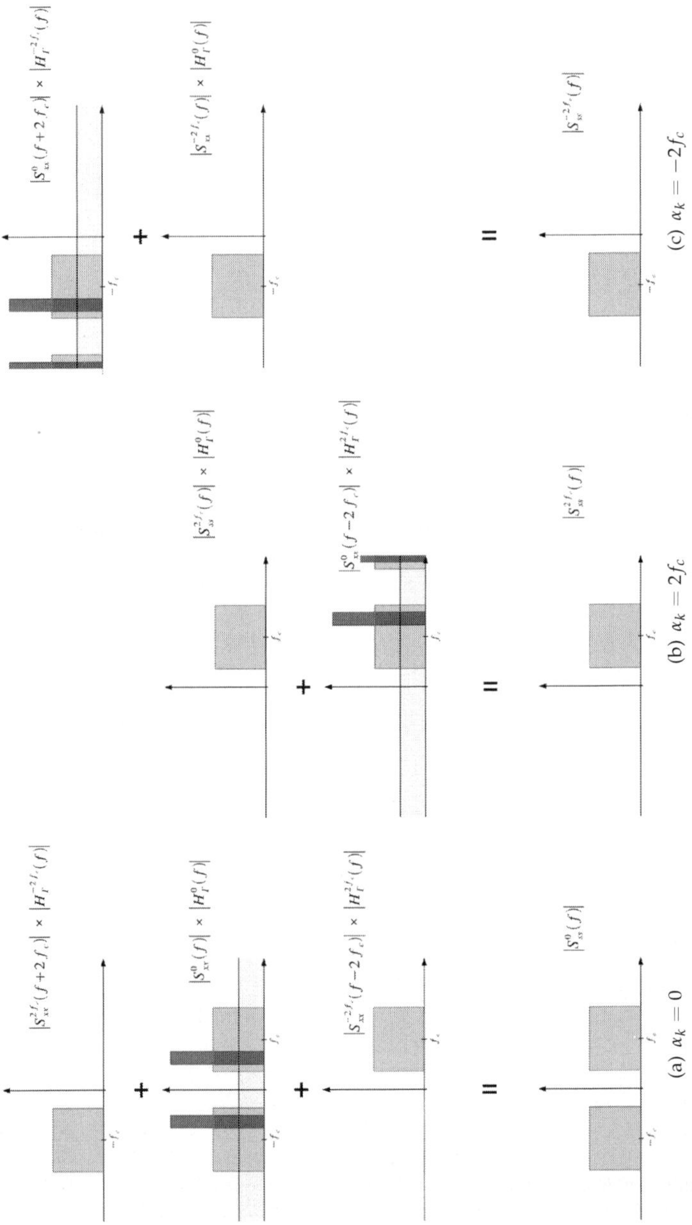

Fig. 3. Graphical representation of the design formula of LAPTV filters, which has been applied to our example. Each plot corresponds to a different value of α_k in (25).

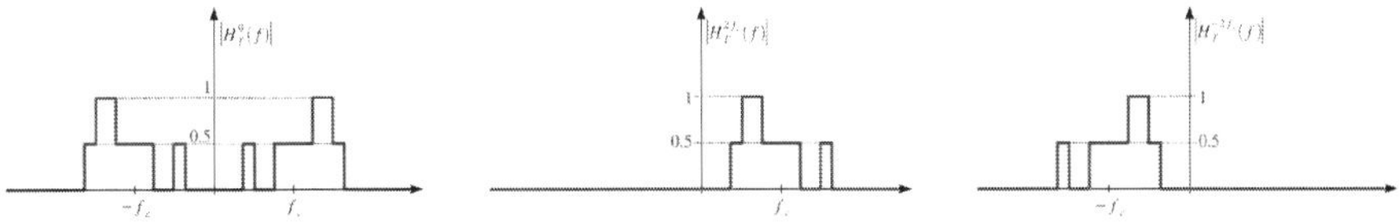

(a) $\alpha = 0$ (b) $\alpha = 2f_c$ (c) $\alpha = -2f_c$

Fig. 4. Fourier coefficients of the optimal LAPTV filter.

$$\begin{cases} (\eta_s + \eta_r + \eta_u)\, H_\Gamma^0(f) + \eta_s\, H_\Gamma^{2f_c}(f) = \eta_s \\ \eta_s\, H_\Gamma^0(f) + (\eta_s + \eta_r)\, H_\Gamma^{2f_c}(f) = \eta_s \\ \eta_r\, H_\Gamma^0(f) = 0 \end{cases} \quad , f \in B_u^+ \tag{28}$$

where B_u^+ stands for the range of positive frequencies occupied by the interference. The solution to the linear system in (28) is:

$$H_\Gamma^0(f) = \frac{\eta_s\, \eta_r}{\eta_s\,(\eta_r + \eta_u) + \eta_r\,(\eta_s + \eta_r + \eta_u)} \quad , f \in B_u^+ \tag{29}$$

$$H_\Gamma^{2f_c}(f) = \frac{\eta_s\,(\eta_r + \eta_u)}{\eta_s\,(\eta_r + \eta_u) + \eta_r\,(\eta_s + \eta_r + \eta_u)} = H_\Gamma^0(f)\left(\frac{\eta_u}{\eta_r} + 1\right) \quad , f \in B_u^+ \tag{30}$$

$$H_\Gamma^{-2f_c}(f) = 0 \quad , f \in B_u^+ \tag{31}$$

The result in (31) is coherent with the fact that there are not any signal spectral components located in B_u^+ after frequency shifting the input downwards by $2f_c$. After using the approximations of high SNR and low SIR, the above results for the other filter coefficients can be approximated by:

$$H_\Gamma^0(f) \approx 0 \quad , f \in B_u^+ \tag{32}$$

$$H_\Gamma^{2f_c}(f) \approx \frac{\text{SNR}}{\text{SNR} + 1} \approx 1 \quad , f \in B_u^+ \tag{33}$$

The underlaying meaning of (32) is that the optimal LAPTV filter cancels the spectral components of the signal which are corrupted by the interference. But contrary to the Wiener filter, these spectral components are restored from other components which are separated $2f_c$ in frequency, which is indicated by (33).

By using a similar approach, the Fourier coefficients of the LAPTV filter are computed for the rest of frequencies (those which do not belong to B_u^+). The result is represented in Fig. 4. We can see in Fig. 4(a) that $|H_\Gamma^0(f)|$ takes three possible values, i.e. 0, 0.5, and 1. $|H_\Gamma^0(f)| = 0$ when $f \in B_u$ (as explained above) or $f \notin B_s$ (out of the signal frequency range). The frequencies at which the Fourier coefficients are plotted with value $|H_\Gamma^\alpha| = 0.5$ correspond to those spectral components of the signal which are estimated from themselves, and jointly from spectral components separated $\alpha = 2f_c$ (or alternatively $\alpha = -2f_c$), since both are only corrupted by noise. For their part, the frequencies at which $|H_\Gamma^0(f)| = 1$ match the spectral components cancelled by $H_\Gamma^{\pm 2f_c}(f)$ (see Fig. 4(b) and 4(c)). These frequencies do not correspond to the spectral band of the interference, but the resulting frequencies after shifting this band by $\pm 2f_c$. Consequently, such spectral components are estimated only from themselves.

The preceding example has been simplified in order to obtain comprehensive results of how an LAPTV filter performs, and to intuitively introduce the idea of frequency shifting and filtering. This idea will become clearer in Section 4, when describing the FRESH implementation of LAPTV filters. In our example, no reference to the cyclostationary properties of the interference has been made. The optimal LAPTV filter also exploits the interference cyclostationarity in order to suppress it more effectively. However, if we had considered the cyclostationary properties of the interference, the closed form expressions for the filter Fourier coefficients would have result more complex, which would have prevented us from obtaining intuitive results. Theoretically, the set of cycle frequencies Γ consists of an infinite number of them, which makes very hard to find a closed form solution to the design formula in (21). This difficulty can be circumvented by forcing the number of cycle frequencies of the linear estimator $h(t, \lambda)$ to be finite, at the cost of performance (the MSE increases and the filter is no longer optimal). This strategy will be described along with the FRESH implementation of LAPTV filters, in Section 4. But firstly, the expression in (22) is generalized for complex signals in the next section.

3. Extension of the study to complex signals

Complex cyclostationary processes require up to four real LAPTV filters in order to achieve optimality, that is:

1. To estimate the real part of $d(t)$ from the real part of $x(t)$,
2. to estimate the real part of $d(t)$ from the imaginary part of $x(t)$,
3. to estimate the imaginary part of $d(t)$ from the real part of $x(t)$ and
4. to estimate the imaginary part of $d(t)$ from the imaginary part of $x(t)$.

This solution can be reduced to two complex LAPTV filters whose inputs are $x(t)$ and the complex conjugate of $x(t)$, that is $x^*(t)$. As a consequence, the optimal filter is not formally a linear filter, but a Widely-Linear Almost-Periodically Time-Variant (WLAPTV) filter (Chevalier & Maurice, 1997) (also known as *Linear-Conjugate Linear*, LCL (Brown, 1987; Gardner, 1993)). Actually, the optimal WLAPTV filter reduces to an LAPTV filter when the observations and the desired signal are jointly circular (Picinbono & Chevalier, 1995). [5] The final output of the WLAPTV filter is obtained by adding together the outputs of the two complex LAPTV filters:

$$\widehat{d}(t) = \int_{-\infty}^{\infty} h(t,u)\, x(u)\, du + \int_{-\infty}^{\infty} g(t,u)\, x^*(u)\, du \tag{34}$$

Since the orthogonality principle establishes that the estimation error must be uncorrelated with the input, it applies to both $x(t)$ and $x^*(t)$, yielding the linear system:

$$\begin{cases} \mathrm{E}\left\{\varepsilon(t)\, x^*(\lambda)\right\} = 0 \\ \mathrm{E}\left\{\varepsilon(t)\, x(\lambda)\right\} = 0 \end{cases} , \quad \forall \lambda, t \in \mathbb{R} \tag{35}$$

$$\begin{cases} R_{dx}(t,\lambda) = \displaystyle\int_{-\infty}^{\infty} h_\Gamma(t,u)\, R_{xx}(u,\lambda)\, du + \int_{-\infty}^{\infty} g_\Gamma(t,u)\, \left[R_{xx^*}(u,\lambda)\right]^*\, du \\ R_{dx^*}(t,\lambda) = \displaystyle\int_{-\infty}^{\infty} h_\Gamma(t,u)\, R_{xx^*}(u,\lambda)\, du + \int_{-\infty}^{\infty} g_\Gamma(t,u)\, R_{xx}(\lambda,u)\, du \end{cases} , \quad \forall \lambda, t \in \mathbb{R} \tag{36}$$

[5] The observed and desired signals, respectively $x(t)$ and $d(t)$, are jointly circular when $x^*(t)$ is uncorrelated with both $x(t)$ and $d(t)$ (Picinbono & Chevalier, 1995).

Analogously to Section 2, it can be demonstrated that the condition in (36) is satisfied if both $h_\Gamma(t,\lambda)$ and $g_\Gamma(t,\lambda)$ are almost-periodic functions, and the linear system in (36) can be reformulated as the design formula (Gardner, 1993):

$$\begin{cases} S_{dx}^{\alpha_k}(f) = \sum\limits_{\gamma_q \in \Gamma} H_\Gamma^{\gamma_q}(f)\, S_{xx}^{\alpha_k-\gamma_q}(f-\gamma_q) + G_\Gamma^{\gamma_q}(f)\left[S_{xx^*}^{\gamma_q-\alpha_k}(\gamma_q - f)\right]^* \\ S_{dx^*}^{\alpha_k}(f) = \sum\limits_{\gamma_q \in \Gamma} H_\Gamma^{\gamma_q}(f)\, S_{xx^*}^{\alpha_k-\gamma_q}(f-\gamma_q) + G_\Gamma^{\gamma_q}(f)\left[S_{xx}^{\gamma_q-\alpha_k}(\gamma_q - f)\right]^* \end{cases}, \quad \forall \alpha_k \in \Gamma, \forall f \in \mathbb{R} \tag{37}$$

where the set of cycle frequencies Γ is defined in this case as the minimum set comprising A_{dx}, A_{dx^*}, B_{xx} and B_{xx^*}, which is closed in the addition and subtraction operations (with A_{dx^*} and B_{xx^*} being the sets of cycle frequencies of the cross-correlation functions of the complex conjugate of the input, $x^*(t)$, with $d(t)$ and $x(t)$, respectively.)

As it occurred for real signals in Section 2, finding a closed-form solution to the design formula in (37) may result too complicated when a large number of cycle frequencies compose the set Γ. In the next section a workaround is proposed based on the FRESH implementation of LAPTV filters and the use of a reduced set of cycle frequencies, $\Gamma_s \subset \Gamma$.

4. Implementation of WLAPTV filters as FRESH (FREquency-SHift) filters

For simplicity reasons, LAPTV filters are often implemented as FREquency SHift (FRESH) filters (Gameiro, 2000; Gardner, 1993; 1994; Gardner & Franks, 1975; Gonçalves & Gameiro, 2002; Loeffler & Burrus, 1978; Ngan et al., 2004; Reed & Hsia, 1990; Zadeh, 1950). FRESH filters consist of a bank of LTI filters, whose inputs are frequency-shifted versions of the input signal. In general, the optimum FRESH filter would require an infinite number of LTI filters. Because this is not feasible, the FRESH filters used in practice are sub-optimal, in the sense that they are limited to a finite set of frequency shifters.

Any WLAPTV filter can be implemented as FRESH filter. [6] This result emerges from using in (34) the generalized Fourier series expansion of LAPTV filters. Let $h(t,\gamma)$ and $g(t,\gamma)$ be two arbitrary LAPTV filters. Then, each of them can be expanded in a generalized Fourier series yielding:

$$\widehat{d}(t) = \int_{-\infty}^{\infty} h(t,u)\, x(u)\, du + \int_{-\infty}^{\infty} g(t,u)\, x^*(u)\, du \tag{38}$$

$$= \int_{-\infty}^{\infty} \sum_k h^{\alpha_k}(t-u)\, e^{j2\pi\alpha_k u}\, x(u)\, du + \int_{-\infty}^{\infty} \sum_p g^{\beta_p}(t-u)\, e^{j2\pi\beta_p u}\, x^*(u)\, du \tag{39}$$

$$= \sum_k \int_{-\infty}^{\infty} h^{\alpha_k}(t-u)\left[e^{j2\pi\alpha_k u}\, x(u)\right] du + \sum_p \int_{-\infty}^{\infty} g^{\beta_p}(t-u)\left[e^{j2\pi\beta_p u}\, x^*(u)\right] du \tag{40}$$

It can be clearly seen that the output of the WLAPTV filter, $\widehat{d}(t)$, is the result of adding together the outputs of the LTI filters $h^{\alpha_k}(t)$ and $g^{\beta_p}(t)$, whose inputs are frequency-shifted versions of the input signal $x(t)$ and its complex conjugate $x^*(t)$, respectively. This is precisely the definition of a FRESH filter.

[6] Formally, two FRESH filters are required respectively for the input and its complex conjugate. Nevertheless, we will refer to the set of both as a FRESH filter herein.

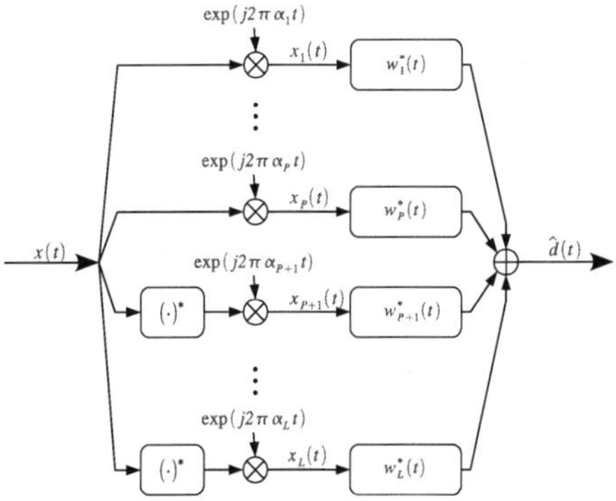

Fig. 5. Block diagram of the FRESH implementation of a WLAPTV filter.

The most difficult problem in the design of sub-optimal FRESH filters concerns the choice of the optimal subset of frequency shifts, $\Gamma_s \subset \Gamma$, under some design constraints. For instance, a common design constraint is the maximum number of branches of the FRESH filter. The optimum Γ_s becomes highly dependent on the spectral correlation function of the input signal and can change with time in nonstationary environments. However, with the aim of simplifying the FRESH implementation, Γ_s is usually fixed beforehand and the common approach to determine the frequency shifts consists in choosing those cycle frequencies at which the spectral cross-correlation functions between $d(t)$ and $x(t)$, or its complex conjugate, exhibits maximum levels (Gardner, 1993; Yeste-Ojeda & Grajal, 2008).
Once the set of frequency shifts has been fixed, the design of FRESH filters is much simpler than that of WLAPTV filters, because FRESH filters only use LTI filters. Because of the nonstationary nature of the input (it is almost-cyclostationary), the optimality criterion used in the design of the set of LTI filters is the MTAMSE criterion, in contrast to the MMSE criterion (Gardner, 1993). The resulting FRESH filter is a sub-optimum solution since it is optimum only within the set of FRESH filters using the same set of frequency shifts.
Let us formulate the output of the FRESH filter by using vector notation:

$$\widehat{d}(t) = \int_{-\infty}^{\infty} \boldsymbol{w}^{\dagger}(t-u)\, \boldsymbol{x}(u)\, du \tag{41}$$

where $\boldsymbol{w}^{\dagger}(t)$ stands for the conjugate transpose of vector $\boldsymbol{w}(t)$, and each component of the input vector $\boldsymbol{x}(t)$ represents the input of an LTI filter according to the scheme represented in Fig. 5:

$$\boldsymbol{x}(t) = \begin{bmatrix} x_1(t) \\ x_2(t) \\ \vdots \\ x_P(t) \\ x_{P+1}(t) \\ \vdots \\ x_L(t) \end{bmatrix} = \begin{bmatrix} x(t)\, e^{j2\pi\alpha_1 t} \\ x(t)\, e^{j2\pi\alpha_2 t} \\ \vdots \\ x(t)\, e^{j2\pi\alpha_P t} \\ x^*(t)\, e^{j2\pi\beta_1 t} \\ \vdots \\ x^*(t)\, e^{j2\pi\beta_{L-P} t} \end{bmatrix} \tag{42}$$

where P is the number of branches used for filtering the frequency shifted versions of $x(t)$, $(L-P)$ is the number of branches used for filtering its complex conjugate $x^*(t)$, and L

is the total number of branches. Note that the first P cycle frequencies can be repeated in the next $P - L$ cycle frequencies, since using a frequency shift for the input $x(t)$ does not exclude it from being used for its complex conjugate. With the aim of computing the MTAMSE optimal set of LTI filters, a stationarized signal model is applied to both the desired signal $d(t)$ and the input vector $\boldsymbol{x}(t)$, which are jointly almost-cyclostationary processes, and therefore stationarizable (Gardner, 1978). The stationary auto- and cross-correlation functions are obtained by taking the stationary part (time-averaging) the corresponding nonstationary correlation functions. As a result, the orthogonality principle is formulated as follows:

$$\mathrm{E}\left\{\varepsilon(t+\tau)\,\boldsymbol{x}^{\dagger}(t)\right\} = \mathbf{0}^{T}, \quad \forall \tau \in \mathbb{R} \tag{43}$$

$$\boldsymbol{R}_{d\boldsymbol{x}}(\tau) = \int_{-\infty}^{\infty} \boldsymbol{w}_{\Gamma_s}^{\dagger}(\tau - u)\,\mathbf{R}_{\boldsymbol{x}\boldsymbol{x}}(u)\,du\,, \quad \forall \tau \in \mathbb{R} \tag{44}$$

where $\mathbf{0}$ is the null vector, and the cross-correlation (row) vector $\boldsymbol{R}_{d\boldsymbol{x}}(\tau)$ and the auto-correlation matrix $\mathbf{R}_{\boldsymbol{x}\boldsymbol{x}}(\tau)$ are computed by time-averaging the corresponding nonstationary correlation functions. For $\boldsymbol{R}_{d\boldsymbol{x}}(\tau)$ this yields:

$$\boldsymbol{R}_{d\boldsymbol{x}}(\tau) = \lim_{T\to\infty} \frac{1}{2T} \int_{-T}^{T} \mathrm{E}\left\{d(t+\tau)\,\boldsymbol{x}^{\dagger}(t)\right\} dt = \begin{bmatrix} R_{dx}^{\alpha_1}(\tau) \\ R_{dx}^{\alpha_2}(\tau) \\ \vdots \\ R_{dx}^{\alpha_P}(\tau) \\ R_{dx^*}^{\alpha_{P+1}}(\tau) \\ \vdots \\ R_{dx^*}^{\alpha_L}(\tau) \end{bmatrix}^{T} \tag{45}$$

where the cyclic cross-correlation functions were defined in (15). The matrix $\mathbf{R}_{\boldsymbol{x}\boldsymbol{x}}(\tau)$ becomes:

$$\mathbf{R}_{\boldsymbol{x}\boldsymbol{x}}(\tau) = \lim_{T\to\infty} \frac{1}{2T} \int_{-T}^{T} \mathrm{E}\left\{\boldsymbol{x}(t+\tau)\,\boldsymbol{x}^{\dagger}(t)\right\} dt \tag{46}$$

where the element in the q-th row and k-th column is:

$$[\mathbf{R}_{\boldsymbol{x}\boldsymbol{x}}(\tau)]_{qk} = \begin{cases} R_{xx}^{\alpha_k-\alpha_q}(\tau)\,e^{j2\pi\alpha_q\tau} & q \le P,\ k \le P \\ R_{xx^*}^{\alpha_k-\alpha_q}(\tau)\,e^{j2\pi\alpha_q\tau} & q \le P,\ k > P \\ \left[R_{xx^*}^{\alpha_q-\alpha_k}(\tau)\right]^{*} e^{j2\pi\alpha_q\tau} & q > P,\ k \le P \\ \left[R_{xx}^{\alpha_q-\alpha_k}(\tau)\right]^{*} e^{j2\pi\alpha_q\tau} & q > P,\ k > P \end{cases} \tag{47}$$

where the cyclic auto-correlation functions were defined in (16).
Finally, the orthogonality principle leads directly to the multidimensional Wiener filter, and the frequency response of the set of filters is obtained by taking the Fourier transform in (44):

$$\boldsymbol{S}_{d\boldsymbol{x}}(f) = \boldsymbol{W}_{\Gamma_s}^{\dagger}(f)\mathbf{S}_{\boldsymbol{x}\boldsymbol{x}}(f) \tag{48}$$

$$\boldsymbol{W}_{\Gamma_s}(f) = \left[\mathbf{S}_{\boldsymbol{x}\boldsymbol{x}}(f)\right]^{-1}\,\boldsymbol{S}_{d\boldsymbol{x}}^{\dagger}(f) \tag{49}$$

where the Hermitian property of matrix $\mathbf{S}_{\boldsymbol{x}\boldsymbol{x}}(f)$ has been used,

$$\boldsymbol{S}_{d\boldsymbol{x}}(f) = \left[S_{dx}^{\alpha_1}(f),\ S_{dx}^{\alpha_2}(f),\ \ldots,\ S_{dx}^{\alpha_P}(f),\ S_{dx^*}^{\alpha_{P+1}}(f),\ \ldots,\ S_{dx^*}^{\alpha_L}(f)\right] \tag{50}$$

and the element of the q-th row and k-th column of matrix $\mathbf{S}_{\boldsymbol{xx}}(f)$ is:

$$[\mathbf{S}_{\boldsymbol{xx}}(f)]_{qk} = \begin{cases} S_{xx}^{\alpha_k-\alpha_q}\left(f-\alpha_q\right) & q \leq P,\ k \leq P \\ S_{xx^*}^{\alpha_k-\alpha_q}\left(f-\alpha_q\right) & q \leq P,\ k > P \\ \left[S_{xx^*}^{\alpha_q-\alpha_k}\left(\alpha_q-f\right)\right]^* & q > P,\ k \leq P \\ \left[S_{xx}^{\alpha_q-\alpha_k}\left(\alpha_q-f\right)\right]^* & q > P,\ k > P \end{cases} \tag{51}$$

It is noteworthy that the expression in (37), which defines the optimal WLAPTV filter, is a generalization of (48) for the case where $\Gamma_s = \Gamma$. In addition, we want to emphasize the main differences between optimal and sub-optimal FRESH filters:

1. Optimal FRESH filters are direct implementations of optimal WLAPTV filters defined by (37), and generally consist of an infinite number of LTI filters. Contrarily, sub-optimal FRESH filters are limited to a finite set of LTI filters.
2. For jointly almost-cyclostationary input and desired signals, optimal FRESH filters are the optimal with respect to any other linear estimator. On the contrary, sub-optimal FRESH filters are defined for a given subset Γ_s and, therefore, they are optimal only in comparison to the rest of FRESH filters using the same frequency shifts.
3. Optimal FRESH filters minimize the MSE at all times (MMSE criterion). However, sub-optimal FRESH filters only minimize the MSE on average (MTAMSE criterion). This means that another FRESH filter, even by making use of the same set of frequency shifts, could exhibit a lower MSE at specific times.

Finally, the inverse of matrix $\mathbf{S}_{\boldsymbol{xx}}(f)$ could not exist for all frequencies, which would invalidate the expression in (49). However, since its main diagonal represents the power spectral density of the frequency shifted versions of the input, this formal problem can be ignored by assuming that a white noise component is always present at the input.
At this point we have finished the theoretical background concerning FRESH filters. The following sections are focused on the applications of adaptive FRESH filters. Firstly, the introduction of an adaptive algorithm in a FRESH filter is reviewed in the next section.

5. Adaptive FRESH filters

The main drawback of using FRESH filters is that the phase of the LTI filters (or alternatively the phase of the frequency shifters) must be "synchronized" with the desired signal. Otherwise, the contribution of the different branches can be destructive rather than constructive. For example, the phase of the signal carrier must be known if the frequency shifts are related to the carrier frequency, or the symbol synchronism must be known if the symbol rate is involved in the frequency shifts. As a consequence, the knowledge required for the design of sub-optimal [7] FRESH filter is rarely available beforehand, which leads to the use adaptive algorithms. Since FRESH filters consist of a set LTI filters, conventional adaptive algorithms can be directly applied, such as Least-Mean-Square (LMS) or Recursive-Least-Squares (RLS). The general scheme of an adaptive FRESH filter is shown in Fig. 6.

[7] Hereinafter, FRESH filters are always limited to a finite set of frequency shifts. Therefore, sub-optimal FRESH filters will be referred to as "optimal" for brevity.

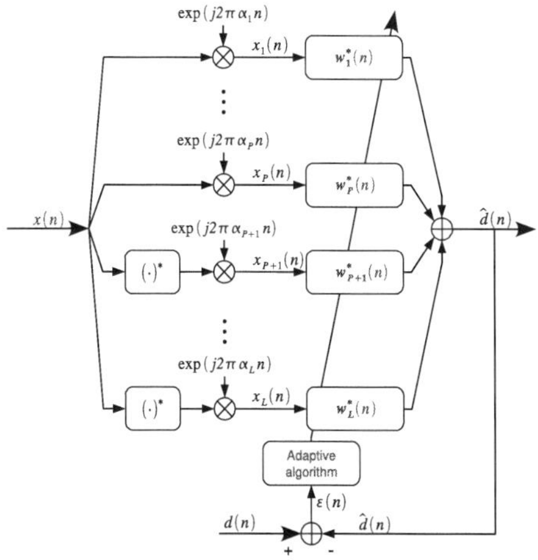

Fig. 6. Block diagram of an adaptive FRESH filter.

In order to simplify the analysis of the adaptive algorithms, the structure of FRESH filters is particularized to the case of discrete-time signals with the set of LTI filters exhibiting Finite Impulse Response (FIR filters). After filtering the received signal, $x(n)$, the output of the adaptive FRESH filter is compared to a desired (or reference) signal, $d(n)$, and the error, $\varepsilon(n)$, is used by an adaptive algorithm in order to update the filter coefficients. Commonly, the desired signal is either a known sequence (as a training sequence for equalizers), or obtained from the received signal (as for blind equalizers).

Let the output of the FRESH filter be defined as the inner product:

$$\widehat{d}(n) \triangleq \boldsymbol{w}^{\dagger}(n)\boldsymbol{x}(n) = \sum_{i=1}^{L} \boldsymbol{w}_i^{\dagger}(n)\boldsymbol{x}_i(n) \tag{52}$$

where the vectors $\boldsymbol{w}(n)$ and $\boldsymbol{x}(n)$ are the concatenation of the filter and the input vectors, respectively:

$$\boldsymbol{w}(n) = \begin{bmatrix} \boldsymbol{w}_1(n) \\ \boldsymbol{w}_2(n) \\ \vdots \\ \boldsymbol{w}_L(n) \end{bmatrix}, \qquad \boldsymbol{x}(n) = \begin{bmatrix} \boldsymbol{x}_1(n) \\ \boldsymbol{x}_2(n) \\ \vdots \\ \boldsymbol{x}_L(n) \end{bmatrix} \tag{53}$$

$\boldsymbol{w}_i(n)$ and $\boldsymbol{x}_i(n)$ are the filter and input vectors, respectively, of the i-th branch:

$$\boldsymbol{w}_i(n) = [w_i(n), w_i(n-1), \ldots, w_i(n-M_i+1)]^T \tag{54}$$

$$\boldsymbol{x}_i(n) = [x_i(n), x_i(n-1), \ldots, x_i(n-M_i+1)]^T \tag{55}$$

where M_i is the length of the i-th filter. Consequently, the total length of vectors $\boldsymbol{w}(n)$ and $\boldsymbol{x}(n)$ is $M = \sum_{i=1}^{L} M_i$.

Using the results in the previous sections, the optimal set of LTI filters is given by multidimensional Wiener filter theory:

$$w_o = (\mathbf{R}_x)^{-1} p \tag{56}$$

where $\mathbf{R}_x$ stands for the time-averaged auto-correlation matrix of the input vector, [8]

$$\mathbf{R}_x = \left\langle \mathrm{E}\left\{ x(n)\, x^{\dagger}(n) \right\} \right\rangle \tag{57}$$

where $\langle \cdot \rangle$ denotes the time average operator:

$$\left\langle \mathrm{E}\left\{ x(n)\, x^{\dagger}(n) \right\} \right\rangle = \lim_{N\to\infty} \frac{1}{2N+1} \sum_{n=-N}^{N} \mathrm{E}\left\{ x(n)\, x^{\dagger}(n) \right\} \tag{58}$$

In Eq. (56), the vector p represents the time-averaged cross-correlation between the input vector x and $d(n)$:

$$p = \langle \mathrm{E}\left\{ x(n) d^{*}(n) \right\} \rangle \tag{59}$$

The correlation functions in (57) and (59) are time-averaged in order to force the LTI characteristic of w_o. The expressions in (56), (57), and (59) allow to follow the classical developments of adaptive algorithms (Haykin, 2001). Despite using classical algorithms, adaptive FRESH filters naturally exploit the cyclostationary properties of the signals as the inputs of the LTI filters are frequency-shifted versions of the input of the adaptive FRESH filter.

5.1 Blind Adaptive FRESH filters (BAFRESH)

One of the main reasons for using adaptive FRESH filters is their inherent ability to operate blindly (Zhang et al., 1999). Commonly, adaptive algorithms require a reference signal which is not available in many applications of adaptive filtering. When the adaptive filter works without such a reference signal, we say that it is "blind". Blind Adaptive FRESH (BAFRESH) filters can be obtained directly by simply using as frequency shifts those cycle frequencies which belong to the cyclic spectrum of the input and satisfy the condition:

$$S_{xx}^{\alpha}(f) = S_{dx}^{\alpha}(f) \tag{60}$$

for the first P branches, and

$$S_{xx^*}^{\alpha}(f) = S_{dx^*}^{\alpha}(f) \tag{61}$$

for the rest of branches (those working with $x^*(t)$). Then, the input signal itself can be used as the reference signal, as it is represented in Fig. 7, while the adaptive algorithm converges to the same solution as if a "clean" reference signal were used. [9] Intuitively, the conditions (60) and (61) mean that a BAFRESH filter must use only those cycle frequencies (among all the cycle frequencies of the input) at which only the part of the input which is correlated with the desired signal exhibits spectral correlation. It is noteworthy that (60) excludes cycle frequency zero from being used in the branches not using the complex conjugate of the input signal. The reason is that all stochastic processes exhibit spectral correlation at cycle frequency zero

[8] We have assumed that the matrix $\mathbf{R}_x$ is nonsingular, which is always true as long as there exists a white noise component at the input.

[9] However, using $x(t)$ instead of a "clean" reference produces an increase in the power of $\varepsilon(n)$, which could influence the adaptive FRESH filter performance.

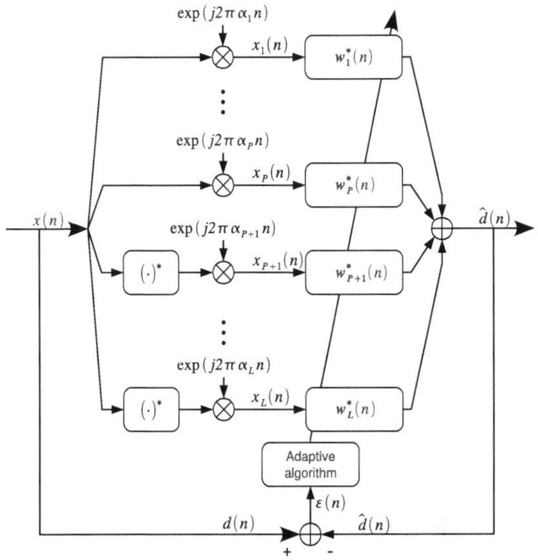

Fig. 7. Block diagram of a BAFRESH filter.

and therefore (60) could only be satisfied if the desired and the input signals are the same, which would eliminate the necessity of a filter. Contrarily, many stochastic processes do not exhibit spectral cross-correlation with their complex conjugate at cycle frequency zero, for instance the circular stochastic processes. This allows the condition (61) to be satisfied without implying that $d(t) = x(t)$.

When adaptive BAFRESH filters use a suitable set of frequency shifts, the correlation between the inputs of the LTI filters, $x_i(n)$, and the reference signal $x(n)$, is only due to the signal to be estimated. Thus, the adaptive algorithm will converge to a solution by which the desired signal is estimated at the output of the BAFRESH filter, while any other component present at the input is minimized. This is a powerful characteristic of adaptive FRESH filters which turns them into a good candidate for those applications where no reference signal is available at the receiver.

6. Adaptive FRESH filters for cycle-frequency errors compensation

This section deals with the problem of uncertainties in the periodicities of LAPTV filters. [10] The purpose in this section is to analyze the nonstationary behavior of adaptive FRESH filters in order to mitigate this problem. Since they exploit the spectral correlation of signals at specific values of frequency separation or cycle frequency, LAPTV filters are severely affected by errors in such cycle frequencies. These errors may be due to non-perfect knowledge of the cyclic spectrum, or natural effects such as the Doppler effect. In such a case, it will be demonstrated that the filter can become totally useless. The reason is that a high enough error (in comparison to the observation time) produces a loss of coherence among the outputs of the FRESH branches. This causes a destructive interference rather than a

[10] The main body of this section can be found in (Yeste-Ojeda & Grajal, 2010).

constructive one when the outputs of the branches are added together. Although this is a well known problem, it has been exhaustively dealt with only in the field of beamforming and direction finding, mainly regarding MUSIC (Schmidt, 1986) and SCORE (Agee et al., 1990) algorithms. Besides describing the problem, some solutions have been proposed. Schell and Gardner stated that the degradation in performance increases with the product of the observation time and the error in cycle frequency (Schell & Gardner, 1990). As a solution, they proposed two alternatives: Using multiple cycle frequencies in order to increase robustness, or adaptively estimating the cycle frequencies by maximizing the magnitude of the FFT of the lag product of the observations. Lee and Lee proposed two procedures for estimating the cycle-frequency offset (Lee & Lee, 1999). Both of them are based on the maximization of the highest eigenvalue of the product of a sample autocorrelation-related matrix. In (Lee et al., 2000), cycle frequencies are estimated iteratively through a gradient descent algorithm which maximizes the output power of an adaptive beamformer, assuming that the initial cycle frequencies are close enough. A similar approach can be found in (Jianhui et al., 2006), where the conjugate gradient algorithm is used instead of gradient descent, and after proper modifications in the cost function. A new approach is described in (Zhang et al., 2004), where the robustness of the beamformer is achieved by minimizing a cost function which is averaged over a range of cycle frequencies, instead of trying to correct the cycle frequency errors.
The approach used in this section is rather different from the cited work. The purpose of this section is to explore an additional advantage of using adaptive filters for FRESH filtering, which is their capability of working in the presence of errors in the frequency shifts. This is possible because the adaptive filter is able to track these errors, by updating the coefficients of the LTI filters in a cyclic manner. As a result, the adaptive filter at each branch of the FRESH filter behaves as a Linear Periodically Time-Variant (LPTV) filter, rather than converging to an LTI filter. This ability is strongly conditioned by the rate of convergence of the adaptive algorithm. For slow convergence, the outputs of the branches with frequency-shift errors are cancelled. As the convergence accelerates, the adaptive filters of those branches with frequency-shift errors behave as LPTV filters in order to compensate the errors. These subjects shall be dealt with later on, but firstly let us highlight the problem of cycle-frequency errors in FRESH filtering.

6.1 Effect of errors in the frequency shifts

The scheme of the adaptive FRESH filter considered in this section has been shown in Fig. 6. The problem of an error in the frequency shifts of the FRESH filter is that the correlation between the desired signal and the corresponding filter input vanishes. For a nonadaptive FRESH filter, the error can be tolerated during a limited observation time. At each branch, the contribution to the signal estimate is constructive for an interval lesser than the inverse of the error of its frequency shift. Therefore, the observation time tolerated by the whole filter is determined by the inverse of the biggest error in the frequency shifts. [11] For an infinite observation time, the optimal LTI filter is null for all branches with an error in their frequency shifts, as we shall demonstrate in this section. This is due to the discrete nature of the cyclic spectrum, which means that the cyclic correlation function is different from zero only at a countable set of cycle-frequency values. Thus, an error in a cycle frequency yields that the signal at the input of the corresponding filter is correlated neither with $d(n)$, nor with the inputs of the rest of filters.

[11] However, the degradation of the estimation error depends on the contribution of the corresponding branch to the signal estimate.

Let us use the definitions introduced in the previous section, specifically from (52) to (59). For convenience, let the auto-correlation matrix of the input vector be expressed in the form

$$\mathbf{R}_x = \begin{bmatrix} \mathbf{R}_{x_{11}} & \langle \mathrm{E}\left\{\boldsymbol{x}_1(n)\boldsymbol{x}_{2L}^{\dagger}(n)\right\}\rangle \\ \langle \mathrm{E}\left\{\boldsymbol{x}_{2L}(n)\boldsymbol{x}_1^{\dagger}(n)\right\}\rangle & \mathbf{R}_{x_{2L}} \end{bmatrix} \tag{62}$$

where $\mathbf{R}_{x_{ij}}$, with $i \leq j$, stands for the auto-correlation matrix of input vectors from the i-th to the j-th branch:

$$\mathbf{R}_{x_{ij}} = \left\langle \mathrm{E}\left\{\boldsymbol{x}_{ij}(n)\ \boldsymbol{x}_{ij}^{\dagger}(n)\right\}\right\rangle \tag{63}$$

Similarly, the vector $\boldsymbol{x}_{ij}(n)$ stands for the concatenation of input vectors from the i-th to the j-th branch:

$$\boldsymbol{x}_{ij}(n) = \left[\boldsymbol{x}_i^T(n),\ \ldots,\ \boldsymbol{x}_j^T(n)\right]^T \tag{64}$$

Let us assume that there is an error in the frequency shift used for the first branch. Then, the time-averaged cross-correlation between $\boldsymbol{x}_1(n)$ and the input vectors of the rest of branches is zero. Moreover, the time-averaged cross-correlation of $\boldsymbol{x}_1(n)$ with the desired signal, $d(n)$, is also zero. Thus, the optimal set of LTI filters when there exist errors in the frequency shift of the first branch results:

$$\boldsymbol{w}_o' = (\mathbf{R}_x)^{-1}\boldsymbol{p} = \begin{bmatrix} \mathbf{R}_{x_{11}}^{-1} & 0 \\ 0 & \mathbf{R}_{x_{2L}}^{-1} \end{bmatrix} \begin{bmatrix} 0 \\ p_{2L} \end{bmatrix} = \begin{bmatrix} 0 \\ \mathbf{R}_{x_{2L}}^{-1}\ p_{2L} \end{bmatrix} \tag{65}$$

Therefore, the optimal LTI filter of the first branch and its output are null. In addition, the optimal set of filters for the other branches is equivalent to not using the first branch. In short, what is happening is that the first frequency shift does not belong to set Γ. When all branches exhibit errors in their frequency shifts, then the optimal filter vector is zero and the FRESH filter becomes useless. It is noteworthy that the cancellation of the branches with an error in their frequency shift is caused by the LTI characteristic of the filters, which has been forced by time-averaging $\mathbf{R}_x$ and $\boldsymbol{p}$. In the next section, it is shown that the errors in the frequency shifts can be compensated by allowing the filters to be time-variant, specifically, LPTV.

6.2 LPTV solution

When there exist errors in the frequency shifts, an adaptive-FRESH filter can compensate them. In order to understand the behavior of the adaptive filter, let us assume that these errors are known. One direct solution to this problem is to substitute the corresponding LTI filters by LPTV filters consisting of a correcting frequency shift followed by an LTI filter, as shown in Fig. 8. Formally, the output of the optimal FRESH filter defined in (56), when there are not errors in the frequency shifts, is:

$$\widehat{d}(n) = \boldsymbol{w}_o^{\dagger}\ \boldsymbol{x}(n) = \sum_{i=1}^{L} \boldsymbol{w}_{oi}^{\dagger}\ \boldsymbol{x}_i(n) \tag{66}$$

where $\boldsymbol{w}_{oi}$ stands for the optimal LTI filter in the i-th branch and $\boldsymbol{x}_i(n)$ are the outputs of the frequency shifters without error. The LPTV solution can be obtained by including the errors

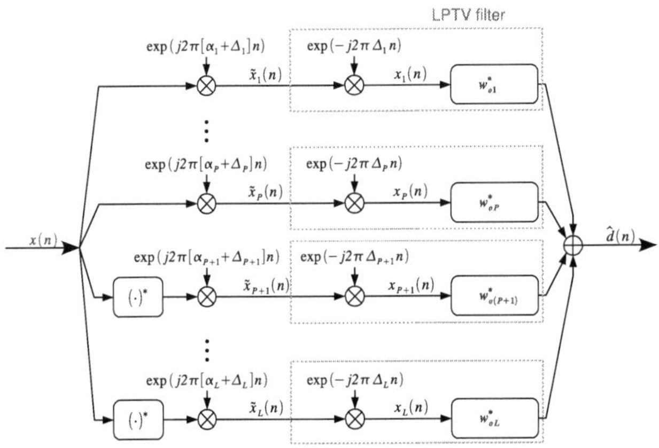

Fig. 8. Cycle frequency errors correction by means of LPTV filters.

in the frequency shifts:

$$\begin{aligned}\widehat{d}(n) &= \sum_{i=1}^{L} \boldsymbol{w}_{oi}^{\dagger}\, \boldsymbol{x}_i(n)\, e^{j2\pi\Delta_i n}\, e^{-j2\pi\Delta_i n} \\ &= \sum_{i=1}^{L} \left(e^{-j2\pi\Delta_i n}\, \boldsymbol{w}_{oi}^{\dagger}\right) \left(\boldsymbol{x}_i(n)\, e^{j2\pi\Delta_i n}\right) \\ &= \sum_{i=1}^{L} \tilde{\boldsymbol{w}}_{oi}^{\dagger}(n)\, \tilde{\boldsymbol{x}}_i(n) = \tilde{\boldsymbol{w}}_{o}^{\dagger}(n)\, \tilde{\boldsymbol{x}}(n)\end{aligned} \tag{67}$$

where $\tilde{\boldsymbol{w}}_o(n)$ is the set of LPTV filters, and $\tilde{\boldsymbol{x}}(n)$ are the input vector to these filters (the output of the first frequency shifters in Fig. 8).
By defining the diagonal matrix

$$\boldsymbol{\Phi} \triangleq \begin{bmatrix} e^{j2\pi\Delta_1}\mathbf{I}_{M_1} & 0 & \cdots & 0 \\ 0 & e^{j2\pi\Delta_2}\mathbf{I}_{M_2} & \cdots & 0 \\ \vdots & \vdots & \ddots & \vdots \\ 0 & 0 & \cdots & e^{j2\pi\Delta_L}\mathbf{I}_{M_L} \end{bmatrix} \tag{68}$$

where $\mathbf{I}_N$ is the $N \times N$ identity matrix, the vectors $\tilde{\boldsymbol{w}}_o(n)$ and $\tilde{\boldsymbol{x}}(n)$ can be expressed in the form:

$$\tilde{\boldsymbol{w}}_o(n) = \boldsymbol{\Phi}^n\, \boldsymbol{w}_o \tag{69}$$

$$\tilde{\boldsymbol{x}}(n) = \boldsymbol{\Phi}^n\, \boldsymbol{x}(n) \tag{70}$$

Additionally, the optimal set of linear time-variant filters is obtained by minimization of the instantaneous MSE. This optimal set (whose input vector is $\tilde{\boldsymbol{x}}(n)$) is (Van Trees, 1968):

$$\tilde{\boldsymbol{w}}_o(n) = \left[\mathbf{R}_{\tilde{x}}(n)\right]^{-1} \tilde{\boldsymbol{p}}(n) \tag{71}$$

where

$$\mathbf{R}_{\tilde{x}}(n) = \mathrm{E}\left\{\tilde{\boldsymbol{x}}(n)\,\tilde{\boldsymbol{x}}^{\dagger}(n)\right\} \tag{72}$$

$$\tilde{\boldsymbol{p}}(n) = \mathrm{E}\left\{\tilde{\boldsymbol{x}}(n)\,d^{*}(n)\right\} \tag{73}$$

Therefore, since (69) is verified, a sufficient condition to obtain (69) from (71), is that:

$$\begin{aligned}\mathbf{R}_{\tilde{x}}(n) &\triangleq \boldsymbol{\Phi}^{n}\left\langle \mathrm{E}\left\{\boldsymbol{x}(n)\,\boldsymbol{x}^{\dagger}(n)\right\}\right\rangle \boldsymbol{\Phi}^{-n}\\ &= \boldsymbol{\Phi}^{n}\,\mathbf{R}_{x}\,\boldsymbol{\Phi}^{-n}\end{aligned} \tag{74}$$

$$\begin{aligned}\tilde{\boldsymbol{p}}(n) &\triangleq \boldsymbol{\Phi}^{n}\left\langle \mathrm{E}\left\{\boldsymbol{x}(n)d^{*}(n)\right\}\right\rangle\\ &= \boldsymbol{\Phi}^{n}\,\boldsymbol{p}\end{aligned} \tag{75}$$

where $\mathbf{R}_x$ and $\boldsymbol{p}$ have been defined in (57) and (59) respectively.

Note that (74) and (75) are not the true auto-correlation matrix and cross-correlation vector between $\tilde{\boldsymbol{x}}(n)$ and $d(n)$. On the contrary, they are based on the stationarized signal model of the input vector $\boldsymbol{x}(n)$ and the desired signal $d(n)$, so that the LTI characteristic of the filters after the second frequency shifters in Fig. 8 is forced.

An additional motivation for introducing (74) and (75) is that these expressions will serve us to develop the convergence of the LMS algorithm mathematically. We have chosen the Least Mean Squares (LMS) adaptive algorithm for the analysis because of its mathematical simplicity, which allows an analytical treatment of the problem. Nonetheless, any adaptive algorithm (for instance, Recursive Least Squares (RLS) (Haykin, 2001)) can be used instead to compensate cycle-frequency errors. The approach herein is the same as as in (Widrow et al., 1976), where the MSE (Mean-Squared-Error) of the adaptive filter is decomposed into the error due to noise in the gradient estimation, and the error due to lag between the optimal and the adaptive filters.

It is straightforward that the LPTV solution in (69) is equivalent to the optimal FRESH filter in the absence of errors. In practice, the errors in the frequency shifts are unknown. Thus, there is not any *fixing* frequency shifter (the second one, in Fig. 8), and the filters of each branch must work with input vector $\tilde{\boldsymbol{x}}(n)$. The advantage of using an adaptive filter is that it can produce the periodic variations of the filters by updating their coefficients. This is only possible for a fast enough rate of convergence. Otherwise, the adaptive filter tends to the LTI optimal solution defined by (56) after substituting the input vector $\boldsymbol{x}(n)$ with $\tilde{\boldsymbol{x}}(n)$ in (57) and (59). This solution implies the cancellation of the branches with errors in their frequency shift. This issue is addressed in next section.

6.3 Excess MSE of the LMS algorithm in the presence of errors in the frequency shifts

In this section we develop an analytical expression for the time-averaged MSE at steady-state of adaptive FRESH filters using the LMS algorithm (LMS-FRESH). The objective is to obtain an expression that accounts for errors in the frequency shifts of the LMS-FRESH filter.

Basically, the LMS algorithm consists in updating the filter weights in the direction of a gradient estimate of the MSE function, which can be thought as a stochastic version of the steepest descent algorithm (Widrow et al., 1976). Let $\tilde{\boldsymbol{w}}(n)$ be the concatenation vector defining the LMS-FRESH filter. The updating algorithm can be formulated as follows:

$$\begin{aligned}\tilde{\boldsymbol{w}}(n+1) &= \tilde{\boldsymbol{w}}(n) + 2\mu\varepsilon^*(n)\tilde{\boldsymbol{x}}(n)\\ \varepsilon(n) &= d(n) - \widehat{d}(n)\\ \widehat{d}(n) &= \tilde{\boldsymbol{w}}^\dagger(n)\ \tilde{\boldsymbol{x}}(n)\end{aligned} \tag{76}$$

where μ is the convergence factor (also known as step-size parameter).
The LMS-FRESH filter exhibits an excess MSE with respect to the set of filters $\tilde{\boldsymbol{w}}_o(n)$ presented in the previous section as the LPTV solution. This excess MSE can be computed as follows (Widrow et al., 1976):

$$\xi_e(n) = \mathrm{E}\left\{[\tilde{\boldsymbol{w}}(n) - \tilde{\boldsymbol{w}}_o(n)]^\dagger\ \mathbf{R}_{\tilde{x}}(n)\ [\tilde{\boldsymbol{w}}(n) - \tilde{\boldsymbol{w}}_o(n)]\right\} \tag{77}$$

Let us separate the excess MSE into two terms: The excess MSE due to gradient noise and the excess MSE due to lag error. The separation is possible by considering the weight error vector as the sum of two terms:

$$\tilde{\boldsymbol{w}}(n) - \tilde{\boldsymbol{w}}_o(n) = [\tilde{\boldsymbol{w}}(n) - \mathrm{E}\{\tilde{\boldsymbol{w}}(n)\}] + [\mathrm{E}\{\tilde{\boldsymbol{w}}(n)\} - \tilde{\boldsymbol{w}}_o(n)] = \tilde{\boldsymbol{u}}(n) + \tilde{\boldsymbol{v}}(n) \tag{78}$$

The first term of the sum in the right hand side, $\tilde{\boldsymbol{u}}(n) = \tilde{\boldsymbol{w}}(n) - \mathrm{E}\{\tilde{\boldsymbol{w}}(n)\}$, produces the excess MSE due to gradient noise, which is related to the gradient estimation process. The second term, $\tilde{\boldsymbol{v}}(n) = \mathrm{E}\{\tilde{\boldsymbol{w}}(n)\} - \tilde{\boldsymbol{w}}_o(n)$, produces the excess MSE due to lag, which quantifies the error due the fact that the adaptive filter cannot follow the variations of $\tilde{\boldsymbol{w}}_o(n)$ with time. By substituting (78) in (77), we obtain:

$$\xi_e(n) = \mathrm{E}\left\{\tilde{\boldsymbol{u}}^\dagger(n)\ \mathbf{R}_{\tilde{x}}(n)\ \tilde{\boldsymbol{u}}(n)\right\} + \mathrm{E}\left\{\tilde{\boldsymbol{v}}^\dagger(n)\ \mathbf{R}_{\tilde{x}}(n)\ \tilde{\boldsymbol{v}}(n)\right\} + 2\mathcal{R}e\left\{\mathrm{E}\left\{\tilde{\boldsymbol{u}}^\dagger(n)\ \mathbf{R}_{\tilde{x}}(n)\ \tilde{\boldsymbol{v}}(n)\right\}\right\} \tag{79}$$

It can be easily shown (from the definitions of $\tilde{\boldsymbol{u}}(n)$ and $\tilde{\boldsymbol{v}}(n)$) that the last term of (79) is zero. Thus, the total time-averaged MSE at steady-state of the LMS-FRESH filters can be expressed as the sum of three terms:

$$\xi_{LMS} \triangleq \left\langle \mathrm{E}\left\{|\varepsilon(n)|^2\right\}\right\rangle = \xi_{min} + \langle \xi_e(n)\rangle = \xi_{min} + \xi_\nabla + \xi_{lag} \tag{80}$$

where ξ_{min} is the minimum time-averaged MSE attained by the optimal FRESH filter, ξ_∇ is the time-averaged excess MSE due to gradient noise, and ξ_{lag} is the time-averaged excess MSE due to lag error.
The minimum time-averaged MSE results from multivariate Wiener theory (Gardner, 1993):

$$\begin{aligned}\xi_{min} &= \sigma_d^2 - \left\langle \tilde{\boldsymbol{w}}_o^\dagger(n)\ \mathbf{R}_{\tilde{x}}(n)\ \tilde{\boldsymbol{w}}_o(n)\right\rangle\\ &= \sigma_d^2 - \boldsymbol{w}_o^\dagger\ \mathbf{R}_x\ \boldsymbol{w}_o\end{aligned} \tag{81}$$

where $\sigma_d^2 = \langle \mathrm{E}\{|d(n)|^2\}\rangle$ is the mean power of the reference signal.
At each instant, the excess MSE due to gradient noise can be computed as follows (Widrow et al., 1976):

$$\xi_\nabla(n) = \mathrm{E}\left\{\tilde{\boldsymbol{u}}^\dagger(n)\ \mathbf{R}_{\tilde{x}}(n)\ \tilde{\boldsymbol{u}}(n)\right\} \tag{82}$$

Assuming that the LMS adaptive filter converges to an LPTV filter at each branch (as shown in Fig. 8), the time-averaged excess MSE at steady-state can be approximated by[12]:

$$\xi_{\nabla} = \langle \xi_{\nabla}(n) \rangle \approx \mu \, \xi_{min} \; \mathrm{tr}\{\mathbf{R}_x\} \tag{83}$$

where $\mathrm{tr}\{\mathbf{R}_x\}$ is the trace of matrix $\mathbf{R}_x$ defined in (57). From (83), ξ_{∇} can be reduced as much as desired by decreasing μ. However, the convergence factor μ controls the rate of convergence of the LMS, so that it is faster as μ increases. Additionally, it will be shown next that the excess MSE due to lag error increases as μ decreases.

The excess MSE due to lag error becomes apparent when the adaptive filter cannot follow the variations of $\tilde{\boldsymbol{w}}_o(n)$ (the LPTV solution) with time. This excess MSE is a function of the weight-error vector $\tilde{\boldsymbol{v}}(n)$, which represents the instantaneous difference between the expected value of the adaptive filter and $\tilde{\boldsymbol{w}}_o(n)$:

$$\xi_{lag}(n) = \tilde{\boldsymbol{v}}^{\dagger}(n) \, \mathbf{R}_{\tilde{x}}(n) \, \tilde{\boldsymbol{v}}(n) \tag{84}$$

The mathematical development of the time-averaged excess MSE at steady-state due to the lag error can be found in the appendix of (Yeste-Ojeda & Grajal, 2010), and yields:

$$\xi_{lag} = \boldsymbol{v}^{\dagger} \, \mathbf{R}_x \, \boldsymbol{v} \tag{85}$$

where $\boldsymbol{v}$, which does not depend on time, is the weight-error vector at steady-state. Under the same conditions that were assumed for (83) (see footnote 12):

$$\begin{aligned} \boldsymbol{v} &= \lim_{n\to\infty} \boldsymbol{\Phi}^{-n} \, \mathrm{E}\{\tilde{\boldsymbol{w}}(n)\} - \boldsymbol{w}_o \\ &= \left(2\mu \left[\boldsymbol{\Phi} - \mathbf{I}_M + 2\mu \mathbf{R}_x\right]^{-1} - \mathbf{R}_x^{-1}\right) \boldsymbol{p} \end{aligned} \tag{86}$$

6.4 Analysis of the results

The study of the previous expressions allows to infer several conclusions:

1. The lag error, ξ_{lag}, tends to zero as μ increases. This is easily seen by taking the limit of (86) as $\mu \to \infty$:

$$\lim_{\mu\to\infty} \boldsymbol{v} = \left(\mathbf{R}_x^{-1} - \mathbf{R}_x^{-1}\right) \boldsymbol{p} = \mathbf{0} \tag{87}$$

   This result indicates that, for a high enough convergence factor, the LMS-FRESH filter is fast enough to follow the variations of the LPTV solution, and therefore the excess MSE due to lag error is zero. However, μ cannot be made as big as desired because then, the adaptive algorithm may not converge, as we shall discuss next.

2. The lag error is also zero when there are not any errors in the frequency shifts. In this case, $\boldsymbol{\Phi} = \mathbf{I}_M$, which substituted in (86) gives $\boldsymbol{v} = \mathbf{0}$. This result is coherent with the concept of lag error. In the absence of errors, the LPTV solution to which the LMS-FRESH filter converges becomes LTI. Consequently, the existence of a lag is not possible.

3. On the contrary, the lag error is maximum when μ tends to zero (and there exist frequency-shift errors). Taking the limit of (86) as $\mu \to 0$ yields:

$$\lim_{\mu\to 0} \boldsymbol{v} = -\mathbf{R}_x^{-1} \, \boldsymbol{p} = -\boldsymbol{w}_o \tag{88}$$

[12] Under small error conditions, and by assuming that $\varepsilon(n)$ and $\tilde{\boldsymbol{x}}(n)$ are Gaussian, and $\tilde{\boldsymbol{x}}(n)$ is uncorrelated over time, i.e. $\mathrm{E}\{\tilde{\boldsymbol{x}}(n)\, \tilde{\boldsymbol{x}}(n+k)\} = 0$, with $k \neq 0$, (Widrow et al., 1975; 1976).

which implies that the LMS-FRESH filter converges to the null vector in a mean sense. Moreover, the filter converges to the null vector also in a mean square sense. This results is derived from the fact that the gradient noise tends to zero as μ tends to zero (see (83)), which entails that $\tilde{\boldsymbol{u}}(n) = 0$, and therefore the LMS-FRESH filter vector matches its expected value, i.e. $\tilde{\boldsymbol{w}}(n) = \mathrm{E}\{\tilde{\boldsymbol{w}}(n)\} = 0$. As a result, the outputs of the branches with an error in their frequency shift are null. The time-averaged excess MSE due to lag error is obtained by substituting (88) in (85), which yields:

$$\lim_{\mu \to 0} \xi_{lag} = \boldsymbol{w}_o^\dagger \, \mathbf{R}_x \, \boldsymbol{w}_o \tag{89}$$

Thus, the total time-averaged MSE at steady-state for μ tending to zero is

$$\lim_{\mu \to 0} \xi_{LMS} = \sigma_d^2 \tag{90}$$

This result could be obtained considering that, since the output of the adaptive-FRESH filter is null, the error signal is $\varepsilon(n) = d(n)$.

4. The optimal convergence factor which minimizes the time-averaged MSE of the LMS algorithm is obtained from (80), (83) and (85), which yields:

$$\mu_o = \arg\min_{\mu} \left\{ \mu \, \xi_{min} \;\; \mathrm{tr}\{\mathbf{R}_x\} + \boldsymbol{v}^\dagger \, \mathbf{R}_x \, \boldsymbol{v} \right\} \tag{91}$$

where vector $\boldsymbol{v}$ is defined by (86).

As regards the convergence of the LMS-FRESH filter, a sufficient condition is that the poles of all components of vector $\boldsymbol{v}(z)$ are located inside the unit circle (Yeste-Ojeda & Grajal, 2010). This is equivalent to the condition that the maximum absolute value of the eigenvalues of matrix

$$(\mathbf{I}_M - 2\mu\mathbf{R}_x)\, \boldsymbol{\Phi}^{-1} \tag{92}$$

is lesser or equal than 1. When a single branch is used for the LMS-FRESH filter, then it is straightforward that the eigenvalues of (92) are $e^{-j2\pi\Delta}(1 - 2\mu\lambda_k)$, with $k = 1, \ldots, M$, and where Δ is the frequency-shift error of the single branch, and λ_k are the eigenvalues of matrix $\mathbf{R}_x$. As a result, the condition for the convergence of the LMS algorithm is:

$$0 < \mu < (\lambda_{max})^{-1} \tag{93}$$

where λ_{max} is the maximum eigenvalue of matrix $\mathbf{R}_x$. This is the same condition as for stationarity environments (Haykin, 2001; Widrow et al., 1976). [13]

6.5 Application

Finally, let us quantify the performance of adaptive FRESH filters for cycle-frequency error compensation through a case study where the received signal consists of a BPSK signal embedded in stationary white Gaussian noise. The receiver incorporates a FRESH filter with the purpose of extracting the BPSK signal from the noise. Two frequency shifts related to the cyclic spectrum of the BPSK signal are used, the inverse of its symbol interval $\alpha_1 = 1/T_s$, and twice its carrier frequency, $\alpha_2 = 2f_c$. These two cycle frequencies have been chosen, according to the common approach mentioned in Section 4, because they exhibit the highest values of

[13] Note that the value of the convergence factor used in (Haykin, 2001) is twice the value used herein.

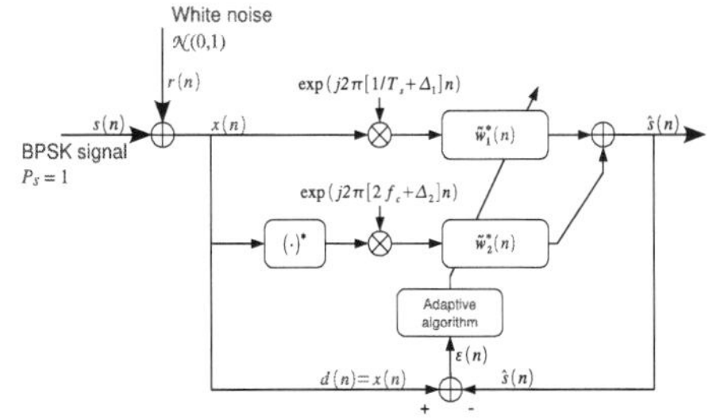

Fig. 9. Blind adaptive FRESH filter for BPSK signal extraction.

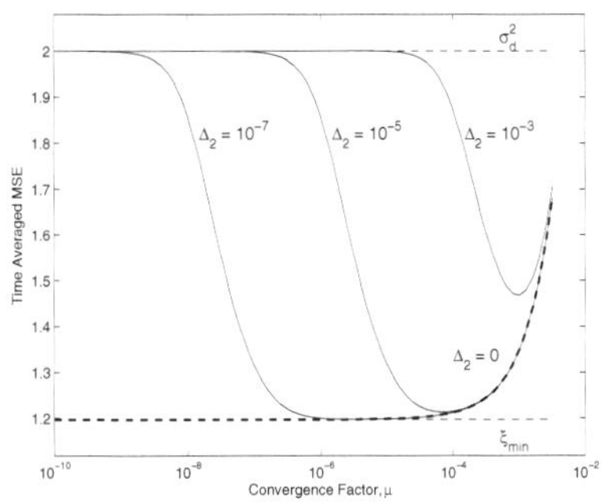

Fig. 10. Analytical time-averaged MSE as a function of the convergence factor, when using only the branch corresponding to frequency shift $\alpha = 2f_c$. The thick dashed line corresponds to $\Delta_2 = 0$.

spectral correlation for a BPSK modulation (Gardner et al., 1987). The desired signal for the adaptive algorithm is the received signal, $d(n) = x(n)$, following the blind scheme described in Section 5.1 (see Fig. 9). In all cases, the carrier frequency and symbol interval have been set to $f_c = 0.3$ (normalized to the sampling frequency) and $T_s = 32$ samples. The noise power is set to $\sigma_r^2 = \mathrm{E}\left\{|r(n)|^2\right\} = 1$, and the SNR is also fixed to SNR= 0 dB, and is defined as the ratio between the mean power of the signal and the noise: SNR= $\left\langle \mathrm{E}\left\{|s(n)|^2\right\}\right\rangle / \sigma_r^2$. Both $\tilde{\boldsymbol{w}}_1(n)$ and $\tilde{\boldsymbol{w}}_2(n)$, are FIR filters with $M_i = 64$ taps.

In order to clarify some concepts, let us consider firstly the case where the FRESH filter is composed of only the branch associated with the frequency shift $\alpha_2 = 2f_c$. The total time-averaged MSE at steady-state (hereinafter referred to as simply "the MSE") is shown in Fig. 10, as a function of the convergence factor and for different values of the frequency-shift error, Δ_2, which are also normalized to the sampling frequency. The MSE of the LMS-FRESH filter when $\Delta_2 = 0$ is plotted with a dashed thick line as a point of reference. This is the lower bound of the MSE attainable by the LMS-FRESH filter, and converges to the MSE of the optimal FRESH filter, ξ_{min}, as μ decreases. Note that the minimum MSE is always greater than the noise power, i.e. $\xi_{min} > 1$, since even if the signal were perfectly estimated ($\hat{s}(n) = s(n)$), the error signal would match the noise ($\varepsilon(n) = r(n)$).

When there exist errors in the frequency shift, the MSE is always higher than the lower bound. Since the lower bound includes the gradient noise effect, the excess MSE over the lower bound

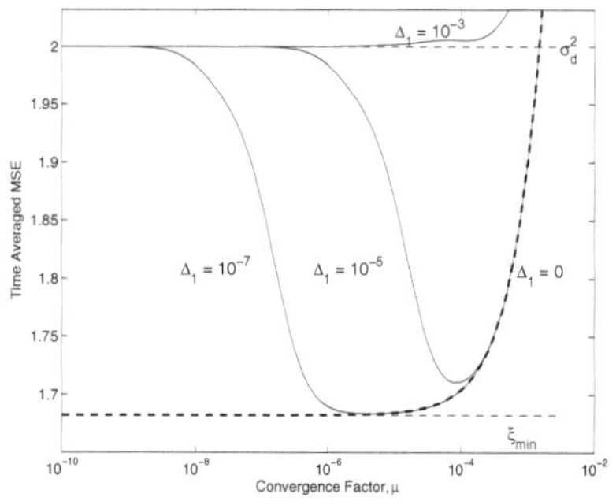

Fig. 11. Analytical time-averaged MSE as a function of the convergence factor, when using only the branch corresponding to frequency shift $\alpha = 1/T_s$. The thick dashed line corresponds to $\Delta_1 = 0$.

is due to the lag error only, and varies from zero (for high μ) up to $\boldsymbol{w}_o^\dagger \mathbf{R}_x \boldsymbol{w}_o = \sigma_d^2 - \xi_{min}$, (see (89), for small μ). Thus, the total MSE tends to σ_d^2 when μ decreases. The curves also show the dependence of the MSE with the error in the frequency shift, which increases with Δ_2 (at any given μ). Therefore, in order to obtain a small excess MSE due to lag, it is required a faster rate of convergence (bigger μ) when Δ_2 increases.

An additional result shown in Fig. 10 is that for high enough errors in the frequency shifts, the MSE does not reach ξ_{min} at any value of μ. In other words, it is impossible to simultaneously reduce the MSE terms due to the lag error and the gradient noise. In such a case, the optimal μ locates at an intermediate value as a result of the trade-off between reducing the lag error and the gradient noise. In practice, the error of the frequency-shifts is commonly unknown. Then the convergence factor should be chosen as a trade-off between the maximum cycle-frequency error which can be compensated by the adaptive filter and the increase of the excess MSE due to gradient noise.

Similar results can be extracted from Fig. 11, which corresponds to the case where only the branch of the FRESH filter with frequency shift $\alpha = 1/T_s$ has been used. The main difference between Figures 10 and 11 is that the minimum MSE, ξ_{min}, is bigger when only $\alpha = 1/T_s$ is used. The reason is that the spectral correlation level exhibited by a BPSK signal is smaller at $\alpha = 1/T_s$ than at $\alpha = 2f_c$ (Gardner et al., 1987). Furthermore, it can be seen that σ_d^2 is not an upper bound for the MSE (as could be thought from Fig. 10), but the limit of the MSE as μ tends to zero.

For the case illustrated in Fig. 12, the two branches shown in Fig. 9 are used, but there is uncertainty only in the symbol rate, that is, the error in the frequency shift related to the carrier frequency, Δ_2, is always zero. The curves show that the improvement in the MSE is not very significant when the error in the symbol rate is compensated. This occurs when the contribution to the signal estimate for a branch is more significant than for the other, which is mainly caused by the different spectral level exhibited by a BPSK signal at cycle frequencies $\alpha = 1/T_s$ and $\alpha = 2f_c$. As a consequence, the minimum MSE when only the second branch is used ($\xi_{min,2}$), and when both branches are used ($\xi_{min,12}$) are very similar. Furthermore, μ tends to zero the MSE tends to $\xi_{min,2}$ instead of σ_d^2, since there is no uncertainty in the carrier frequency.

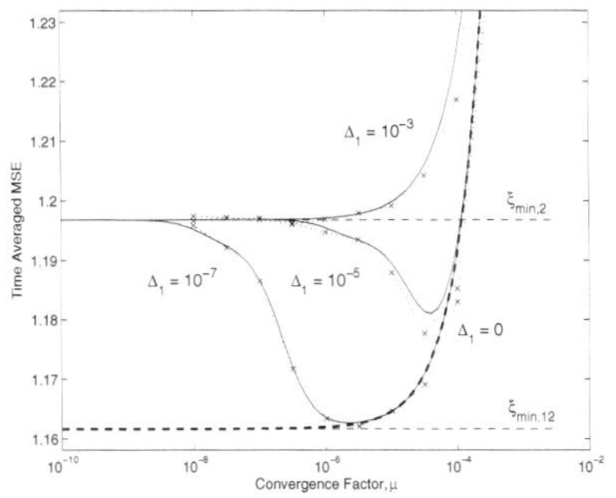

Fig. 12. Time-averaged MSE as a function of the convergence factor, when using the two branches. $\Delta_2 = 0$ in all cases, also for the thick dashed line which corresponds to $\Delta_1 = 0$. Simulation results are represented by cross marks.

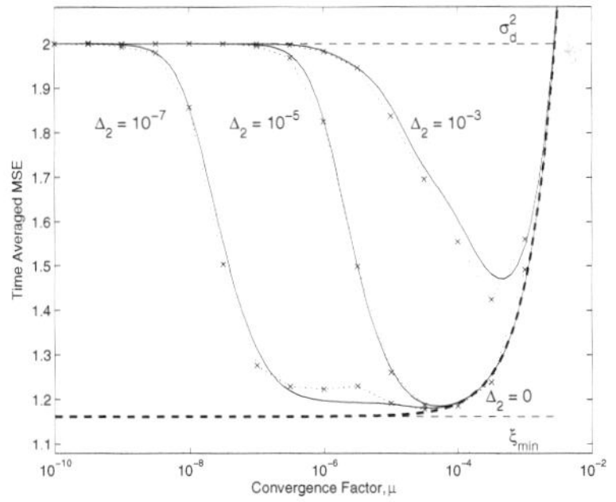

Fig. 13. Time-averaged MSE as a function of the convergence factor, when using the two branches. $\Delta_1 = 10^{-5}$ in all cases, except for the thick dashed line which corresponds to $\Delta_1 = 0$ and $\Delta_2 = 0$. Simulation results are represented by cross marks.

Fig. 13 shows the MSE when there exist errors in both frequency shifts. The curves correspond to an error in the symbol rate $\Delta_1 = 10^{-5}$ and different errors for the carrier frequency. In this case, the minimum MSE is attained at a convergence factor such that the lag error of both branches is compensated. However, compensating the error in the carrier frequency is critical, while compensating the error in the symbol rate only produces a slight improvement. This conclusion can be deduced from the curve for $\Delta_2 = 10^{-7}$. Since $\Delta_1 = 10^{-5}$, it is required a convergence factor close to $\mu = 10^{-4}$ or higher in order to compensate the frequency-shift error at the first branch (see Fig. 11). However, the excess MSE due to lag error is small for $\mu = 10^{-6}$ or higher, where only the frequency-shift error at the second branch can be compensated.

The analytical expression for the MSE has been obtained under some assumptions (Gaussianity, small error conditions and input uncorrelated over time) which in practice are only approximations, and also in the case studies presented. Therefore, in order to check its accuracy, Figures 12 and 13 also include the MSE obtained by simulation, which is represented

Parameter	Min. value	Max. value
INR (interference-to-noise ratio)	-20 dB	20 dB
T_{s2} (interference symbol interval)	1 sample	64 samples
f_{c2} (interference carrier frequency)	0	1
Δ_1	-10^{-5}	10^{-5}
Δ_2	-10^{-5}	10^{-5}

Table 1. Range of the random variables used in the simulation with a BPSK interference. The INR is defined analogously to SNR. f_{c2} is normalized with the sampling rate. Δ_1 and Δ_2 are the absolute cycle-frequency errors of the branches with cycle frequencies $\alpha_1 = 1/T_s$ and $\alpha_2 = 2f_c$, respectively.

by the lines with cross marks: 200 realizations have been used for the ensemble averages in order to obtain the instantaneous MSE. Then, the instantaneous MSE has been time-averaged over 200.000 samples after the convergence of the LMS. The agreement between theoretical and simulation results is excellent in all cases, which confirms the validity of the assumptions made.

A last case study is presented with a twofold purpose: 1) To demonstrate that the adaptive algorithm compensates cycle-frequency errors also in the presence of interferences. 2) To demonstrate that an adaptive algorithm different from the LMS exhibits a similar behavior. For this reason, we shall use the RLS algorithm in this last case study, despite the lack of an analytical expression for the MSE. The scheme for the adaptive FRESH filter presented in Fig. 9 is valid also in this case study, but a BPSK interference having random parameters has been added to the input, along with the BPSK signal and the noise defined for the previous case studies. The errors in the frequency shifts of the FRESH filter are also random. All random variables are constant at each trial, but change from trial to trial according an uniform distribution within the ranges gathered in Table 1. As regards the RLS algorithm, it is exponentially weighted with a convergence factor $\lambda = 1 - \mu$, where μ is known as the forgetting rate (Haykin, 2001). Also, we have used in this case study the BPSK signal as the reference signal, so that the MSE does not depend on the random interference power.

Fig. 14 shows the MSE obtained by simulation (using 100 trials for computing the ensemble averages and 20000 samples for the time averages). The results show the capability of the RLS algorithm for compensating errors in the frequency shifts in the presence of the interference. Otherwise, the RLS algorithm would have converged to a FRESH filter which cancels its output, and the obtained MSE would have been equal to σ_d^2. Analogously to the previous case studies using the LMS algorithm, the RLS algorithm cannot compensate errors in the frequency shifts if the forgetting rate is too small (slow convergence). In such a case, the adaptive FRESH filter tends to cancel its output and the error is σ_d^2. For moderate forgetting rates, the cycle-frequency errors are compensated, and the MSE approaches ξ_{min}. Contrarily, an excessively high forgetting rate increases the MSE as a consequence of the gradient noise.

In summary, the possible existence of cycle-frequency errors in LAPTV filtering is a serious problem that must be managed. When using the non-adaptive FRESH implementation, the minimum time-averaged MSE is obtained when the branches with uncertainties in their frequency shifts are not used (or equivalently, their output is cancelled). On the contrary, adaptive-FRESH filters can work in the presence of errors in the frequency shifts. In such a case, the adaptive-FRESH filter behaves as an LPTV filter for those branches with an error in the frequency shift. In order to be effective, the rate of convergence of the adaptive algorithm must be carefully chosen. The optimal rate of convergence results from the trade-off between

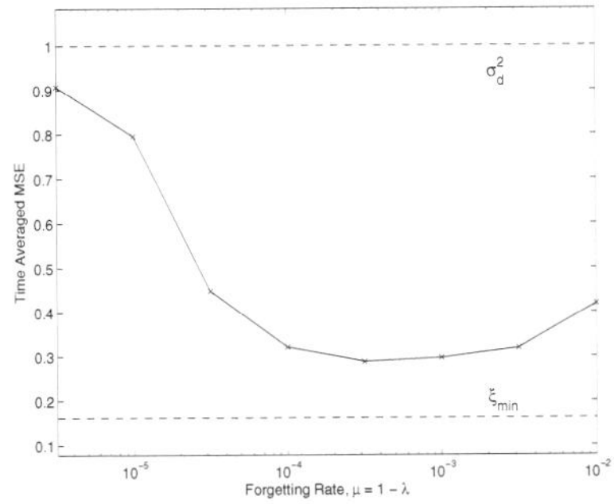

Fig. 14. Simulated time-averaged MSE as a function of the forgetting rate of the RLS algorithm, in the presence of a BPSK interference with random parameters.

decreasing the excess MSE due to gradient noise (slow rate of convergence) and decreasing the excess MSE due to lag error (fast rate of convergence). The analytical expressions in this section allow to compute the optimal convergence factor and the time-averaged MSE at steady-state of the LMS-FRESH filter.

7. Adaptive FRESH filters for interference rejection in signal detection

Finally, we end this chapter with the description of a real application example of adaptive-FRESH filters. The system developed in this section, previously presented in (Yeste-Ojeda & Grajal, 2008), finds application in fields such as electronic warfare or spectrum management. The increasing saturation of the radio-electric spectrum has led modern radar and communication systems to employ complex signal waveforms capable of operating under the presence of interferences. On the contrary, interception systems face serious problems in the detectiong unknown or partially known signals if the signal of interest (SOI) is hidden by temporally and spectrally overlapping interferences. Therefore, hostile transmitters can take advantage of this fact and reduce their probability of interception by following this strategy.

The problem dealt with in this section consists in detecting an unknown signal hidden by an interference with known parameters when only one sensor is available. The SOI and the interference are overlapped simultaneously in time and frequency, with the interference being more powerful that the SOI. As the reader will have guessed, the solution adopted to solve this problem is to exploit the cyclostationary properties of the interference in order to extract it from the received signal. This procedure requires knowing, at least, the cyclic spectrum of the interference. On the other hand, much work has been done when only the SOI cyclic spectrum is known, mainly with the aim of robust signal detection and estimation (Gardner, 1993; Mirbagheri et al., 2006; Zhang et al., 1999). The approach in this section is significantly different from these works, since it exploits the cyclostationarity of those signals to be removed, i.e. the interference.

Our approach is based on a *"divide and conquer"* strategy, by which the global problem is split into two sub-problems: A signal separation problem and a signal detection one. Firstly, the interference is separated by means of a blind adaptive FRESH filter. Once the interference has

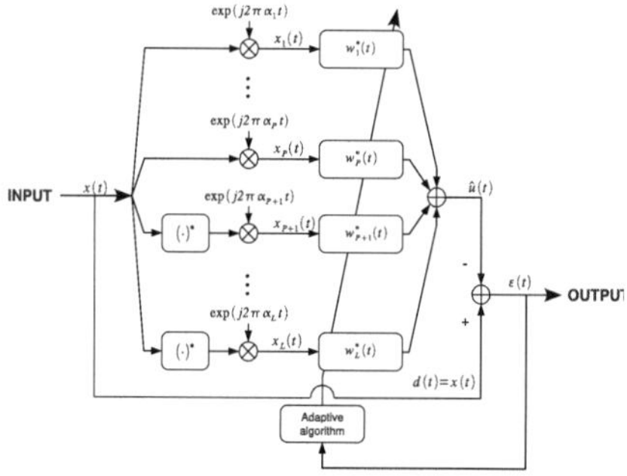

Fig. 15. Block diagram of the interference rejection system.

been removed, the detection is performed on the residual, which is assumed to consist of only the noise and the SOI.

7.1 The interference rejection system

This system is mainly based on an BAFRESH filter, following the scheme represented in Fig. 15. This scheme is the same as the one represented in Fig. 7, but after rearranging it so that the error signal is the output of the system, that is the input of the detection system. Let the received signal be composed by the SOI, $s(t)$, the interferences, $u(t)$, and a stationary white noise, $r(t)$:

$$x(t) = s(t) + u(t) + r(t) \tag{94}$$

where $s(t)$, $u(t)$, and $r(t)$, are assumed to be independent from one another. If the interferences were perfectly estimated, that is $\widehat{u}(t) = u(t)$, the estimation error would only consist of the SOI plus noise, $\varepsilon(t) = s(t) + r(t)$. Thus, the input of the detector must be the estimation error, $\varepsilon(t)$, as indicated by Fig. 15.

The next step in the design of the FRESH filter is to choose a suitable set of frequency shifts. Since the adaptive FRESH filters is blind, these cycle frequencies must belong uniquely to the cyclic spectrum of the signal to be estimated, i.e. the interference. We shall follow the strategy mentioned in Section 4 consisting in taking those cycle frequencies related with the interferences which exhibit the highest spectral correlation level, with the exception of cycle frequency zero for the branches not using the complex conjugate of the input. Since the cyclic spectrum of the SOI is unknown, we can only assume that the chosen cycle frequencies do not belong to its cyclic spectrum (which would be very infrequent in practice as the interference and the SOI are transmitted by different sources).

Given the set of frequency shifts used, Γ_s, the adaptive FRESH filter will converge to the optimum set of LTI filters, whose frequency response has been defined in (49). In our case, the desired signal is the interference, which is the only signal correlated with the inputs of the LTI

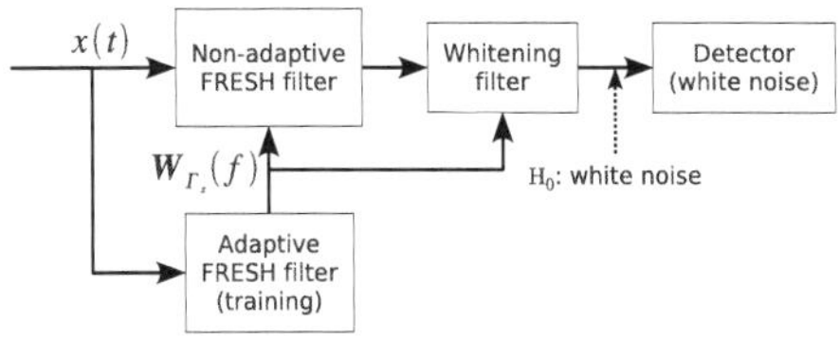

Fig. 16. Scheme for the whole interception system.

filters. As a result, the frequency response of the optimum set of LTI filters becomes:

$$\begin{aligned} \boldsymbol{W}_{\Gamma_s}(f) &= \left[\mathbf{S}_{\boldsymbol{xx}}(f)\right]^{-1} \boldsymbol{S}_{d\boldsymbol{x}}^{\dagger}(f) \\ &= \left[\mathbf{S}_{\boldsymbol{ss}}(f) + \mathbf{S}_{\boldsymbol{uu}}(f) + \eta_r \mathbf{I}_{\mathrm{L}}\right]^{-1} \boldsymbol{S}_{u\boldsymbol{u}}^{\dagger}(f) \end{aligned} \tag{95}$$

where η_r is the noise Power Spectral Density (PSD), and $\mathbf{I}_{\mathrm{L}}$ is the identity matrix of size $L \times L$. In addition, the definition of the spectral correlation vector $\boldsymbol{S}_{u\boldsymbol{u}}(f)$ is analogous to (50), while the spectral autocorrelation matrices $\mathbf{S}_{\boldsymbol{ss}}(f)$ and $\mathbf{S}_{\boldsymbol{uu}}(f)$ are defined analogously to (51).

7.2 Intermediate whitening filter and FRESH filter training

Although the separation and detection problems have been considered independently, the noise PSD at the output of the interference rejection system depends on the adaptive FRESH filter and may change with time during the convergence of the adaptive algorithm. As a result, it is advisable the use of an intermediate stage in order to effectively separate the detection problem from the FRESH filter. A whitening filter previously to the detector (as indicated in Fig. 16) can do this task, so that the detector can be designed for a white noise. The optimum detector to be used depends on the specific SOI to be detected. The whitening filter is defined as the inverse of the squared root of the noise PSD at the output of the separator. This output consists of the white noise at the input plus the noise leakage at the output of the FRESH filter, which can be expressed as a function of the FRESH filter vector. Therefore, the frequency response of the whitening filter becomes:

$$H_w(f) = \frac{1}{\sqrt{1 + |\boldsymbol{W}_{\Gamma_s}(f)|^2}} \tag{96}$$

Moreover, using an adaptive algorithm requires some training time, during which the detector decisions could be wrong. The scheme proposed in Fig. 16 consists of a branch for training the interference rejection system which incorporates the adaptive FRESH filter, and an independent non-adaptive FRESH filter which effectively performs the signal separation task and is the one connected to the detector. The coefficients of the non-adaptive FRESH filter are fixed once the adaptive one has converged. This requires some mechanism for controlling the beginning and ending of a learning interval, in which the detector decisions are considered wrong. Such a mechanism might be based on monitoring the power variations of the interferences estimate and the SOI plus noise estimate, updating the non-adaptive FRESH system when both powers stabilize.

7.3 Application

Finally, let us quantify the performance of the described interception system through a case study whose scenario is represented in Fig. 17. In that scenario, the SOI is a Continuous-Wave

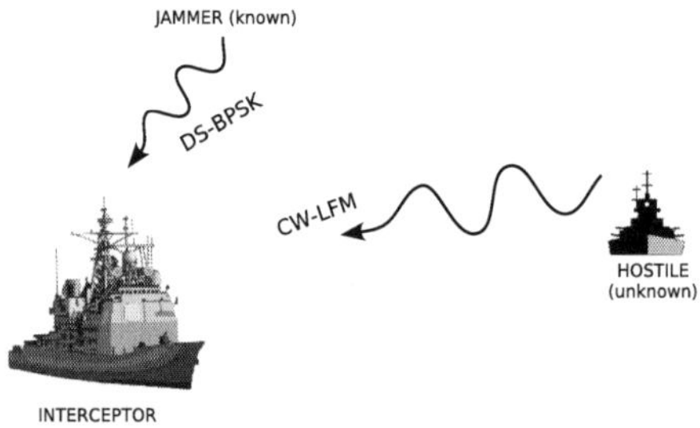

Fig. 17. Scenario for the detection of a CW-LFM signal hidden by a DS-BPSK interference.

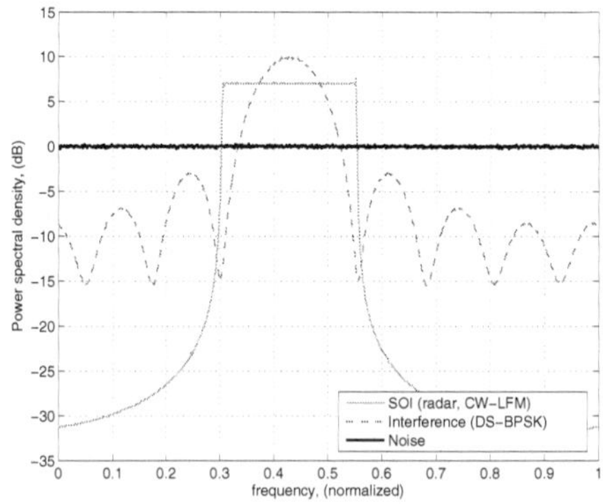

Fig. 18. PSD of noise, the CW-LFM signal (SOI) and the DS-BPSK interference (interference). SNR and INR fixed at 0 dB.

Linear Frequency Modulated (CW-LFM) radar signal which is being transmitted by a hostile equipment and, therefore, unknown. This signal is intentionally transmitted in the spectral band of a known Direct-Sequence Binary Phase Shift Keying (DS-BPSK) spread-spectrum communication signal, with the aim of hindering its detection. The SOI sweeps a total bandwidth of $BW = 20$ MHz with a sweeping time $T_p = 0.5$ ms, while the DS-BPSK interfering signal employs a chip rate $1/T_c = 10.23$ Mcps. The PSDs of the SOI, the interference and the noise are shown in Fig. 18.

The structure of the FRESH filter is designed based on a previous study of the performance of the sub-optimal FRESH filters. As a result, the interference rejection system incorporates an adaptive FRESH filter consisting of 5 branches, each one using a FIR filter of 1024 coefficients. The frequency shifts of the FRESH filter correspond to the 5 cycle frequencies of the DS-BPSK interference with the highest spectral correlation level, which are (Gardner et al., 1987): $\{\pm 1/T_c\}$ for the input $x(t)$, and $\{2f_c, 2f_c \pm 1/T_c\}$ for the complex conjugate of the input $x^*(t)$; where f_c is the carrier frequency and T_c is the chip duration of the DS-BPSK interference. The adaptive algorithm used is Fast-Block Least Mean Squares (FB-LMS) (Haykin, 2001), with a convergence factor $\mu = 1$.

Next, we present some simulation results on the interception system performance obtained after the training interval has finished. Firstly, the improvement in the SIR obtained at the output of the interference rejection system is represented in Fig. 19, as a function of the input

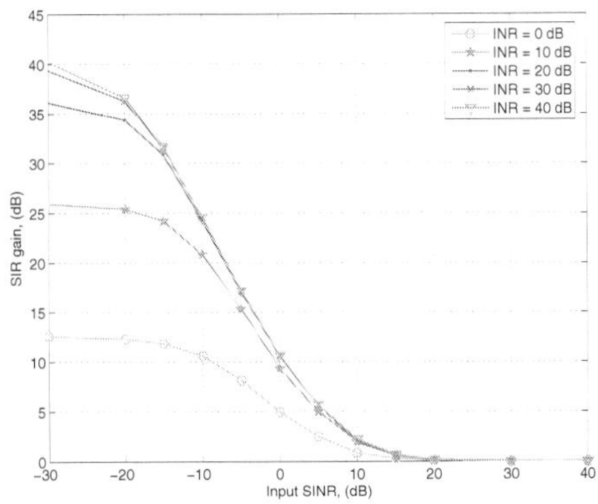

Fig. 19. Simulated SIR improvement as a function of the input SINR and INR.

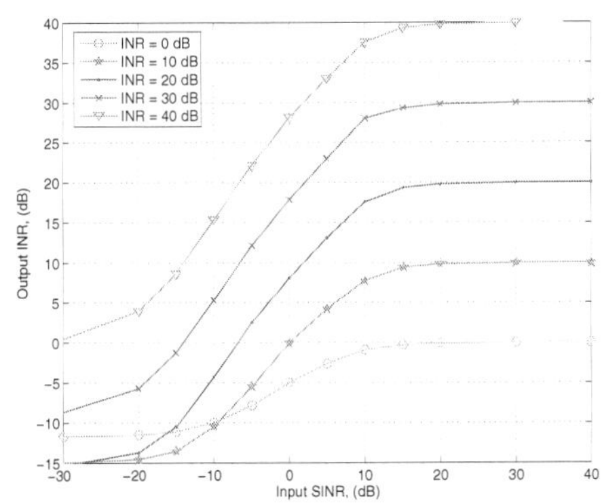

Fig. 20. Simulated INR at the output of the interference rejection system.

Signal-to-Interference-plus-Noise Ratio (SINR), for several values of Interference-to-Noise Ratio (INR). Two main results are revealed in Fig. 19:

1. The SIR improvement tends to zero as the SINR increases, because the SOI is powerful enough to mask the interference which makes the FRESH filter fail to estimate the interference. This is corroborated through Fig. 20, where the simulated INR at the output of the interference rejection system is shown. For high enough input SINR, the ouput INR matches the input INR, indicating that the FRESH filter cannot extract any of the interference power. This allows to define a "useful region", where the interference rejection system obtains a significant SIR improvement. In our example, the useful region comprises an input SINR$\leq$ 0 dB.
2. The SIR improvement saturates for high input INR values, which is shown by the fact that the SIR improvement for INR= 40 dB matches the curve obtained for INR= 30 dB. This is a limitation is due to the adaptive algorithm and does not appear when the optimal FRESH filter is used instead.
3. In addition, although it seems logical that the output INR increases with the input one, Fig. 20 reveals that this is not true for low input SINR and INR. The reason is that the

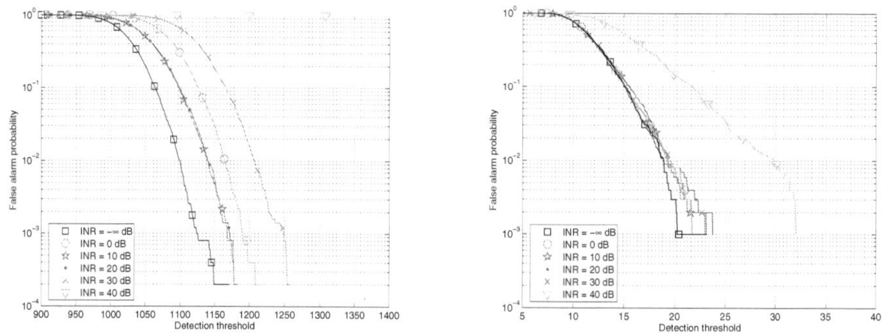

(a) Energy detector (b) Atomic decomposition detector

Fig. 21. Degradation of the P_{FA} when the interference is present (with the interference rejection system).

interference becomes masked by noise if the input INR is low enough (i.e. INR= 0 dB). As the input INR increases, the interference rejection system increases its effectiveness, so that the output INR decreases. That is why the output INR is lower for INR= 10 dB and INR= 20 dB than for INR= 0 dB.

The output INR can provide an idea about the degradation of the probability of false alarm (P_{FA}) of the detector (the probability of detection when the SOI is not present). However, each particular detector is affected in a different way. We shall illustrate this fact with two different detectors. The first one is an energy detector (ED), which consists of comparing the total energy to a detection threshold set to attain a desired P_{FA}. The second one is a detector based on atomic decomposition (AD), such as that proposed in (López Risueño et al., 2003). This detector exhibits an excellent performance for LFM signals, as the SOI considered in our case study. The AD-based detector can be thought as a bank of correlators or matched filters, each one matched to a chirplet (a signal with Gaussian envelope and LFM), whose maximum output is compared to a detection threshold. Both detectors process the signal by blocks, taking a decision each 1024 samples.

Fig. 21 shows the degraded P_{FA} of the whole interception system in the presence of the interference, and when the detection threshold has been determined for an input consisting of only noise. The curves clearly show the different dependence of the P_{FA} of both detectors on the input INR. The energy detector exhibits a higher sensitivity to the interference than the AD-based one. Thus, the AD-based detector visibly degrades its P_{FA} only for an input INR= 40 dB and above. On the contrary, ED always exhibits a degraded P_{FA} in the presence of the interference due to the energy excess, which is proportional to the output INR shown in Fig. 20.

Finally, we end this application example by showing the sensitivity improvement of the interception system obtained thanks to the interference rejection system. The sensitivity is defined as the SNR at the input of the interception system required to attain an objective probability of detection ($P_D = 90\%$), for a given probability of false alarm ($P_{FA} = 10^{-6}$). Thus, the detection threshold takes a different value depending on the input INR so that the P_{FA} holds for all the INR values. The simulation results are gathered in Tab. 2, with all values expressed in dB. At each INR value, the sensitivities of both detectors, AD and ED, with and

	With interf. rej. system		Without interf. rej. system		Sensitivity improvement	
INR	AD	ED	AD	ED	AD	ED
$-\infty$	-12.1	-6.1	-12.1	-6.1	0.0	0.0
0	-9.6	-4.3	-4.0	-3.5	5.6	0.8
10	-9.0	-4.3	5.8	1.1	14.8	5.4
20	-9.2	-4.3	15.9	6.8	27.1	11.1
30	-8.3	-3.4	26.0	14.3	34.3	17.7
40	-4.1	-0.5	35.8	21.6	39.9	22.1

Table 2. Sensitivity (SNR, dB) for the CW-LFM signal as a function of the INR. $P_{FA} = 10^{-6}$, $P_D = 90\%$.

without the interference rejection system, are shown. The sensitivity improvement obtained by using the interference rejection system is also shown.
As can be seen, the improvement is very significant and proves the benefit of using the interference rejection system. Moreover, the improvement is higher for increasing input INR. However, there is still a sensitivity degradation as the INR increases due to an increase in the detection threshold and/or a distortion produced by the interference rejection system to the SOI because of the signal leakage at the FRESH output (the latter only applies to AD, since ED is insensitive to the signal waveform). And, as expected, the AD-based detector outperforms ED (López Risueño et al., 2003).

8. Summary

This chapter has described the theory of adaptive FRESH filtering. FRESH filters represent a comprehensible implementation of LAPTV filters, which are the optimum filters for estimating or extracting signal information when the signals are modelled as almost-cyclostationary stochastic processes. When dealing with complex signals, both the signal and its complex conjugate must be filtered, resulting in WLAPTV filters. The knowledge required for the design optimal FRESH filters is rarely available beforehand in practice, which leads to the incorporation of adaptive scheme. Since FRESH filters consist of a set of LTI filters, classical algorithms can be applied by simply use the stationarized versions of the inputs of these LTI filters, which are obtained by time-averaging their statistics. Then, the optimal set of LTI filters is given by the multidimensional Wiener filter theory. In addition, thanks to their properties of signal separation in the cycle frequency domain, adaptive FRESH filters can operate blindly, that is without reference of the desired signal, by simply using as frequency shifts the cycle frequencies belonging uniquely to the desired signal cyclic spectrum. Furthermore, adaptive FRESH filters have the advantage of being able to compensate small errors in their frequency shifts, which can be present in practice due to non-ideal effects such as Doppler or the oscillators stability. In this case, the convergence rate of the adaptive algorithm must be carefully chosen in order to simultaneously minimize the gradient noise and the lag errors. The chapter is finally closed by presenting an application example, in which an adaptive FRESH filter is used to suppress known interferences for an unknown hidden signal interception system, demonstrating the potentials of adaptive FRESH filters in this field of application.

9. References

Adlard, J., Tozer, T. & Burr, A. (1999). Interference rejection in impulsive noise for VLF communications, *IEEE Military Communications Conference Proceedings, 1999. MILCOM 1999.*, pp. 296–300.

Agee, B. G., Schell, S. V. & Gardner, W. A. (1990). Spectral self-coherence restoral: A new approach to blind adaptive signal extraction using antenna arrays, *Proceedings of the IEEE* 78(4): 753–767.

Brown, W. A. (1987). *On the Theory of Cyclostationary Signals*, Ph.D. dissertation.

Chen, Y. & Liang, T. (2010). Application study of BA-FRESH filtering technique for communication anti-jamming, *IEEE 10th International Conference on Signal Processing (ICSP)*, pp. 287–290.

Chevalier, P. & Blin, A. (2007). Widely linear MVDR beamformers for the reception of an unknown signal corrupted by noncircular interferences, *IEEE Transactions on Signal Processing* 55(11): 5323–5336.

Chevalier, P. & Maurice, A. (1997). Constrained beamforming for cyclostationary signals, *International Conference on Acoustics, Speech, and Signal Processing, ICASSP-97*.

Chevalier, P. & Pipon, F. (2006). New insights into optimal widely linear array receivers for the demodulation of BPSK, MSK, and GMSK signals corrupted by noncircular interferences - Application to SAIC, *IEEE Transactions on Signal Processing* 54(3): 870–883.

Corduneanu, C. (1968). *Almost Periodic Functions*, Interscience Publishers.

Franks, L. E. (1994). Polyperiodic linear filtering, *in* W. A. Gardner (ed.), *Cyclostationarity in Communicactions and Signal Processing*, IEEE Press.

Gameiro, A. (2000). Capacity enhancement of DS-CDMA synchronous channels by frequency-shift filtering, *Proceedings of the IEEE International Symposium on Personal, Indoor and Mobile Radio Communications*.

Gardner, W. A. (1978). Stationarizable random processes, *IEEE Transactions on Information Theory* 24(1): 8–22.

Gardner, W. A. (1986). *Introduction to Random Processes with Applications to Signals and Systems*, Macmillan Publishing Company.

Gardner, W. A. (1987). Spectral correlation of modulated signals: Part I – analog modulation, *IEEE Transactions on Communications* 35(6): 584–594.

Gardner, W. A. (1991). Exploitation of spectral redundancy in cyclostationary signals, *IEEE Signal Processing Magazine* 8(2): 14–36.

Gardner, W. A. (1993). Cyclic Wiener filtering: Theory and method, *IEEE Transactions on Communications* 41(1): 151–163.

Gardner, W. A. (1994). *Cyclostationarity in Communications and Signal Processing*, IEEE Press.

Gardner, W. A., Brown, W. A. & Chen, C. K. (1987). Spectral correlation of modulated signals: Part II – digital modulation, *IEEE Transactions on Communications* 35(6): 595–601.

Gardner, W. A. & Franks, L. E. (1975). Characterization of cyclostationary random signal processes, *IEEE Transactions on Information Theory* 21(1): 4–14.

Gelli, G. & Verde, F. (2000). Blind LPTV joint equalization and interference suppression, *Acoustics, Speech, and Signal Processing, 2000. ICASSP '00. Proceedings. 2000 IEEE International Conference on*.

Giannakis, G. B. (1998). Cyclostationary signal analysis, *in* V. K. Madisetti & D. Williams (eds), *The Digital Signal Processing Handbook*, CRC Press.

Gonçalves, L. & Gameiro, A. (2002). Frequency shift based multiple access interference canceller for multirate UMTS-TDD systems, *The 13th IEEE International Symposium on Personal, Indoor and Mobile Radio Communications*.

Haykin, S. (2001). *Adaptive Filter Theory*, Prentice Hall.

Hu, Y., Xia, W. & Shen, L. (2007). Study of anti-interference mechanism of multiple WPANs accesing into a HAN, *International Symposium on Intelligent Signal Processing and Communication Systems*.

Jianhui, P., Zhongfu, Y. & Xu, X. (2006). A novel robust cyclostationary beamformer based on conjugate gradient algorithm, *2006 International Conference on Communications, Circuits and Systems Proceedings*, Vol. 2, pp. 777–780.

Lee, J. H. & Lee, Y. T. (1999). Robust adaptive array beamforming for cyclostationary signals under cycle frequency error, *IEEE Transactions on Antennas and Propagation* 47(2): 233–241.

Lee, J. H., Lee, Y. T. & Shih, W. H. (2000). Efficient robust adaptive beamforming for cyclostationary signals, *IEEE Transactions on Signal Processing* 48(7): 1893–1901.

Li, X. & Ouyang, S. (2009). One reduced-rank blind fresh filter for spectral overlapping interference signal extraction and DSP implementation, *International Workshop on Intelligent Systems and Applications, ISA*, pp. 1–4.

Loeffler, C. M. & Burrus, C. S. (1978). Optimal design of periodically time-varying and multirate digital filters, *IEEE Transactions on Acoustic, Speech and Signal Processing* 66(1): 51–83.

López Risueño, G., Grajal, J. & Yeste-Ojeda, O. A. (2003). Atomic decomposition-based radar complex signal interception, *IEE Proceedings on Radar, Sonar and Navigation* 150: 323–331.

Martin, V., Chabert, M. & Lacaze, B. (2007). Digital watermarking of natural images based on LPTV filters, *Acoustics, Speech and Signal Processing, 2007. ICASSP 2007. IEEE International Conference on*.

Mirbagheri, A., Plataniotis, K. & Pasupathy, S. (2006). An enhanced widely linear CDMA receiver with OQPSK modulation, *IEEE Transactions on Communications* 54(2): 261–272.

Napolitano, A. & Spooner, C. M. (2001). Cyclic spectral analysis of continuous-phase modulated signals, *IEEE Transactions on Signal Processing* 49(1): 30–44.

Ngan, L. Y., Ouyang, S. & Ching, P. C. (2004). Reduced-rank blind adaptive frequency-shift filtering for signal extraction, *IEEE International Conference on Acoustics, Speech, and Signal Processing, ICASSP*, Vol. 2.

Petrus, P. & Reed, J. H. (1995). Time dependent adaptive arrays, *IEEE Signal Processing Letters* 2(12): 219–222.

Picinbono, B. & Chevalier, P. (1995). Widely linear estimation with complex data, *IEEE Transactions on Signal Processing* 43(8): 2030–2033.

Reed, J. H. & Hsia, T. C. (1990). The performance of time-dependent adaptive filters for interference rejection, *IEEE Transactions on Acoustic, Speech and Signal Processing* 38(8): 1373–1385.

Schell, S. V. & Gardner, W. A. (1990). Progress on signal-selective direction finding, *Fifth ASSP Workshop on Spectrum Estimation and Modeling*, pp. 144–148.

Schmidt, R. O. (1986). Multiple emitter location and signal parameter estimation, *IEEE Transactions on Antennas and Propagation* 34(3): 276–280.

Van Trees, H. L. (1968). *Detection, Estimation, and Modulation Theory*, Vol. 1, John Wiley and Sons.

Whitehead, J. & Takawira, F. (2004). Low complexity constant modulus based cyclic blind adaptive multiuser detection, *AFRICON, 2004. 7th AFRICON Conference in Africa*, Vol. 1, pp. 115–120.

Whitehead, J. & Takawira, F. (2005). Blind adaptive multiuser detection for periodically time varying interference suppression [DS-CDMA system applications], *IEEE Wireless Communications and Networking Conference, 2005*, Vol. 1, pp. 273–279.

Widrow, B., Glover, Jr., J. R., McCool, J. M., Kaunitz, J., Williams, C. S., Hearn, R. H., Zeidler, J. R., Dong, Jr., E. & Goodlin, R. C. (1975). Adaptive noise cancelling: Principles and applications, *Proceedings of the IEEE* 63(12): 1692–1717.

Widrow, B., McCool, J. M., Larimore, M. G. & Johnson, Jr., C. R. (1976). Stationary and nonstationary learning characteristics of the LMS adaptive filter, *Proceedings of the IEEE* 64(8): 1151–1162.

Wong, H. E. & Chambers, J. A. (1996). Two-stage interference immune blind equaliser which exploits cyclostationary statistics, *Electronic Letters* 32(19): 1763–1764.

Yeste-Ojeda, O. A. & Grajal, J. (2008). Cyclostationarity-based signal separation in interceptors based on a single sensor, *IEEE Radar Conference 2008*, pp. 1–6.

Yeste-Ojeda, O. A. & Grajal, J. (2010). Adaptive-FRESH filters for compensation of cycle-frequency errors, *IEEE Transactions on Signal Processing* 58(1): 1–10.

Zadeh, L. A. (1950). Frequency analysis of variable networks, *Proceedings of the I.R.E.* pp. 291–299.

Zhang, H., Abdi, A. & Haimovich, A. (2006). Reduced-rank multi-antenna cyclic Wiener filtering for interference cancellation, *Military Communications Conference, 2006. MILCOM 2006*.

Zhang, J., Liao, G. & Wang, J. (2004). A novel robust adaptive beamforming for cyclostationary signals, *The 7th International Conference on Signal Processing, ICSP*, Vol. 1, pp. 339–342.

Zhang, J., Wong, K. M., Luo, Z. Q. & Ching, P. C. (1999). Blind adaptive FRESH filtering for signal extraction, *IEEE Transactions on Signal Processing* 47(5): 1397–1402.

12

Transient Analysis of a Combination of Two Adaptive Filters

Tõnu Trump
Department of Radio and Telecommunication Engineering,
Tallinn University of Technology
Estonia

1. Introduction

The Least Mean Square (LMS) algorithm is probably the most popular adaptive algorithm. The algorithm has since its introduction in Widrow & Hoff (1960) been widely used in many applications like system identification, communication channel equalization, signal prediction, sensor array processing, medical applications, echo and noise cancellation etc. The popularity of the algorithm is due to its low complexity but also due to its good properties like e.g. robustness Haykin (2002); Sayed (2008). Let us explain the algorithm in the example of system identification.

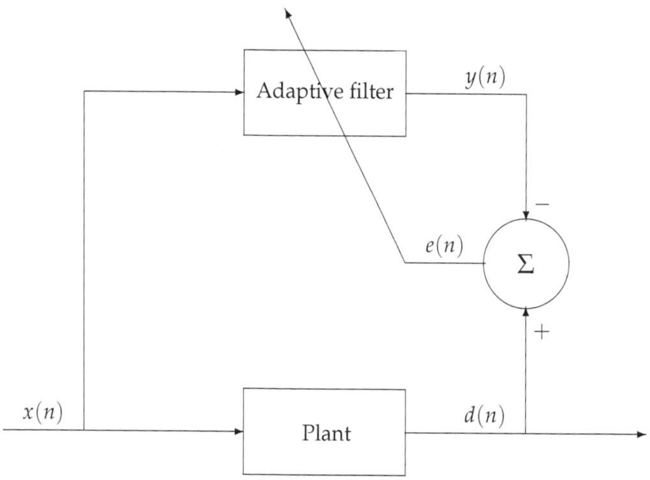

Fig. 1. Usage of an adaptive filter for system identification.

As seen from Figure 1, the input signal to the unknown plant, is $x(n)$ and the output signal from the plant is $d(n)$. We call the signal $d(n)$ the desired signal. The signal $d(n)$ also contains noise and possible nonlinear effects of the plant. We would like to estimate the impulse response of the plant observing its input and output signals. To do so we connect an adaptive filter in parallel with the plant. The adaptive filter is a linear filter with output signal $y(n)$. We then compare the output signals of the plant and the adaptive filter and form the error signal $e(n)$. Obviously one would like have the error signal to be as small as possible in some sense. The LMS algorithm achieves this by minimizing the mean squared error but doing this in instantaneous fashion. If we collect the impulse response coefficients of our adaptive filter computed at iteration n into a vector $\mathbf{w}(n)$ and the input signal samples into a vector $\mathbf{x}(n)$, the LMS algorithm updates the weight vector estimate at each iteration as

$$\mathbf{w}(n) = \mathbf{w}(n-1) + \mu e^*(n)\mathbf{x}(n), \tag{1}$$

where μ is the step size of the algorithm. One can see that the weight update is in fact a low pass filter with transfer function

$$H(z) = \frac{\mu}{1-z^{-1}} \tag{2}$$

operating on the signal $e^*(n)\mathbf{x}(n)$. The step size determines in fact the extent of initial averaging performed by the algorithm. If μ is small, only a little of new information is passed into the algorithm at each iteration, the averaging is thus over a large number of samples and the resulting estimate is more reliable but building the estimate takes more time. On the other hand if μ is large, a lot of new information is passed into the weight update each iteration, the extent of averaging is small and we get a less reliable estimate but we get it relatively fast.

When designing an adaptive algorithm, one thus faces a trade–off between the initial convergence speed and the mean–square error in steady state. In case of algorithms belonging to the Least Mean Square family this trade–off is controlled by the step-size parameter. Large step size leads to a fast initial convergence but the algorithm also exhibits a large mean–square error in the steady state and in contrary, small step size slows down the convergence but results in a small steady state error.

Variable step size adaptive schemes offer a possible solution allowing to achieve both fast initial convergence and low steady state misadjustment Arenas-Garcia et al. (1997); Harris et al. (1986); Kwong & Johnston (1992); Matthews & Xie (1993); Shin & Sayed (2004). How successful these schemes are depends on how well the algorithm is able to estimate the distance of the adaptive filter weights from the optimal solution. The variable step size algorithms use different criteria for calculating the proper step size at any given time instance. For example squared instantaneous errors have been used in Kwong & Johnston (1992) and the squared autocorrelation of errors at adjacent time instances have been used in Arenas-Garcia et al. (1997). The reference Matthews & Xie (1993) ivestigates an algorithm that changes the time–varying convergence parameters in such a way that the change is proportional to the negative of gradient of the squared estimation error with respect to the convergence parameter. In reference Shin & Sayed (2004) the norm of projected weight error vector is used as a criterion to determine how close the adaptive filter is to its optimum performance.

Recently there has been an interest in a combination scheme that is able to optimize the trade–off between convergence speed and steady state error Martinez-Ramon et al. (2002). The scheme consists of two adaptive filters that are simultaneously applied to the same inputs as depicted in Figure 2. One of the filters has a large step size allowing fast convergence and the other one has a small step size for a small steady state error. The outputs of the filters are combined through a mixing parameter λ. The performance of this scheme has been studied for some parameter update schemes Arenas-Garcia et al. (2006); Bershad et al. (2008);

Candido et al. (2010); Silva et al. (2010). The reference Arenas-Garcia et al. (2006) uses convex combination i.e. λ is constrained to lie between 0 and 1. The references Silva et al. (2010) and Candido et al. (2010) present transient analysis of a slightly modified versions of this scheme. The parameter λ is in those papers found using an LMS type adaptive scheme and possibly computing the sigmoidal function of the result. The reference Bershad et al. (2008) takes another approach computing the mixing parameter using an affine combination. This paper uses the ratio of time averages of the instantaneous errors of the filters. The error function of the ratio is then computed to obtain λ.

In Mandic et al. (2007) a convex combination of two adaptive filters with different adaptation schemes has been investigated with the aim to improve the steady state characteristics. One of the adaptive filters in that paper uses LMS algorithm and the other one Generalized Normalized Gradient Decent algorithm. The combination parameter λ is computed using stochastic gradient adaptation. In Zhang & Chambers (2006) the convex combination of two adaptive filters is applied in a variable filter length scheme to gain improvements in low SNR conditions. In Kim et al. (2008) the combination has been used to join two affine projection filters with different regularization parameters. The work Fathiyan & Eshghi (2009) uses the combination on parallel binary structured LMS algorithms. These three works use the LMS like scheme of Azpicueta-Ruiz et al. (2008b) to compute λ.

It should be noted that schemes involving two filters have been proposed earlier Armbruster (1992); Ochiai (1977). However, in those early schemes only one of the filters have been adaptive while the other one has used fixed filter weights. Updating of the fixed filter has been accomplished by copying of all the coefficients from the adaptive filter, when the adaptive filter has been performing better than the fixed one.

In this chapter we compute the mixing parameter λ from output signals of the individual filters. The scheme was independently proposed in Trump (2009a) and Azpicueta-Ruiz et al. (2008a), the steady state performance of it was investigated in Trump (2009b) and the tracking performance in Trump (2009c). The way of calculating the mixing parameter is optimal in the sense that it results from minimization of the mean-squared error of the combined filter. In the main body of this chapter we present a transient analysis of the algorithm. We will assume throughout the chapter that the signals are complex–valued and that the combination scheme uses two LMS adaptive filters. The italic, bold face lower case and bold face upper case letters will be used for scalars, column vectors and matrices respectively. The superscript $*$ denotes complex conjugation and H Hermitian transposition of a matrix. The operator $E[\cdot]$ denotes mathematical expectation, $tr[\cdot]$ stands for trace of a matrix and $\mathcal{R}e\{\cdot\}$ denotes the real part of a complex variable.

2. Algorithm

Let us consider two adaptive filters, as shown in Figure 2, each of them updated using the LMS adaptation rule

$$\mathbf{w}_i(n) = \mathbf{w}_i(n-1) + \mu_i e_i^*(n)\mathbf{x}(n), \tag{3}$$

$$e_i(n) = d(n) - \mathbf{w}_i^H(n-1)\mathbf{x}(n), \tag{4}$$

$$d(n) = \mathbf{w}_o^H\mathbf{x}(n) + v(n). \tag{5}$$

In the above equations the vector $\mathbf{w}_i(n)$ is the length N vector of coefficients of the i-th adaptive filter, with $i = 1, 2$. The vector $\mathbf{w}_o$ is the true weight vector we aim to identify with our adaptive scheme and $\mathbf{x}(n)$ is the N input vector, common for both of the adaptive filters.

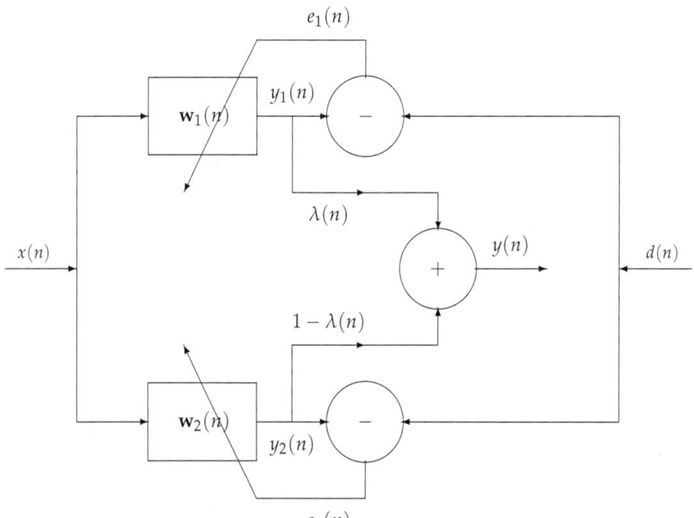

Fig. 2. The combined adaptive filter.

The input process is assumed to be a zero mean wide sense stationary Gaussian process. The desired signal $d(n)$ is a sum of the output of the filter to be identified and the Gaussian, zero mean i.i.d. measurement noise $v(n)$. We assume that the measurement noise is statistically independent of all the other signals. μ_i is the step size of i–th adaptive filter. We assume without loss of generality that $\mu_1 > \mu_2$. The case $\mu_1 = \mu_2$ is not interesting as in this case the two filters remain equal and the combination renders to a single filter.
The outputs of the two adaptive filters are combined according to

$$y(n) = \lambda(n)y_1(n) + [1 - \lambda(n)]y_2(n), \tag{6}$$

where $y_i(n) = \mathbf{w}_i^H(n-1)\mathbf{x}(n)$ and the mixing parameter λ can be any real number.
We define the *a priori* system error signal as difference between the output signal of the true system at time n, given by $y_o(n) = \mathbf{w}_o^H\mathbf{x}(n) = d(n) - v(n)$, and the output signal of our adaptive scheme $y(n)$

$$e_a(n) = y_o(n) - \lambda(n)y_1(n) - (1 - \lambda(n))y_2(n). \tag{7}$$

Let us now find $\lambda(n)$ by minimizing the mean square of the *a priori* system error. The derivative of $E[|e_a(n)|^2]$ with respect to $\lambda(n)$ reads

$$\begin{aligned}\frac{\partial E[|e_a(n)|^2]}{\partial\lambda(n)} &= 2E[(y_o(n) - \lambda(n)y_1(n) - (1 - \lambda(n))y_2(n)) \\ &\quad \cdot (-y_1(n) + y_2(n))^*] \\ &= 2E[\mathcal{R}e\{(y_o(n) - y_2(n))(y_2(n) - y_1(n))^*\} \\ &\quad +\lambda(n)|(y_2(n) - y_1(n))|^2].\end{aligned}$$

Setting the derivative to zero results in

$$\lambda(n) = \frac{E[\mathcal{R}e\{(d(n) - y_2(n))(y_1(n) - y_2(n))^*\}]}{E[|(y_1(n) - y_2(n))|^2]}, \tag{8}$$

where we have replaced the true system output signal $y_o(n)$ by its observable noisy version $d(n)$. Note however, that because we have made the standard assumption that the input signal $\mathbf{x}(n)$ and measurement noise $v(n)$ are independent random processes, this can be done without introducing any error into our calculations.
The denominator of equation (8) comprises expectation of the squared difference of the two filter output signals. This quantity can be very small or even zero, particularly in the beginning of adaptation if the two step sizes are close to each other. Correspondingly λ computed directly from (8) may be large. To avoid this from happening we add a small regularization constant ϵ to the denominator of (8).

3. Transient analysis

In this section we are interested in finding expressions that characterize transient performance of the combined algorithm i.e. we intend to derive formulae that characterize entire course of adaptation of the algorithm. Before we can proceed we need, however, to introduce some notations. First let us denote the weight error vector of i–th filter as

$$\tilde{\mathbf{w}}_i(n) = \mathbf{w}_o - \mathbf{w}_i(n). \tag{9}$$

Then the equivalent weight error vector of the combined adaptive filter will be

$$\tilde{\mathbf{w}}(n) = \lambda\tilde{\mathbf{w}}_1(n) + (1-\lambda)\tilde{\mathbf{w}}_2(n). \tag{10}$$

The mean square deviation of the combined filter is given by

$$\begin{aligned} MSD = E[\tilde{\mathbf{w}}^H(n)\tilde{\mathbf{w}}(n)] &= \lambda^2 E[\tilde{\mathbf{w}}_1^H(n)\tilde{\mathbf{w}}_1(n)] \\ &+2\lambda(1-\lambda)\mathcal{R}e\{E[\tilde{\mathbf{w}}_2^H(n)\tilde{\mathbf{w}}_1(n)\}] \\ &+(1-\lambda)^2 E[\tilde{\mathbf{w}}_2^H(n)\tilde{\mathbf{w}}_2(n)]. \end{aligned} \tag{11}$$

The *a priori* estimation error of an individual filter is defined as

$$e_{i,a}(n) = \tilde{\mathbf{w}}_i^H(n-1)\mathbf{x}(n). \tag{12}$$

It follows from (7) that we can express the *a priori* error of the combination as

$$e_a(n) = \lambda(n)e_{1,a}(n) + (1-\lambda(n))\,e_{2,a}(n) \tag{13}$$

and because $\lambda(n)$ is according to (8) a ratio of mathematical expectations and, hence, deterministic, we have for the excess mean square error of the combination

$$E[|e_a(n)|^2] = \lambda^2 E[|e_{1,a}(n)|^2] + 2\lambda(1-\lambda)E[\mathcal{R}e\{e_{1,a}(n)e_{2,a}^*(n)\}] + (1-\lambda)^2 E[|e_{2,a}(n)|^2]. \tag{14}$$

As $e_{i,a}(n) = \tilde{\mathbf{w}}_i^H(n-1)\mathbf{x}(n)$, the expression of the excess mean square error becomes

$$\begin{aligned} E[|e_a(n)|^2] &= \lambda^2 E[\tilde{\mathbf{w}}_1^H(n-1)\mathbf{x}\mathbf{x}^H\tilde{\mathbf{w}}_1(n-1)] \\ &+2\lambda(1-\lambda)E[\mathcal{R}e\{\tilde{\mathbf{w}}_1^H(n-1)\mathbf{x}\mathbf{x}^H\tilde{\mathbf{w}}_2(n-1)\}] \\ &+(1-\lambda)^2 E[\tilde{\mathbf{w}}_2^H(n-1)\mathbf{x}\mathbf{x}^H\tilde{\mathbf{w}}_2(n-1)]. \end{aligned} \tag{15}$$

In what follows we often drop the explicit time index n as we have done in (15), if it is not necessary to avoid a confusion.
Noting that $y_i(n) = \mathbf{w}_i^H(n-1)\mathbf{x}(n)$, we can rewrite the expression for $\lambda(n)$ in (8) as

$$\lambda(n) = \frac{E[\tilde{\mathbf{w}}_2^H \mathbf{x}\mathbf{x}^H \tilde{\mathbf{w}}_2] - E[\mathcal{R}e\{\tilde{\mathbf{w}}_2^H \mathbf{x}\mathbf{x}^H \tilde{\mathbf{w}}_1\}]}{E[\tilde{\mathbf{w}}_1^H \mathbf{x}\mathbf{x}^H \tilde{\mathbf{w}}_1] - 2E[\mathcal{R}e\{\tilde{\mathbf{w}}_1^H \mathbf{x}\mathbf{x}^H \tilde{\mathbf{w}}_2\}] + E[\tilde{\mathbf{w}}_2^H \mathbf{x}\mathbf{x}^H \tilde{\mathbf{w}}_2]}. \tag{16}$$

We thus need to investigate the evolution of the individual terms of the type $EMSE_{k,l} = E[\tilde{\mathbf{w}}_k^H(n-1)\mathbf{x}(n)\mathbf{x}^H(n)\tilde{\mathbf{w}}_l(n-1)]$ in order to reveal the time evolution of $EMSE(n)$ and $\lambda(n)$. To do so we, however, concentrate first on the mean square deviation defined in (11).
For a single LMS filter we have after subtraction of (3) from $\mathbf{w}_o$ and expressing $e_i(n)$ through the error of the corresponding Wiener filter $e_o(n)$

$$\tilde{\mathbf{w}}_i(n) = \left(\mathbf{I} - \mu_i \mathbf{x}\mathbf{x}^H\right) \tilde{\mathbf{w}}_i(n-1) - \mu_i \mathbf{x} e_o^*(n). \tag{17}$$

We next approximate the outer product of input signal vectors by its correlation matrix $\mathbf{x}\mathbf{x}^H \approx \mathbf{R}_\mathbf{x}$. The approximation is justified by the fact that with small step size the weight error update of the LMS algorithm (17) behaves like a low pass filter with a low cutoff frequency. With this approximations we have

$$\tilde{\mathbf{w}}_i(n) \approx (\mathbf{I} - \mu_i \mathbf{R}_\mathbf{x}) \tilde{\mathbf{w}}_i(n-1) - \mu_i \mathbf{x} e_o^*(n). \tag{18}$$

This means in fact that we apply the small step size theory Haykin (2002) even if the assumption of small step size is not really true for the fast adapting filter. In our simulation study we will see, however, that the assumption works in practice rather well.
Let us now define the eigendecomposition of the correlation matrix as

$$\mathbf{Q}^H \mathbf{R}_x \mathbf{Q} = \mathbf{\Omega}, \tag{19}$$

where $\mathbf{Q}$ is a unitary matrix whose columns are the orthogonal eigenvectors of $\mathbf{R}_x$ and $\mathbf{\Omega}$ is a diagonal matrix having eigenvalues associated with the corresponding eigenvectors on its main diagonal. We also define the transformed weight error vector as

$$\mathbf{v}_i(n) = \mathbf{Q}^H \tilde{\mathbf{w}}_i(n) \tag{20}$$

and the transformed last term of equation (18) as

$$\mathbf{p}_i(n) = \mu_i \mathbf{Q}^H \mathbf{x} e_o^*(n). \tag{21}$$

Then we can rewrite the equation (18) after multiplying both sides by $\mathbf{Q}^H$ from the left as

$$\mathbf{v}_i(n) = (\mathbf{I} - \mu_i \mathbf{\Omega}) \mathbf{v}_i(n-1) - \mathbf{p}_i(n). \tag{22}$$

We note that the mean of $\mathbf{p}_i$ is zero by the orthogonality theorem and the crosscorrelation matrix of $\mathbf{p}_k$ and $\mathbf{p}_l$ equals

$$E[\mathbf{p}_k \mathbf{p}_l^H] = \mu_k \mu_l \mathbf{Q}^H E[\mathbf{x} e_o^*(n) e_o(n) \mathbf{x}^H] \mathbf{Q}. \tag{23}$$

We now invoke the Gaussian moment factoring theorem to write

$$E[\mathbf{x} e_o^*(n) e_o(n) \mathbf{x}^H] = E[\mathbf{x} e_o^*(n)] E[e_o(n) \mathbf{x}^H] + E[\mathbf{x}\mathbf{x}^H] E[|e_o|^2]. \tag{24}$$

The first term in the above is zero due to the principle of orthogonality and the second term equals $\mathbf{R}J_{min}$. Hence we are left with

$$E[\mathbf{p}_k\mathbf{p}_l^H] = \mu_k\mu_l J_{min}\mathbf{\Omega}, \tag{25}$$

where $J_{min} = E[|e_o|^2]$ is the minimum mean square error produced by the corresponding Wiener filter. As the matrices $\mathbf{I}$ and $\mathbf{\Omega}$ in (22) are diagonal, it follows that the m-th element of vector $\mathbf{v}_i(n)$ is given by

$$\begin{aligned} v_{i,m}(n) &= (1-\mu_i\omega_m)\,v_{i,m}(n-1) - p_{i,m}(n) \\ &= (1-\mu_i\omega_m)^n\,v_m(0) + \sum_{i=0}^{n-1}(1-\mu_i\omega_m)^{n-1-i}\,p_{i,m}(i), \end{aligned} \tag{26}$$

where ω_m is the m-th eigenvalue of $\mathbf{R}_x$ and $v_{i,m}$ and $p_{i,m}$ are the m-th components of the vectors $\mathbf{v}_i$ and $\mathbf{p}_i$ respectively.
We immediately see that the mean value of $v_{i,m}(n)$ equals

$$E[v_{i,m}(n)] = (1-\mu_i\omega_m)^n\,v_m(0) \tag{27}$$

as the vector $\mathbf{p}_i$ has zero mean.
The expected values of $v_{i,m}(n)$ exhibit no oscillations as the correlation matrix $\mathbf{R}$ is positive semidefinite with all its eigenvalues being nonnegative real numbers. In order the LMS algorithm to converge in mean, the weight errors need to decrease with time. This will happen if

$$|1-\mu_i\omega_m| < 1 \tag{28}$$

for all m. In that case all the natural modes of the algorithm die out as the number of iterations n approaches infinity. The condition needs to be fulfilled for all the eigenvalues ω_m and is obviously satisfied if the condition is met for the maximum eigenvalue. It follows that the individual step size μ_i needs to be selected such that the double inequality

$$0 < \mu_i < \frac{2}{\lambda_{max}} \tag{29}$$

is satisfied.
In some applications the input signal correlation matrix and its eigenvalues are not known *a priori*. In this case it may be convenient to use the fact that

$$tr\{\mathbf{R}_x\} = \sum_{i=0}^{N-1} r_x(i,i) = \sum_{i=0}^{N-1}\omega_i > \omega_{max}, \tag{30}$$

where $r_x(i,i)$ is the i-th diagonal element of the matrix $\mathbf{R}$. Then we can normalize the step size with the instantaneous estimate of the trace of correlation matrix $\mathbf{x}^H(n)\mathbf{x}(n)$ to get so called normalized LMS algorithm. The normalized LMS algorithm uses the normalized step size

$$\mu_i = \frac{\alpha_i}{\mathbf{x}^H(n)\mathbf{x}(n)}$$

and is convergent if

$$0 < \alpha_i < 2.$$

The normalized LMS is more convenient for practical usage if the properties of the input signal are unknown or are varying in time like this is for example the case with speech signals.
To proceed with our development for the combination of two LMS filters we note that we can express the MSD and its individual components in (11) through the transformed weight error vectors as

$$E[\tilde{\mathbf{w}}_k^H(n)\tilde{\mathbf{w}}_l(n)] = E[\mathbf{v}_k^H(n)\mathbf{v}_l(n)] = \sum_{m=0}^{N-1} E[v_{k,m}(n)v_{l,m}^*(n)] \tag{31}$$

so we also need to find the auto- and cross correlations of v. Let us concentrate on the m-th component in the sum above corresponding to the cross term and denote it as $\Upsilon_m = E[v_{k,m}(n)v_{l,m}^*(n)]$. The expressions for the component filters follow as special cases. Substituting (26) into the expression of Υ_m above, taking the mathematical expectation and noting that the vector $\mathbf{p}$ is independent of $\mathbf{v}(0)$ results in

$$\begin{aligned}\Upsilon_m &= E\left[(1-\mu_k\omega_m)^n v_k(0)\,(1-\mu_l\omega_m)^n v_l^*(0)\right] \\ &+E\left[\sum_{i=0}^{n-1}\sum_{j=0}^{n-1}(1-\mu_k\omega_m)^{n-1-i}(1-\mu_l\omega_m)^{n-1-j}\,p_{k,m}(i)p_{l,m}^*(j)\right].\end{aligned} \tag{32}$$

We now note that most likely the two component filters are initialized to the same value

$$v_{k,m}(0) = v_{l,m}(0) = v_m(0)$$

and that

$$E\left[p_{k,m}(i)p_{l,m}^*(j)\right] = \begin{cases}\mu_k\mu_l\omega_m J_{min}, & i=j\\ 0, & \text{otherwise}\end{cases}. \tag{33}$$

We then have for the m-th component of MSD

$$\begin{aligned}\Upsilon_m &= (1-\mu_k\omega_m)^n(1-\mu_l\omega_m)^n|v_m(0)|^2 \\ &+\mu_k\mu_l\omega_m J_{min}(1-\mu_k\omega_m)^{n-1}(1-\mu_l\omega_m)^{n-1}\sum_{i=0}^{n-1}(1-\mu_k\omega_m)^{-i}(1-\mu_l\omega_m)^{-i}.\end{aligned} \tag{34}$$

The sum over i in the above equation can be recognized as a geometric series with n terms. The first term is equal to 1 and the geometric ratio equals $(1-\mu_k\omega_m)^{-1}(1-\mu_l\omega_m)^{-1}$. Hence we have

$$\begin{aligned}&\sum_{i=0}^{n-1}(1-\mu_k\omega_m)^{-i}(1-\mu_l\omega_m)^{-i} \\ &=\frac{(1-\mu_k\omega_m)(1-\mu_l\omega_m)}{\mu_k\mu_l\omega_m^2-\mu_k\omega_m-\mu_l\omega_m}-\frac{(1-\mu_k\omega_m)^{-n+1}(1-\mu_l\omega_m)^{-n+1}}{\mu_k\mu_l\omega_m^2-\mu_k\omega_m-\mu_l\omega_m}.\end{aligned} \tag{35}$$

After substitution of the above into (34) and simplification we are left with

$$\begin{aligned}\Upsilon_m &= E[v_{k,m}(n)v_{l,m}^*(n)] \\ &= (1-\mu_k\omega_m)^n(1-\mu_l\omega_m)^n\left[|v_m(0)|^2+\frac{J_{min}}{\omega_m^2-\frac{\omega_m}{\mu_l}-\frac{\omega_m}{\mu_k}}\right] \\ &-\frac{J_{min}}{\omega_m^2-\frac{\omega_m}{\mu_l}-\frac{\omega_m}{\mu_k}},\end{aligned} \tag{36}$$

which is our result for a single entry to the MSD crossterm vector. It is easy to see that for the terms involving a single filter we get an expressions that coincide with the one available in the literature Haykin (2002).
Let us now focus on the cross term

$$EMSE_{kl} = E\left[\tilde{\mathbf{w}}_k^H(n-1)\mathbf{x}(n)\mathbf{x}^H(n)\tilde{\mathbf{w}}_l(n-1)\right],$$

appearing in the EMSE equation (15). Due to the independence assumption we can rewrite this using the properties of trace operator as

$$\begin{aligned} EMSE_{kl} &= E\left[\tilde{\mathbf{w}}_k^H(n-1)\mathbf{R}_\mathbf{x}\tilde{\mathbf{w}}_l(n-1)\right] \\ &= tr\left\{E\left[\mathbf{R}_\mathbf{x}\tilde{\mathbf{w}}_l(n-1)\tilde{\mathbf{w}}_k^H(n-1)\right]\right\} \\ &= tr\left\{\mathbf{R}_\mathbf{x}E\left[\tilde{\mathbf{w}}_l(n-1)\tilde{\mathbf{w}}_k^H(n-1)\right]\right\}. \end{aligned} \tag{37}$$

Let us now recall that for any of the filters $\tilde{\mathbf{w}}_i(n) = \mathbf{\Omega}\mathbf{v}_i(n)$ to write

$$\begin{aligned} EMSE_{kl} &= tr\left\{\mathbf{R}_\mathbf{x}E\left[\mathbf{Q}\mathbf{v}_l(n-1)\mathbf{v}_k^H(n-1)\mathbf{Q}^H\right]\right\} \\ &= tr\left\{E\left[\mathbf{v}_k^H(n-1)\mathbf{Q}^H\mathbf{R}_\mathbf{x}\mathbf{Q}\mathbf{v}_l(n-1)\right]\right\} \\ &= tr\left\{E\left[\mathbf{v}_k^H(n-1)\mathbf{\Omega}\mathbf{v}_l(n-1)\right]\right\} \\ &= \sum_{i=0}^{N-1}\omega_i E\left[v_{k,i}^*(n-1)v_{l,i}(n-1)\right]. \end{aligned} \tag{38}$$

The EMSE of the combined filter can now be computed as

$$EMSE = \sum_{i=0}^{N-1}\omega_i E\left[|\lambda(n)v_{k,i}(n-1) + (1-\lambda(n)v_{l,i}(n-1)|^2\right], \tag{39}$$

where the components of type $E[v_{k,i}(n-1)v_{l,i}(n-1)]$ are given by (36). To compute $\lambda(n)$ we use (16) substituting (38) for its individual components.

4. Simulation results

A simulation study was carried out with the aim of verifying the approximations made in the previous Section. In particular we are interested in how well the small step-size theory applies to our combination scheme of two adaptive filters.
We have selected the sample echo path model number one shown in Figure 3 from *ITU-T Recommendation G.168 Digital Network Echo Cancellers* (2009), to be the unknown system to identify.
We have combined two 64 tap long adaptive filters. In order to obtain a practical algorithm, the expectation operators in both numerator and denominator of (8) have been replaced by exponential averaging of the type

$$P_u(n) = (1-\gamma)P_u(n-1) + \gamma u^2(n), \tag{40}$$

where $u(n)$ is the signal to be averaged, $P_u(n)$ is the averaged quantity and $\gamma = 0.01$. The averaged quantities were then used in (8) to obtain λ. With this design the numerator and

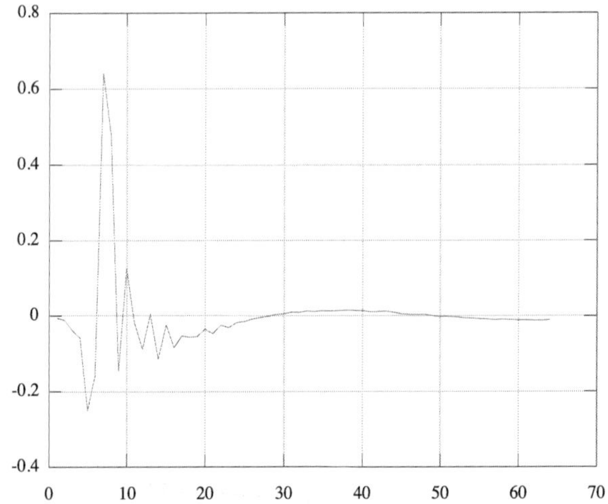

Fig. 3. The true impulse response.

denominator of in the λ expression (8) are relatively small random variables at the beginning of the test cases. For practical purposes we have therefore restricted λ to be less than unity and added a small constant to the denominator to avoid division by zero.
In the Figures below the noisy blue line represents the simulation result and the smooth red line is the theoretical result. The curves are averaged over 100 independent trials.
In our first simulation example we use Gaussian white noise with unity variance as the input signal. The measurement noise is another white Gaussian noise with variance $\sigma_v^2 = 10^{-3}$. The step sizes are $\mu_1 = 0.005$ for the fast adapting filter and $\mu_2 = 0.0005$ for the slowly adapting filter. Figure 4 depicts the evolution of EMSE in time. One can see that the system converges fast in the beginning. The fast convergence is followed by a stabilization period between sample times 1000 – 7000 followed by another convergence to a lower EMSE level between the sample times 8000 – 12000. The second convergence occurs when the mean squared error of the filter with small step size surpasses the performance of the filter with large step size. One can observe that the there is a good accordance between the theoretical and the simulated curves.
In the Figure 5 we show the time evolution of mean square deviation of the combination in the same test case. Again one can see that the theoretical and simulation curves fit well.
We continue with some examples with coloured input signal. In those examples the input signal x is formed from the Gaussian white noise with unity variance by passing it through the filter with transfer function

$$H(z) = \frac{1}{1 - 0.5z^{-1} - 0.1z^{-2}}$$

to get a coloured input signal. The measurement noise is Gaussian white noise, statistically independent of x.

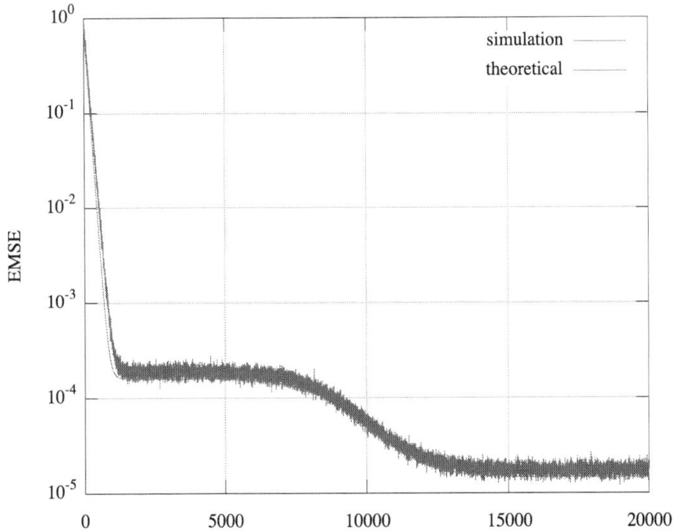

Fig. 4. Time–evolutions of EMSE with $\mu_1 = 0.005$ and $\mu_2 = 0.0005$ and $\sigma_v^2 = 10^{-3}$.

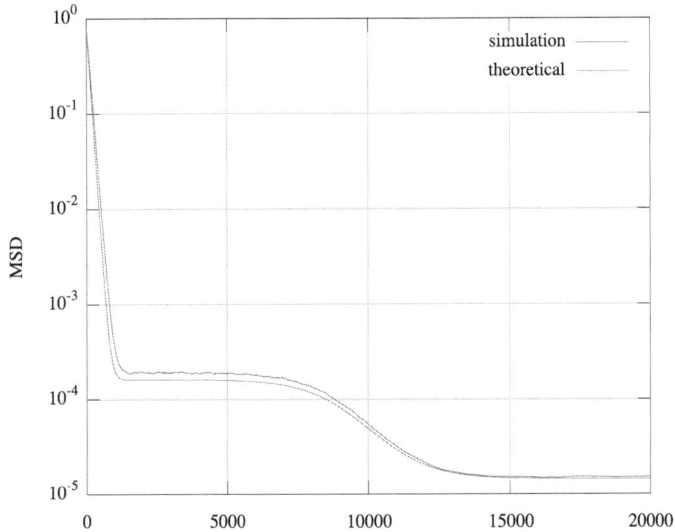

Fig. 5. Time–evolutions of EMSE with $\mu_1 = 0.005$ and $\mu_2 = 0.0005$ and $\sigma_v^2 = 10^{-3}$.

In our first simulation example with coloured input we have used observation noise with variance $\sigma_v^2 = 10^{-4}$. The step size of the fast filter is $\mu_1 = 0.005$ and the step size of the slow filter $\mu_2 = 0.001$. As seen from Figure 6 there is a a rapid convergence, determined by the fast converging filter in the beginning followed by a stabilization period. When the EMSE of the slowly adapting filter becomes smaller than that of the fast one, between sample times 10000 and 15000, a second convergence occurs. One can observe a good resemblance between simulation and theoretical curves.

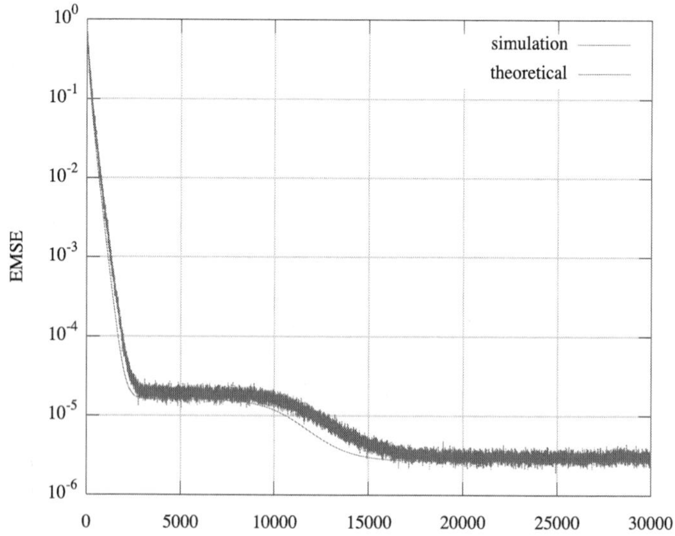

Fig. 6. Time–evolutions of EMSE with $\mu_1 = 0.005$ and $\mu_2 = 0.001$ and $\sigma_v^2 = 10^{-4}$.

In Figure 7 we have made the difference between the step sizes small. The step size of the fast adapting filter is now $\mu_1 = 0.003$ and the step size of the slowly adapting filter is $\mu_2 = 0.002$. One can see that the characteristic horizontal part of the learning curve has almost disappeared. We have also increased the measurement noise level to $\sigma_v^2 = 10^{-2}$. The simulation and theoretical curves show a good match.
In Figure 8 we have increased the measurement noise level even more to $\sigma_v^2 = 10^{-1}$. The step size of the fast adapting filter is $\mu_1 = 0.004$ and the step size of the slowly adapting filter is $\mu_2 = 0.0005$. One can see that the theoretical simulation results agree well.
Figure 9 depicts the time evolution of the combination parameter λ in this simulation. At the beginning of the test case the combination parameter is close to one. Correspondingly the output signal of the fast filter is used as the output of the combination. After a while, when the slow filter catches up the fast one and becomes better, λ changes toward zero and eventually becomes a small negative number. In this state the slow but more accurate filter determines the combined output. Again one can see that there is a clear similarity between the lines.

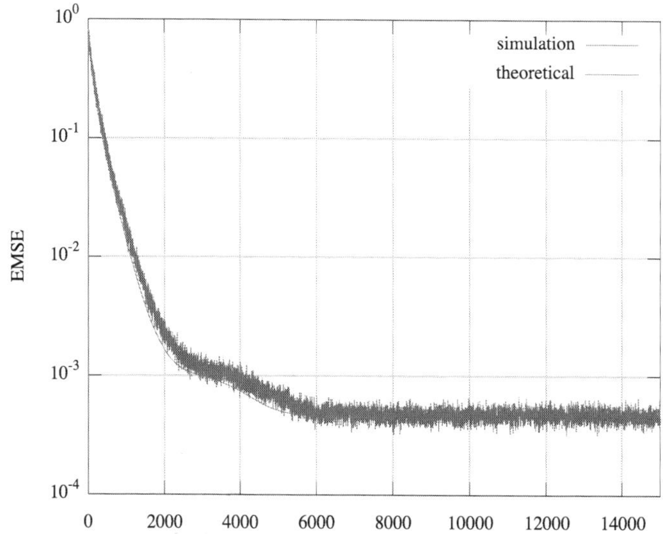

Fig. 7. EMSE with $\mu_1 = 0.003$ and $\mu_2 = 0.002$. and $\sigma_v^2 = 10^{-2}$.

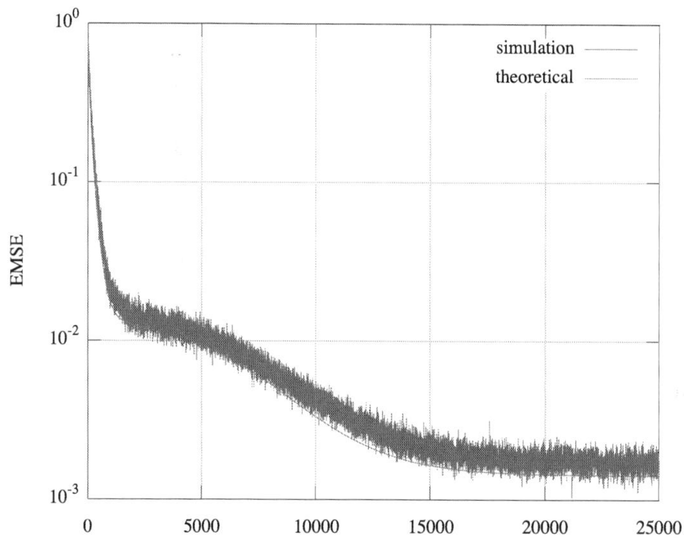

Fig. 8. EMSE with $\mu_1 = 0.004$ and $\mu_2 = 0.0005$ and $\sigma_v^2 = 10^{-1}$.

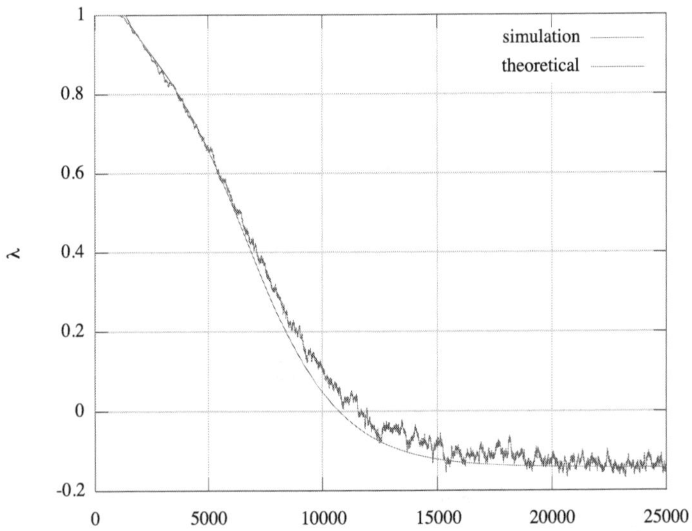

Fig. 9. Time–evolutions of λ with $\mu_1 = 0.004$ and $\mu_2 = 0.0005$. and $\sigma_v^2 = 10^{-1}$.

5. Conclusions

In this chapter we have investigated a combination of two LMS adaptive filters that are simultaneously applied to the same input signals. The output signals of the two adaptive filters are combined together using an adaptive mixing parameter. The mixing parameter λ was computed using the output signals of the individual filters and the desired signal. The transient behaviour of the algorithm was investigated using the assumption of small step size and the expressions for evolution of $EMSE(n)$ and $\lambda(n)$ were derived. Finally it was shown in the simulation study that the derived formulae fit the simulation results well.

6. References

Arenas-Garcia, J., Figueiras-Vidal, A. R. & Sayed, A. H. (1997). A robust variable step–size lms–type algorithm: Analysis and simulations, *IEEE Transactions on Signal Processing* 45: 631–639.

Arenas-Garcia, J., Figueiras-Vidal, A. R. & Sayed, A. H. (2006). Mean-square performance of convex combination of two adaptive filters, *IEEE Transactions on Signal Processing* 54: 1078–1090.

Armbruster, W. (1992). *Wideband Acoustic Echo Canceller with Two Filter Structure, Signal Processing VI, Theories and Applications, J Vanderwalle, R. Boite, M. Moonen and A. Oosterlinck ed.*, Elsevier Science Publishers B.V.

Azpicueta-Ruiz, L. A., Figueiras-Vidal, A. R. & Arenas-Garcia, J. (2008a). A new least squares adaptation scheme for the affine combination of two adaptive filters, *Proc. IEEE*

International Workshop on Machine Learning for Signal Processing, Cancun, Mexico, pp. 327–332.

Azpicueta-Ruiz, L. A., Figueiras-Vidal, A. R. & Arenas-Garcia, J. (2008b). A normalized adaptation scheme for the convex combination of two adaptive filters, *Proc. IEEE International Conference on Acoustics, Speech, and Signal Processing*, Las Vegas, Nevada, pp. 3301–3304.

Bershad, N. J., Bermudez, J. C. & Tourneret, J. H. (2008). An affine combination of two lms adaptive filters – transient mean–square analysis, *IEEE Transactions on Signal Processing* 56: 1853–1864.

Candido, R., Silva, M. T. M. & Nascimento, V. H. (2010). Transient and steady-state analysis of the affine combination of two adaptive filters, *IEEE Transactions on Signal Processing* 58: 4064–4078.

Fathiyan, A. & Eshghi, M. (2009). Combining several pbs-lms filters as a general form of convex combination of two filters, *Journal of Applied Sciences* 9: 759–764.

Harris, R. W., Chabries, D. M. & Bishop, F. A. (1986). Variable step (vs) adaptive filter algorithm, *IEEE Transactions on Acoustics, Speech and Signal Processing* 34: 309–316.

Haykin, S. (2002). *Adaptive Filter Theory, Fourth Edition,*, Prentice Hall.

ITU-T Recommendation G.168 Digital Network Echo Cancellers (2009). ITU-T.

Kim, K., Choi, Y., Kim, S. & Song, W. (2008). Convex combination of affine projection filters with individual regularization, *Proc. 23rd International Technical Conference on Circuits/Systems, Computers and Communications (ITC-CSCC)*, Shimonoseki, Japan, pp. 901–904.

Kwong, R. H. & Johnston, E. W. (1992). A variable step size lms algorithm, *IEEE Transactions on Signal Processing* 40: 1633–1642.

Mandic, D., Vayanos, P., Boukis, C., Jelfs, B., Goh, S. I., Gautama, T. & Rutkowski, T. (2007). Collaborative adaptive learning using hybrid filters, *Proc. IEEE International Conference on Acoustics, Speech, and Signal Processing*, Honolulu, Hawaii, pp. 901 – 924.

Martinez-Ramon, M., Arenas-Garcia, J., Navia-Vazquez, A. & Figueiras-Vidal, A. R. (2002). An adaptive combination of adaptive filters for plant identification, *Proc. 14th International Conference on Digital Signal Processing*, Santorini, Greece, pp. 1195–1198.

Matthews, V. J. & Xie, Z. (1993). A stochastic gradient adaptive filter with gradient adaptive step size, *IEEE Transactions on Signal Processing* 41: 2075–2087.

Ochiai, K. (1977). Echo canceller with two echo path models, *IEEE Transactions on Communications* 25: 589–594.

Sayed, A. H. (2008). *Adaptive Filters*, John Wiley and sons.

Shin, H. C. & Sayed, A. H. (2004). Variable step–size nlms and affine projection algorithms, *IEEE Signal Processing Letters* 11: 132–135.

Silva, M. T. M., Nascimento, V. H. & Arenas-Garcia, J. (2010). A transient analysis for the convex combination of two adaptive filters with transfer of coefficients, *Proc. IEEE International Conference on Acoustics, Speech, and Signal Processing*, Dallas, TX, USA, pp. 3842–3845.

Trump, T. (2009a). An output signal based combination of two nlms adaptive algorithms, *Proc. 16th International Conference on Digital Signal Processing*, Santorini, Greece.

Trump, T. (2009b). Steady state analysis of an output signal based combination of two nlms adaptive filters, *Proc. 17th European Signal Processing Conference*, Glasgow, Scotland.

Trump, T. (2009c). Tracking performance of a combination of two nlms adaptive filters, *Proc. IEEE Workshop on Statistical Signal Processing*, Cardiff, UK.

Widrow, B. & Hoff, M. E. J. (1960). Adaptive switching circuits, *IRE WESCON Conv. Rec.*, pp. 96–104.

Zhang, Y. & Chambers, J. A. (2006). Convex combination of adaptive filters for a variable tap–length lms algorithm, *IEEE Signal Processing Letters* 13: 628–631.

13

Adaptive Harmonic IIR Notch Filters for Frequency Estimation and Tracking

Li Tan[1], Jean Jiang[2] and Liangmo Wang[3]
[1,2]Purdue University North Central
[3]Nanjing University of Science and Technology
[1,2]USA
[3]China

1. Introduction

In many signal processing applications, adaptive frequency estimation and tracking of noisy narrowband signals is often required in communications, radar, sonar, controls, biomedical signal processing, and the applications such as detection of a noisy sinusoidal signal and cancellation of periodic signals. In order to achieve the objective of frequency tracking and estimation, an adaptive finite impulse response (FIR) filter or an adaptive infinite impulse response (IIR) notch filter is generally applied. Although an adaptive FIR filter has the stability advantage over an adaptive IIR notch filter, it requires a larger number of filter coefficients. In practical situations, an adaptive IIR notch filter (Chicharo & Ng, 1990; Kwan & Martin, 1989; Nehorai, 1985) is preferred due to its less number of filter coefficients and hence less computational complexity. More importantly, a second-order adaptive pole/zero constrained IIR notch filter (Xiao et al, 2001; Zhou & Li, 2004) can effectively be applied to track a single sinusoidal signal. If a signal contains multiple frequency components, then we can estimate and track its frequencies using a higher-order adaptive IIR notch filter constructed by cascading second-order adaptive IIR notch filters (Kwan & Martin, 1989). To ensure the global minimum convergence, the filter algorithm must begin with initial conditions, which require prior knowledge of the signal frequencies.
However, in many practical situations, a sinusoidal signal may be subjected to nonlinear effects (Tan & Jiang, 2009a, 2009b) in which possible harmonic frequency components are generated. For example, the signal acquired from a sensor may undergo saturation through an amplifier. In such an environment, we may want to estimate and track the signal's fundamental frequency as well as any harmonic frequencies. Using a second-order adaptive IIR notch filter to estimate fundamental and harmonic frequencies is insufficient, since it only accommodates one frequency component. On the other hand, applying a higher-order IIR notch filter may not be effective due to adopting multiple adaptive filter coefficients and local minimum convergence of the adaptive algorithm. In addition, monitoring the global minimum using a grid search method requires a huge number of computations, and thus makes the notch filter impractical in real time processing. Therefore, in this chapter, we propose and investigate a novel adaptive harmonic IIR notch filter with a single adaptive coefficient to efficiently perform frequency estimation and tracking in a harmonic frequency environment.

The proposed chapter first reviews the standard structure of a cascaded second-order pole/zero constrained adaptive IIR notch filter and its associated adaptive algorithm. Second, we describe the structure and algorithm for a new adaptive harmonic IIR notch filter under a harmonic noise environment. The key feature is that the proposed filter contains only one adaptive parameter such that its global minimum of the MSE function can easily be monitored during adaptation. For example, when the input fundamental signal frequency has a step change (the signal frequency switches to a different frequency value), the global minimum location of the MSE function is also changed. The traditional cascaded second-order adaptive IIR notch filter may likely converge to local minima due to its slow convergence; and hence an incorrect estimated fundamental frequency value could be obtained. However, with the proposed algorithms, when a possible local minimum is detected, the global minimum can easily be detected and relocated so that adaptive filter parameters can be reset based on the estimated global minimum, which is determined from the computed MSE function.

In this chapter, we perform convergence analysis of the adaptive harmonic IIR notch filter (Tan & Jiang, 2009). Although such an analysis is a very challenging task due to the extremely complicated plain gradient and MSE functions, with reasonable simplifications we are still able to achieve some useful theoretical results such as the convergence upper bound of the adaptive algorithm. Based on convergence analysis, we further propose a new robust algorithm. Finally, we demonstrate simulation results to verify the performance of the proposed adaptive harmonic IIR notch filters.

2. Background on adaptive IIR notch filters

In this section, we will describe frequency tracking and estimation using standard adaptive IIR notch filters and illustrate some issues when we apply them in a harmonic noise environment.

2.1 Adaptive second-order IIR notch filters

Fig. 1 presents a basic block diagram for a second-order adaptive IIR notch filter for estimation of a single sinusoid. As shown in Fig. 1, the input sinusoid with frequency f needed be estimated and tracked is given below:

$$x(n) = A\cos(2\pi fn / f_s + \alpha) + v(n) \tag{1}$$

where A and α are the amplitude and phase angle; and $v(n)$ is a zero-mean Gaussian noise process. f_s and n are the sampling rate and time index, respectively.

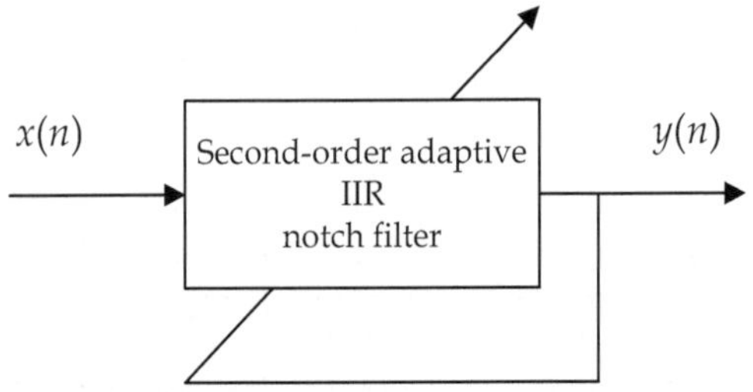

Fig. 1. Second-order adaptive IIR notch filter

To estimate the signal frequency, a standard second-second order adaptive IIR notch filter (Zhou & Li, 2004) is applied with its transfer function given by

$$H(z) = \frac{1 - 2\cos(\theta)z^{-1} + z^{-2}}{1 - 2r\cos(\theta)z^{-1} + r^2 z^{-2}} \tag{2}$$

The transfer function has one notch frequency parameter θ and has zero on the unit circle resulting in an infinite-depth notch. r is the pole radius which controls the notch bandwidth. It requires $0 << r < 1$ for achieving a narrowband notch. Making the parameter θ to be adaptive, that is, $\theta(n)$. The filter output can be expressed as

$$y(n) = x(n) - 2\cos[\theta(n)]x(n-1) + x(n-2) + 2r\cos[\theta(n)]y(n-1) - r^2 y(n-2) \tag{3}$$

Again, when r is close to 1, the 3-dB notch filter bandwidth can be approximated as $BW \approx 2(1-r)$ radians (Tan, 2007). Our objective is to minimize the filter output power $E[y^2(n)]$. Once the output power is minimized, the filter parameter θ will converge to its corresponding frequency f Hz. For a noise free case, the minimized output power should be zero. Note that for frequency tracking, our expected result is the parameter $\theta(n)$ rather than the filtered signal $y(n)$. A least mean square (LMS) algorithm to minimize the instantaneous output power $y^2(n)$ is often used and listed below:

$$\theta(n+1) = \theta(n) - 2\mu y(n)\beta(n) \tag{4}$$

where the gradient function $\beta(n) = \partial y(n) / \partial \theta(n)$ can be derived as following:

$$\beta(n) = 2\sin[\theta(n)]x(n-1) - 2r\sin[\theta(n)]y(n-1) + 2r\cos[\theta(n)]\beta(n-1) - r^2\beta(n-2) \tag{5}$$

and u is the convergence factor which controls the speed of algorithm convergence. Fig. 2 illustrates the behavior of tacking and estimating a sinusoid with its frequency value of 1 kHz at a sampling rate of 8 kHz for a noise free situation. As shown in Fig. 2, the LMS algorithm converges after 2600 iterations. Again, note that the estimated frequency is 1 kHz

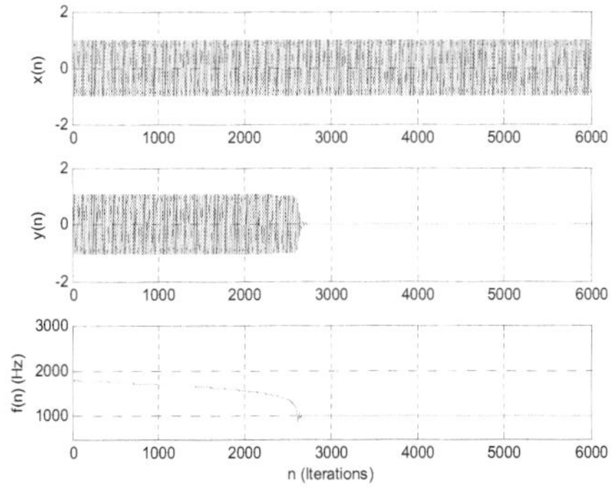

Fig. 2. Frequency tracking of a single sinusoid using a second-order adaptive IIR notch filter (sinusoid: $A = 1$, $f = 1000$ Hz, $f_s = 8000$; adaptive notch filter: $r = 0.95$ and $\mu = 0.005$)

while the filter output approaches to zero. However, when estimating multiple frequencies (or tracking a signal containing not only its fundamental frequency but also its higher-order harmonic frequencies), a higher-order adaptive IIR notch filter using cascading second-order adaptive IIR notch filter is desirable.

2.2 Cascaded higher-order adaptive IIR notch filters

In order to track the fundamental frequency under a harmonic environment, we can cascade second-order IIR notch filters to obtain a higher-order IIR notch filter whose transfer function is yielded as

$$H(z) = \prod_{k=1}^{K} H_k(z) = \prod_{k=1}^{K} \frac{1 - 2\cos\theta_k(n) z^{-1} + z^{-2}}{1 - 2r\cos\theta_k(n) z^{-1} + r^2 z^{-2}} \tag{6}$$

The filter contains K stages (K sub-filters). $\theta_k(n)$ is the adaptive parameter for the k th sub-filter while r is the pole radius as defined in Section 2.1. For an adaptive version, the output from each sub-filter is expressed as

$$y_k(n) = y_{k-1}(n) - 2\cos[\theta_k(n)]y_{k-1}(n-1) + y_{k-1}(n-2) + 2r\cos[\theta_k(n)]y_k(n-1) - r^2 y_k(n-2) \tag{7}$$

Note that the notch filter output $y(n)$ is from the last stage sub-filter, that is, $y(n) = y_K(n)$. After minimizing its instantaneous output power $y_K^2(n)$, we achieve LMS update equations as

$$\theta_k(n+1) = \theta_k(n) - 2 \times 2^{k-1} \mu y_K(n) \beta_{Kk}(n) \tag{8}$$

where $\beta_{Kk}(n)$ is the gradient function which can be determined from the following recursions:

$$\begin{aligned}\beta_{Kk}(n) &= \beta_{(K-1)k}(n) + 2\sin[\theta_k(n)]y_{K-1}(n) - 2\cos[\theta_k(n)]\beta_{(K-1)k}(n-1) \\ &+ \beta_{(K-1)k}(n-2) - 2r\sin[\theta_k(n)]y_{K-1}(n) + 2r\cos[\theta_k(n)]\beta_{Kk}(n-1) - r^2\beta_{Kk}(n-2)\end{aligned} \tag{9}$$

Fig. 3 shows an example of tracking a signal containing up to its third harmonic components, that is, $\sin(2\pi \times f_a \times n / f_s) + 0.5\cos(2\pi \times 2f_a \times n / f_s) - 0.25\cos(2\pi \times 3f_a \times n / f_s)$, where f_a represents the fundamental frequency in Hz and the sampling rate f_s is 8000 Hz. We cascade three second-order adaptive IIR notch filters for this application. For our LMS algorithm, the initial conditions are set to $\theta_1(0) = 2\pi \times 1200 / f_s = 0.3\pi$ radians, $\theta_2(0) = 0.6\pi$ radians, $\theta_3(0) = 0.9\pi$ radians. The fundamental frequency starts from 1225 Hz, and then switches to 1000 Hz and 875 Hz after 10000 iterations and 20000 iterations, respectively. Fig. 3a shows the input and outputs from each filter stage while Fig. 3b displays the tracked frequency values, where $f_1(n) = f_a$, $f_2(n) = 2f_a$ and $f_3(n) = 3f_a$.

With the prior knowledge of the fundamental frequency, the notch filter initially starts from the location nearby the global minimum. The fundamental frequency and harmonic frequencies are tracked with corrected frequency values, that is, 1225, 2x1225, 3x1225 Hz for first 10000 iterations, 1000, 2x1000, 3x1000 Hz from 10001 to 20000 iterations, and 875, 1750,

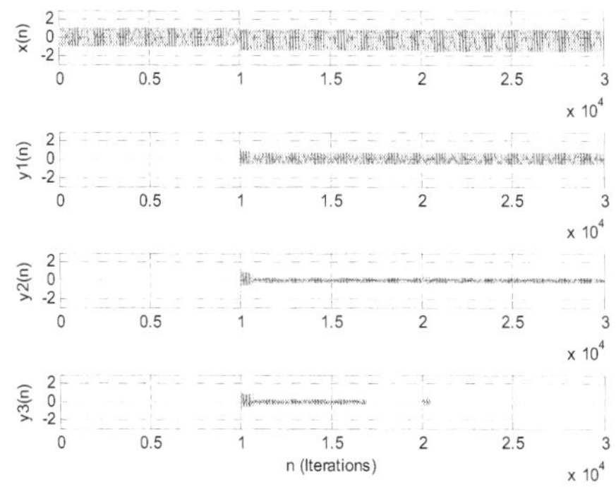

(a)

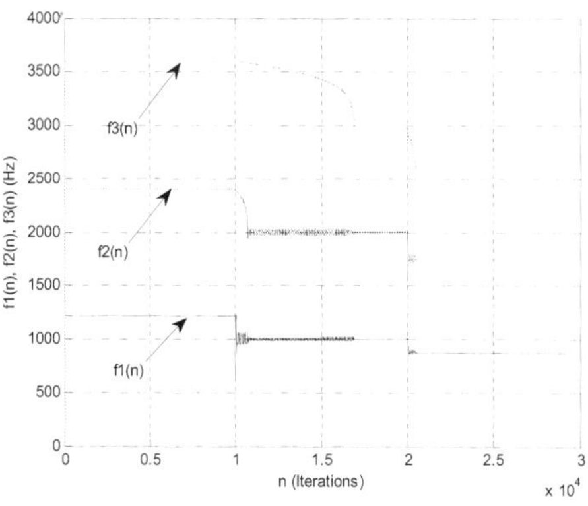

(b)

Fig. 3. Frequency tracking of a signal with its fundamental component, second and third harmonics by using second-order adaptive IIR notch filters in cascade ($r = 0.95$ and $\mu = 0.002$)

2625 Hz from 20001 to 30000 iterations, respectively. We can see that the algorithm exhibits slow convergence when the fundamental frequency switches. Another problem is that the algorithm may converge to a local minimum if it starts at arbitrary initial conditions. As shown in Fig. 4, if the algorithm begins with initial conditions: $\theta_1(0) = 2\pi \times 400 / f_s = 0.1\pi$ radians, $\theta_2(0) = 0.2\pi$ radians, $\theta_2(0) = 0.3\pi$ radians, it converges to local minima with wrong estimated frequencies when the fundamental frequency of the input signal is 1225 Hz. When this fundamental frequency steps to 1000 Hz and 875 Hz, respectively, the algorithm continuously converges to local minima with incorrectly estimated frequency values.

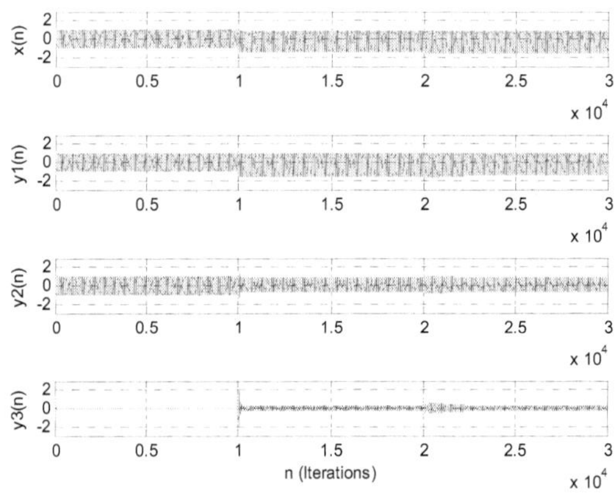

(a)

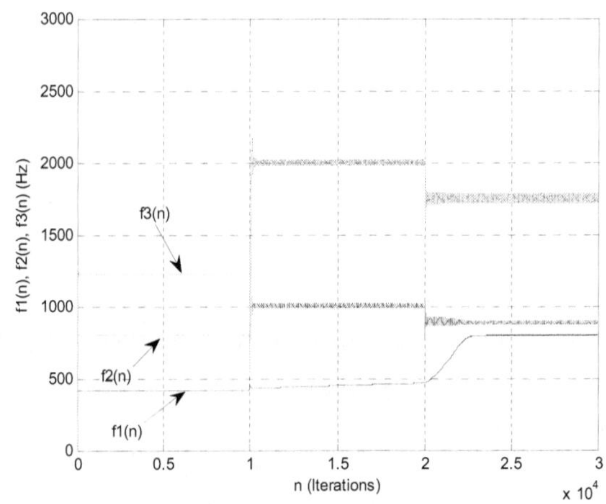

(b)

Fig. 4. Frequency tracking of a single with its fundamental component, second and third harmonics by using second-order adaptive IIR notch filters in cascade

(sinusoid: $A = 1$, $f = 1000$ Hz, $f_s = 8000$; adaptive notch filter: $r = 0.95$ and $\mu = 0.005$).

3. Adaptive harmonic IIR Notch filter structure and algorithm

As described in Section 2.2, a generic higher-order adaptive IIR notch filter suffers from slow convergence and local minimum convergence. To apply the filter successfully, we must have prior knowledge about the frequencies to be tracked. The problem becomes more severe again after the frequencies switch to different values. Using a grid search method to achieve the initial conditions may solve the problem but requires a huge number of computations. However, if we only focus on the fundamental frequency tracking and estimation, this problem can significantly be alleviated.

3.1 Harmonic IIR notch filter structure

Consider a measured signal $x(n)$ containing a fundamental frequency component and its harmonics up to M th order as

$$x(n) = \sum_{m=1}^{M} A_m \cos[2\pi(mf)n / f_s + \alpha_m] + v(n) \tag{10}$$

where A_m, mf, and α_m are the magnitude, frequency (Hz), and phase angle of the m th harmonic component, respectively. To estimate the fundamental frequency in such harmonic frequency environment, we can apply a harmonic IIR notch filter with a structure illustrated in Fig. 5 for the case of $M = 3$ (three harmonics).

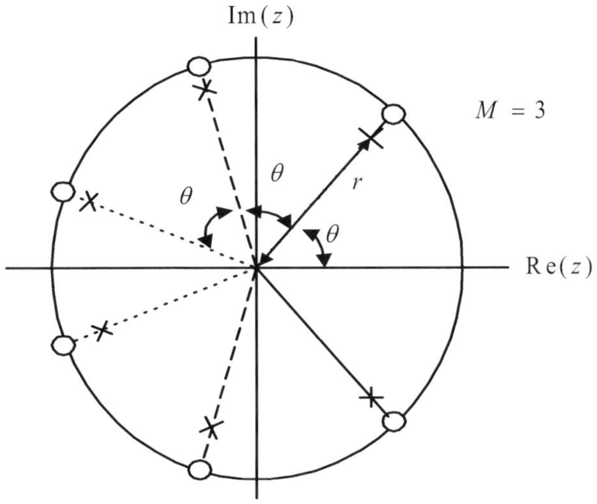

Fig. 5. Pole-zero plot for the harmonic IIR notch filter for $M = 3$

As shown in Fig. 5, to construct a notch filter transfer function, two constrained pole-zero pairs (Nehorai, 1985) with their angles equal to $\pm m\theta$ (multiple of the fundamental frequency angle θ) relative to the horizontal axis are placed on the pole-zero plot for $m=1,2,\cdots,M$, respectively. Hence, we can construct M second-order IIR sub-filters. In a cascaded form (Kwan & Martin, 1989), we have

$$H(z)=H_1(z)H_2(z)\cdots H_M(z)=\prod_{m=1}^{M}H_m(z) \tag{11}$$

where $H_m(z)$ denotes the mth second-order IIR sub-filter whose transfer function is defined as

$$H_m(z)=\frac{1-2z^{-1}\cos(m\theta)+z^{-2}}{1-2rz^{-1}\cos(m\theta)+r^2z^{-2}} \tag{12}$$

We express the output $y_m(n)$ from the mth sub-filter with an adaptive parameter $\theta(n)$ as

$$y_m(n)=y_{m-1}(n)-2\cos[m\theta(n)]y_{m-1}(n-1)+y_{m-1}(n-2)+2r\cos[m\theta(n)]y_m(n-1)-r^2y_m(n-2) \tag{13}$$

$$m=1,2,\cdots,M$$

with $y_0(n)=x(n)$. From (12), the transfer function has only one adaptive parameter $\theta(n)$ and has zeros on the unit circle resulting in infinite-depth notches. Similarly, we require $0<<r<1$ for achieving narrowband notches. When r is close to 1, its 3-dB notch bandwidth can be approximated by $BW\approx 2(1-r)$ radians. The MSE function at the final stage, $E[y_M^2(n)]=E[e^2(n)]$, is minimized, where $e(n)=y_M(n)$. It is important to notice that once the single adaptive parameter $\theta(n)$ is adapted to the angle corresponding to the fundamental frequency, each $m\theta(n)$ ($m=2,3,\cdots,M$) will automatically lock to its harmonic frequency. To examine the convergence property, we write the mean square error (MSE) function (Chicharo & Ng, 1990) below:

$$E\left[e^2(n)\right]=E\left[y_M^2(n)\right]=\frac{1}{2\pi j}\oint\left|\prod_{m=1}^{M}\frac{1-2z^{-1}\cos[m\theta(n)]+z^{-2}}{1-2rz^{-1}\cos[m\theta(n)]+r^2z^{-2}}\right|^2\Phi_{xx}\frac{dz}{z} \tag{14}$$

where Φ_{xx} is the power spectrum of the input signal. Since the MSE function in (14) is a nonlinear function of adaptive parameter θ, it may contain local minima. A closed form solution of (14) is difficult to achieve. However, we can examine the MSE function via a numerical example. Fig. 6 shows the plotted MSE function versus θ for a range from 0 to π/M radians [0 to $f_s/(2M)$ Hz] assuming that all harmonics are within the Nyquist limit for the following conditions: $M=3$, $r=0.95$, $f_a=1000$ Hz, $f_s=8000$ Hz (sampling rate), signal to noise power ratio (SNR)=22 dB, and 400 filter output samples. Based on Fig. 6, we observe that there exit four (4) local minima in which one (1) global minimum is located at 1 kHz. If we let the adaptation initially start from any point inside the global minimum valley (frequency capture range), the adaptive harmonic IIR notch filter will converge to the global minimum of the MSE error function.

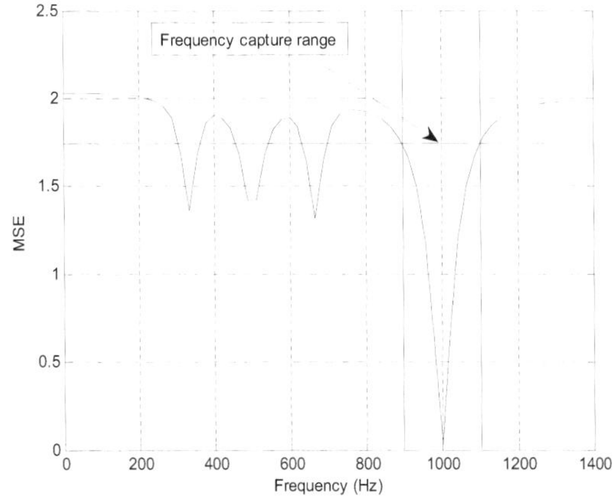

Fig. 6. Error surface of the harmonic IIR notch filter for $M = 3$ and $r = 0.95$

3.2 Adaptive harmonic IIR notch filter algorithms

Similar to Section 2.2, we can derive the LMS algorithm (Tan & Jiang, 2009a, 2009b) by taking the derivative of the instantaneous output power $e^2(n) = y_M^2(n)$ and substituting the result to zero. We achieve

$$\theta(n+1) = \theta(n) - 2\mu y_M(n)\beta_M(n) \tag{15}$$

where the gradient function $\beta_m(n) = \partial y_m(n) / \partial\theta(n)$ is recursively computed as

$$\begin{aligned}\beta_m(n) &= \beta_{m-1}(n) - 2\cos[m\theta(n)]\beta_{m-1}(n-1) + 2m\sin[m\theta(n)]y_{m-1}(n-1) + \beta_{m-1}(n-2) \\ &\quad + 2r\cos[m\theta(n)]\beta_m(n-1) - r^2\beta_m(n-2) - 2rm\sin[m\theta(n)]y_m(n-1)\end{aligned} \tag{16}$$

$$m = 1, 2, \cdots, M$$

with $\beta_0(n) = \partial y_0(n) / \partial\theta(n) = \partial x(n) / \partial\theta(n) = 0$, $\beta_0(n-1) = \beta_0(n-2) = 0$.

To prevent local minima convergence, the algorithm will start with an optimal initial value θ_0, which is coarsely searched over the frequency range: $\theta = \pi / (180M)$, ..., $179\pi / (180M)$, as follows:

$$\theta_0 = \underset{0<\theta<\pi/M}{\arg} (\min E[e^2(n,\theta)]) \tag{17}$$

where the estimated MSE function, $E[e^2(n,\theta)])$, can be determined by using a block of N signal samples:

$$E[e^2(n,\theta)]) \approx \frac{1}{N}\sum_{i=0}^{N-1} y_M^2(n-i,\theta) \tag{18}$$

There are two problems depicted in Fig. 7 as an example. When the fundamental frequency switches from 875 Hz to 1225 Hz, the algorithm starting at the location of 875 Hz on the MSE function corresponding to 1225 Hz will converge to the local minimum at 822 Hz. On the other hand, when the fundamental frequency switches from 1225 Hz to 1000 Hz, the algorithm will suffer a slow convergence rate due to a small gradient value of the MSE function in the neighborhood at the location of 1225 Hz. We will solve the first problem in this section and fix the second problem in next section.

To prevent the problem of local minima convergence due to the change of a fundamental frequency, we monitor the global minimum by comparing a frequency deviation

$$\Delta f = | f(n) - f_0 | \tag{19}$$

with a maximum allowable frequency deviation chosen below:

$$\Delta f_{\max} = 0.5 \times (0.5BW) \tag{20}$$

where $f_0 = 0.5 f_s \theta_0 / \pi$ Hz is the pre-scanned optimal frequency via (17) and (18); BW is the 3-dB bandwidth of the notch filter, which is approximated by $BW = (1-r) f_s / \pi$ in Hz. If

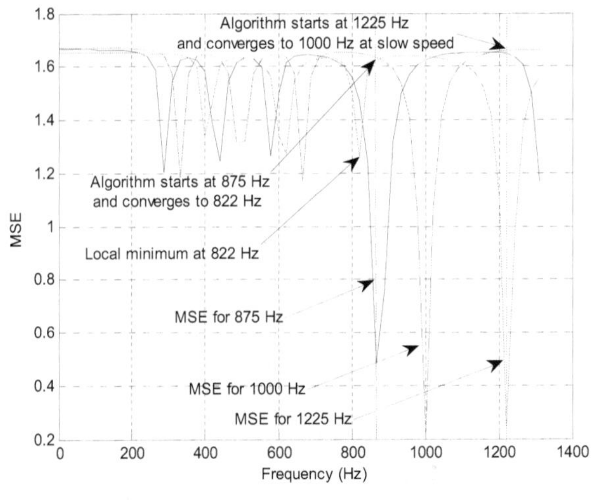

Fig. 7. MSE functions for the fundamental frequencies, 875 Hz, 1000 Hz, and 1225 Hz ($M = 3$, $r = 0.96$, $N = 200$, and $f_s = 8$ kHz)

$\Delta f > \Delta f_{\max}$, the adaptive algorithm may possibly converge to its local minima. Then the adaptive parameter $\theta(n)$ should be reset to its new estimated optimal value θ_0 using (17) and (18) and then the algorithm will resume frequency tracking in the neighborhood of the global minimum. The LMS type algorithm is listed in Table 1.

Step 1: Determine the initial θ_0 using (17) and (18):
Search for $\theta_0 = \underset{0<\theta<\pi/M}{\arg} (\min E[e^2(n,\theta)])$ for $\theta = \pi/(180M),\cdots,179\pi/(180M)$
Set the initial condition: $\theta(0)=\theta_0$ and $f_0 = 0.5 f_s \theta_0 / \pi$ Hz
Step 2: Apply the LMS algorithm:
For $m = 1,2,\cdots,M$
$y_m(n) = y_{m-1}(n) - 2\cos(m\theta) y_{m-1}(n-1) + y_{m-1}(n-2) + 2r\cos(m\theta) y_m(n-1) - r^2 y_m(n-2)$
$\beta_m(n) = \beta_{m-1}(n) - 2\cos[m\theta(n)]\beta_{m-1}(n-1) + 2m\sin[m\theta(n)] y_{m-1}(n-1) + \beta_{m-1}(n-2)$
$+ 2r\cos[m\theta(n)]\beta_m(n-1) - r^2\beta_m(n-2) - 2rm\sin[m\theta(n)] y_m(n-1)$
$\theta(n+1) = \theta(n) - 2\mu y_M(n)\beta_M(n)$
Step 3: Convert $\theta(n)$ to the desired estimated fundamental frequency in Hz:
$f(n) = 0.5 f_s \theta(n)/\pi$
Step 4: Monitor the global minimum:
if $\lvert f(n) - f_0 \rvert > \Delta f_{\max}$, go to step 1
otherwise continue Step 2

Table 1. Adaptive Harmonic IIR notch LMS algorithm

3.3 Convergence performance analysis

We focus on determining a simple and useful upper bound for (15) using the approach in references (Handel & Nehorai, 1994; Petraglia, et al, 1994; Stoica & Nehorai, 1998; Xiao, et al, 2001). For simplicity, we omit the second and higher order terms in the Taylor series expansion of the filter transfer function. We achieve the following results:

$$H(e^{j\omega}, m\theta) \approx H_\omega(m\theta)(\omega - m\theta) \tag{21}$$

where

$$H_\omega(m\theta) = \frac{-2\sin(m\theta)}{(1-r)(e^{jm\theta} - re^{-jm\theta})} \prod_{k=1,k\neq m}^{M} H_k(e^{jm\theta}) = B(m\theta)\angle\phi_m \tag{22}$$

The magnitude and phase of $H_\omega(m\theta)$ in (22) are defined below:

$$B(m\theta) = \lvert H_\omega(m\theta) \rvert \text{ and } \phi_m = \angle H_\omega(m\theta) \tag{23}$$

Considering the input signal $x(n)$ in (10), we now can approximate the harmonic IIR notch filter output as

$$y_M(n) = \sum_{m=1}^{M} m A_m B(m\theta) \cos[(m\theta)n + \alpha_m + \phi_m]\delta_\theta(n) + v_1(n) \tag{24}$$

where $v_1(n)$ is the filter output noise and note that

$$\omega - m\theta = m[\theta(n) - \theta] = m\delta_\theta(n) \tag{25}$$

To derive the gradient filter transfer function defined as $S_M(z) = \beta_M(z) / X(z)$, we obtain the following recursion:

$$S_m(z) = H_m(z)S_{m-1}(z) + \frac{2mz^{-1}\sin(m\theta)[1 - rH_m(z)]}{1 - 2r\cos(m\theta)z^{-1} + r^2z^{-2}} H_1(z)\cdots H_{m-1}(z) \tag{26}$$

Expanding (26) leads to

$$S_M(z) = \sum_{n=1}^{M}\left[\prod_{k=1,k\neq n}^{M} H_k(z)\right]\frac{2\times n\sin(n\theta)z^{-1}}{1 - 2r\cos(n\theta)z^{-1} + r^2z^{-2}} - H(z)\sum_{n=1}^{M}\frac{2r\times n\sin(n\theta)z^{-1}}{1 - 2r\cos(n\theta)z^{-1} + r^2z^{-2}} \tag{27}$$

At the optimal points, $\omega = m\theta$, the first term in (27) is approximately constant, since we can easily verify that these points are essentially the centers of band-pass filters (Petranglia, et al, 1994). The second-term is zero due to $H(e^{jm\theta}) = 0$. Using (22) and (23), we can approximate the gradient filter frequency response at $\omega = m\theta$ as

$$S_M(e^{jm\theta}) = \left[\prod_{k=1,k\neq m}^{M} H_k(e^{jm\theta})\right]\frac{2\times m\sin(m\theta)}{(1-r)(e^{jm\theta} - re^{-jm\theta})} = mB(m\theta)\angle(\phi_m + \pi) \tag{28}$$

Hence, the gradient filter output can be approximated by

$$\beta_M(n) = \sum_{m=1}^{M} mB(m\theta)A_m\cos[(m\theta)n + \alpha_m + \phi_m + \pi] + v_2(n) \tag{29}$$

where $v_2(n)$ is the noise output from the gradient filter. Substituting (24) and (29) in (15) and assuming that the noise processes of $v_1(n)$ and $v_2(n)$ are uncorrelated with the first summation terms in (24) and (29), it leads to the following:

$$E[\delta_\theta(n+1)] = E[\delta_\theta(n)] - E[2\mu y_M(n)\beta_M(n)] \tag{30}$$

$$E[\delta_\theta(n+1)] = E[\delta_\theta(n)] + \mu\sum_{m=1}^{M} m^2A_m^2B^2(m\theta)E[\delta_\theta(n)] - 2\mu E[v_1(n)v_2(n)] \tag{31}$$

$$E[v_1(n)v_2(n)] = \frac{\sigma_v^2}{2\pi j}\oint H(z)S_M(1/z)\frac{dz}{z} \tag{32}$$

where σ_v^2 is the input noise power in (10). To yield a stability bound, it is required that

$$\left|1 + \mu\sum_{m=1}^{M} m^2A_m^2B^2(m\theta)\right| < 1 \tag{33}$$

Then we achieve the stability bound as

$$\mu(\theta) < 2 / \sum_{m=1}^{M} m^2 A_m^2 B^2(m\theta) \tag{34}$$

The last term in (31) is not zero, but we can significantly suppress it by using a varying convergence factor developed later in this section. Since evaluating (34) still requires knowledge of all the harmonic amplitudes, we simplify (34) by assuming that each frequency component has the same amplitude to obtain

$$\mu(\theta) < M / \sigma_x^2 \sum_{m=1}^{M} m^2 B^2(m\theta) \tag{35}$$

where σ_x^2 is the power of the input signal. Practically, for the given M, we can numerically search for the upper bound $\mu_{\max}$ which works for the required frequency range, that is,

$$\mu_{\max} = \min_{0<\theta<\pi/M}[\arg(u(\theta))] \tag{36}$$

Fig. 8 plots the upper bounds based on (36) versus M using $\sigma_x^2 = 1$ for $r = 0.8$, $r = 0.9$, and $r = 0.96$, respectively.

We can see that a smaller upper bound will be required when r and M increase. We can also observe another key feature described in Fig. 9.

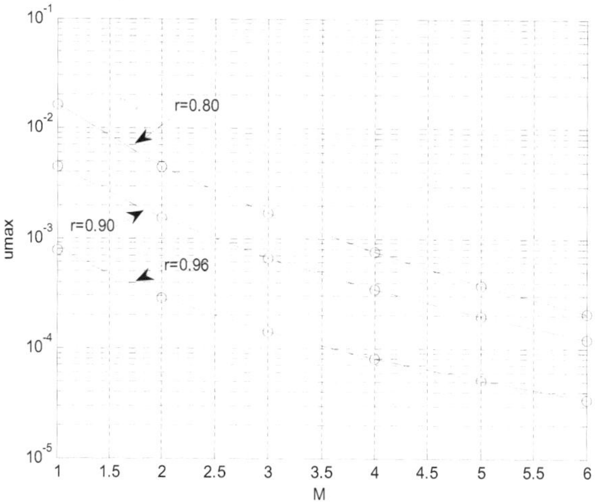

Fig. 8. Plots of the upper bounds in Equation (36) versus M using $\sigma_x^2 = 1$.

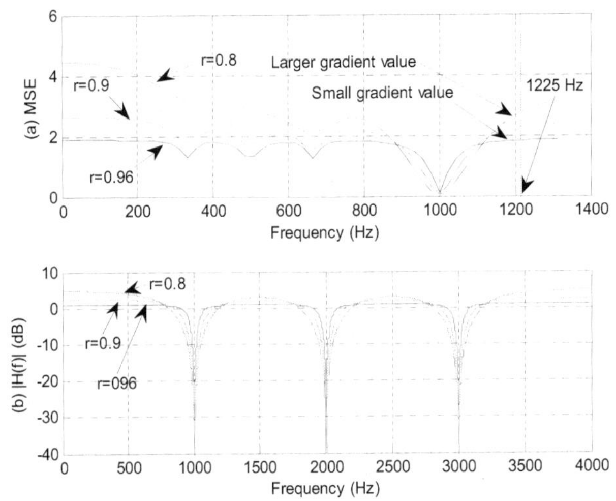

Fig. 9. (a) MSE functions; (b) Magnitude frequency responses ($M=3$, $N=200$, $f_s=8$ kHz)

As shown in Fig. 9, when the pole radius r is much smaller than 1 ($r=0.8$), we will have a larger MSE function gradient starting at 1225 Hz and then the convergence speed will be increased. But using the smaller r will end up with a degradation of the notch filter frequency response, that is, a larger notch bandwidth. On the other hand, choosing r close to 1 ($r=0.96$) will maintain a narrow notch bandwidth but result in a slow convergence rate, since the algorithm begins with a small MSE function gradient value at 1225 Hz. Furthermore, we expect that when the algorithm approaches to its global minimum, the cross-correlation $c(n)$ between the final filter output $e(n)=y_M(n)$ and its delayed signal $y_M(n-1)$ becomes uncorrelated, that is, $c(n)=E[y_M(n)y_M(n-1)]\approx 0$. Hence, the cross-correlation measurement can be adopted to control the notch bandwidth and convergence factor. We propose the improved algorithm with varying bandwidth and convergence factor below:

$$c(n)=\lambda c(n)+(1-\lambda)y_M(n)y_M(n-1) \tag{37}$$

$$r(n)=r_{\min}+\Delta r\cdot e^{-\alpha|c(n)|} \tag{38}$$

$$\mu(n)=\mu_{\max}(1-e^{-\alpha|c(n)|}) \tag{39}$$

where $0<<\lambda<1$, $r_{\min}<r(n)\leq r_{\min}+\Delta r<1$ with $r_{\min}=0.8$ (still providing a good notch filter frequency response), $\mu_{\max}$ is the upper bound for $r(n)=r_{\min}+\Delta r$, and α is the damping constant, which controls the speed of change for the notch bandwidth and convergence factor. From (37), (38), and (39), our expectation is as follows: when the algorithm begins to work, the cross-correlation $c(n)$ has a large value due to a fact that the filter output contains fundamental and harmonic signals. The pole radius $r(n)$ in (38) starts with a smaller value to increase the gradient value of the MSE function at the same time the

step size $u(n)$ in (39) changes to a larger value. Considering both factors, the algorithm achieves a fast convergence speed. On the other hand, as $c(n)$ approach to zeroe, $r(n)$ will increases its value to preserve a narrow notch bandwidth while $u(n)$ will decay to zero to reduce a misadjustment as described in (31).
To include (37), (38), and (39) in the improved algorithm, the additional computational complexity over the algorithm proposed in the reference (Tan & Jiang, 2009a, 2009b) for processing each input sample requires six (6) multiplications, four (4) additions, two (2) absolute operations, and one (1) exponential function operation. The new improved algorithm is listed in Table 2.

Step 1: Determine the initial θ_0 using (17) and (18):
Search for $\theta_0 = \underset{0<\theta<\pi/M}{\arg}(\min E[e^2(n,\theta)])$ for $\theta = \pi/(180M), \cdots, 179\pi/(180M)$
Set the initial condition: $\theta(0) = \theta_0$ and $f_0 = 0.5 f_s \theta_0 / \pi$ Hz,
u_{max}, r_{min}, λ, α
Step 2: Apply the LMS algorithm:
For $m = 1, 2, \cdots, M$
$y_m(n) = y_{m-1}(n) - 2\cos(m\theta) y_{m-1}(n-1) + y_{m-1}(n-2)$
$+ 2r(n)\cos(m\theta) y_m(n-1) - r^2(n) y_m(n-2)$
$\beta_m(n) = \beta_{m-1}(n) - 2\cos[m\theta(n)]\beta_{m-1}(n-1) + 2m\sin[m\theta(n)] y_{m-1}(n-1) + \beta_{m-1}(n-2)$
$+ 2r(n)\cos[m\theta(n)]\beta_m(n-1) - r^2(n)\beta_m(n-2) - 2r(n) m \sin[m\theta(n)] y_m(n-1)$
$c(n) = \lambda c(n) + (1-\lambda) y_M(n) y_M(n-1)$
$r(n) = r_{min} + \Delta r \cdot e^{-\alpha \lvert c(n) \rvert}$
$\mu(n) = \mu_{max}(1 - e^{-\alpha \lvert c(n) \rvert})$
$\theta(n+1) = \theta(n) - 2\mu(n) y_M(n) \beta_M(n)$
Step 3: Convert $\theta(n)$ to the desired estimated fundamental frequency in Hz:
$f(n) = 0.5 f_s \theta(n) / \pi$
Step 4: Monitor the global minimum:
if $\lvert f(n) - f_0 \rvert > \Delta f_{max}$, go to step 1
otherwise continue Step 2

Table 2. New adaptive harmonic IIR notch LMS algorithm with varying notch bandwidth and convergence factor

3.4 Simulation results

In our simulations, an input signal containing up to third harmonics is used, that is,

$$x(n) = \sin(2\pi \times f_a \times n / f_s) + 0.5\cos(2\pi \times 2 f_a \times n / f_s) - 0.25\cos(2\pi \times 3 f_a \times n / f_s) + v(n) \quad (41)$$

where f_a is the fundamental frequency and $f_s = 8000$ Hz. The fundamental frequency changes for every $n = 2000$ samples. Our developed algorithm uses the following parameters:

$$M = 3,\ N = 200,\ \alpha = 10,\ c(0) = 0.2,\ \lambda = 0.997,$$

$$r_{\min} = 0.8\,,\ \Delta r = 0.16$$

The upper bound $\mu_{\max} = 2.14 \times 10^{-4}$ is numerically searched using (35) for $r = 0.96$. The behaviors of the developed algorithm are demonstrated in Figs. 10-13. Fig. 10a shows a plot of the MSE function to locate the initial parameter, $\theta(0) = 2\pi \times 1222 / f_s = 0.3055\pi$ when the fundamental frequency is 1225 Hz. Figs. 10b and 10c show the plots of MSE functions for resetting initial parameters $\theta(0) = 0.25\pi$ and $\theta(0) = 0.22225\pi$ when the fundamental frequency switches to 1000 Hz and then 875 Hz, respectively. Fig. 11 depicts the noisy input signal and each sub-filter output. Figs. 12a to 12c depicts the cross correlation $c(n)$, pole radius $r(n)$, and adaptive step size $\mu(n)$. Fig. 12d shows the tracked fundamental frequencies. As expected, when the algorithm converges, $c(n)$ approaches to zero (uncorrelated), $r(n)$ becomes $r_{\max} = 0.96$ to offer a narrowest notch bandwidth. At the same time, $\mu(n)$ approaches to zero so that the misadjustment can be reduced. In addition, when

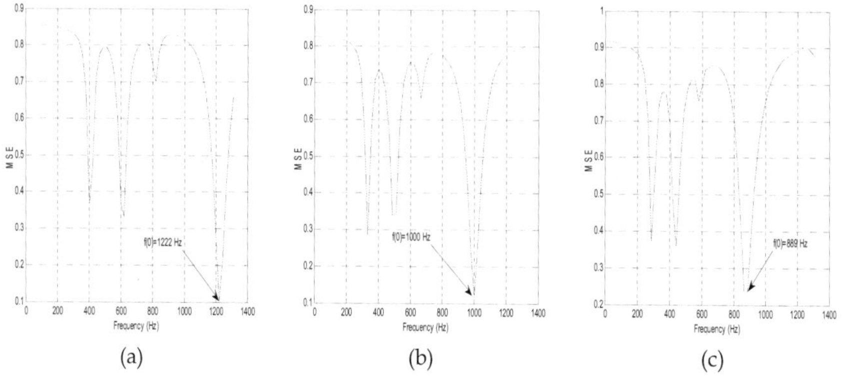

Fig. 10. Plots of MSE functions for searching the initial adaptive parameter

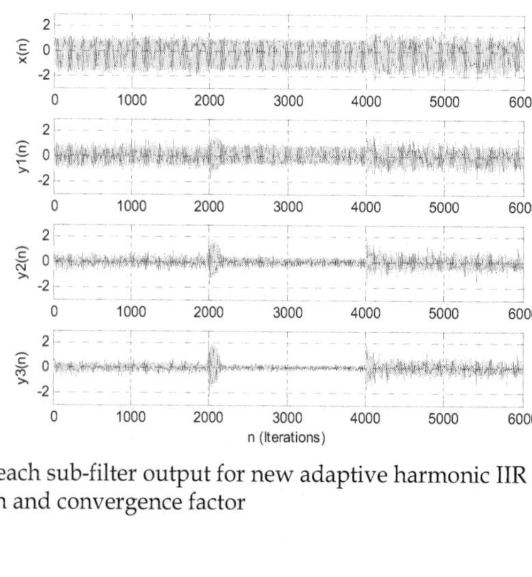

Fig. 11. Input and each sub-filter output for new adaptive harmonic IIR notch filter with varying bandwidth and convergence factor

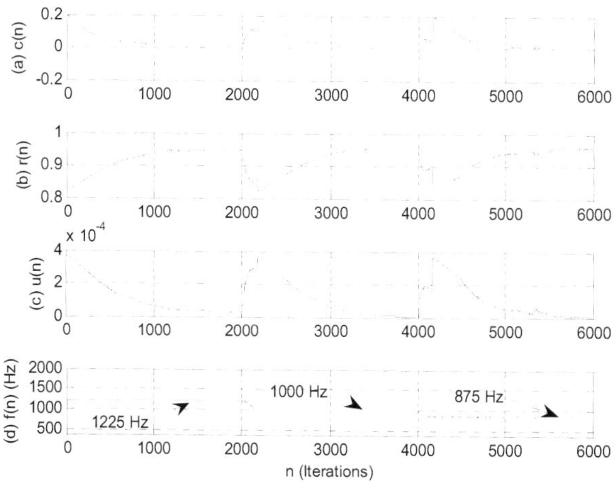

Fig. 12. (a) The cross correlation $c(n)$ between the notch filter output and its delayed output; (b) Varying notch filter parameter $r(n)$; (c) Varying convergence factor $\mu(n)$; (d) Tracked fundamental frequencies $f(n)$.

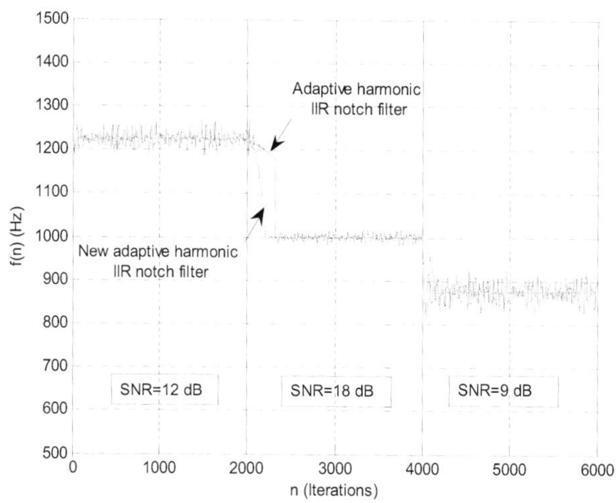

New algorithm: $\mu_{max} = 2.14 \times 10^{-4}$, $r_{min} = 0.8$ and $r_{max} = 0.96$

Algorithm (Tan & Jiang, 2009): $r = 0.96$ and $\mu = 2 \times 10^{-4}$

Fig. 13. Frequency tracking comparisons in the noise environment the frequency changes from 1225 Hz to 1000 Hz, the algorithm starts moving away from its original global minimum, since the MSE function is changed. Once the tracked frequency is moved beyond the maximum allowable frequency deviation $\Delta f_{\max}$, the algorithm relocates θ_0 and reset $\theta(n) = \theta_0$; and $\theta(n)$ is reset again after the frequency is switched from 1000 Hz to 875 Hz. The improved algorithm successfully tracks the signal fundamental frequency and its changes.

To compare with the algorithm recently proposed in the reference (Tan & Jiang, 2009b), we apply the same input signal to the adaptive harmonic IIR notch filter using a fixed notch bandwidth ($r = 0.96$) and a fixed convergence factor, $\mu = 2.14 \times 10^{-4}$. As shown in Fig. 13, the improved algorithm is much robust to noise under various SNR conditions. This is because when the algorithm converges, the varying convergence factor approaches to zero to offer a smaller misadjustment.

Fig. 14 shows the comparison of standard deviation of the estimated frequency between two algorithms, where we investigate the following condition: $f_a = 1000$ Hz, $M = 3$ using 5000 iterations. For the previous algorithm, we use $r = 0.96$ and $\mu = 10^{-4}$ while for the improved algorithm, all the parameters are the same except that $\mu_{\max} = 10^{-4}$. For each algorithm, we obtain the results using 50 independent runs under each given signal to noise ratio (SNR). From Fig. 14, it is evident that the developed adaptive harmonic IIR notch filter with varying notch bandwidth and convergence factor offers a significant improvement.

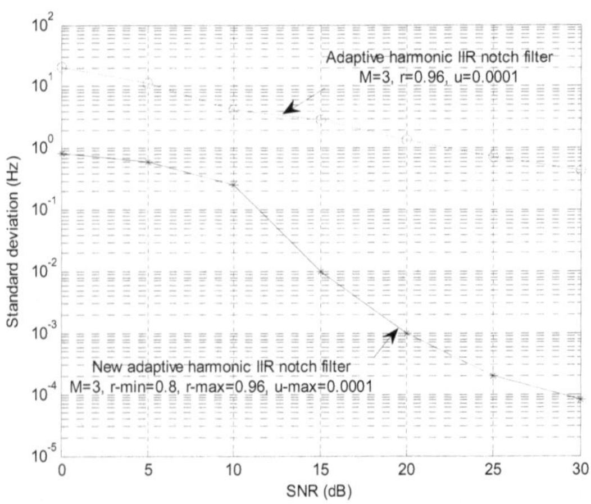

Fig. 14. Tracking error performance of the proposed algorithm

4. Conclusion

In this chapter, we have reviewed the standard adaptive IIR notch filters for applications of single frequency and multiple frequency estimation as well as tracking in the harmonic noise environment. The problems of slow convergence speed and local minima convergence are addressed when applying a higher-order adaptive IIR notch filter for tracking multiple frequencies or harmonic frequencies. We have demonstrated that the adaptive harmonic IIR notch filter offers an effective solution for frequency estimation and tracking in a harmonic noise environment. In addition, we have derived a simple and useful stability bound for the adaptive harmonic IIR notch filter. In order to achieve the noise robustness and accuracy of frequency tracking in the noisy environment, we have developed an improved adaptive harmonic IIR notch filter with varying notch bandwidth and convergence factor. The developed algorithm is able to prevent its local minima convergence even when the signal fundamental frequency switches in the tracking process.

5. Acknowledgment

This work was supported in part by the Purdue University 2010 Summer Faculty Research Grant, Indiana, USA.

6. References

Nehorai, A. (1985). A Minimal Parameter Adaptive Notch Filter with Constrained Poles and Zeros. *IEEE Trans. Acoust., Speech, Signal Process.*, Vol. 33, No. 4, pp. 983-996, August 1985.

Kwan, T. & Martin, K. (1989). Adaptive Detection and Enhancement of Multiple Sinusoids Using a Cascade IIR Filter. *IEEE Trans Circuits Syst.*, Vol. 36, No. 7, pp. 937-947, July 1989.

Chicharo, J. & Ng, T. (1990). Gradient-based Adaptive IIR Notch Filtering for Frequency Estimation. *IEEE Trans. Acoust., Speech, Signal Process.*, Vol. 38, No. 5, pp. 769-777, May 1990.

Zhou, J. & Li, G. (2004). Plain Gradient-based Direct Frequency Estimation Using Second-order Constrained Adaptive IIR Notch filter. *Electronics Letters*, vol. 40, No. 5, pp. 351-352, March 2004.

Xiao, Y., Takeshita, Y. & Shida, K. (2001). Steady-state Analysis of a Plain Gradient Algorithm for a Second-order Adaptive IIR Notch Filter with Constrained Poles and Zeros. *IEEE Trans. on Circuits and Systems-II: Analog and Digital Signal Processing*, Vol. 48, No. 7, pp 733-740, July 2001.

Tan, L. & Jiang, J. (2009). Novel Adaptive IIR Notch Filter for Frequency Estimation and Tracking. *IEEE Signal Processing Magazine*, Vol. 26, Issue 6, pp. 168-189, November 2009.

Tan, L. & Jiang, J. (2009). Real-Time Frequency Tracking Using Novel Adaptive Harmonic IIR Notch Filter. *the Technology Interface Journal*, Vol. 9, No. 2, Spring 2009

Tan, L. (2007). *Digital Signal Processing: Fundamentals and Applications*. pp. 358-362, ISBN: 978-0-12-374090-8, Elsevier/Academic Press, 2007.

Stoica, P., & Nehorai, A. (1998). Performance Analysis of an Adaptive Notch Filter with Constrained Poles and Zeros. *IEEE Trans. Acoust., Speech, Signal Process.*, Vol. 36, No. 6, pp. 911-919, June 1998.

Handel, P. & Nehorai, A. (1994). Tracking Analysis of an Adaptive Notch Filterwith Constrained Poles and Zeros. *IEEE Trans. Signal Process.*, Vol. 42, No. 2, pp. 281-291, February 1994.

Petraglia, M., Shynk, J. & Mitra, S. (1994). Stability Bounds and Steady-state Coefficient Variance for a Second-order Adaptive IIR Notch Filter. *IEEE Trans. Signal Process.*, Vol. 42, No. 7, pp. 1841-1845, July 1994.

14

Echo Cancellation for Hands-Free Systems

Artur Ferreira and Paulo Marques
Instituto de Telecomunicações
Instituto Superior de Engenharia de Lisboa
Portugal

1. Introduction

Echo is defined as the delayed and attenuated version of the original signal produced by some device, such as a loudspeaker. As a consequence a person listens to a delayed replica of its own voice signal. This is an undesired effect that appears whenever the output signal is fed back into the system's input and it can be quite disturbing on voice conversations.

Echo arises in long distance communication scenarios such as hands-free systems Hänsler (1994); Jeannès et al. (2001); Liu (1994), *voice over internet protocol* (VoIP) Witowsky (1999), teleconferencing Kuo & Pan (1994), mobile phone conversation, and satellite communications among others.

In order to minimize or even remove the presence of echo in communications, echo suppression and echo cancellation techniques have been proposed in the last three decades Sondhi (2006). An echo suppressor is a voice-operated switch that disconnects the communication path (or introduces a very large attenuation) whenever some decision mechanism indicates that we are in the presence of echo. The emitting circuit is disconnected whenever we have signal on the reception part of the circuit; the reception circuit is disconnected whenever we have signal emission. Their behavior is not adequate for cross conversation (full duplex) scenarios. Echo suppressors were the first approach to this problem. In the last decade, due to their unsatisfactory results, they have been replaced by digital echo cancelers. An echo canceler device, as opposed to an echo suppressor, does not interrupt the echo path; it operates by removing (subtracting) the detected echo replicas from the information signal. The term usually coined for the cancellation of echoes with acoustic coupling is *acoustic echo cancellation* (AEC) Gilloire & Hänsler (1994).

In the past years, adaptive filtering techniques Haykin (2002); Sayed (2003); Widrow & Stearns (1985) have been employed for the purpose of AEC Breining (1999); Widrow et al. (1975). Typically, these techniques rely on the use of *finite impulse response* (FIR) filters Oppenheim & Schafer (1999); Veen & Haykin (1999) whose coefficients are updated along the time by an efficient rule guided by some statistical criterion. Usually, one employs a gradient descent technique in order to minimize some cost (error) function. The most popular of these techniques is the Widrow-Hoff *least mean squares* (LMS) algorithm as well as its variants, that minimize the *mean square error* (MSE) between two signals. Moreover, in many cases such as real-time conversations over mobile phones, AEC algorithms must run in real-time to be useful. We thus have the need for efficient implementations of echo cancellation techniques on digital embedded devices like *field programmable gate array* (FPGA) and/or *digital signal processor* (DSP), to fulfill real-time requirements of many applications, these days.

This chapter reviews and compares existing solutions for AEC based on adaptive filtering algorithms. We also focus on real-time solutions for this problem on DSP platforms. Section 2 states the echo cancellation problem. Section 3 reviews some basic concepts of adaptive filtering techniques and algorithms. Section 4 describes some existing solutions for AEC. Section 5 details real-time implementations of AEC systems with DSP from Texas Instruments. Section 6 presents some experimental results and Section 7 ends the chapter with some concluding remarks and future directions and challenges for AEC techniques.

2. The echo cancellation problem

2.1 What is echo?

Echo signal is defined as the delayed and attenuated version of the original signal produced by some device, such as a loudspeaker. Lets consider some signal $x(t)$ and its attenuated and delayed version

$$x_d(t) = \alpha x(t - t_d), \tag{1}$$

where α is the attenuation factor and t_d is time delay of the echo replica. Whenever we have a delay (t_d) larger than 35 ms, echo becomes perceptible to the listener Oh et al. (1994). As t_d increases, the more annoying is the echo effect. Larger values of t_d imply that we should have larger attenuation on the echo signal to minimize the undesired echo effect. For satellite communications, a typical delay value between two end-points is about 270 ms. This leads to a total round trip delay of at least 540 ms, including the terrestrial circuits Texas Instruments (1986). In these situations, we must apply a large attenuation to the echo signal, to make conversation possible. The worst case happens when the feedback is sustained (non-decaying); this makes the most annoying effect named as howling and it happens whenever α is not small enough.

The existence of undesired echo is a well-known problem that frequently arises in telecommunications, being most probable to happen in long distance communications and most problematic in voice conversations. Therefore, echo cancellation is needed for long-distance communications which have shown a growing use in the last decade. For instance, in the VoIP application the network load changes the transmission time and the time delay of the echo(es). Another challenging problem is that the echo path is not static because the channel characteristics change over time, due to many factors such as the distance between the loudspeaker and the microphone. Fig. 1 shows the existence of acoustic echo. The received signal from the far end talker, $r[n]$, is transmitted through the loudspeaker to the near end. A version of this signal is received by the microphone (due, for example, to direct coupling between the loudspeaker and the microphone), together with the near end speech, constituting the received signal from the acoustic channel, $r_A[n]$. The echo path is defined by functions f and g on both ends; these functions represent the linear or non-linear behavior of the echo path.

2.2 Sources of echo

In the telecommunications field, we can find many sources of echo caused by long distance communications and/or the hands-free voice conversation setup Sondhi (2006). For instance we have echoes:

- on the hands-free VoIP setup, in which we have a microphone and a loudspeaker;
- on a (satellite) mobile telephone connection;

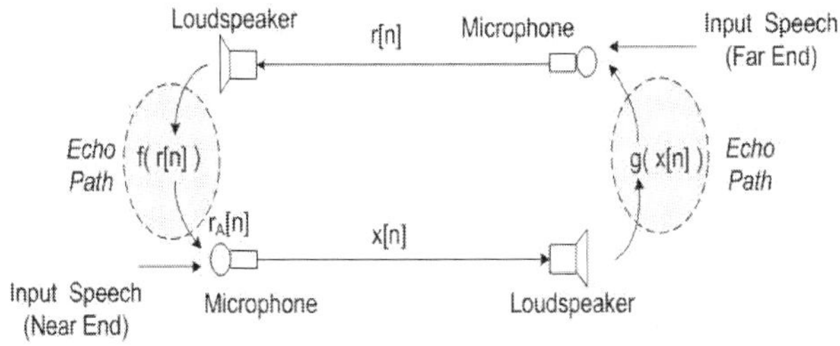

Fig. 1. The acoustic echo scenario. A version of the received signal trough the loudspeaker is fed back into the microphone re-entering the system leading to undesired feedback. The worst case happens when the feedback is sustained (non-decaying); this makes the most annoying effect named as howling. Functions f and g represent the echo path on both ends.

- whenever someone makes a speech on some room; each room has its own acoustic conditions leading to echo Antweller & Symanzik (1995);
- the two-wire/four-wire conversion Sondhi & Berkeley (1980) in telephony carried out by a hybrid circuit on a telephone line, as depicted in Fig. 2, in which we consider a simplified connection between two subscribers S_1 and S_2.

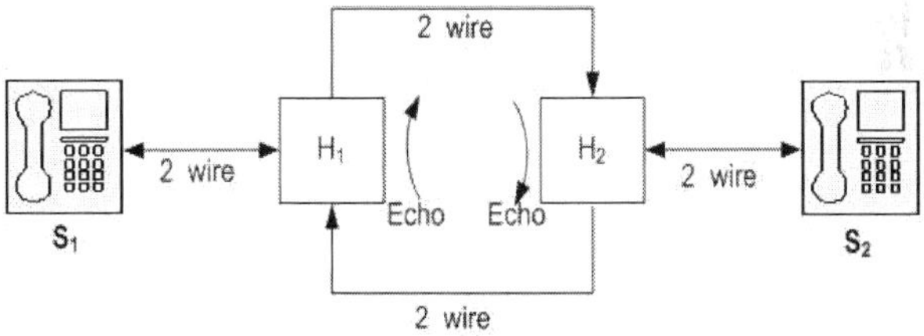

Fig. 2. Simplified long distance connection between two subscribers, using a hybrid circuit for the two-wire/four-wire conversion. The impedance mismatch on the two-wire/four-wire conversion originates the return of a portion of the emitted signal. This causes echo on both ends of the conversation system.

The subscriber loop connects the analog telephone with a two-wire line. In order to establish a connection, the central office must connect the two-wire line from one subscriber to another. This way, long distance telephone connections are four-wire connections with two-wires for transmission and the other two for reception. The hybrid circuit is a device that establishes the connection and conversion between the two-wire and the four-wire circuits. The connection between S_1 and H_1 (or between S_2 and H_2) is a two-wire connection between the subscriber and the central office. Between central offices, we have four-wire connections (between H_1 and H_2). Each two-wire connection is usually designated as *the subscriber loop*; in this portion of the circuit, both directions of communication are supported in the same pair of wires.
The hybrid circuit H_1 converts the signal from S_2 to the two-wire connection to S_1, whitout back reflection of energy from this signal. In practice, this is not possible to accomplish because due to many varying characteristics such as the length of the subscriber loop, the individual subscriber devices and line impedance; these factors altogether inhibit the perfect separation between emission and reception signals. Since there is some energy reflection from

the emmited signal, as a consequence S_2 (or S_1) receives a delayed version of its own voice signal with some attenuation and distortion.
Applications such as hands-free telephony, tele-conferencing and video-conferencing require the use of *acoustic echo cancellation* (AEC) techniques to eliminate acoustic feedback from the loudspeaker to the microphone Gay & J.Benesty (2000).
Echo cancellation is usually achieved by using an adaptive filter which attempts to synthesize a replica of the echo signal and subtract it from the returned signal. An adaptive filter changes its coefficients along the time; as a consequence it changes its frequency response in order to satisfy the adaptation criterion. This is the principle illustrated in Fig. 3 in the AEC context. The adaptive filter operates on the voice signal and tries to replicate the echo signal, which is

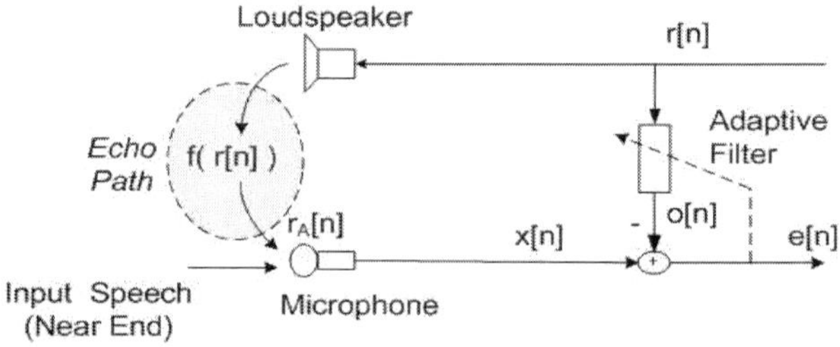

Fig. 3. The acoustic echo cancellation scenario for the setup of Fig. 1. Echo cancellation is achieved by using an adaptive filter which attempts to synthesize a replica of the echo signal and subtract it from the returned signal.

subtracted from the emitted signal. The adaptive filter imitates the echo path thus canceling its effects. In the case of the two-wire/four-wire conversion, depicted in Fig. 2, AEC is performed with the block diagram of Fig. 4.

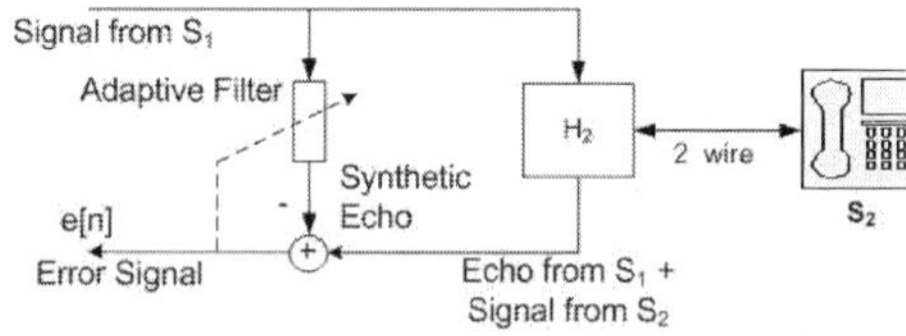

Fig. 4. Echo cancellation on the telephone line using an adaptive filter. The adaptive filter compensates the non-ideal behavior of the hybrid circuit.

The adaptive filter synthesizes a replica of the echo, which is subtracted from the returned signal. This removes/minimizes the echo whitout interrupting the echo path. The adaptive filter compensates the undesired effects of the non-ideal hybrid circuit.

3. Adaptive filtering techniques

In order to model the referred time-changing echo characteristics and to cancel its undesired effects on the conversation, adaptive filtering Haykin (2002); Sayed (2003); Widrow & Stearns (1985) has been used extensively in the last three decades (see for instance, Benesty et al. (2001); Greenberg (1998); J.Ni & Li (2010); Krishna et al. (2010); Marques et al. (1997); Sondhi & Berkeley (1980)). The main reasons for the success of adaptive filtering to solve the AEC problem are:

- its efficiency, allowing real-time implementations;
- its ability to cope with statistically changing environments;
- its adequate results in noisy environments.

Due to the time varying characteristics of the echo path and the devices in the circuit, it is not possible to cancel echo with (static) classic filtering which removes some frequency band. The filter coefficients and thus its frequency response must change along the time to efficiently model (imitate) the behavior of the echo path, thus leading to echo cancellation.

3.1 FIR and IIR filtering structures

A *finite impulse response* (FIR) filter Oppenheim & Schafer (1999); Veen & Haykin (1999) has difference equation given by

$$o[n] = \sum_{k=0}^{M-1} w_k x[n-k], \tag{2}$$

where w_k with $k \in \{0, \ldots, M-1\}$ are the filter coefficients and $x[n-k]$ are the (past) samples on the input of the filter. Using vector notation, we compute each output sample of the filter by the inner product between row vectors $\mathbf{w} = [w_0,\ w_1,\ \ldots, w_{M-1}]$ and $\mathbf{x} = [x[n],\ x[n-1], \ldots, x[n-(M-1)]]$,

$$o[n] = \mathbf{w}\mathbf{x}^T = \mathbf{x}\mathbf{w}^T. \tag{3}$$

The *infinite impulse response* (IIR) Oppenheim & Schafer (1999); Veen & Haykin (1999) difference equation is

$$o[n] = \sum_{k=0}^{M-1} w_k x[n-k] + \sum_{k=1}^{N-1} v_k o[n-k], \tag{4}$$

with feedback coefficients v_k. Depending on the value of the feedback coefficients, the filter can become an unstable system. In order to prevent this situation to happen, adaptive filtering algorithms with IIR filters must take additional measures to assure the stability of the filter. Fig. 5 depicts the FIR and IIR structures for digital filtering, corresponding to (2) and (4), respectively. In the case in which these structures are applied on adaptive filtering scenarios, the filter coefficients are periodically updated.

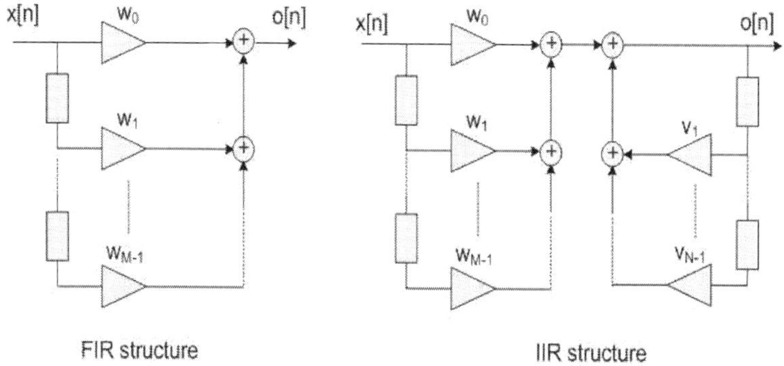

Fig. 5. FIR and IIR structures for digital filtering. When these structures are applied on adaptive filtering problems, their coefficients are time-changing, being updated by some rule.

3.1.1 Analysis on the z-plane

In the z-transform domain, the FIR filter has a rational transfer function

$$H(z) = \sum_{k=0}^{M-1} w_k z^{-k} = w_0 \prod_{k=1}^{M} (1 - q_k z^{-1}), \tag{5}$$

with M zeros represented by q_k, whereas a IIR filter has a transfer function

$$H(z) = \frac{\sum_{k=0}^{M-1} w_k z^{-k}}{1 - \sum_{k=1}^{N-1} v_k z^{-k}} = \frac{w_0 \prod_{k=1}^{M} (1 - q_k z^{-1})}{\prod_{k=1}^{N} (1 - r_k z^{-1})}, \tag{6}$$

with M zeros (given by q_k) and N poles (given by r_k). The zeros correspond to the direct connections between input and output whereas the poles indicate the feedback connections. It is well-known that the use of poles can lead to accomplish a given filter specification more easily that using only zeros. However, for causal filters poles cause instability whenever placed outside the unit circle in the z-plane; the adaptation algorithm has to assure stability. IIR filters are, by definition, systems with infinite impulse response and thus we can theoretically accommodate any echo path of largest length. In the case of IIR filters, the adaptive filtering algorithm must take additional steps in order to keep the N poles of the filter inside the unit circle on the z-plane. Since a FIR filter is stable independently of its coefficients, adaptive filtering algorithms usually employ FIR filtering instead of IIR filtering.

3.2 Statistical and adaptive filtering

Fig. 6 shows the block diagram of a typical statistical filtering problem. The adaptive filter operates on the sequence $x[n]$ which is made up by the desired signal with uncorrelated aditive white noise. The impulse response of the adaptive filter is given by $w[n]$. At each time instant n, the filter outputs $o[n]$ which is an estimate of the desired response $d[n]$. Since both these signals are instances of stochastic processes, the error estimate $e[n]$ has specific statistical properties. The goal of statistical filtering is to minimize the estimation error, according to some statistical criterion, like the *mean square error* (MSE) between the output and the desired signal.

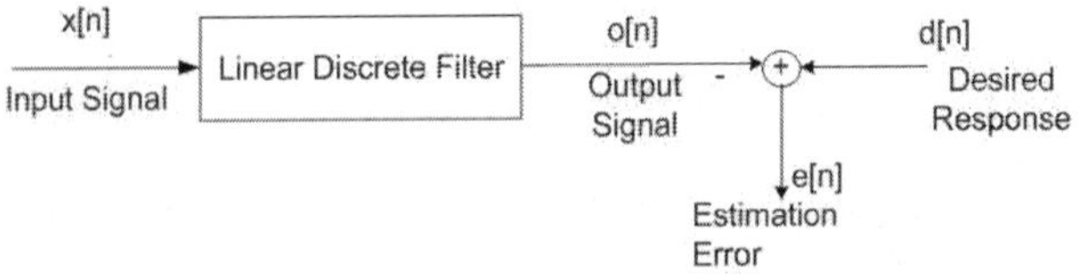

Fig. 6. Block diagram of statistical filtering. The discrete filter is applied to the input signal $x[n]$ and produces output $o[n]$, which is compared against the desired signal $d[n]$. The error signal (to be minimized) is the difference between $o[n]$ and $d[n]$. The discrete filter is learned with the statistics from the input signal.

Fig. 7 shows the block diagram of a typical adaptive filtering application. The error signal is used as input to the coefficient update algorithm of the adaptive (FIR or IIR) filter. As time goes by and samples move along vector $\mathbf{x}$, the coefficients in vector $\mathbf{w}$ are updated by some

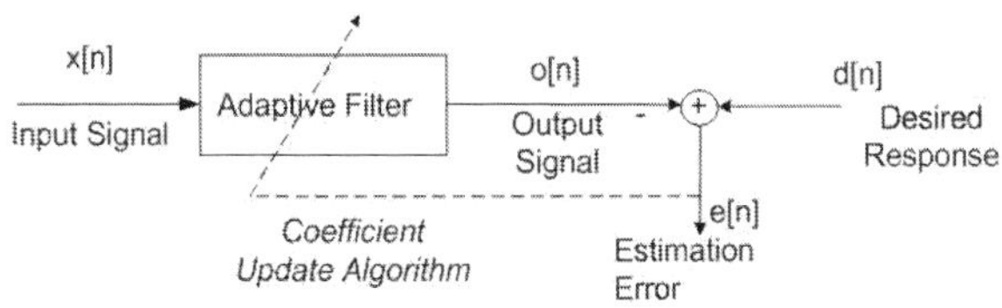

Fig. 7. Block diagram of adaptive filtering. The discrete filter is applied to the input signal $x[n]$ and produces output $o[n]$, which is compared against the desired signal $d[n]$. The error signal is used as input to the coefficient update algorithm of the adaptive filter. The adaptive filter coefficients are updated according to the error signal produced at each time instant.

rule using a statistical criterion. The minimization of the *mean square error* (MSE) between the output and the desired signal, leads to minimization of the energy of the error signal. If we define the error signal as the difference between the desired signal $d[n]$ and the output signal $o[n]$, we get

$$e[n] = d[n] - o[n] = d[n] - \mathbf{x}\mathbf{w}^T = d[n] - \mathbf{w}\mathbf{x}^T. \tag{7}$$

The energy of the error signal is defined as

$$\begin{aligned} E_e &= \sum_{n=-\infty}^{\infty} e^2[n] = \sum_{n=-\infty}^{\infty} (d[n] - o[n])^2 \\ &= \sum_{n=-\infty}^{\infty} (d^2[n] - 2d[n]o[n] + o^2[n]). \end{aligned} \tag{8}$$

Each term of the sum in (8) is given by

$$\begin{aligned} e^2[n] &= d^2[n] - 2d[n]o[n] + o^2[n] \\ &= d^2[n] - 2d[n]\mathbf{x}\mathbf{w}^T + \mathbf{w}\mathbf{x}^T\mathbf{x}\mathbf{w}^\mathbf{T}. \end{aligned} \tag{9}$$

Taking the expectation operator $\mathcal{E}$ on (9) and since $\mathcal{E}[\mathbf{w}] = \mathbf{w}$ we get

$$\begin{aligned} \mathcal{E}[e^2[n]] &= \mathcal{E}[d^2[n]] - 2\mathcal{E}[d[n]\mathbf{x}\mathbf{w}^T] + \mathcal{E}[\mathbf{w}\mathbf{x}^T\mathbf{x}\mathbf{w}^\mathbf{T}] \\ &= \mathcal{E}[d^2[n]] - 2\mathcal{E}[d[n]\mathbf{x}]\mathbf{w}^T + \mathbf{w}\mathcal{E}[\mathbf{x}^T\mathbf{x}]\mathbf{w}^\mathbf{T} \\ &= \mathcal{E}[d^2[n]] - 2\mathbf{p}\mathbf{w}^\mathbf{T} + \mathbf{w}\mathbf{R}\mathbf{w}^\mathbf{T}, \end{aligned} \tag{10}$$

where $\mathbf{R}$ is the square auto-correlation matrix of the input vector

$$\begin{aligned} \mathbf{R} &= \mathcal{E}[\mathbf{x}^\mathbf{T}\mathbf{x}] \\ &= \begin{bmatrix} x^2[n] & x[n]x[n-1] & \ldots & x[n]x[n-(M-1)] \\ x[n-1]x[n] & x^2[n-1] & \ldots & x[n-1]x[n-(M-1)] \\ \vdots & \vdots & & \vdots \\ x[n-(M-1)]x[n] & x[n-(M-1)]x[n-1] & \ldots & x^2[n-(M-1)] \end{bmatrix}, \end{aligned} \tag{11}$$

and $\mathbf{p}$ is the vector with the cross-correlation between the desired and the input signal

$$\mathbf{p} = \mathcal{E}[d[n]\mathbf{x}] = [d[n]x[0],\ d[n]x[n-1],\ \ldots,\ d[n]x[n-(M-1)]]. \tag{12}$$

The error surface is a multidimensional paraboloid with concavity aligned along the positive axis, leading to a surface with a single minimum. In order to find this minimum, we search for the optimal weight vector $\mathbf{w}^*$ that leads to a null gradient

$$\nabla \frac{\delta \mathcal{E}[e^2[n]]}{\delta \mathbf{w}} = 0. \quad (13)$$

For stationary input signals, the minimization of (13) leads to the Wiener filter Orfanidis (2007); Widrow & Stearns (1985) solution that computes the optimal weight vector given by

$$\mathbf{w}^* = \mathbf{R}^{-1}\mathbf{p}, \quad (14)$$

leading to the optimal solution in the MSE sense. However, Wiener filter is not adequate for non stationary situations, because it requires prior knowledge of the statistical properties of the input signal. This way, Wiener filter is optimal only if these statistics match with the ones considered for the design of the filter. In cases which we do not have such information, it may not be possible to design the Wiener filter, or at least it can not be optimal. We can overcome this problem with a two step approach:

1. estimation of the statistical parameters of those signals;
2. compute the filter parameters.

For real-time applications, the computational complexity of this approach is prohibitive. An efficient method to solve this problem consists on the use of an adaptive filter. These filters exhibit a satisfactory behavior in environments in which there is no prior knowledge of the statistical properties of the signals under consideration. The adaptive filter designs itself automatically, with some recursive learning algorithm to update its parameters, minimizing some cost function. It starts with a set of parameters which reflect the absence of knowledge of the environment; if we have a stationary environment the adaptive filter parameters converge, at each iteration step, to the Wiener filter solution given by (14) Haykin (2002); Sayed (2003); Widrow & Stearns (1985). On a non-stationary environment, the adaptive filtering algorithm provides a way to follow the variation of the statistical properties of the signal, along the time, provided that this variation is slow enough.

Adaptive filtering has been used in a variety of applications such as communications, radar, sonar, seismology, and biomedical engineering. Altough these applications come from such different fields, they all share a common characteristic: using an input vector and a desired response, we compute an estimation error; this error is then used to update the adaptive filter coefficients. Table 1 summarizes classes and some applications of adaptive filtering. The echo cancellation problem belongs to the class IV-Interference Cancellation.

3.2.1 Echo cancellation

The block diagram for AEC depicted in Fig. 2, operates by synthesizing an echo replica subtracting it from the received signal. This synthetic echo is generated from the speech signal. The result of this subtraction is named acoustic error signal, which can be used to adjust the filter coefficients. In the ideal case, the adaptive filter has a transfer function which is equal to the echo path, leading to a total echo cancellation. The principle shown in Fig. 6 is applied in Fig. 2. Notice that if the echo paths given by functions f and g in Fig. 2 are non-linear, it is not possible to achieve full echo cancellation because we are using linear filters to imitate the echo path. In practice, linear filters achieve adequate results.

Class	**Applications**
I. Identification	System Identification
	Terrestrial Layer Modelization
II. Inverse Modelization	Predictive Deconvolution
	Adaptive Equalization
III. Prediction	Linear Predictive Coding
	Auto-Regressive Spectral Analysis
	Signal Detection
IV. Interference Cancellation	Noise Cancellation
	Echo Cancellation
	Adaptive Beamforming

Table 1. Classes and applications of adaptive filtering techniques.

The adaptive filter coefficients adjustment has been addressed using the *least mean squares* (LMS) adaptive filtering algorithm and its variants Haykin (2002); Widrow & Stearns (1985). The choice of the adaptive filter adjustment coefficients must be made taking into account some important characteristics of the algorithm such as:

- rate of convergence and precision;
- numerical complexity;
- filter structure and stability.

The rate of convergence is defined as the number of iterations that the algorithm requires, operating on stationary signals, to approximate the optimal Wiener solution. The higher the rate of convergence, the faster the algorithm adapts to non stationary environments with unknown characteristics.

The numerical complexity is the number of operations needed to complete an iteration of the algorithm. Depending on the adaptation algorithm and on the processor where the algorithm runs, it is possible to have numerical problems. The most common source of problems of this kind is the so-called *finite precision effects*, due to limited number of bits used to represent data types for coefficients and samples. As the algorithm performs its computations, it is possible to accumulate quantization errors. If this situation is not monitored, the adaptive filter coefficients may enter into an overflow (or underflow) problem. These factors prevent that the adaptive algorithm converges to an acceptable solution. In the worst case of overflow and underflow, we say that the algorithm is numerically unstable.

The filter stability is assured by choosing a FIR filter; whatever are its coefficients, a FIR filter is always stable since it has no feedback from the output to the input. If the filter input becomes zero at a given time instant, then its output will be zero after M/F_S, where M is the order of the filter and F_s is the sampling frequency. The longest echo path (time delay) that we can accommodate is given by the order of the filter; long echo paths lead to higher order filters that are computationally more demanding to store in memory and to update in real-time. Thus, the computational complexity that we can put into the adaptive filter limits the longest echo path.

On the other hand, if we use an adaptive IIR filter care must be taken to assure stability. In any case (FIR or IIR filter) we have a time varying impulse response, due to the adaptation of the filter coefficients.

3.3 Adaptive filter update: Least mean squares algorithm and variants

In this section, we review the most common adaptive filtering techniques. For the purpose of explanation we consider adaptive FIR filters. The *least mean square* (LMS) algorithm operates by updating the filter coefficients $\mathbf{w}$ according to a gradient descent rule given by

$$\mathbf{w}_{(i+1)} \leftarrow \mathbf{w}_{(i)} + 2\mu e_{(i)} \mathbf{x}_{(i)}, \tag{15}$$

where $\mathbf{w}_{(i)}$ is the value of the coefficient vector $\mathbf{w}$ at time instant i, μ is the step size, $e_{(i)}$ is the error signal and $\mathbf{x}_{(i)}$ represents the present and previous samples at the filter taps, at time instant i.

The LMS step μ must be chosen carefully in order to assure proper convergence. A small μ will assure convergence but the rate of convergence can be quite slow that is not adequate for a real-time conversation. A large μ can cause that the LMS algorithm does not find an adequate local minimum, thus leading to unsatisfactory echo cancellation. It can be shown Haykin (2002); Widrow & Stearns (1985) that the choice

$$0 < \mu < \frac{1}{(M+1)P_{(i)}}, \tag{16}$$

assures adequate convergence rate; M is the order of the adaptive filter and $P_{(i)}$ is the average power of the signal present in the input of the filter. In Özbay & Kavsaoğlu (2010), the choice of the optimal value for the LMS adaptation step is discussed.

3.3.1 Variants of LMS

Some acceleration techniques have been proposed to improve LMS convergence. Moreover, in the presence of speech signals, one must be careful in the coefficient update because speech signals have a power which exhibit a large dynamic range, making ineffective the use of a constant step size. To overcome this difficulty, the *normalized least mean squares* (NLMS) Birkett & Goubran (1995); Kuo & Lee (2001) algorithm (a variant of LMS) uses a variable step size, $\mu_{(i)}$, computed by

$$\mu_{(i)} = \frac{\eta}{a + P_{(i)}}, \tag{17}$$

in which $\eta > 0$, $P_{(i)}$ is the instantaneous power of signal $\mathbf{x}$ at time index i and $a > 0$ is a suitably chosen value to avoid numerical problems caused by zero division. This way, we have an adaptation step given by

$$\mathbf{w}_{(i+1)} \leftarrow \mathbf{w}_{(i)} + 2\mu_{(i)} e_{(i)} \mathbf{x}_{(i)}, \tag{18}$$

for NLMS, which has a relatively low convergence speed but it is quite stable and has low complexity. The *leaky least mean squares* (LLMS) algorithm is another variant of LMS Kuo & Lee (2001), which introduces a leakage factor β such that $(0 < \beta < 1)$ into the coefficient update

$$\mathbf{w}_{(i+1)} \leftarrow \beta\mathbf{w}_{(i)} + 2\mu e_{(i)} \mathbf{x}_{(i)}. \tag{19}$$

Thus, for the following iteration we use a portion of the coefficient value (they have leaks caused by β). The NLMS and LLMS can be used simultaneously in the coefficient update process, leading to

$$\mathbf{w}_{(i+1)} \leftarrow \beta\mathbf{w}_{(i)} + 2\mu_{(i)} e_{(i)} \mathbf{x}_{(i)}. \tag{20}$$

The *recursive least squares* algorithm (RLS) Haykin (2002) recursively computes the filter coefficients such that minimize a weighted linear least squares cost function. Notice that the LMS algorithm aims at minimizing the mean square error. RLS algorithm considers the input signals as deterministic, while for the LMS and variants these are considered as instances of stochastic processes. RLS has extremely fast convergence at the expense of high computational complexity, which makes it uninteresting for real-time implementations. The main drawback of RLS is its poor performance when the filter to be estimated changes its statistical properties.
A LMS variant named *frequency-response-shaped least mean squares* (FRS-LMS) was proposed in Kukrera & Hocanin (2006) and shown to have good convergence properties. The FRS-LMS algorithm has improved performance when a sinusoidal input signal is corrupted by correlated noise. The algorithm shapes the frequency response of the transversal filter. This shaping action is performed on-line using an additional term similar to leakage β in LLMS shown in (19). This term involves the multiplication of the filter coefficient vector by a matrix, and it is computed efficiently with the *fast Fourier Transform* (FFT) Oppenheim & Schafer (1999). The authors show analytically that the adaptive filter converges in both the mean and mean-square senses. They also analyze the filter in the steady state in order to show its frequency-response-shaping capability. The experimental results show that FRS-LMS is very effective even for highly correlated noise.
The *decoupled partitioned block frequency domain adaptive filter* (DPBFAD) approach is quite demanding regarding computational requirements in the number of operations as well as the required memory, when compared to LMS, NLMS, and LLMS. The coefficients are updated in blocks, to allow real-time implementation, on the frequency domain. It requires the computation of the DFT (using FFT) and its inverse at each iteration.
Table 2 compares three algorithms that have proven effective for adaptive filtering, namely the *least mean squares* (LMS), *recursive least squares* (RLS), and fast RLS (also known as fast Kalman) Orfanidis (2007). This list is by no means exhaustive, since there are many different algorithms for this purpose.

Algorithm	Rate of Convergence	Complexity	Stability
LMS	Slow	Low	Stable
RLS	Fast	High	Stable
Fast RLS	Fast	Low	Unstable

Table 2. Rate of convergence, complexity, and stability of well-known adaptive filtering algorithms.

4. Solutions for echo cancellation

This section presents some solutions for the AEC problem. We focus on real-time solutions carried out over DSP platforms.

4.1 Short-length centered adaptive filter approach

In Marques (1997); Marques & Sousa (1996); Marques et al. (1997) we have an implementation of a long distance echo canceler which copes with double talking situations and exceeds the CCITT (now ITU-T, International Telecommunication Union-Telecommunications) G.165 recommendation levels for echo cancellation. The proposed solution is based on short length adaptive FIR filters centered on the positions of the most significant echoes, which are tracked by time-delay estimators. To deal with double talking situations a speech detector is employed. The resulting algorithm enables long-distance echo cancellation with low computational requirements. It reaches high *echo return loss enhancement* (ERLE) and shows fast convergence. The key issue to use centered adaptive filters is that the echo-path impulse response is characterized mainly by two active regions, corresponding to the near-end and the far-end signal echo respectively, as shown in Fig. 8.

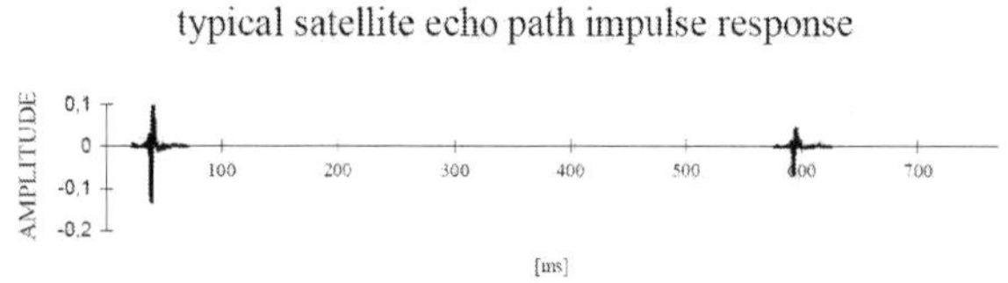

Fig. 8. Typical echo path impulse response (adapted from Marques et al. (1997)). We have two active regions corresponding to the near-end and far-end echo, respectively.

Each active region has a length usually much shorter than the total supported echo-path length. The proposed system is based on time-delay estimators to track the position of these active regions, where short-length adaptive filters have to be centered.
Fig. 9 shows the impulse response of an acoustic echo path, resulting from the direct coupling between the speaker and the microphone of an IRISTEL telephone. Although the supported echo path length is 64 delay elements, only a small region is active. Knowing its position and length, the adaptive filter has to adjust only the corresponding coefficients.

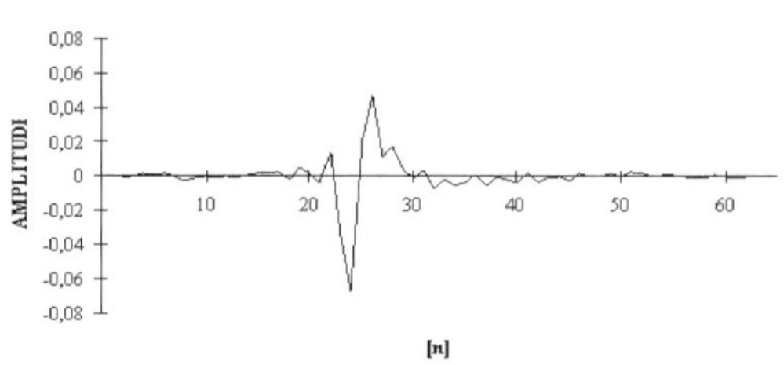

Fig. 9. Acoustic echo path impulse response for an IRISTEL telephone. Most of the coefficients are near zero and only a small subset of the coefficients has a significant value (adapted from Marques et al. (1997)).

In Marques et al. (1997) the authors compare the traditional full-tap FIR and short-length centered filter solution in an echo path with a delay of half a second. The conventional structure converges to a solution where the ERLE is less than 10 dB, while the centered filter achieves approximately 80 dB, as depicted in Fig. 10.

4.1.1 System architecture

Fig. 11 shows the proposed system architecture which is a combined echo cancellation structure including two echo cancelers, one for each communication direction, and a speech detector. Each echo canceler is composed by a centered adaptive filter and a time delay estimator. The delay estimator tracks the corresponding main signal reflection position where the short length adaptive filter is to be centered. The near-end and far-end speech detectors inhibit the adaptation of the filter whenever speech is present.

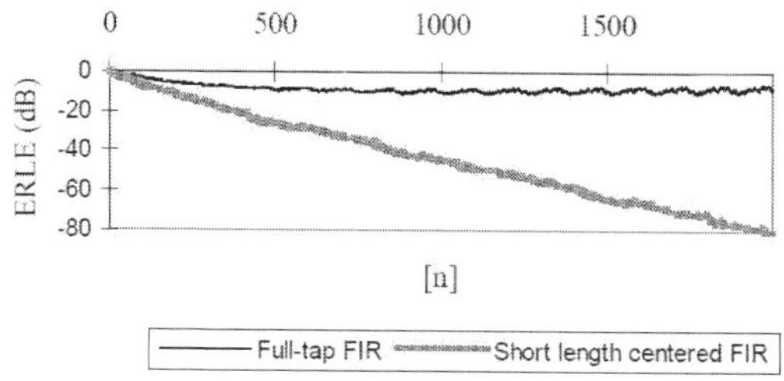

Fig. 10. Convergence of the traditional FIR structure compared to the centered adaptive filter, for a delay of 4000 taps (adapted from Marques et al. (1997)).

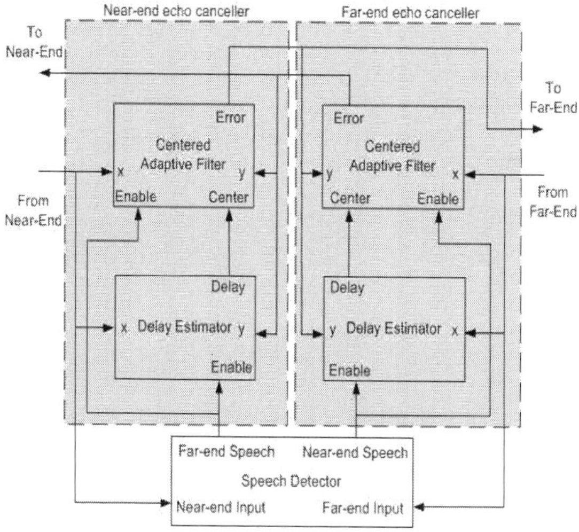

Fig. 11. The block diagram of the proposed system with two echo cancelers and a speech detector. Each echo canceler has a short-length centered adaptive filter and a time delay estimator (from Marques et al. (1997)).

The speech detector is very important in echo cancellation systems where double talking may occur (full duplex mode) as this situation originates the abrupt increase of the adjustment error. The common solution of using adaptive FIR filters to approximate the echo-path impulse response becomes insufficient; if this situation occurs and no action is taken, drift of the adaptive filter coefficients is possible Johnson (1995). Additionally, in this system, erroneous *time-delay estimation* (TDE) may happen. To overcome this problem, the strategy is to inhibit the filters adjustment and the delay estimation when double talking is detected. In Fig. 12 a centered adaptive filter example is shown. The supported echo path length is M taps, the position of the active region is $(M-1)T_s$ and for illustration purposes only, the considered length is 3 taps. $T_s = 1/F_s$ is the sampling time, that is, the time between two consecutive samples. The main advantages of the centered adaptive filter, as compared to the typical full-length FIR solution, are:

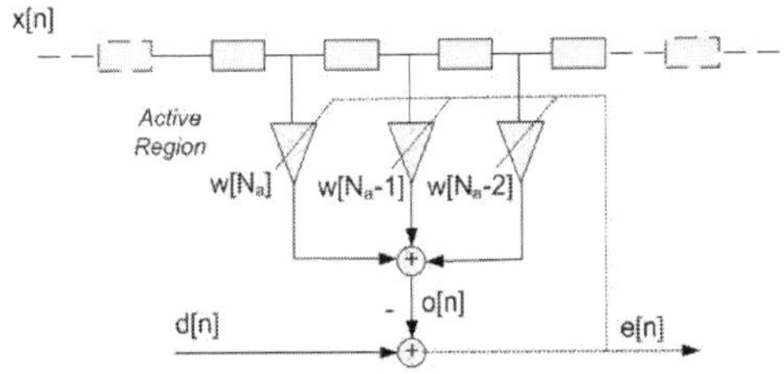

Fig. 12. Centered adaptive filter. The supported echo path length is N_a taps, but considering an active region of 3 taps, only the corresponding 3 coefficients need adjustment.

- reduced computational cost, due to the lower number of coefficients that need adjustment, when compared with the total supported echo path length;
- greater convergence speed, since the adaptation step can now be larger;
- reduced residual error because the coefficients which would otherwise converge to zero, now take precisely that value.

To adjust the short length centered adaptive filter coefficients, the NLMS algorithm was employed, due to its adequacy in the presence of speech signals Haykin (2002).

4.1.2 Time delay estimation

The TDE block estimates the presence of the echo as well as its delay, given by parameter t_d in (1). The basic aspects of TDE are discussed in Jacovitti & Scarano (1993). The *direct cross correlation* (DCC) method is analyzed and compared with the *average square difference function* (ASDF) and the *average magnitude difference function* (AMDF).
The DCC method computes the cross-correlation between signals $x[n]$ and $y[n]$ given by

$$DCC_{xy}[k] = \sum_{k=0}^{L-1} x[n]y[n-k] =< x[n], y[n-k] >, \tag{21}$$

where $< .,. >$ denotes the inner product between its two arguments. Essentially, DCC is the inner product between $x[n]$ and shifted versions of $y[n]$. The DCC can be computed efficiently on the frequency domain using the *fast Fourier transform* (FFT) and its inverse Oppenheim & Schafer (1999) by

$$DCC_{xy}[k] = \text{IFFT}[\text{FFT}[x[n]]. * \text{FFT}[y[-n]]], \tag{22}$$

using L-point FFT/IFFT and $.*$ being the dot product between vectors. The maximum value of $DCC_{xy}[k]$ corresponds to the estimated location of the delay $\hat{k} = \arg\max_k DCC_{xy}[k]$; the value of t_d as in (1) is given by $t_d = \hat{k}T_s$. The ASDF estimator is given by

$$ASDF_{xy}[k] = \frac{1}{L}\sum_{k=0}^{L-1} (x[n] - y[n-k])^2, \tag{23}$$

which is similar to the Euclidian distance between two signals. Finally, the AMDF estimator computes

$$AMDF_{xy}[k] = \frac{1}{L}\sum_{k=0}^{L-1} |x[n] - y[n-k]|, \tag{24}$$

with the advantage, over the previous two measures, that it requires no multiplications to measure the similarity between two signals. For ASDF and AMDF we are interested in finding indexes $\hat{k} = \arg\min_k ASDF_{xy}[k]$ and $\hat{k} = \arg\min_k AMDF_{xy}[k]$.
Supported on many experimental tests, the authors in Marques et al. (1997) chose the DCC method, because it outperforms the other two (AMDF and ASDF) for low *signal-to-noise ratio* (SNR) scenarios. The TDE component is the most demanding block on the entire system; it takes about 90 % of the total processing time.

4.1.3 Speech detector

The speech detector copes with double talking situations. When both speakers are talking, the received signal is a composition of the received echo and the other speaker's signal. If no action is taken, adaptive filter coefficient drift may happen as well as erroneous time delay estimation, so the common solution of using adaptive FIR filters to approximate the echo path impulse response becomes insufficient. Thus, whenever speech is present we have to inhibit the coefficients adjustment as well as delay estimation. The speech detector criterion, based on Messerschmidt et al. (1986), is as follows:

- the far-end speaker is considered present when the power of the original signal is above a given threshold, established by the noise average power; we consider that the speaker is still present for more 75 ms, after the power level gets below this threshold;
- the near-end speaker is considered present when the power of the echoed signal is 6 dB below the power of the original signal.

Each filter is adapted only when the corresponding speaker is detected. This way, when speech is detected on both directions, echo cancellation is performed using the coefficients that were updated just before the beginning of the presence of speech.

4.2 Improved short-length centered adaptive filter approach

In Ferreira & Marques (2008) we have an improvement on the approach detailed in Subsection 4.1, and depicted in Fig. 11. The system architecture is the same, but some modifications were placed on the centered adaptive filter as well as on the TDE block. The DSP platform and the hands-free conversation setup used in the experimental tests are also different.
The centered adaptive FIR filter has a small number of coefficients, corresponding to the length of the active area of the echo, with 32 and 64 coefficients for a sampling rate of 8 kHz; this assures fast convergence. The experimental tests showed that is preferable to set to (absolute) zero all the filter coefficients that are near zero and to keep with a non-zero value, only the coefficients on the active area.
On the TDE block, both DCC and ASDF methods were considered. The authors also considered a new approach with a *maximum delay FIR filter*, that has a (large) number of coefficients $\mathbf{c} = [c_0, c_1, \ldots, c_{M-1}]$ corresponding to the maximum expected delay. These coefficients are updated by

$$\mathbf{c}_{(i+1)} \leftarrow \mathbf{c}_{(i)} + 2\mu e_{(i)}\mathbf{x}_{(i)}, \tag{25}$$

but only a small fraction ($t \ll M$) of these coefficients is updated between two consecutive sampling times (125 μs), in order to meet real-time requirements. For the typical scenario, there is no need to update the entire set of coefficients in order to get an accurate estimation of the time delay. The main component of the echo is given by the coefficient with the highest (absolute) amplitude value. Using the DSP parallel instructions Kehtarnavaz (2004), this update is carried out simultaneously with the update of the centered filter coefficients. In the experimental tests, this delay estimator with low complexity, has obtained good results even in situations of low signal-to-noise ratio. The number of coefficients that need adjustment is small when compared with the total number of elements in the supported delay line, thus enabling a larger step.

4.3 Normalized subband adaptive filter

In J.Ni & Li (2010), the authors address two well-known problems of AEC:

- high correlation between both speech signals (on the input of the adaptive filter);
- the large length of the impulse response of the echo path.

These characteristics slow down the convergence rate of the adaptive filter whenever NLMS algorithm is used. The *normalized subband adaptive filter* (NSAF) offers a good solution to this problem due to its decorrelating property. However, similar to the NLMS-based adaptive filter, the NSAF requires a tradeoff between fast convergence rate and small steady-state MSE. In J.Ni & Li (2010), the authors propose an adaptive combination scheme to address this tradeoff. The combination is carried out in subband domain and the mixing parameter is adapted by means of a stochastic gradient algorithm which employs the sum of squared subband errors as the cost function. The proposed combination scheme obtains both fast convergence rate and small steady-state MSE.

4.4 Hirschman optimal transform

In Krishna et al. (2010), the transform domain adaptive filter approach finds an adequate solution for AEC as it results in a significant reduction in the computational burden, as compared to the traditional approaches. There are some different orthogonal transform based adaptive filters for echo cancellation. In Krishna et al. (2010), the authors present *Hirschman optimal transform* (HOT) based adaptive filter for elimination of echo from audio signals. Simulations and analysis show that HOT based LMS adaptive filter is computationally efficient and has fast convergence compared to LMS, NLMS and Discrete Fourier Transform -LMS (DFT-LMS). The spectral flatness measure shows a significant improvement in canceling the acoustic echo.

4.5 An optimal step approach

The optimal step approach described in Özbay & Kavsaoğlu (2010) deals with the AEC problem in the context of practical applications in which the positions of talker, microphone and loudspeaker are not stationary. They explore the fact that the amplitude of the speech signals depend on the acoustic properties of the environment. Choosing a constant step μ does not always yield an optimal result as echo power spectrum density depends on the distance between speaker microphone and loudspeaker which can not be known a priori. The authors show the need for a dynamic choice of the LMS step value. They provide an algorithm for obtaining an optimal step value for any AEC problem.

The authors show that for the optimal μ value in the case that the microphone of the speaker is far from its loudspeaker, adaptive filter output power spectrum density is approximately equal to that of the one obtained for a small μ value. Therefore, in AEC application, the optimal μ value is computed as a function of the echo power spectrum density. By using the proposed algorithm, the step is adaptively set depending on the distance between speaker microphone and loudspeaker and the acoustic properties of the environment.

5. Real-time DSP implementations

This section addresses real-time implementations of long-distance AEC systems on DSP from Texas Instruments with code optimized for real-time processing. We consider AEC on a hands-free system developed on the TMS320C50 and TMS320C6713 DSP platforms.
The TMS320C50 operates at 41 MHz, has a on-chip RAM of 10 K word and a 32 kB PROM with communication kernel Texas Instruments (1993). The *analog interface circuit* (AIC) has 14 bit resolution. The TMS320C6713 Kehtarnavaz (2004) has a master clock of 225 MHZ, delivering 1800 MIPS and 1350 MFLOPS. The analog stereo interface is carried out by the AIC 23 codec, with sampling rates from 8 to 96 kHz, with 16, 20 and 24 bits per sample. Fig. 13 shows the block diagram of the *development starter kit* (DSK) C6713 developed by Spectrum Digital[1] for Texas Instruments; the DSK has 192 kB of internal RAM and 16 MB of external RAM.

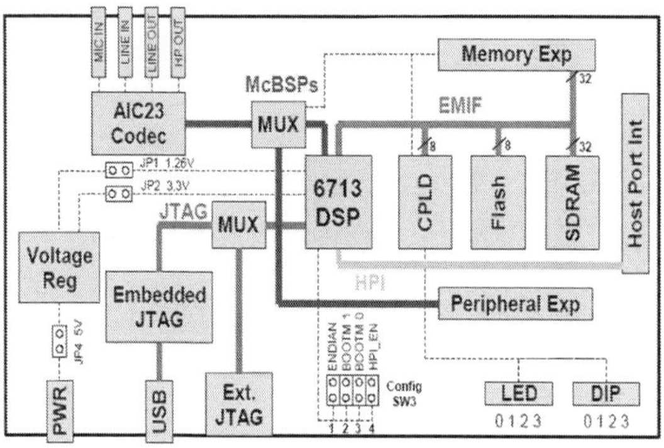

Fig. 13. The block diagram of the Development Starter Kit C6713 developed by Spectrum Digital for Texas Instruments (adapted from Spectrum Digital Inc., DSP Development Systems (2003)).

5.1 The (improved) short-length centered adaptive filter approach

The first approach of AEC system based on centered adaptive filter reported in Marques et al. (1997) and described in Subsection 4.1 was implemented on the TMS320C50 DSP. The approach described in Subsection 4.2 and reported in Ferreira & Marques (2008) was implemented with TMS320C6713 using the DSKC6713. The code, written in C++ programming language, is located on the 192 kB internal RAM, along with the data. The code was compiled with level-3 optimization Kehtarnavaz (2004), for faster execution:

- using allocation of variables to registers;
- elimination of unused code, unused assignments and local common expressions;
- simplification of expressions and statements;
- software pipelining;
- loop optimizations and loop unrolling;
- removal of functions that are never called; simplification of functions with return values that are never used.

[1] www.c6000.spectrumdigital.com

The filters are managed as circular buffers and inline functions are used whenever possible. The sampling rate is 8 kHz, and the number of bits per sample is 16 (the minimum allowed by the AIC23 codec), suited for speech signals. This way, we have 125 μs between two consecutive samples, and this is the maximum processing time to meet real-time requirements (28125 instructions, under a 225 MHz clock). The time delay estimator has the largest amount of total processing time, being not possible to completely update the time delay estimation, within 125 μs. Between two consecutive samples, we update only a small portion of the filter coefficients.

5.2 An optimal step approach

The optimal step approach of Özbay & Kavsaoğlu (2010) also uses the Texas Instruments TMS320C6713 with DSKC6713, because it is an up to date architecture. The authors established an experimental setup including the DSKC6713 board, a laptop computer, an amplifier, a loudspeaker, and two microphones. They have considered two scenarios of application:

- in the first scenario, two microphones were placed close to the loudspeaker;
- in the second scenario one microphone was placed close to the loudspeaker and speech trial was implemented in the far-end microphone.

The experimental results show the adequacy of the proposed solution.

6. Experimental results

This section presents some experimental results obtained with the AEC systems described in Subsections 4.1 and 4.2, respectively.

6.1 The short-length centered adaptive filter approach

Using a single TM5320C50 DSP with no external memory, the system detects and cancels an echo with a delay of more than 380 ms. Considering a configuration with 64 Kwords of data memory, the maximum supported delay is larger than 2.5 seconds.
Table 3 shows the computational requirements for a TMS320C50 DSP. Considering an unidirectional configuration and an active region of 4 miliseconds, the maximum supported echo delay is very significant (greater than 2.5 seconds).

Module function	Processor clock-cycles	Percentage
Speech detector	65	2.6
Time-delay estimator	82+18*corrl	3.28+0.72*corrl
Centered adaptive filter	114+6*M	4.56+0.24*M
Main Cycle	31	1.2

Table 3. Computational requirements for a TMS320C50 DSP with the AEC approach described in Subsection 4.1. M is the supported echo region length (order of FIR filter). The number of computations per sampling period has been reduced by dividing the computation of the cross-correlation function into blocks, each with length $corrl$.

Table 4 describes the main features of the developed AEC system. The maximum length of the echo path is proportional to the available amount of memory. We have two values for this parameter, corresponding to the internal memory of the DSP and the external memory available on the DSK (64 kB), respectively.

Feature	Value
Maximum supported echo delay	381 ms // 2643 ms
Maximum length of dispersion area	4 ms
Absolute delay	0.375 ms
Minimum attenuation on the returned echo	6 dB
Convergence	Improvement of 41 dB in 80 ms
Residual echo level	-51 dBm0
Speech detector level	6 dB below emission level
Hold time after speech detection	75 ms

Table 4. Main features of the AEC approach with TMS320C50 DSP described in Subsection 4.1. The maximum supported echo delay depends on the amount of internal//external memory.

Fig. 14 shows the ERLE (in dB) obtained by the AEC system with simulated, electric, and real echo paths, as a function of time. As expected, we get the best results on the simulated echo path, due to the adequacy of the adaptive filter to this path. The electric echo path is easier to cancel than the acoustic echo path, in which due to its non-linearities, the experimental results show less attenuation than for the other two paths. Even on the acoustic echo path which is the most difficult, we rapidly get 10 dB of attenuation, in less than 30 ms (which is roughly the delay time that a human user perceives the echo); this attenuation stops about -20 dB which is a very interesting value. In summary, ERLE is greater than 41 dB in just 80 ms in a simulated echo path; with real electrical and acoustic echo paths, 24.5 dB and 19.2 dB have been measured, respectively.

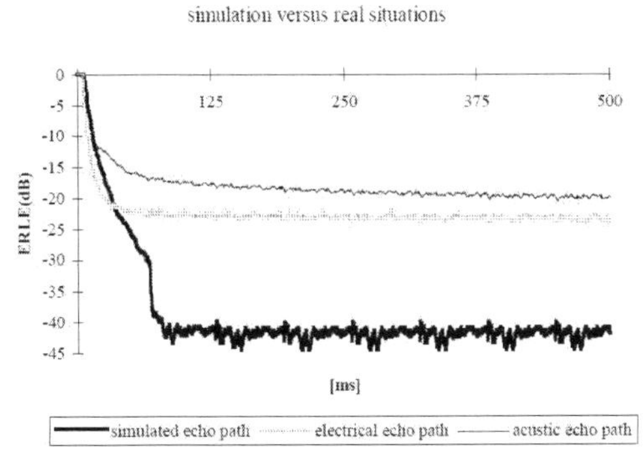

Fig. 14. Echo canceller ERLE in simulated, electric and acoustic paths. On the acoustic path, which is the most difficult we get about 10 dB of attenuation in less than 30 ms.

Table 5 compares this system with the CCITT G.165 recommendation, for a real situation, on the following tests:

- CR - Convergence Rate;
- FERLAC - Final Echo Return Loss After Convergence;
- IRLC - Infinite Return Loss Convergence;
- LR - Leak Rate.

Test Description	CCITT G.165 Requirement	System Performance
CR	$\geq$ 27 dB (500 ms)	41 dB
FERLAC	-40 dBm0	-51 dBm0
IRLC	-40 dBm0	-51 dBm0
LR	$\leq$ 10 dB	$\approx$ 0 dB

Table 5. System performance - comparison with CCITT G.165 recommendation levels for AEC.

We conclude that the system exceeds the recommendation levels for all these tests. The CR and FERLAC measures are taken on the single-talk scenario. Fig. 15 shows the time delay estimator ability to track time varying delays in the presence of real speech signals. On the voiced parts of the speech signals the TDE block tracks the delays accurately.

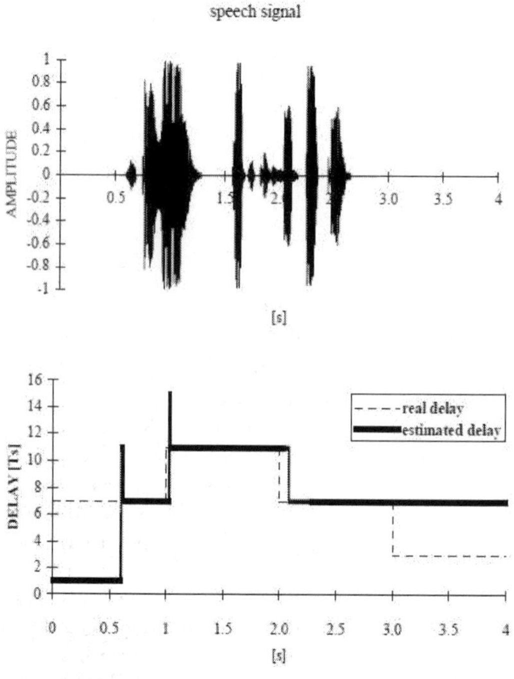

Fig. 15. Real speech signal (top) and real/estimated delay obtained by the TDE module. The TDE block has a good performance on the presence of real speech. Adapted from Marques et al. (1997).

In Fig. 16 the usefulness of the speech detector to prevent the filter coefficient drift is emphasized. In the presence of double talk, with the speech detector disabled the coefficient drift happens.

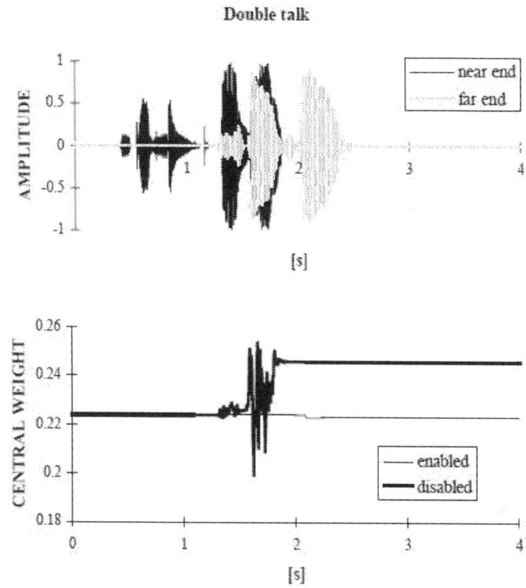

Fig. 16. The speech detector prevents filter coefficient drift in the case of double talk. With the speech detector disabled, coefficient drift happens. Adapted from Marques et al. (1997).

Feature	Value
Absolute delay	0.375 ms
Convergence speed	27 dB (125 ms)
Digitalization	$F_s = 8000H_z$ $n = 16$ bit/sample
Hold time after speech	75 ms
Max. length	256 ms
Max. length of dispersion area	4 ms
Max. memory (data + code)	$<$ 192 kB
Residual echo	-42.26 dBm0
Returned echo minimum loss	6 dB
Speech detector	6 dB below threshold

Table 6. Main features of the AEC approach with TMS320C6713 DSP described in Subsection 4.2.

6.2 The improved short-length centered adaptive filter approach

The tests were carried out in DSP Code Composer Studio (CCS) environment, with code written in C++, using real signals. Table 6 summarizes the developed system features. The total amount of memory needed for the echo canceler data and code is low (and proportional to the maximum expected delay) making it suited for an embedded system. The total amount of memory required can be reduced, using a fixed-point DSP. The adaptive centered filters have 32 or 64 coefficients, while FIR-based time delay estimator uses up to M=4000 coefficients (delays up to 0.5 seconds), giving a reasonable range of delays, suited for several applications. Fig. 17 shows the (typical) centered adaptive filter coefficients (with 32 active coefficients), for a speech signal. Only a small subset of coefficients is far from zero according to the echo path characteristics, as expected; this is a typical test situation. Fig. 18 displays the echo and error

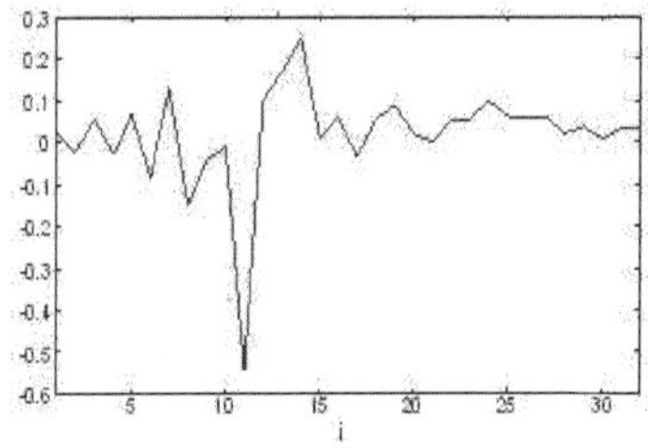

Fig. 17. Centered adaptive filter coefficients. Only a small subset of coefficients is far from zero.

signals for a speech signal, while Fig. 19 displays the achieved attenuation, of about 20 dB, for the speech signal on its voiced parts. It is interesting to note that how attenuation increases on the voiced parts of the speech signal, according to the AEC fundamental concepts presented in Subsections 2.1 and 2.2.

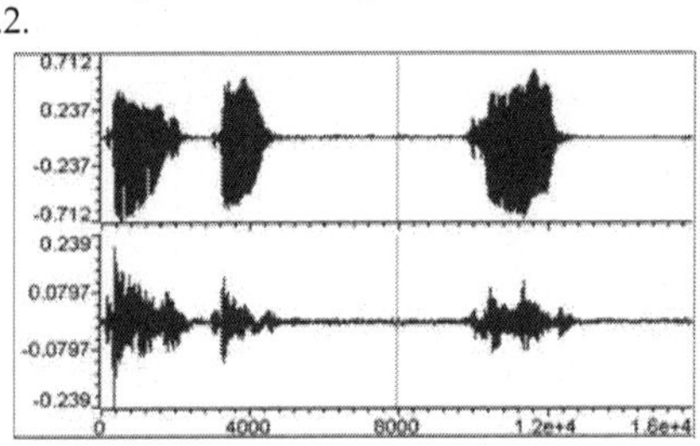

Fig. 18. Echo (top) and error (bottom) signal. Whenever there is echo with higher energy the adaptive filter error signal follows it. On its portions with higher energy, the error signal shows a decaying behavior that corresponds to the convergence of the adaptive filter.

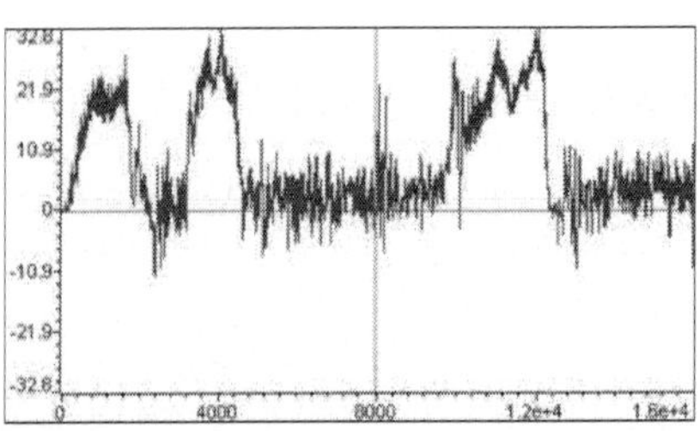

Fig. 19. Attenuation obtained for the speech signal of Fig. 18. We have increased attenuation on the voiced parts of the speech signal.

Table 7 compares our system with the CCITT G.165 recommendation levels, for a real conversation. We conclude that this system approaches the recommendation levels for

Test Description	CCITT G.165 Requirement	System Performance
CR	$\geq$ 27 dB (500 ms)	27 dB (125 ms)
FERLAC	-40 dBm0	-37.39 dBm0
IRLC	-40 dBm0	-37.39 dBm0
LR	$\leq$ 10 dB	$\approx$ 0 dB

Table 7. System performance - comparison with CCITT G.165 recommendation levels for AEC.

FERLAC and IRLC measures, matches for CR and exceeds it for the LR measure. The CR and FERLAC measures are taken on the single-talk scenario.
Fig. 20 displays the attenuation obtained for several electric and acoustic echo paths, using the average power of the received echo as the reference value, because the attenuation on the acoustic channel is not constant along these tests. The attenuation for the simulated echo path

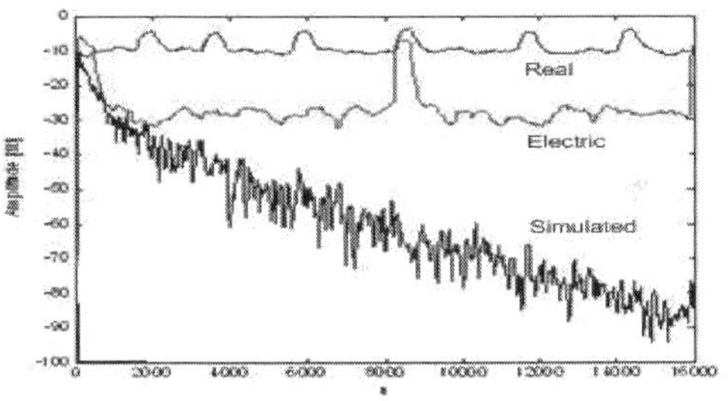

Fig. 20. Attenuation for the echo paths real (acoustic), electric and simulated (real-time on CCS).

is much larger than the other two, as expected. On the other hand, the attenuation for the electric echo path is around 30 dB, which is a considerable value. Finally, for the acoustic path we get about 10 dB of attenuation, which is also an acceptable practical value. This result was expected due to the strong non-linearities in the acoustic echo path, caused by the loudspeakers and microphone.

7. Conclusions

In this chapter, we have addressed the problem of acoustic echo cancellation. Echo being a delayed and attenuated version of the original signal produced by some device, such as a loudspeaker, causes disturbing effects on a conversation. This problem arises in many telecommunication applications such those as hands-free systems, leading to need of its cancellation in real-time. The echo cancellation techniques have better performance than the oldest and simpler echo suppression techniques.
We have reviewed some concepts of digital, statistical, and adaptive filtering. Some solutions for real-time acoustic echo cancellation based on adaptive filtering techniques, on digital signal processors were described in detail.
We have addressed some implementation issues of adaptive filtering techniques in real-time. After the description of the acoustic echo cancellation solutions in some detail, we have focused on their real-time implementations on well known digital signal processor platforms,

discussing its main characteristics as well as their experimental results according to standard measures.

7.1 Open challenges: future work

Altough adaptive filtering techniques have been proved efficient for the echo cancellation problem, there are some open challenges that lead to directions of future work. One of the most important directions of current and future research, due to its importance and difficulty is to model the non-linear echo path. Since we use linear filters to model the echo path, it is not possible to guarantee a complete echo cancellation when the echo path is non-linear. In these situations, better results can be obtained with non-linear filters or with linear filters complemented by non-linear functions. The challenge is thus positioned at choosing adequate non-linear filters and non-linear functions that accurately model the echo path, being able to achieve even better and faster cancellation results.

8. Acknowledgments

This work has been partly supported by the Portuguese *Fundação para a Ciência e Tecnologia* (FCT) Project FCT PTDC/EEA-TEL/71996/2006.

9. References

Antweller, C. & Symanzik, H. (1995). Simulation of time variant room impulse responses, *IEEE International Conference on Acoustics, Speech, and Signal Processing - ICASSP'95*, Vol. 5, Detroit, USA, pp. 3031–3034.

Benesty, J., Gaensler, T., Morgan, D., Sondhi, M. & Gay, S. (2001). *Advances in Network and Acoustic Echo Cancellation*, Springer-Verlag.

Birkett, A. & Goubran, R. (1995). Acoustic echo cancellation using NLMS-neural network structures, *IEEE International Conference on Acoustics, Speech, and Signal Processing - ICASSP'95*, Detroit, USA.

Breining, C. (1999). Acoustic echo control. an application of very-high-order adaptive filters, *Digital Signal Processing* 16(6): 42–69.

Ferreira, A. & Marques, P. (2008). An efficient long distance echo canceler, *International Conference on Signals and Electronic Systems, ICSES'08*, Krakow, pp. 331–334.

Gay, S. & J.Benesty (2000). *Acoustic signal processing for telecommunications*, Kluwer Academic Publishers.

Gilloire, A. & Hänsler, E. (1994). Acoustic echo control, *Annals of Telecommunications* 49: 359–359. 10.1007/BF02999422.
URL: *http://dx.doi.org/10.1007/BF02999422*

Greenberg, J. (1998). Modified LMS algorithms for speech processing with an adaptive noise canceller, *IEEE Transactions on Signal Processing* 6(4): 338–351.

Hänsler, E. (1994). The hands-free telephone problem: an annotated bibliography update, *Annals of Telecommunications* 49: 360–367. 10.1007/BF02999423.
URL: *http://dx.doi.org/10.1007/BF02999423*

Haykin, S. (2002). *Adaptive Filter Theory*, 4th edn, Prentice-Hall.

Instruments, T. (1986). Digital voice echo canceler with a TMS32020, I: 415–454.

Instruments, T. (1993). TMS 320C5X users guide.

Jacovitti, G. & Scarano, G. (1993). Discrete time techniques for time delay estimation, *IEEE Transactions on Signal Processing* 41(2): 525–533.

Jeannès, R., Scalart, P., Faucon, G. & Beaugeant, C. (2001). Combined noise and echo reduction in hands-free systems: A survey, *IEEE Transactions on Speech And Audio Processing* 9(8): 808–820.

J.Ni & Li, F. (2010). Adaptive combination of subband adaptive filters for acoustic echo cancellation, *IEEE Transactions on Consumer Electronics* 56(3): 1549 – 1555.

Johnson, C. (1995). Yet still more on the interaction of adaptive filtering, identification, and control, *IEEE Signal Processing Magazine* pp. 22 – 37.

Kehtarnavaz, N. (2004). *Real-Time Digital Signal Processing*, Newnes.

Krishna, E., Raghuram, M., Madhav, K. & Reddy, K. (2010). Acoustic echo cancellation using a computationally efficient transform domain lms adaptive filter, *10th International Conference on Information Sciences Signal Processing and their Applications (ISSPA)*, Kuala Lumpur, Malaysia, pp. 409–412.

Kukrera, O. & Hocanin, A. (2006). Frequency-response-shaped LMS adaptive filter, *Digital Signal Processing* 16(6): 855–869.

Kuo, S. & Lee, B. (2001). *Real-Time Digital Signal Processing*, John Wiley & Sons.

Kuo, S. & Pan, Z. (1994). Acoustic echo cancellation microphone system for large-scale videoconferencing, *IEEE International Conference on Acoustics, Speech, and Signal Processing - ICASSP'94*, Vol. 1, Adelaide, Australia, pp. 7–12.

Liu, Z. (1994). A combined filtering structure for echo cancellation in hand-free mobile phone applications, *International Conference on Signal Processing Applications & Technology*, Vol. 1, Dallas, USA, pp. 319–322.

Marques, P. (1997). *Long distance echo cancellation using centered short length transversal filters*, Master's thesis, Instituto Superior Técnico, Lisbon, Portugal.

Marques, P. & Sousa, F. (1996). TMS320C50 echo canceller based on low resolution time delay estimation, *The First European DSP Education and Research Conference*, Paris.

Marques, P., Sousa, F. & Leitao, J. (1997). A DSP based long distance echo canceller using short length centered adaptive filters, *IEEE International Conference on Acoustics, Speech, and Signal Processing - ICASSP'97*, Munich.

Messerschmidt, D., Hedberg, D., Cole, C., Haoui, A. & Winship, P. (1986). Digital voice echo canceller with a TMS320C30, *Digital Signal Processing Applications* 1: 415–454.

Oh, D., Shin, D., Kim, S. & Lee, D. (1994). Implementation of multi-channel echo canceler for mobile communication with TMS320C50, *International Conference on Signal Processing Applications & Technology*, Vol. 1, Dallas, USA, pp. 259–263.

Oppenheim, A. & Schafer, R. (1999). *Discrete-Time Signal Processing*, 2nd edn, Prentice Hall International, Inc.

Orfanidis, S. (ed.) (2007). *Optimum Signal Processing*, 2nd edn, McGraw-Hill.

Özbay, Y. & Kavsaoğlu, A. (2010). An optimum algorithm for adaptive filtering on acoustic echo cancellation using tms320c6713 dsp, *Digit. Signal Process.* 20: 133–148.
URL: *http://portal.acm.org/citation.cfm?id=1663653.1663859*

Sayed, A. (2003). *Fundamentals of Adaptive Filtering*, Wiley-IEEE Press.

Sondhi, M. (2006). The history of echo cancellation, *IEEE Signal Processing Magazine* 23(5): 95 – 102.

Sondhi, M. & Berkeley, D. (1980). Silencing echoes on the telephone network, *Proceedings of the IEEE* 68(8): 948–963.

Spectrum Digital Inc., DSP Development Systems (2003). TMS320C6713 DSK technical reference.

Veen, B. & Haykin, S. (1999). *Signals and Systems*, John Wiley & Sons.

Widrow, B., Glover, J., McCool, J., Kaunitz, J., Williams, C., Hearn, R., Zeidler, J., Dong, E. & Goodlin, R. (1975). Adaptive noise cancelling: Principles and applications, *Proceedings of the IEEE* 63(12): 1692 – 1716.

Widrow, B. & Stearns, S. (1985). *Adaptive Signal Processing*, Prentice Hall.

Witowsky, W. (1999). Understanding echo cancellation in voice over IP networks, *International Conference on Signal Processing Applications and Technology (ICSPAT)*, Orlando.

15

Adaptive Heterodyne Filters

Michael A. Soderstrand
University of California (Retired)
Department of Electrical and Computer Engineering,
Oklahoma State University (Retired)
Washington, D.C.
United States of America

1. Introduction

The heterodyne process has been an important part of electronic communications systems for over 100 years. The most common use of the heterodyne process is in modulation and demodulation where a local oscillator produces the heterodyne signal which is then mixed with (multiplied by) the signal of interest to move it from one frequency band to another. For example, the superheterodyne receiver invented by U.S. Army Major Edwin Armstrong in 1918 uses a local oscillator to move the incoming radio signal to an intermediate band where it can be easily demodulated with fixed filters rather than needing a variable filter or series of fixed filters for each frequency being demodulated (Butler, 1989, Duman 2005). Today you will find heterodyne as a critical part of any modern radio or TV receiver, cell phone, satellite communication system, etc.

In this chapter we will introduce the concept of making a tunable or adaptive filter using the heterodyne process. The concept is very similar to that of the superheterodyne receiver, but applied to tunable filters. Most tunable filters require a complicated mechanism for adjusting the coefficients of the filter in order to tune the filter. Using the heterodyne approach, we move the signal to a fixed filter and then move the signal back to its original frequency band minus the noise that has been removed by the fixed filter. Thus complicated fixed filters that would be virtually impossible to tune using variation of the filter parameters can be easily made tuneable and adaptive.

1.1 Applications of adaptive heterodyne filters

Modern broad-band wireless systems are designed to be co-located with older narrow-band communications so as to be able to share valuable spectrum (Etkin et al., 2005, Peha, 1998, 2000). This is accomplished by using a pseudorandom number sequence to control the spreading of the spectrum of the modern wireless transmitter so that it appears to be background noise that is easily filtered out by the narrow-band receiver. The five most common techniques for achieving spread-spectrum communications are (1) Frequency Hopping Spread Spectrum (FHSS, e.g.: IEEE 802.11-1997) in which the signal is transmitted at a random series of frequencies across the spectrum, (2) Direct Sequence Spread Spectrum (DSSS, e.g.: IEEE 802.11b and 802.11g) in which the transmitter multiplies the signal by a random sequence to make it appear like background noise, (3) Time Hopping Spread

Spectrum (THSS, e.g.: IEEE 802.15) in which the carrier is turned on and off by the random code sequence, (4) Chirp Spread Spectrum (CSS, e.g.: IEEE 802.15.4a-2007) which uses wideband linear frequency modulated chirp pulses to encode the information, and (5) Ultra Wide Band (UWB, e.g.: IEEE 802.15.3a - Note: No standard assigned, MB-OFDM and DS-UWB will compete in market) based on transmitting short duration pulses.
When working properly, the narrow-band transmissions licensed to the frequency spectrum do not affect the broadband systems. They either interfere with a small portion of the broad-band transmission (which may be re-sent or reconstructed) or the narrow-band signals are themselves spread by the receiver demodulation process (Pickholtz et al., 1982). However, in practice the narrow-band transmissions can cause serious problems in the spread-spectrum receiver (Coulson, 2004, McCune, 2000). To alleviate these problems, it is often necessary to include narrow-band interference attenuation or suppression circuitry in the design of the spread-spectrum receiver. Adaptive heterodyne filters are an attractive approach for attenuation of narrow-band interference in such broadband systems. Other approaches include smart antennas and adaptive analog and digital filters, but adaptive heterodyne filters are often a good choice for attenuation of narrow band interference in broadband receivers (Soderstrand, 2010a).

1.2 Preliminary concepts

Figure 1 shows the most common digital heterodyne circuit. The incoming signal x(n) is multiplied by the heterodyne signal cos(ω_0n). The parameter ω_0 is the heterodyne frequency which, along with all frequencies contained in x(n), must be less than $\pi/2$ in order to avoid aliasing.

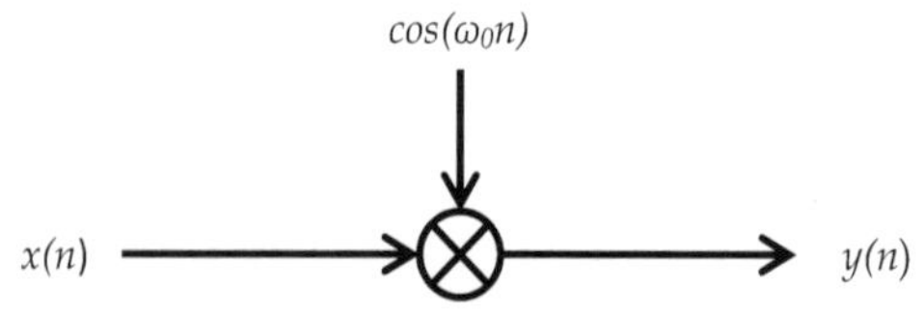

Fig. 1. Basic digital heterodyne operation.

Most textbooks analyze this basic heterodyne operation in the time domain making use of trigonometric identities to show that the effect of the heterodyne operation is to generate two images of the input signal x(n), one translated up in frequency by ω_0 and the other translated down in frequency by ω_0. However, for our purposes it is better to view things in the frequency domain (z-domain).
The time domain multiplication of x(n) by $e^{j\omega_0 n}$ rotates the z-domain representation of the signal X(z) left by ω_0 to X($ze^{-j\omega_0}$). The signal that was at DC, now appears at -ω_0. Similarly, the time domain multiplication of x(n) by $e^{-j\omega_0 n}$ rotates the z-domain representation of the signal X(z) right by ω_0 to X($ze^{j\omega_0}$). The signal that was at DC, now appears at -ω_0. This important relationship is expressed in the following equation (Dorf & Wan, 2000, Roberts, 2007):

$$x(n)e^{j\omega_0 n} \overset{Z}{\Leftrightarrow} X(ze^{-j\omega_0}) \tag{1}$$

If we express $\cos(\omega_0 n)$ in terms of the complex exponential, we get the following:

$$x(n)\cos(\omega_0 n) = \frac{1}{2}x(n)[e^{j\omega_0 n} + e^{-j\omega_0 n}] \overset{Z}{\Leftrightarrow} \frac{1}{2}[X(ze^{-j\omega_0}) + X(ze^{j\omega_0})] \quad (2)$$

From equation (2) we can clearly see the separation of the input signal into two signals, one translated in frequency by rotation to the left ω_0 and the other translated in frequency by rotation to the right ω_0 in the z-plane. In a modulation system, we would filter out the lower frequency and send the higher frequency to the antenna for transmission. In a demodulator, we would filter out the higher frequency and send the lower frequency to the IF stage for detection.

1.3 A simple tunable heterodyne band-pass filter

The basic heterodyne operation of Figure 1 can be used to implement a simple tunable narrow-band band-pass filter using the circuit of Figure 2.

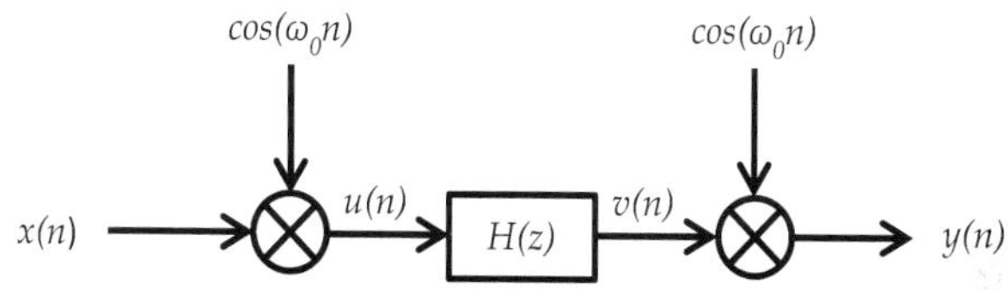

Fig 2. Simple tunable heterodyne band-pass filter ($H(z)$ must be a narrow-band low-pass filter)

Using the same analysis as equation (2) we obtain:

$$u(n) = x(n)\cos(\omega_0 n) = \frac{1}{2}x(n)[e^{j\omega_0 n} + e^{-j\omega_0 n}] \overset{Z}{\Leftrightarrow} U(z) = \frac{1}{2}[X(ze^{-j\omega_0}) + X(ze^{j\omega_0})] \quad (3)$$

After the filter stage we have:

$$V(z) = \frac{1}{2}[X(ze^{-j\omega_0}) + X(ze^{j\omega_0})]H(z) \quad (4)$$

The final heterodyne operation then results in the output Y(z):

$$Y(z) = \frac{1}{4}[H(ze^{-j\omega_0}) + H(ze^{j\omega_0})]X(z) + \frac{1}{4}[H(ze^{-j\omega_0})X(ze^{-2j\omega_0}) + H(ze^{j\omega_0})X(ze^{2j\omega_0})] \quad (5)$$

Equation (5) is obtained by the straight-forward application of equation (1) for the multiplication of equation (4) by the cosine heterodyne function. Equation (5) consists of four separate terms. If H(z) is a narrow-band low-pass filter, then the first two terms of equation (5) represent a narrow-band band-pass filter centered at the heterodyne frequency ω_0.

$$Y_{BP}(z) = \frac{1}{4}[H(ze^{-j\omega_0}) + H(ze^{j\omega_0})]X(z) \quad (6)$$

This narrow-band band-pass filter has only half the energy, however, because the other half of the energy appears in the high-frequency last terms in equation (5).

$$Y_{HF}(z) = \frac{1}{4}[H(ze^{-j\omega_0})X(ze^{-2j\omega_0}) + H(ze^{j\omega_0})X(ze^{2j\omega_0})] \quad (7)$$

However, if H(z) is of sufficiently narrow bandwidth, these high-frequency terms will be attenuated by H(z) and equation (6) will substantially represent the output of the simple tunable heterodyne filter of Figure 2.
Figure 3 shows the impulse response of the circuit of Figure 1 as simulated in MatLab for four different values of the heterodyne frequency. Figure 3 was implemented by the following MatLab script (COSHET):

```
% COSHET   (Lab book p. 129 12/11/2010)
% Function to implement cosine heterodye filter
% Set the following inputs before calling COSHET:
%        inp = 0 (provide input file inpf)
%            = 1 (impulse response)
%        npoints = number of points in input
%        w0 = heterodyne frequency
%        [b a] = coefficients of filter H(z)
%
% OUTPUTS:  hdb = frequency response of the filter
if inp==1
    for index=1:npoints
        inpf(index)=0;
    end
    inpf(1)=1;
end
for index=1:npoints
    x(index)=inpf(index)*sqrt(2)*cos(w0*(index-1));
end
y=filter(b,a,x);
for index=1:npoints
    yout(index)=y(index)*sqrt(2)*cos(w0*(index-1));
end
h=fft(yout);
hdb=20*log10(abs(h));
plot(hdb,'k')
```

Before invoking the above script each of the input values was set (inp=1, npoints=1000, $\omega_0 = \pi/5$, $\omega_0 = 2\pi/5$, $\omega_0 = 3\pi/5$ and $\omega_0 = 4\pi/5$). The filter H(z) was selected as an inverse-Chebyshev filter designed as [b,a] = cheby2(11, 40, 0.1). As can be seen from Figure 3, we have been able to implement a tunable narrow-band band-pass filter that can be tuned by the changing the heterodyne frequency.
Figure 4 shows a MatLab simulation of the ability of the circuit of Figure 2 to attenuate frequencies outside the band-pass filter and pass frequencies inside the bandwidth of the band-pass filter. The following MatLab script (GENINP) generates an input signal consisting of nine cosine waves spaced by $\pi/10$ in the z-plane:

```
% GENINP  (Lab book p. 129 12/11/2010)
% Generates nine sinusoidal inputs spaced by pi/10
% INPUTS:  npoints = number of points
for index=1:npoints
    inpf(index)=cos(pi*(index-1)/10);
    inpf(index)=inpf(index)+cos(2*pi*(index-1)/10);
    inpf(index)=inpf(index)+cos(3*pi*(index-1)/10);
    inpf(index)=inpf(index)+cos(4*pi*(index-1)/10);
    inpf(index)=inpf(index)+cos(5*pi*(index-1)/10);
    inpf(index)=inpf(index)+cos(6*pi*(index-1)/10);
    inpf(index)=inpf(index)+cos(7*pi*(index-1)/10);
    inpf(index)=inpf(index)+cos(8*pi*(index-1)/10);
    inpf(index)=inpf(index)+cos(9*pi*(index-1)/10);
end
```

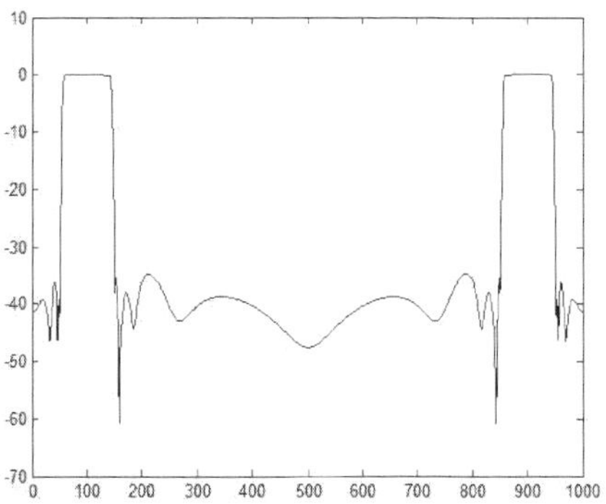

Fig. 3a. Tunable band-pass filter with $\omega_0 = \pi/5$

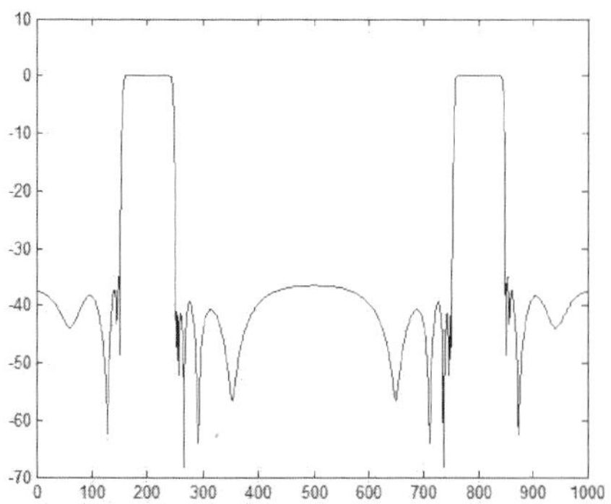

Fig. 3b. Tunable band-pass filter with $\omega_0 = 2\pi/5$

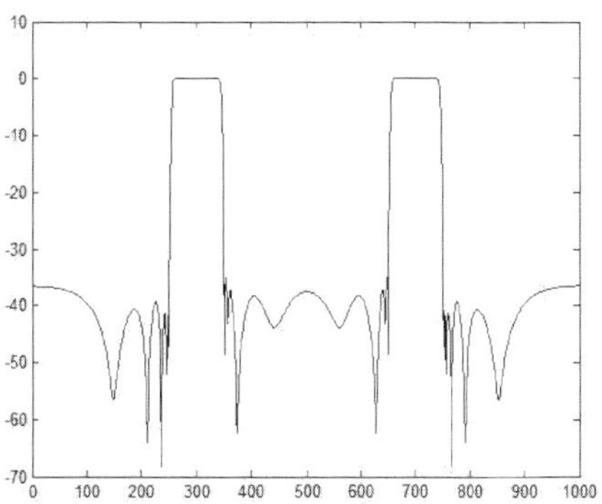

Fig. 3c. Tunable band-pass filter with $\omega_0 = 4\pi/5$

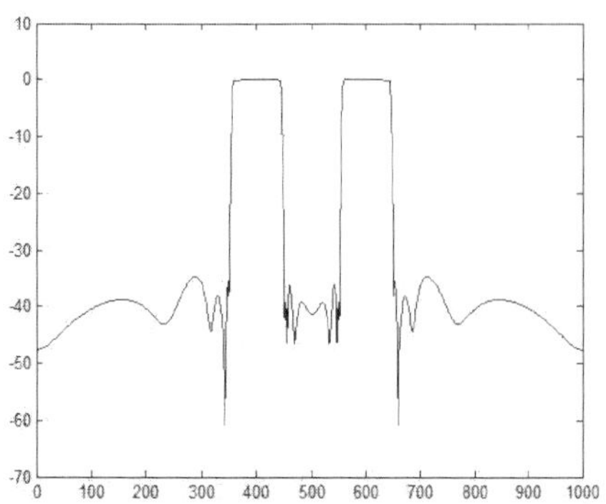

Fig. 3d. Tunable band-pass filter with $\omega_0 = 4\pi/5$

Fig. 3. MatLab simulation of circuit of Figure 2 for various values of the heterodyne frequency ω_0.

This input is then used with the previous script (COSHET) to generate Figure 4 (inp=0).

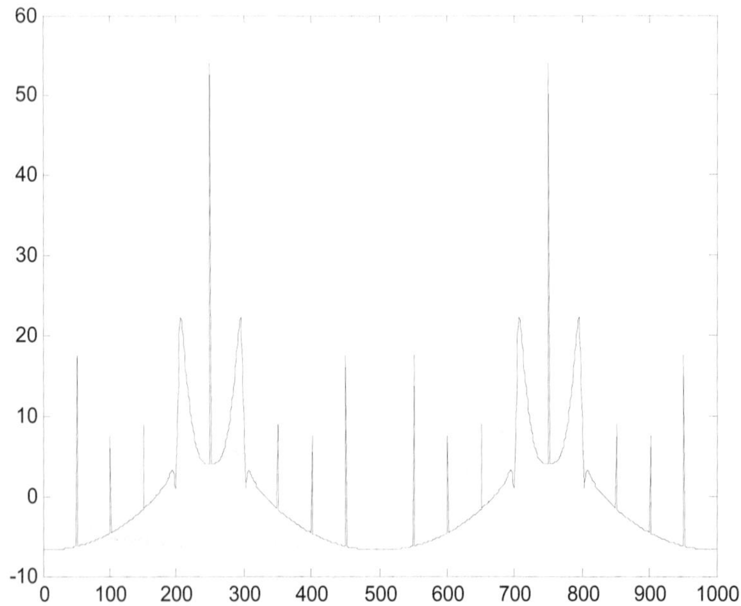

Fig. 4. Output of circuit of figure 2 when input is nine equally-spaced cosine waves.

In Figure 4 you can see the nine equally spaced cosine waves. The heterodyne frequency was set to $\pi/2$. Thus the cosine waves at all frequencies except $\pi/2$ are severely attenuated. There is nearly 40db difference between the cosine output at $\pi/2$ and the cosine output at other frequencies. Once again, this verifies the ability of the circuit of Figure 2 to implement a tunable narrow-band band-pass filter. (NOTE: The plots obtained from MatLab label the Nyquist frequency π as 500. The plots show the entire frequency response from 0 to 2π. Hence, the cosine at $\pi/2$ appears at 250 on the x-axis.).

1.4 Problems with the simple tunable heterodyne structure

While the Simple Tunable Heterodyne Band-Pass Filter of Section 1.3 works very well, attempts to use the structure of Figure 2 to realize tunable wide-band filters such as tunable Band-Stop or Notch Filters, tunable cut-off frequency Low Pass or High Pass Filters or tunable bandwidth Band-Pass Filters will fail. Equation (7) represents the high-frequency components at $2\omega_0$ that must be substantially attenuated by H(z) in order to prevent interference with the desired filter of equation (6). In the case of a wide-band H(z), this attenuation does not happen and interference destroys the operation of the filter.

But an even more serious problem is in equation (6) itself. For example, if we try to design a tunable Band-Stop Filter by making H(z) a wide-band High-Pass Filter, equation (6) indicates that the stop-band of the High-Pass Filter H(z) has been moved to $\pm\omega_0$ as desired to attenuate frequencies around $\pm\omega_0$. However, since H(z) passes frequencies away from $\pm\omega_0$, the maximum attenuation that can be achieved across the stop band is only 6db! This is illustrated in Figure 5 where we have replaced the narrow-band band-pass H(z) from the previous section with a wide-band high-pass H(z).

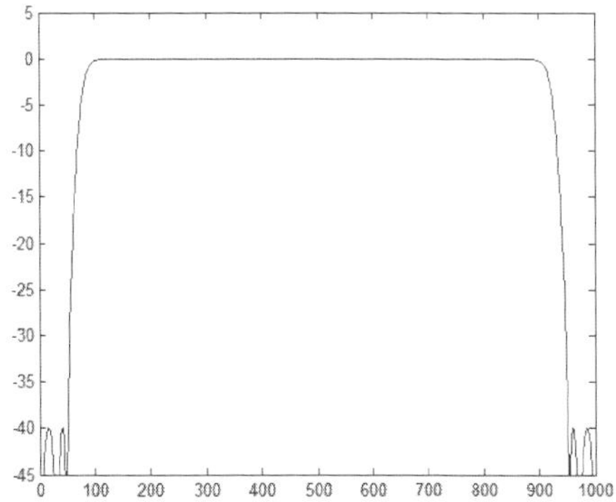

Fig. 5a. H(z) for a wideband high-pass filter

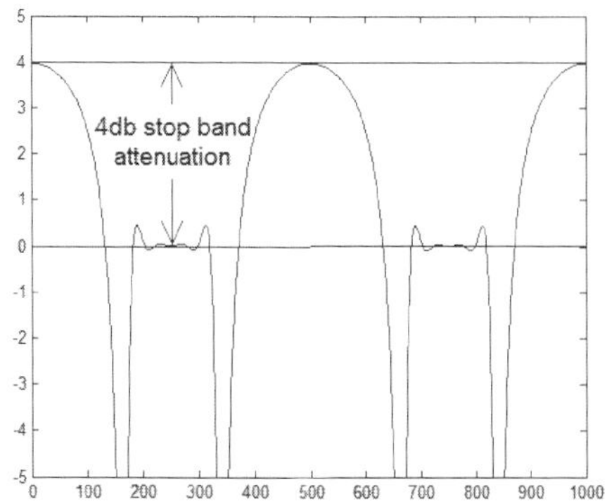

Fig. 5b. Tunable band-stop filter (poor attenuation)

Fig. 5. Demonstration of failure of circuit 2 to work with wide-band functions.

2. The complex digital heterodyne circuit

The key to designing Complex Heterodyne Tunable Filters is in the modification of the Basic Digital Heterodyne Circuit of Figure 1 into the Complex Digital Heterodyne Circuit shown in Figure 6a. When implemented in software or in hardware that supports complex arithmetic, the circuit is of little more complexity than the Basic Digital Heterodyne circuit of Figure 1. However, in standard hardware we must implement the complex arithmetic using standard digital hardware as shown in Figure 6b. Figure 6b is the complete implementation of the Complex Digital Heterodyne Circuit of Figure 6a. Figures 6c and 6d show simplified hardware for real input and for real output respectively. In the remainder of this chapter, we shall use the circuit diagram of Figure 6a to represent all the circuits of Figure 6.

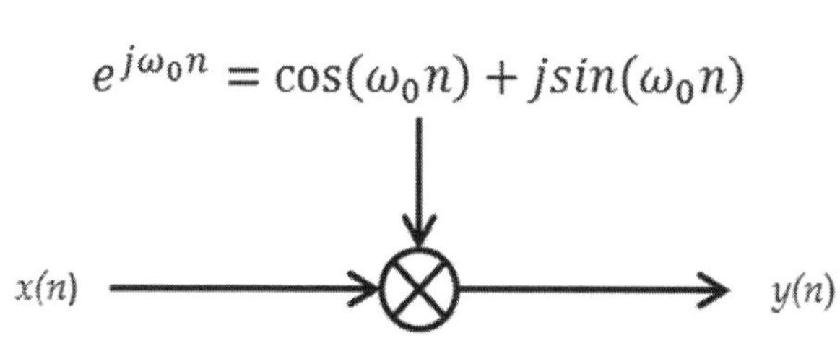

Fig. 6a. Complex heterodyne circuit for software or hardware that supports complex arithmetic

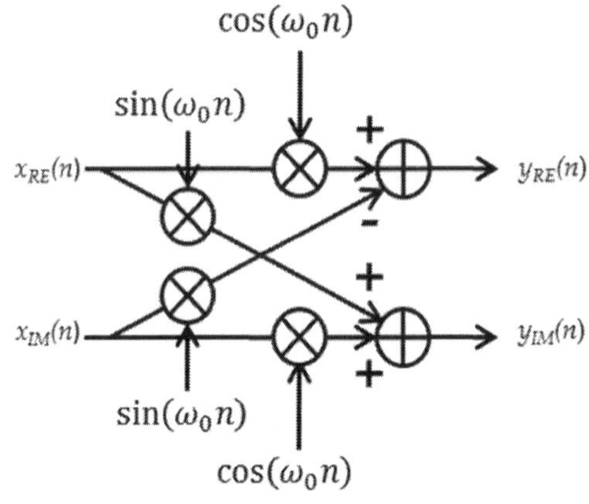

Fig. 6b. Complete hardware implementation of complex digital heterodyne circuit.

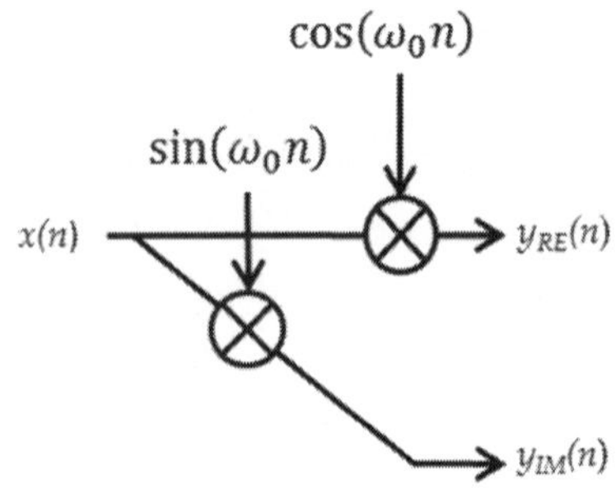

Fig. 6c. Implementation of real-input complex digital heterodyne

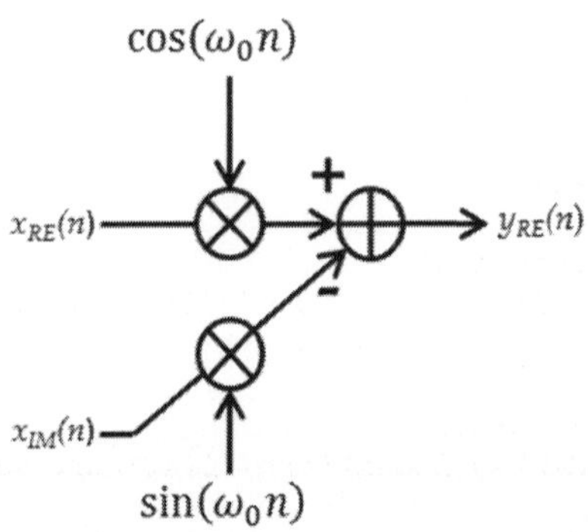

Fig. 6d. Implementation of real-output complex digital heterodyne.

Fig. 6. Implementations of the complex heterodyne circuit

2.1 Complex heterodyne rotation

Now we consider what happens when we replace the basic digital heterodyne circuit in Figure 2 with the complex digital heterodyne unit of Figure 6 to obtain the Complex Heterodyne Rotation Circuit of Figure 7.

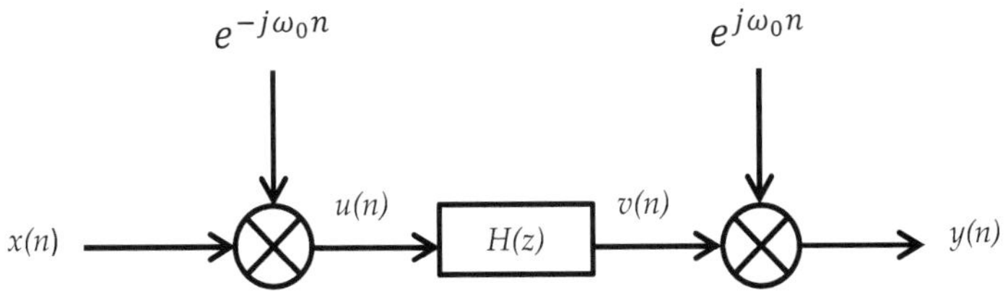

Fig. 7. Complex heterodyne rotation circuit (Rotates *H(z)* by ω_0 in the z-plane so that what was at DC is now at ω_0)

The MatLab code to implement Figure 7 is as follows:

```
% EXPHET  (Lab book p. 129 12/11/2010)
% Function to implement complex exponential heterodyne
filter
% Set the following inputs before calling EXPHET:
%       inp = 0 (provide input file inpf)
%           = 1 (impulse response)
%       npoints = number of points in input
%       w0 = heterodyne frequency
%       [b a] = coefficients of filter H(z)
% OUTPUTS:  hdb = frequency response of the filter
clear x y yout hdb
if inp==1
    for index=1:npoints
        inpf(index)=0;
    end
    inpf(1)=1;
end
for index=1:npoints
    x(index)=inpf(index)*exp(-1i*w0*(index-1));
end
y=filter(b,a,x);
for index=1:npoints
    yout(index)=y(index)*exp(1i*w0*(index-1));
end
hdb=20*log10(abs(fft(yout)));
plot(hdb,'k')
```

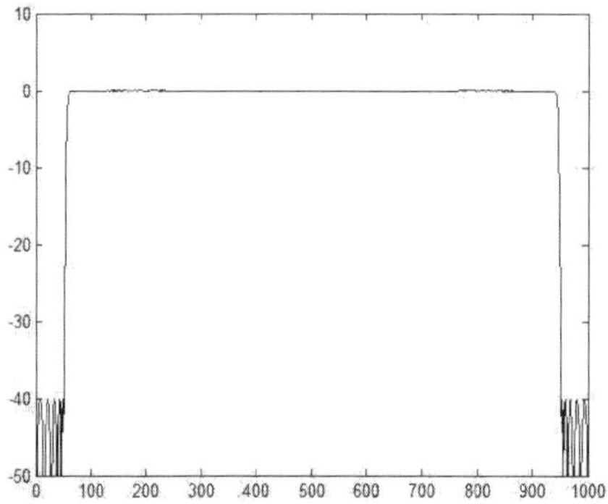

Fig. 8a. Frequency response of prototype filter

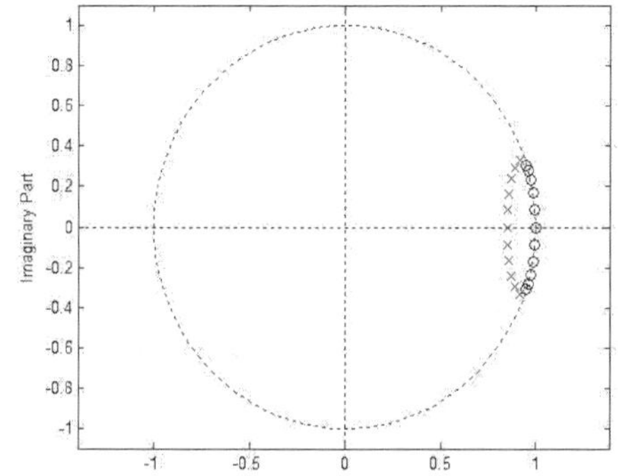

Fig. 8b. Pole-zero plot of prototype filter

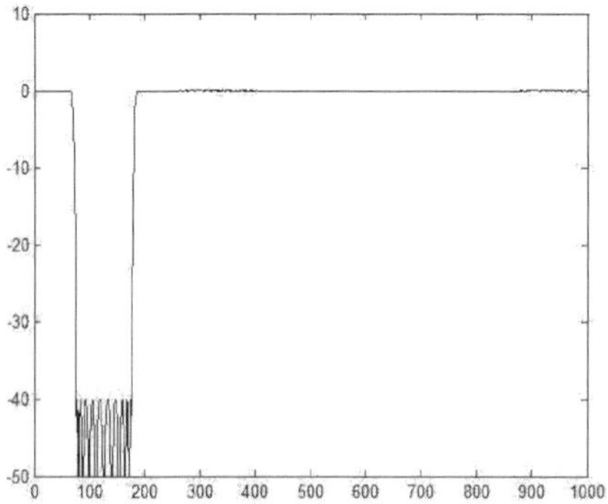

Fig. 8c. Frequency response of rotated filter

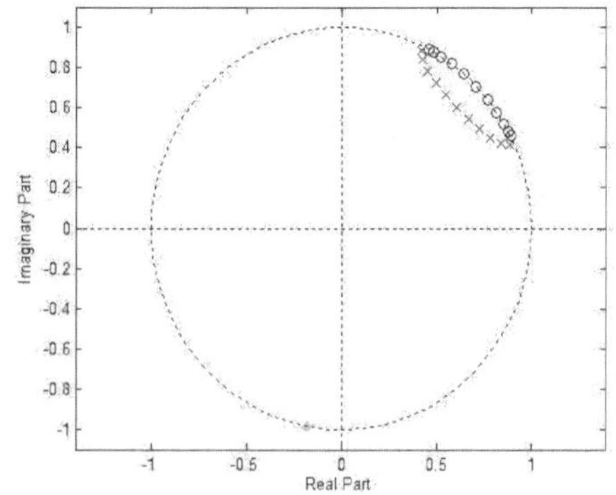

Fig. 8d. Pole-zero plot of rotated filter

Fig. 8. Demonstration of complex heterodyne rotation circuit of Figure 7

Using the same prototype wideband High-Pass Filter as we used in Section 1.4 to get Figures 5a and 5b, let's use this prototype filter in the Complex Heterodyne Rotation Circuit if Figure 7. The results are shown in Figure 8. Figure 8a shows the frequency response of the prototype wideband High-Pass Filter, Figure 8b shows the pole-zero plot for this prototype filter, Figure 8c shows the frequency response of the rotated filter at the output of Figure 7, and Figure 8d shows the pole-zero plot for the circuit of Figure 7 with the wideband High-Pass prototype filter used for H(z).

Figure 8 demonstrates the ability of the Complex Heterodyne Rotation Circuit of Figure 7 to rotate poles and zeros in the z-plane. However, the output of Figure 7 is not real. It is a complex output generating a frequency response that is not symmetric around the Nyquist frequency. This means that the filter will attenuate frequencies at $+\omega_0$ but not at $-\omega_0$. Since real systems have frequencies at both $+\omega_0$ and $-\omega_0$, the circuit of Figure 7 cannot be used to implement a band-stop filter for real systems. In sections 3, 4 and 5 we shall see three different ways we can make use of the basic circuit of Figure 7 to implement tunable band-stop and notch filters, tunable cut-off frequency high-pass and low-pass filters, and tunable bandwidth band-pass filters.

3. Three-way tunable complex heterodyne filter (Azam's technique)

The basic structure for Tunable Complex Heterodyne filters is shown in Figure 9. This Three-Way Tunable Complex Heterodyne circuit consists of three complex heterodyne units of Figure 6 and two identical prototype filters H(z). By selecting the correct prototype filter, we are able to design tunable band-stop and notch filters, tunable cut-off frequency low-pass and high-pass filters and tunable bandwidth band-pass and band-stop filters. These filters are maximally tunable in that the band-pass and band-stop filters can be tuned from DC to the Nyquist frequency and the other filters can be tuned such that their bandwidth varies from zero to half the Nyquist frequency. There is no distortion in the filters, the prototype design transfers directly except that the pass-band ripple is doubled, thus we must design prototype filters with half the desired pass-band ripple.

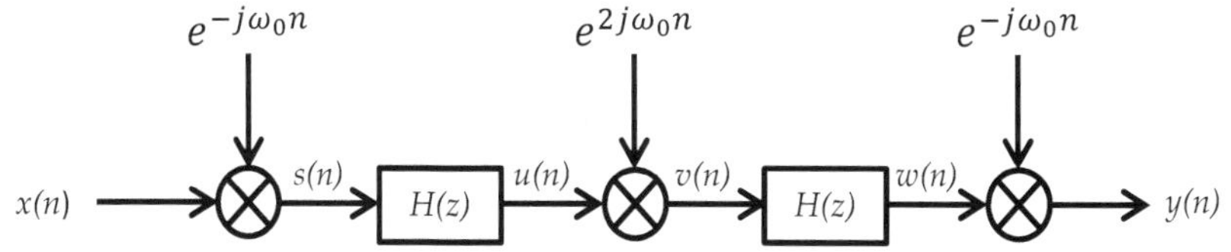

Fig. 9. Three-way tunable complex heterodyne filter (Azam's method)

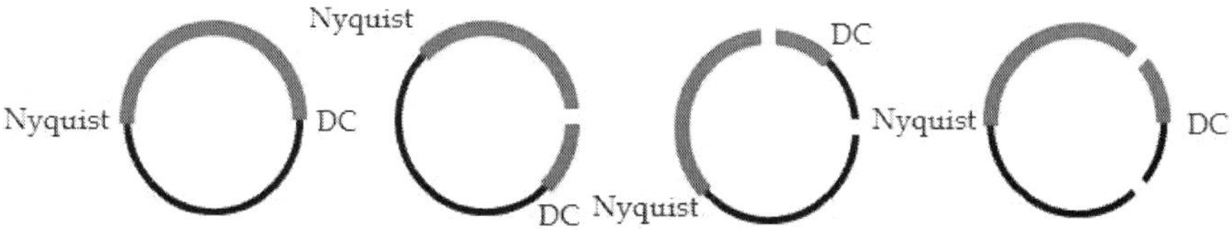

Fig. 10a. Input $X(z)$ Fig. 10b. Rotate ω_0 to DC Fig. 10c. Rotate - ω_0 to DC Fig. 10d. Rotate back

Fig. 10. Creation of a notch at $\pm\omega_0$ using the three-way tunable complex heterodyne filter of Figure 9 (z-plane).

Before we look at the detailed analysis of Figure 9, let's take an overview of its operation. In order to make the procedure clear, let's assume that H(z) is a wide-band high-pass filter like that of Figure 8a and 8b. Then the first heterodyne operation rotates the input signal x(n) (shown in Figure 10a.) by $-\omega_0$ so that the frequencies that were at DC are now located at $-\omega_0$ (see Figure 10b). H(z) is then applied attenuating frequencies that were at ω_0 in x(n) before the rotation (indicated by white spot in Figure 10b). At this point if we simply rotated back like we did in the circuit of Figure 7, we would get the rotated H(z) as shown in Figure 8c and 8d. However, in Figure 9 we now rotate back $2\omega_0$ so that the frequencies of x(n) that were at DC are now at $+\omega_0$ in x(n) (see Figure 10c) The second identical H(z) then attenuates frequencies in x(n) that were at $-\omega_0$ before any of these rotations (indicated by second white spot in Figure 10c). Finally, we rotate the signal back to its original frequencies with the attenuation having been applied both at $+\omega_0$ (first H(z)) and $-\omega_0$ (second H(z)) as shown in Figure 10d. Since H(z) is applied twice, we will experience twice the pass-band ripple. Hence, the prototype filter H(z) must be designed with one-half the ripple desired in the final filter. Also because H(z) is applied twice, some portions of the stop-band will have twice the attenuation while other parts will have the desired attenuation. Having more attenuation than specified is not a problem, so we will design the prototype filter H(z) with the desired stop-band attenuation (not half the stop-band attenuation).

Now let's look at the detailed mathematics of Figure 9. Making use of the relationship of Equation 1, we have the following as a result of passing x(n) (see Figure 10a) through the first complex heterodyne unit in Figure 9:

$$x(n)e^{-j\omega_0 n} \overset{Z}{\Leftrightarrow} X\left(ze^{j\omega_0}\right) \tag{8}$$

Next we apply the prototype filter H(z) (see Figure 10b):

$$x(n)e^{-j\omega_0 n} * h(n) \overset{Z}{\Leftrightarrow} X\left(ze^{j\omega_0}\right)H(z) \tag{9}$$

Now we rotate back $2\omega_0$ by passing through the second complex heterodyne unit (see Figure 10c):

$$[x(n)e^{-j\omega_0 n} * h(n)]e^{2j\omega_0 n} \overset{Z}{\Leftrightarrow} X\left(ze^{-j\omega_0}\right)H(ze^{-2j\omega_0 n}) \tag{10}$$

We then apply the second identical prototype filter H(z) (see Figure 10c):

$$\left\{\left[x(n)e^{-j\omega_0 n} * h(n)\right]e^{2j\omega_0 n}\right\} * h(n) \overset{Z}{\Leftrightarrow} X\left(ze^{-j\omega_0}\right)H\left(ze^{-2j\omega_0 n}\right)H(z) \tag{11}$$

Finally we pass through the last complex heterodyne unit returning the signal to its original location (see Figure 10d):

$$(\left\{\left[x(n)e^{-j\omega_0 n} * h(n)\right]e^{2j\omega_0 n}\right\} * h(n))e^{-j\omega_0 n} \overset{Z}{\Leftrightarrow} X(z)H\left(ze^{-j\omega_0 n}\right)H(ze^{j\omega_0 n}) \tag{12}$$

The transfer function shown in equation (12) above is the effect of the entire Three-Way Tunable Complex Heterodyne Filter shown in Figure 9. By choosing different prototype filters H(z) we are able to implement tunable center-frequency band-stop and notch filters, tunable cut-off frequency low-pass and high-pass filers, and tunable bandwidth band-pass and band-stop filters. In the following sections we will look at the details for each of these designs.

Designing tunable filters using the Three-Way Complex Heterodyne circuit of Figure 9 is simply a matter of choosing the correct prototype filter H(z). Table 1 on the next page shows the types of tunable filters that can be designed using the Three-Way Complex Heterodyne Technique including the requirements for the prototype filter H(z) and the tunable range. In the following sections we shall make use of this table to design examples of each of these tunable filters.

3.1 Design of tunable center-frequency band-stop filter

In this and the following five sections we will give an example of each of the filter designs in Table 1. In all of these designs the prototype filter H(z) may be designed using any of the many filter design techniques. For example, in MatLab we may design Butterworth (butter), Chebyshev (cheby1), inverse Chebyshev (cheby2), elliptical (ellip) or Parks-McClellan Linear Phase Filters (firpm) to name a few. The Three-Way Complex Heterodyne Circuit of Figure 9 and Table 1 will preserve the key characteristics of the prototype filter except as noted in Table 1. The examples in this chapter will all be based on linear-phase Parks-McClellan filters. The prototype filter H(z) will use a 64-tap prototype filter with weights designed to obtain 40db attenuation in the stop band and a maximum ripple of 1.5db in the prototype filter pass-band (3db in the tunable filter pass-band).

Desired Tunable Filter	**Required** H(z)	**Tunable Range**
Tunable center-frequency band-stop filter	High-pass filter with cut-off frequency equal to one-half of the desired band-width, pass-band ripple equal to one-half the desired pass-band ripple and stop-band attenuation equal to the desire stop-band attenuation for the tunable center-frequency band-stop filter.	Fully tunable from DC to the Nyquist frequency.
Tunable cut-off frequency low-pass filter	Low-pass filter with cut-off frequency equal to one-half of the Nyquist frequency, pass-band ripple equal to one-half the desired pass-band ripple and stop-band attenuation equal to the desire stop-band attenuation for the tunable cut-off frequency low-pass filter.	Cut-off frequency tunable from DC to one-half the Nyquist frequency
Tunable cut-off high-pass filter	High-pass filter with cut-off frequency equal to one-half of the Nyquist frequency, pass-band ripple equal to one-half the desired pass-band ripple and stop-band attenuation equal to the desire stop-band attenuation for the tunable cut-off frequency high-pass filter.	Cut-off frequency tunable from DC to one-half the Nyquist frequency
Tunable band-width band-pass filter	Band-pass filter centered at $\pi/2$ with band-width of $\pi/2$, pass-band ripple equal to one-half the desired pass-band ripple and stop-band attenuation equal to the desired stop-band attenuation for the tunable band-width band-pass filter.	Bandwidth tunable from Δ to $\pi/2$
Tunable band-width band-stop filter	Band-stop filter centered at $\pi/2$ with band-width of $\pi/2$, pass-band ripple equal to one-half the desired pass-band ripple and stop-band attenuation equal to the desired stop-band attenuation for the tunable band-width band-stop filter.	Bandwidth tunable from Δ to $\pi/2$
NOTE: In bandwidth tuning, Δ is the smallest bandwidth available. The actual value of Δ depends on the transition band of the prototype filter H(z). The narrower the transition band, the smaller the value of Δ. Attempts to tune the bandwidth to less than Δ will result in leakage at DC and the Nyquist frequency.		

Table 1. Design of tunable filters using the three-way complex heterodyne circuit of Figure 9

The following MatLab code is used to implement the Three-Way Complex Heterodyne Circuit of Figure 9:

```
% N3WAYHET
% Implements the Three-Way Heterodyne Rotion Filter
% Also known as the Full-Tunable Digital Heterodyne Filter
% INPUTS:
% Set the following inputs before calling 3WAYHET:
%       inp = 0 (provide input file inpf)
%           = 1 (impulse response)
%       npoints = number of points in input
%       w0 = heterodyne frequency
%       [b a] = coefficients of filter H(z)
%       scale = 0 (do not scale the output)
%             = 1 (scale the output to zero db)
%
% OUTPUTS:  ydb = frequency response of the filter
%           hdb, sdb, udb, vdb, wdb (intermediate outputs)
clear y ydb hdb s sdb u udb v vdb w wdb
if inp==1
    for index=1:npoints
        inpf(index)=0;
    end
    inpf(1)=1;
end
for index=1:npoints
    s(index)=inpf(index)*exp(-1i*w0*(index-1));
end
u=filter(b,a,s);
for index=1:npoints
    v(index)=u(index)*exp(+2*1i*w0*(index-1));
end
w=filter(b,a,v);
for index=1:npoints
    y(index)=w(index)*exp(-1i*w0*(index-1));
end
[h,f]=freqz(b,a,npoints,'whole');
hdb=20*log10(abs(h));
sdb=20*log10(abs(fft(s)));
udb=20*log10(abs(fft(u)));
vdb=20*log10(abs(fft(v)));
wdb=20*log10(abs(fft(w)));
ydb=20*log10(abs(fft(y)));
if scale==1
    ydbmax=max(ydb)
    ydb=ydb-ydbmax;
end
plot(ydb,'k')
```

To design a tunable center-frequency band-pass filter, the prototype filter must be a narrow-band low-pass filter with the bandwidth equal to half the bandwidth of the desired tunable band-pass filter. Before calling the MatLab m-file n3wayhet, we initialize the input variables as follows:

```
inp=1;npoints=1000;w0=0;a=1;b=firpm(64,[0 .1*.8 .1/.8 1],[0 0 1 1],[10 1]);scale=1 n3wayhet;
```

Figure 11 shows the design criteria for the prototype wide-band high-pass filter needed to implement the tunable band-stop filter. The prototype high-pass filter needs a stop-band bandwidth of one-half the desired bandwidth of the tunable notch filter. The prototype filter must have one-half the pass-band ripple of the desired pass-band ripple for the tunable band-pass filter. However, the prototype high-pass filter should have the same stop-band attenuation as is desired in the tunable band-stop filter.

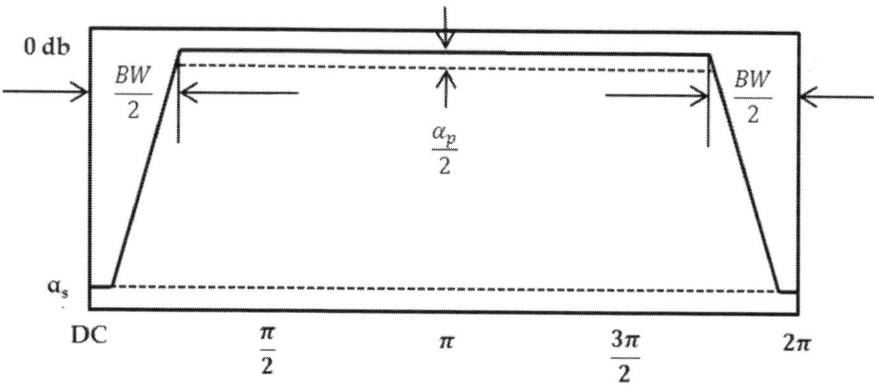

Fig. 11. Design criteria for prototype wide-band high-pass filter *H(z)* required to implement a tunable band-stop filter using the three-way complex heterodyne circuit of Figure 9.

Figure 12 shows the result of running this MatLab m-file simulation of the circuit of Figure 9 for four different values of ω_0, $\omega_0 = 0$, $\omega_0 = \frac{\pi}{4}$, $\omega_0 = \frac{\pi}{2}$ and $\omega_0 = \frac{3\pi}{4}$. Key features of the Three-Way Complex Heterodyne Technique can be seen in Figure 12. First, when $\omega_0 = 0$ we get the frequency response shown in Figure 12a which is the prototype filter convolved with itself (H(z)H(z)). Thus we have over 80db attenuation in the stop band and the desired less that 3db ripple in the pass-band. The prototype filter is High-Pass. Figure 12b shows the circuit with $\omega_0 = \pi/4$. This tunes the center frequency to $\pi/4$ which shows up as 125 on the x-axis of Figure 12b. Figure 12c shows the circuit with $\omega_0 = \pi/2$. This tunes the center frequency to $\pi/2$ which shows up as 250 on the x-axis of Figure 12c. Figure 12d shows the circuit with $\omega_0 = 3\pi/4$. This tunes the center frequency to $3\pi/4$ which shows up as 375 on the x-axis of Figure 12d. Notice that the attenuation of the tuned band-stop filters is over 40db which is the same stop-band attenuation as the prototype filter. All of these filters retain the linear-phase property of the prototype filter that was designed using the Parks-McClellan algorithm.

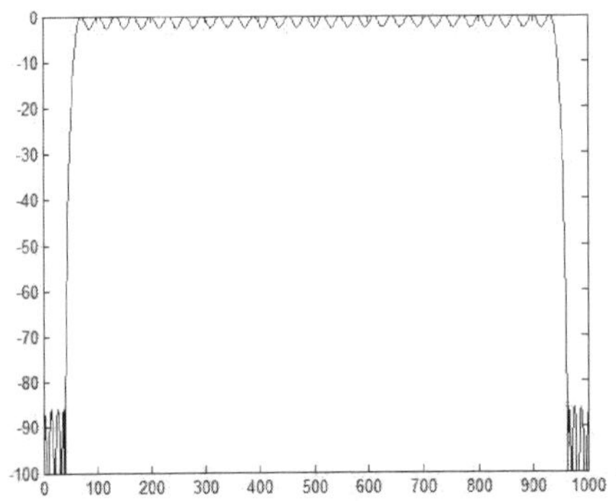

Fig. 12a. Tunable band pass $\omega_0 = 0$ $[H(z)H(z)]$

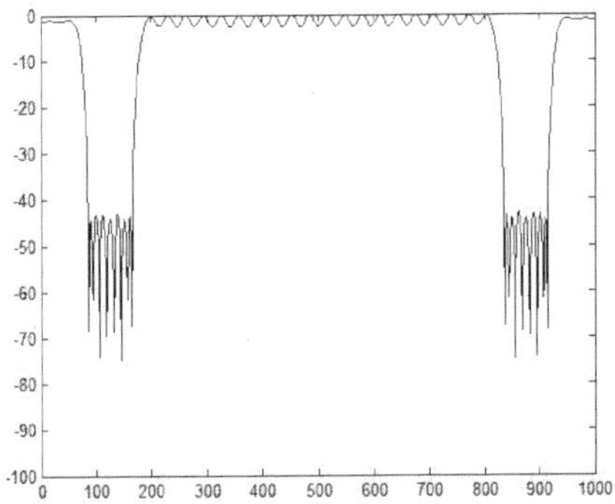

Fig. 12b. Tunable band pass $\omega_0 = \pi/4$

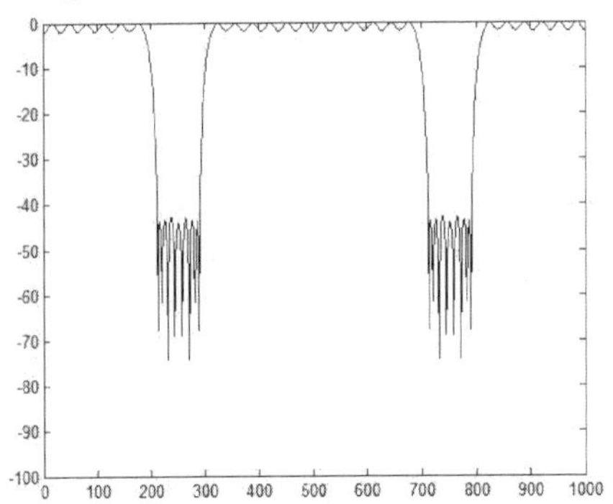

Fig. 12c. Tunable band pass $\omega_0 = \pi/2$

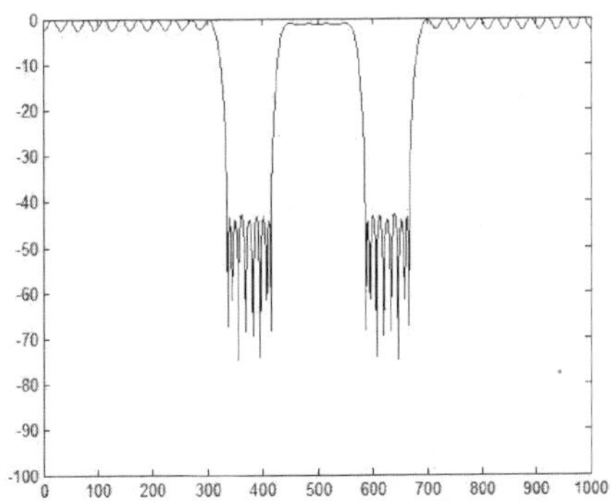

Fig. 12d. Tunable band pass $\omega_0 = 3\pi/4$

Fig. 12. Tunable center-frequency linear-phase band-stop filter using the three-way Complex heterodyne circuit

3.2 Tunable cut-off frequency low-pass filter

To design a tunable cut-off frequency low-pass filter, the prototype filter must be a wide-band low-pass filter with the bandwidth equal to half the Nyquist Frequency. Before calling the MatLab m-file n3wayhet, we initialize the input variables as follows:

```
inp=1;npoints=1000;w0=0;a=1;b=firpm(64,[0 .5*.955 .5/.955 1],[1 1 0 0],[1 10]);
scale=1;n3wayhet
```

Figure 13 shows the design criteria for the prototype low-pass filter with cut-off frequency at $\pi/2$ that is needed to implement the tunable cut-off frequency low-pass filter. The prototype low-pass filter needs a cut-off frequency of $\pi/2$. The prototype filter must have one-half the pass-band ripple of the desired pass-band ripple and the same stop band attenuation as for the tunable cut-off frequency low-pass filter.

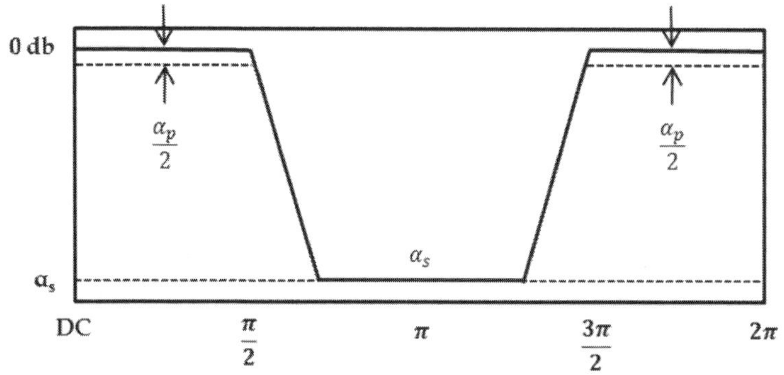

Fig. 13. Design criteria for prototype low-pass filter $H(z)$ with cut-off frequency at $\pi/2$ required to implement a tunable cut-off frequency low-pass filter using the three-way complex heterodyne circuit of Figure 9.

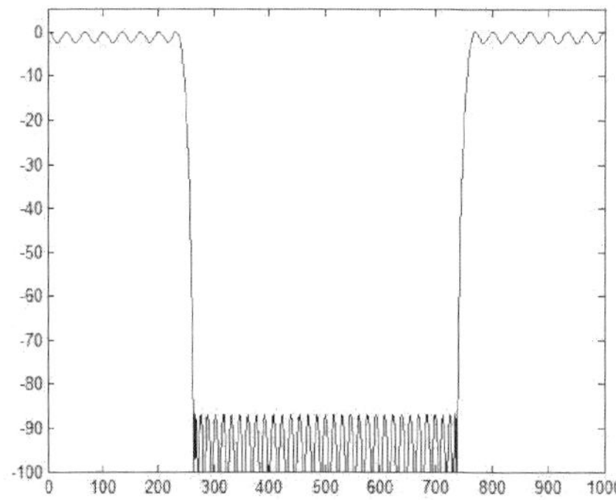

Fig. 14a. Tunable cut-off low-pass filter $\omega_0 = 0$ $[H(z)H(z)]$

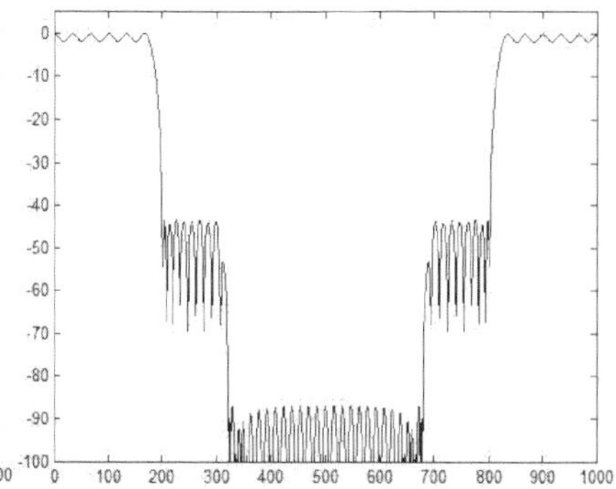

Fig. 14b. Tunable cut-off low-pass $\omega_0 = \pi/4$

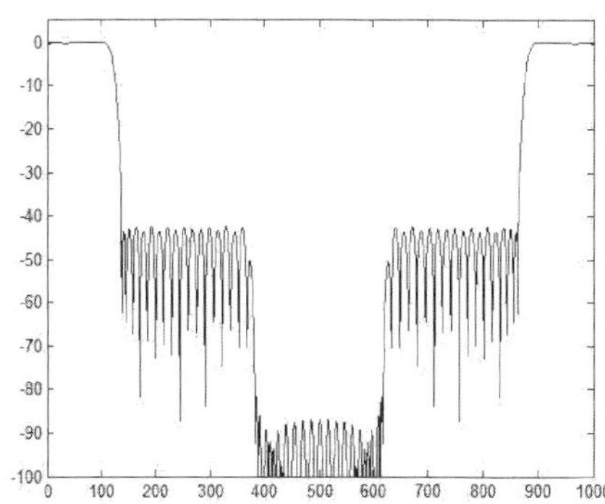

Fig. 14c. Tunable cut-off low-pass $\omega_0 = \pi/2$

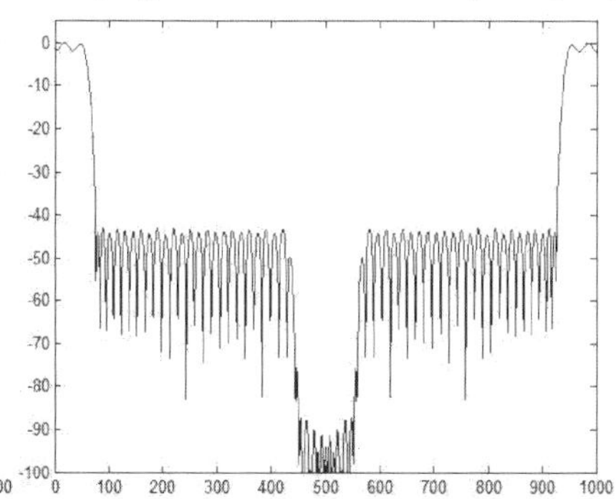

Fig. 14d. Tunable cut-off low-pass $\omega_0 = 3\pi/4$

Fig. 14. Tunable cut-off frequency linear-phase low-pass filter using three-way complex heterodyne circuit

Figure 14 shows the tunable cut-off frequency low-pass filter. First, when $\omega_0 = 0$ we get the frequency response shown in Figure 14a which is the prototype filter convolved with itself (H(z)H(z)). Thus we have over 80db attenuation in the stop band and the desired less that 3db ripple in the pass-band. The prototype filter is Low-Pass with bandwidth set to one-half the Nyquist frequency (250 on the x-axis). Figure 14b shows the circuit with $\omega_0 = \pi/8$. This tunes the cut-off frequency to $\pi/2 - \pi/8 = 3\pi/8$ which shows up as 187.5 on the x-axis of Figure 14b. Figure 14c shows the circuit with $\omega_0 = \pi/4$. This tunes the cut-off frequency to $\pi/2 - \pi/4 = \pi/4$ which shows up as 125 on the x-axis of Figure 14c. Figure 14d shows the circuit with $\omega_0 = 3\pi/8$. This tunes the center frequency to $\pi/2 - 3\pi/8 = \pi/8$ which shows up as 62.5 on the x-axis of Figure 14d. Notice that the attenuation of the tuned low-pass filters is over 40db which is the same stop-band attenuation as the prototype filter. All of these filters retain the linear-phase property of the prototype filter that was designed using the Parks-McClellan algorithm.

3.3 Tunable cut-off frequency high-pass filter

To design a tunable cut-off frequency high-pass filter, the prototype filter must be a wide-band high-pass filter with the bandwidth equal to half the Nyquist Frequency. Before calling the MatLab m-file n3wayhet, we initialize the input variables as follows:

```
inp=1;npoints=1000;w0=0;a=1;b=firpm(64,[0 .1*.8 .1/.8 1],[0 0 1 1],[10 1]);
scale=1;n3wayhet;
```

Figure 15 shows the design criteria for the prototype high-pass filter with cut-off frequency at $\pi/2$ that is needed to implement the tunable cut-off frequency high-pass filter. The prototype high-pass filter needs a cut-off frequency of $\pi/2$. The prototype filter must have one-half the pass-band ripple of the desired pass-band ripple and the same stop band attenuation as for the tunable cut-off frequency high-pass filter.

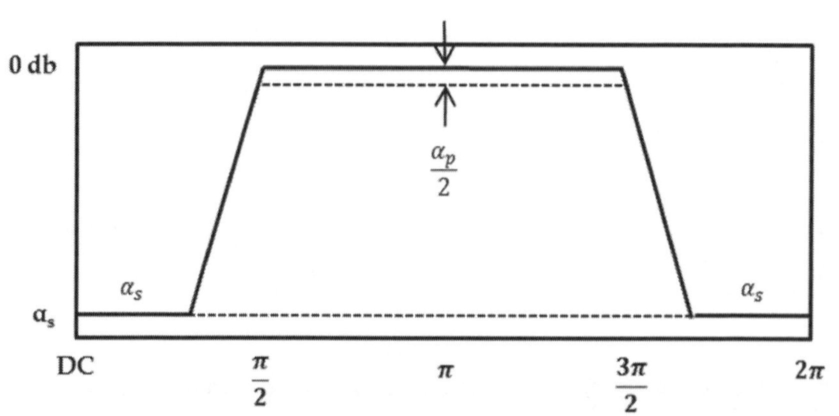

Fig. 15. Design criteria for prototype high-pass filter *h(z)* with cut-off frequency at $\pi/2$ required to implement a tunable cut-off frequency high-pas filter using the three-way complex heterodyne circuit of figure 9.

Figure 16 shows the tunable cut-off frequency high-pass filter. First, when $\omega_0 = 0$ we get the frequency response shown in Figure 16a which is the prototype filter convolved with itself (H(z)H(z)). Thus we have over 80db attenuation in the stop band and the desired less that 3db ripple in the pass-band. The prototype filter is High-Pass with bandwidth set to one-half the Nyquist frequency (250 on the x-axis). Figure 16b shows the circuit with $\omega_0 = \pi/8$. This tunes the cut-off frequency to $\pi/2 + \pi/8 = 5\pi/8$ which shows up as 312.5 on the x-axis of Figure 16b. Figure 16c shows the circuit with $\omega_0 = \pi/4$. This tunes the cut-off frequency to $\pi/2 + \pi/4 = 3\pi/4$ which shows up as 375 on the x-axis of Figure 16c. Figure 16d shows the circuit with $\omega_0 = 3\pi/8$. This tunes the center frequency to $\pi/2 + 3\pi/8 = 7\pi/8$ which shows up as 437.5 on the x-axis of Figure 16d. Notice that the attenuation of the tuned high-pass filters is over 40db which is the same stop-band attenuation as the prototype filter. All of these filters retain the linear-phase property of the prototype filter that was designed using the Parks-McClellan algorithm.

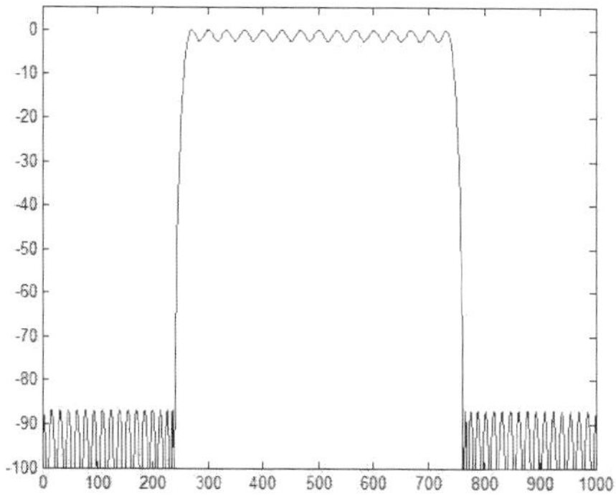

Fig. 16a. Tunable high-pass filter $\omega_0 = 0$ $(H(z)H(z))$

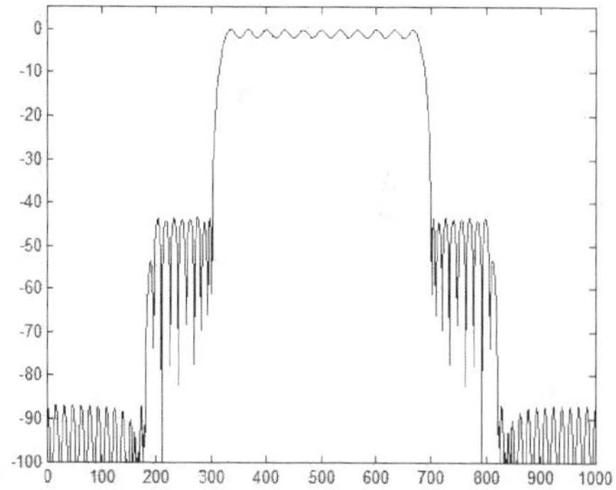

Fig. 16b. Tunable high-pass filter $\omega_0 = \pi/8$

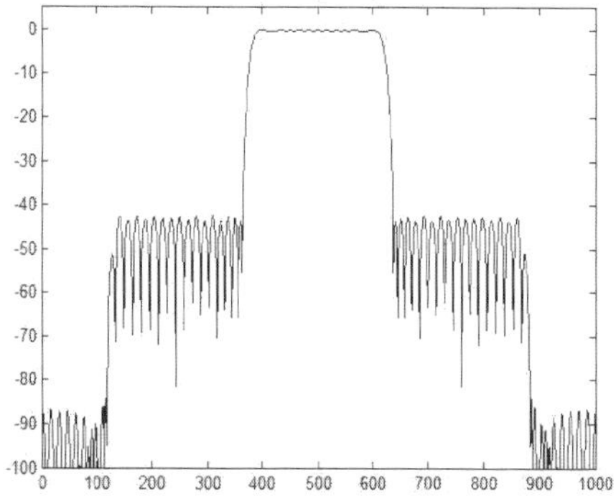

Fig. 16c. Tunable high-pass filter $\omega_0 = \pi/4$

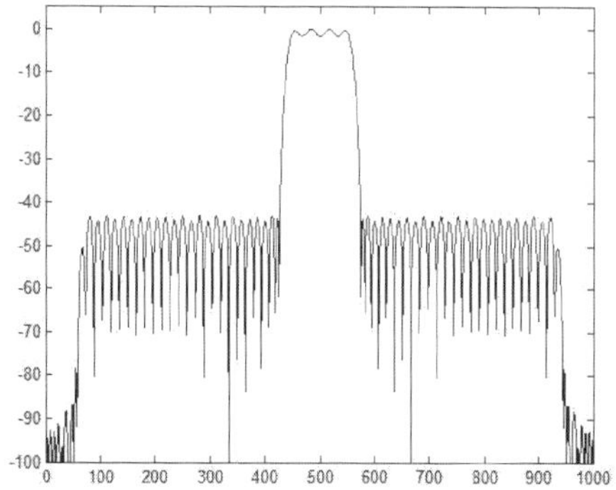

Fig. 16d. Tunable high-pass filter $\omega_0 = 3\pi/8$

Fig. 16. Tunable cut-off frequency linear-phase high-pass filter using three-way complex heterodyne circuit

3.4 Tunable bandwidth band-pass filter

To design a tunable bandwidth band-pass filter, the prototype filter must be a wide-band band-pass filter with the bandwidth equal to half the Nyquist Frequency. Before calling the MatLab m-file n3wayhet, we initialize the input variables as follows:

```
inp=1;npoints=1000;w0=0;a=1;b=firpm(64,[0 .25*.9 .25/.9 .75*.95 .75/.95 1],
                [0 0 1 1 0 0],[10 1 10]);scale=1;n3wayhet
```

Figure 17 shows the design criteria for the prototype band-pass filter with bandwidth of π/2 that is needed to implement the tunable bandwidth band-pass filter. The prototype band-pass filter needs a bandwidth of π/2. The prototype filter must have one-half the pass-band ripple of the desired pass-band ripple and the same stop band attenuation as for the tunable bandwidth band-pass filter.

Figure 18 shows the tunable bandwidth band-pass filter. First, when $\omega_0 = 0$ we get the frequency response shown in Figure 18a which is the prototype filter convolved with itself (H(z)H(z)). Thus we have over 80db attenuation in the stop band and the desired less that 3db ripple in the pass-band. The prototype filter is Band-Pass centered at π/2 with bandwidth of π/2 (125 to 375 on the x-axis). Figure 18b shows the circuit with $\omega_0 = \pi/16$. This tunes the lower band edge to π/2 - π/4 + π/16 = 5π/16 (156.25 on the x-axis of Figure 18b) and the upper band edge to π/2 + π/4 - π/16 = 11π/16 (343.75 on the x-axis of Figure 18b). Figure 18c shows the circuit with $\omega_0 = \pi/8$. This tunes the lower band edge to π/2 - π/4 + π/8 = 3π/8 (187.5 on the x-axis of Figure 16c) and the upper band edge to π/2 + π/4 - π/8 = 5π/8 (312.5 on the x-axis in Figure 18c). Figure 18d shows the circuit with $\omega_0 = 3\pi/16$. This tunes the lower band edge to π/2 - π/4 + 3π/16 = 7π/16 (218.75 on the x-axis of Figure 18d) and the upper band edge to π/2 + π/4 - 3π/16 = 9π/16 (281.25 on the x-axis of Figure 18d). Notice that the attenuation of the tuned band-pass filters is over 40db which is the same stop-band attenuation as the prototype filter. All of these filters retain the linear-phase property of the prototype filter that was designed using the Parks-McClellan algorithm.

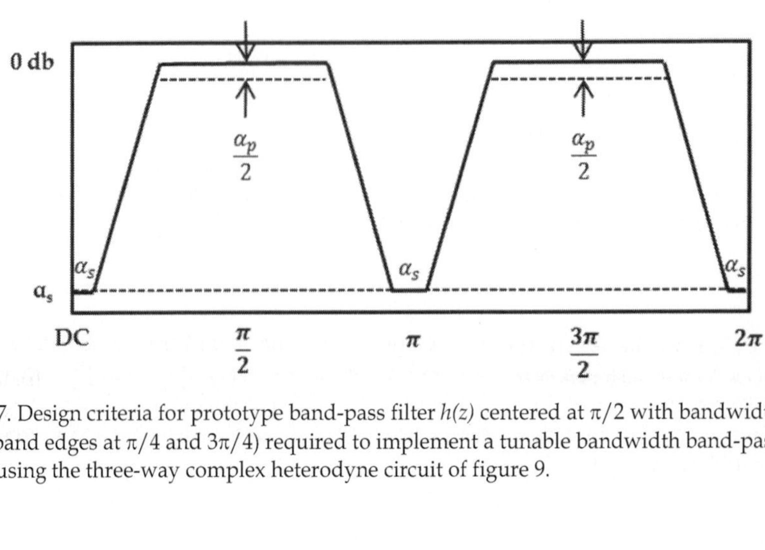

Fig. 17. Design criteria for prototype band-pass filter *h(z)* centered at π/2 with bandwidth of π/2 (band edges at π/4 and 3π/4) required to implement a tunable bandwidth band-pass filter using the three-way complex heterodyne circuit of figure 9.

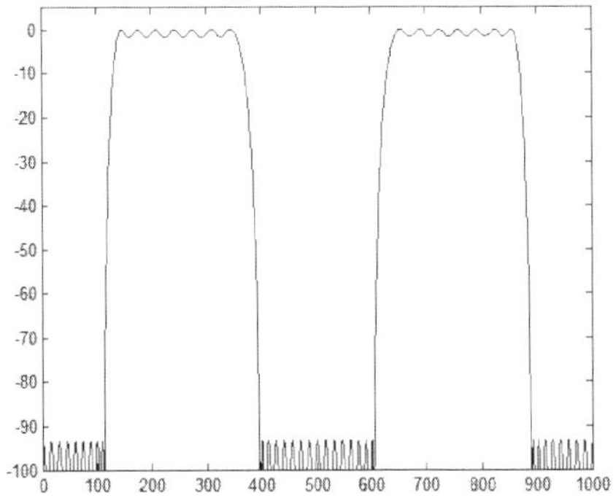

Fig. 18a. Tunable bandwidth BP filter $\omega_0 = 0$ $(H(z)H(z))$

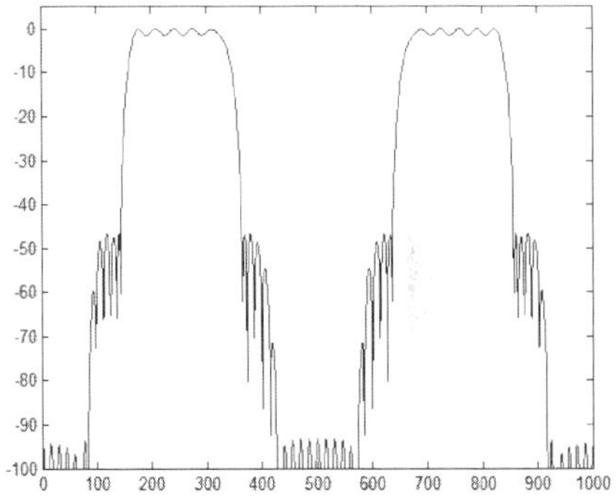

Fig. 18b. Tunable bandwidth BP filter $\omega_0 = \pi/8$

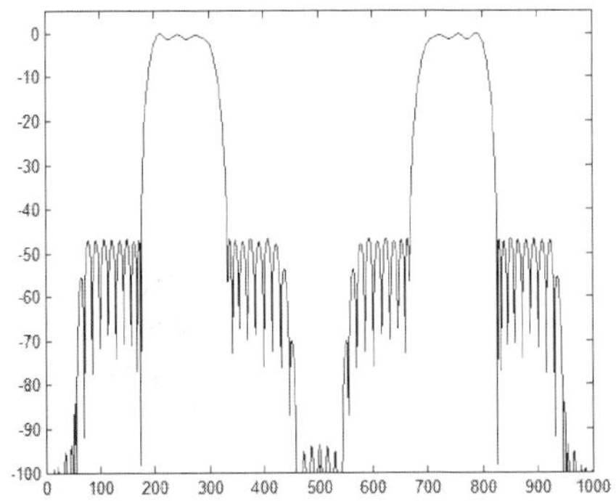

Fig. 18c. Tunable bandwidth BP filter $\omega_0 = \pi/4$

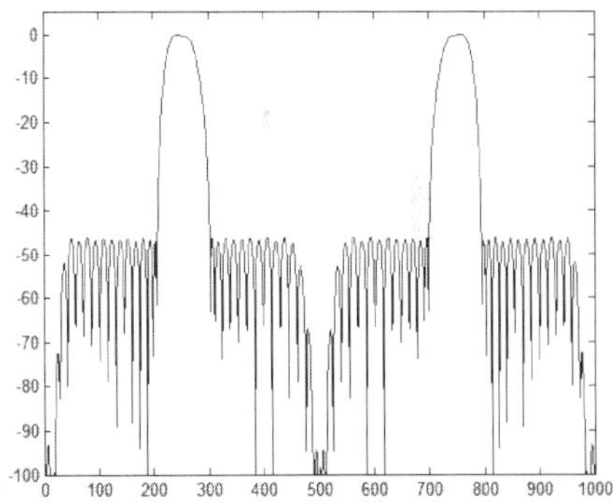

Fig. 18d. Tunable bandwidth BP filter $\omega_0 = 3\pi/8$

Fig. 18. Tunable bandwidth linear-phase band-pass filter using three-way complex heterodyne circuit

3.5 Tunable bandwidth band-stop filter

To design a tunable bandwidth band-stop filter, the prototype filter must be a wide-band band-stop filter with the bandwidth equal to half the Nyquist Frequency. Before calling the MatLab m-file n3wayhet, we initialize the input variables as follows:

```
inp=1;npoints=1000;w0=0;a=1;b=firpm(64,[0 .25*.9 .25/.9 .75*.95 .75/.95 1],[1 1 0 0 1 1],
[1 10 1]);scale=1;n3wayhet
```

Figure 19 shows the design criteria for the prototype band-stop filter with bandwidth of $\pi/2$ that is needed to implement the tunable bandwidth band-stop filter. The prototype band-stop filter needs a bandwidth of $\pi/2$. The prototype filter must have one-half the pass-band ripple of the desired pass-band ripple and the same stop band attenuation as for the tunable bandwidth band-stop filter.

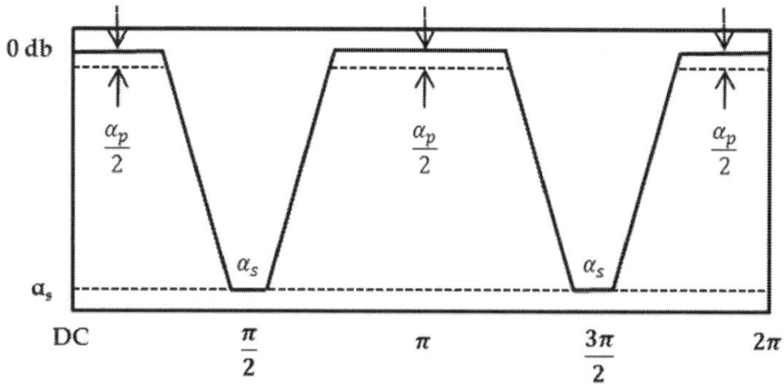

Fig. 19. Design criteria for prototype band-stop filter $H(z)$ centered at $\pi/2$ with bandwidth of $\pi/2$ (band edges at $\pi/4$ and $3\pi/4$) required to implement a tunable bandwidth band-stop filter using the three-way complex heterodyne circuit of Figure 9.

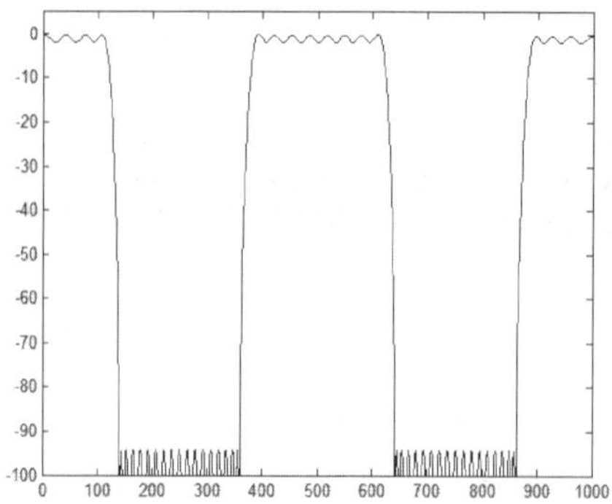

Fig. 20a. Tunable bandwidth BS filter $\omega_0 = 0$ ($H(z)H(z)$)

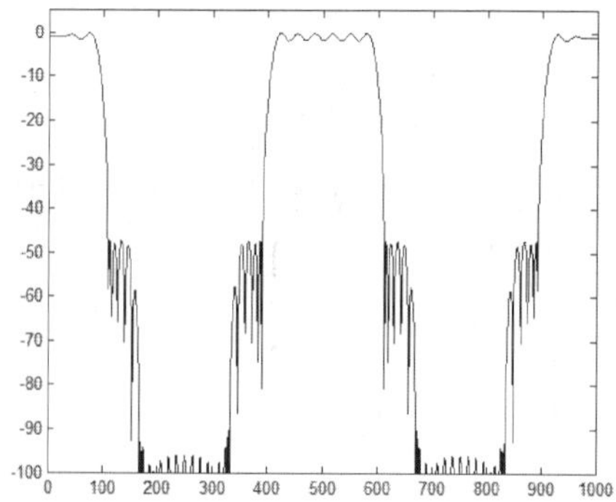

Fig. 20b. Tunable bandwidth BS filter $\omega_0 = \pi/8$

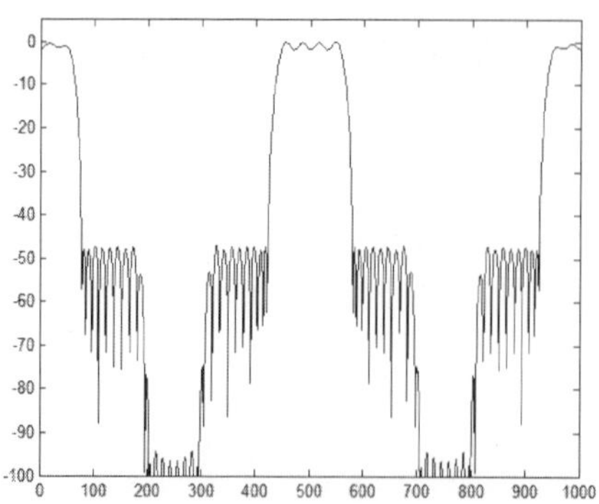

Fig. 20c. Tunable bandwidth BS filter $\omega_0 = \pi/4$

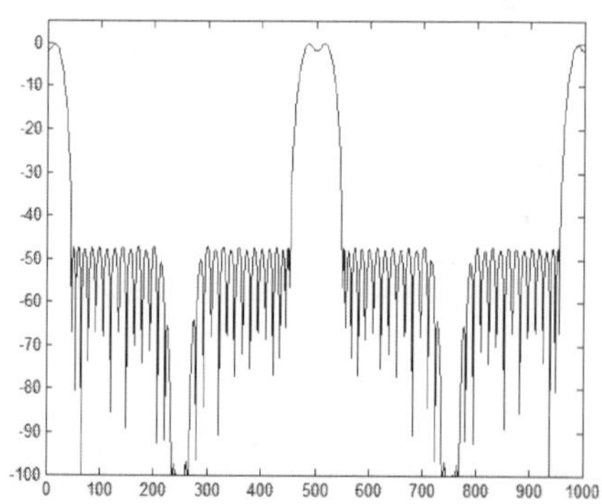

Fig. 20d. Tunable bandwidth Bs filter $\omega_0 = 3\pi/8$

Fig. 20. Tunable bandwidth linear-phase band-stop filter using three-way complex heterodyne circuit

Figure 20 shows the tunable bandwidth band-stop filter. First, when $\omega_0 = 0$ we get the frequency response shown in Figure 20a which is the prototype filter convolved with itself (*H(z)H(z)*). Thus we have over 80db attenuation in the stop band and the desired less that 3db ripple in the pass-band. The prototype filter is Band-Stop centered at $\pi/2$ with bandwidth of $\pi/2$ (125 to 375 on the x-axis). Figure 20b shows the circuit with $\omega_0 = \pi/16$. This tunes the lower band edge to $\pi/2 - \pi/4 + \pi/16 = 5\pi/16$ (156.25 on the x-axis of Figure 18b) and the upper band edge to $\pi/2 + \pi/4 - \pi/16 = 11\pi/16$ (343.75 on the x-axis of Figure 20b). Figure 20c shows the circuit with $\omega_0 = \pi/8$. This tunes the lower band edge to $\pi/2 - \pi/4 + \pi/8 = 3\pi/8$ (187.5 on the x-axis of Figure 20c) and the upper band edge to $\pi/2 + \pi/4 - \pi/8 = 5\pi/8$ (312.5 on the x-axis in Figure 20c). Figure 20d shows the circuit with $\omega_0 = 3\pi/16$. This tunes the lower band edge to $\pi/2 - \pi/4 + 3\pi/16 = 7\pi/16$ (218.75 on the x-axis of Figure 20d) and the upper band edge to $\pi/2 + \pi/4 - 3\pi/16 = 9\pi/16$ (281.25 on the x-axis of Figure 20d). Notice that the attenuation of the tuned band-stop filters is over 40db which is the same stop-band attenuation as the prototype filter. All of these filters retain the linear-phase property of the prototype filter that was designed using the Parks-McClellan algorithm.

3.6 Summary of three-way tunable complex heterodyne filter (Azam's technique)

The Three-Way Complex Heterodyne Technique is capable of designing tunable center frequency band-stop and notch filter, tunable cut-off frequency low-pass and high-pass filters and tunable bandwidth band-pass and band-stop filters. The technique is not able to implement tunable center-frequency band-pass filters, but these are easily implementable by the simple cosine heterodyne circuit of Figure 2.

Figure 9 is the basic Three-Way Complex Heterodyne Circuit used to implement these filters in software or hardware. A very nice FPGA implementation of this circuit has been reported in the literature in a paper that won the Myril B. Reed Best Paper Award at the 2000 IEEE International Midwest Symposium on Circuits and Systems (Azam et. al., 2000). For further information on this paper and the award, visit the MWSCAS web page at http://mwscas.org. Table 1 provides the design details for the five possible tunable filters. Sections 3.1 through 3.5 provide examples of each of the five tunable filters from Table 1. In section 6 of this chapter we shall show how to make these tunable filters adaptive so that they can automatically very center frequency, cut-off frequency or bandwidth to adapt to various signal processing needs.

4. Bottom-top tunable complex heterodyne filters (Cho's technique)

The Three-Way Tunable Complex Heterodyne Circuit of section 3 implemented by the circuit of Figure 9 is a special case of a more general technique referred to as the Bottom-Top Tunable Complex Heterodyne Filter Technique. Figure 21 below shows the complete circuit for the Bottom-Top Tunable Complex Heterodyne Filter:

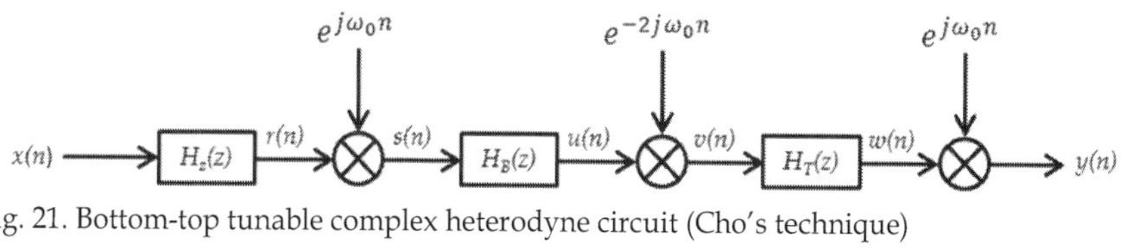

Fig. 21. Bottom-top tunable complex heterodyne circuit (Cho's technique)

Comparing the circuit of Figure 21 to the circuit of Figure 9, we see that the circuit of Figure 21 has one additional fixed filter block $H_z(z)$ between the input and the first heterodyne stage. This block allows for fixed signal processing that is not subject to the rotations of the other two blocks. Otherwise, this is the same circuit as Figure 9. However, the addition of this extra block gives us the flexibility to do many more signal processing operations.

We do not have sufficient room in this chapter to explore all the possibilities of the circuit of Figure 9, so we shall limit ourselves to three: (1) Tunable filters with at least some real poles and zeros, (2) Tunable filters with poles and zeros clustered together on the unit circle, and (3) Tunable filters realized with a Nyquist filter that allows the elimination of the last heterodyne stage. This third option is so important that we will cover it as a separate topic in section 5. The first two are covered here in section 4.1 and 4.2 respectively.

4.1 Tunable filters with real poles and zeros

When the prototype filter has some of its poles and zeros located on the real axis, it is often useful to remove these poles and zeros from the rotation process and allow them to remain on the real axis. An example of this is the design of a tunable cut-off frequency low-pass (or high-pass) filter. Such filters typically have some poles and zeros on the real axis. An excellent example of this is a Butterworth Low-Pass Filter. An nth order Butterworth Filter has n zeros located at -1 on the real axis. If we wish to design a tunable cut-off frequency Butterworth Low-Pass Filter, the prototype filter will have a cut-off frequency at $\pi/2$. The only other specification for a Butterworth Filter is the order of the filter. Here we pick an 11th order Butterworth Low-Pass Filter with cut-off frequency of $\pi/2$:

```
[b,a]=butter(11,0.5);
```

To design a tunable cut-off frequency low-pass filter using the circuit of Figure 21, we will divide the poles and zeros of the prototype filter between the three transfer function boxes such that $H_z(z)$ contains all the real poles and zeros, $H_B(z)$ contains all the complex poles and zeros with negative imaginary parts (those located in the bottom of the z-plane) and $H_T(z)$ contains all the complex poles and zeros with positive imaginary parts (those located in the top of the z-plane). The following MatLab m-file accomplishes this:

```
% BOTTOMTOP
% Extracts the bottom and top poles and zeros from a filter
function
% INPUT:   [b,a] = filter coefficients
%          delta = maximum size of imaginary part to consider
it zero
% OUTPUT:
%          [bz,az] = real poles and zeros
%          [bb,ab] = bottom poles and zeros
%          [bt,at] = top poles and zeros
clear rb rbz rbt rbb ra raz rat rab bz bt bb az at ab
rb=roots(b);
lb=length(b)-1;
% find real zeros
rbz=1;
nbz=0;
nbt=0;
nbb=0;
for index=1:lb
```

```
            if abs(imag(rb(index)))<delta
            nbz=nbz+1;
            rbz(nbz,1)=real(rb(index));
% find top zero
        elseif imag(rb(index))>0
            nbt=nbt+1;
            rbt(nbt,1)=rb(index);
% find bottom zero
         else
            nbb=nbb+1;
            rbb(nbb,1)=rb(index);
        end
end
ra=roots(a);
la=length(a)-1;
% find real poles
raz=1;
naz=0;
nat=0;
nab=0;
for index=1:la
    if abs(imag(ra(index)))<delta
        naz=naz+1;
        raz(naz,1)=real(ra(index));
% find top zero
    elseif imag(ra(index))>0
        nat=nat+1;
        rat(nat,1)=ra(index);
% find bottom zero
    else
        nab=nab+1;
        rab(nab,1)=ra(index);
    end
end
if nbz==0
    bz=1;
else
    bz=poly(rbz);
end
if nbt==0
    bt=1;
else
    bt=poly(rbt);
end
if nbb==0
    bb=1;
else
    bb=poly(rbb);
end
if naz==0
    az=1;
else
    az=poly(raz);
```

```
end
if nat==0
  at=1;
else
    at=poly(rat);
end
if nab==0
    ab=1;
else
    ab=poly(rab);
end
```

Figure 22 shows the results of applying the above m-file to the prototype 11th order Butterworth Low-Pass Filter with cut-off frequency at $\pi/2$.

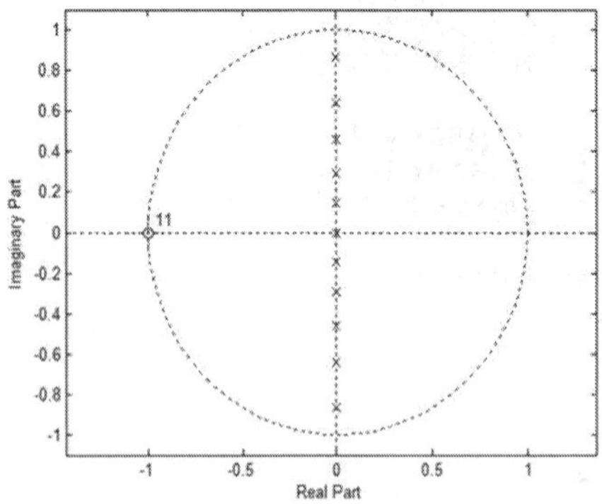

Fig. 22a. Pole-zero plot of H (z) (11th order butterworth LP)

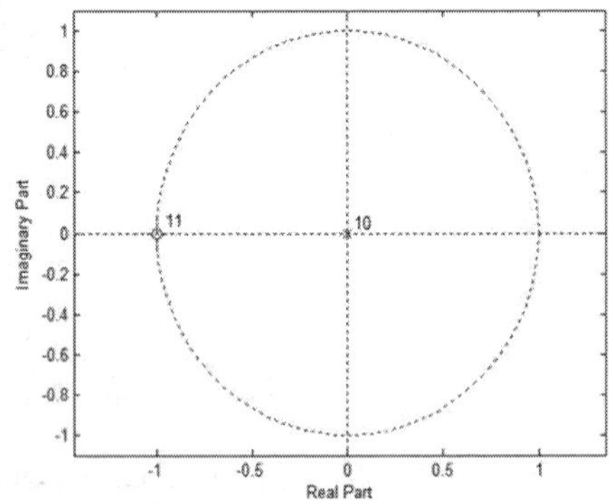

Fig. 22b. Pole-zero plot of $H_z(z)$ (real poles and zeros)

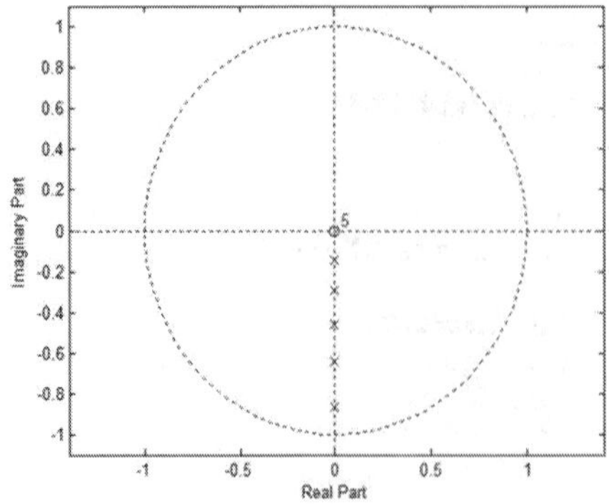

Fig. 22c. Pole-Zero Plot of $H_B(z)$ (bottom poles and zeros).

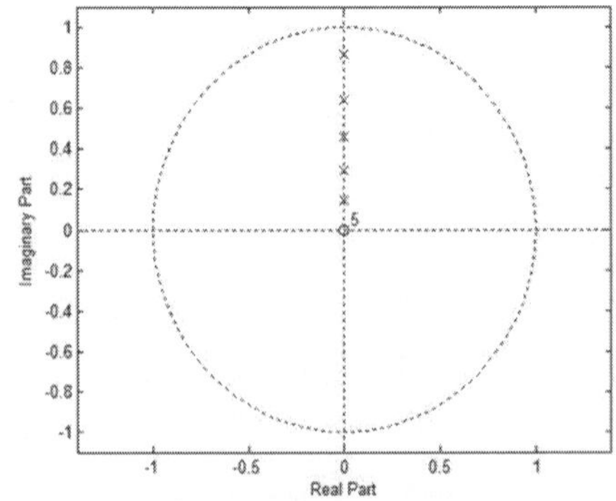

Fig. 22b. Pole-Zero Plot of $H_T(z)$ (top poles and zeros)

Fig. 22. Illustration of the result of the Matlab m-file dividing the poles and zeros in the prototype 11th order butterworth low-pass filter designed with a cut-off frequency of $\pi/2$. The resulting transfer functions $H_z(z)$, $H_B(z)$ and $H_T(z)$ are then implanted in the appropriate boxes in the circuit of Figure 21.

To simulate the Bottom-Top Tunable Complex Heterodyne Filter of Figure 21, we make use of the following MatLab m-file:

```
% CMPLXHET
% Implements the Complex Heterodyne Filter
% INPUTS:
% Set the following inputs before calling 3WAYHET:
%       inp = 0 (provide input file inpf)
%           = 1 (impulse response)
%       npoints = number of points in input
%       w0 = heterodyne frequency
%       [bz az] = coefficients of filter Hz(z)
%       [bb ab] = coefficients of filter Hb(z)
%       [bt at] = coefficients of filter Ht(z)
%       scale = 0 (do not scale the output)
%             = 1 (scale the output to zero db)
%
% OUTPUTS:  ydb = frequency response of the filter
%           hdb, sdb, udb, vdb, wdb (intermediate outputs)
clear y ydb hdb s sdb u udb v vdb w wdb h f
if inp==1
    for index=1:npoints
        inpf(index)=0;
    end
    inpf(1)=1;
end
r=filter(bz,az,inpf);
for index=1:npoints
    s(index)=r(index)*exp(1i*w0*(index-1));
end
u=filter(bb,ab,s);
for index=1:npoints
    v(index)=u(index)*exp(-2*1i*w0*(index-1));
end
w=filter(bt,at,v);
for index=1:npoints
    y(index)=w(index)*exp(1i*w0*(index-1));
end
[h,f]=freqz(b,a,npoints,'whole');
hdb=20*log10(abs(h));
rdb=20*log10(abs(fft(r)));
sdb=20*log10(abs(fft(s)));
udb=20*log10(abs(fft(u)));
vdb=20*log10(abs(fft(v)));
wdb=20*log10(abs(fft(w)));
ydb=20*log10(abs(fft(y)));
if scale==1
    ydbmax=max(ydb)
    ydb=ydb-ydbmax;
end
plot(ydb,'k')
```

Figure 23 shows the results of this simulation for the 11th order Butterworth Low Pass prototype filter with cut-off frequency of $\pi/2$ (250). Figure 23a shows the result for $\omega_0 = 0$. This is the prototype filter. Unlike the Three-Way Tunable Complex Heterodyne Technique of the previous section, we do not need to design for half the desired pass-band ripple. We can design for exactly the desired properties of the tunable filter. Figure 23b shows the result for $\omega_0 = -\pi/8$. This subtracts $\pi/8$ from the cut-off frequency of $\pi/2$ moving the cut-off frequency to $3\pi/8$ (187.5). Figure 23c shows the result for $\omega_0 = -\pi/4$. This subtracts $\pi/4$ from the cut-off frequency of $\pi/2$ moving the cut-off frequency to $\pi/4$ (125). Figure 23d shows the result for $\omega_0 = -3\pi/8$. This subtracts $3\pi/8$ from the cut-off frequency of $\pi/2$ moving the cut-off frequency to $\pi/8$ (62.5). The horizontal line on each of the plots indicates the 3db point for the filter. While there is some peaking in the pass-band as the filter is tuned, it is well within the 3db tolerance of the pass-band.

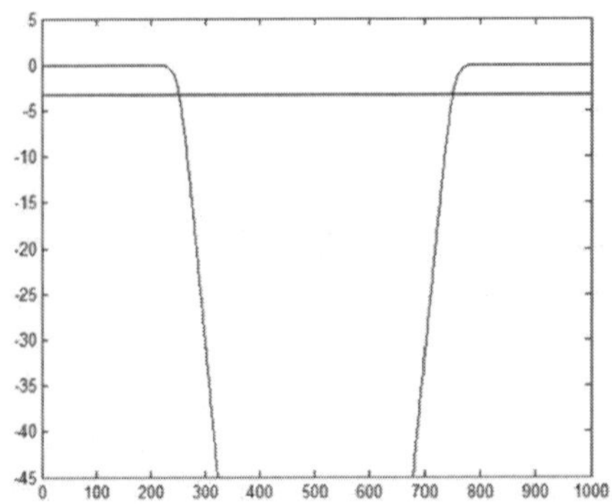

Fig. 23a. Tunable low-pass with $\omega_0 = 0$

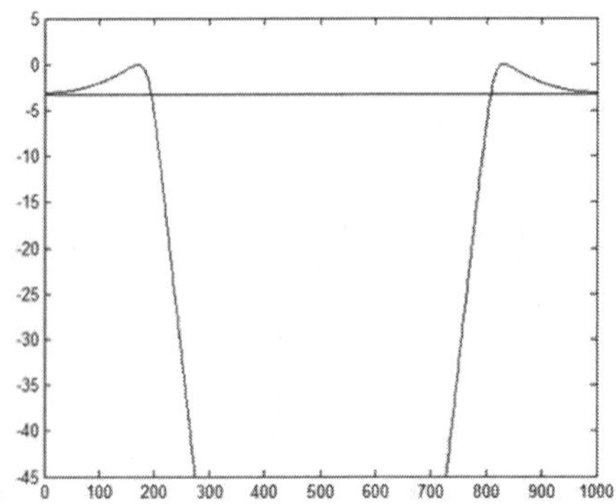

Fig. 23b. Tunable low-pass with $\omega_0 = -\pi/8$

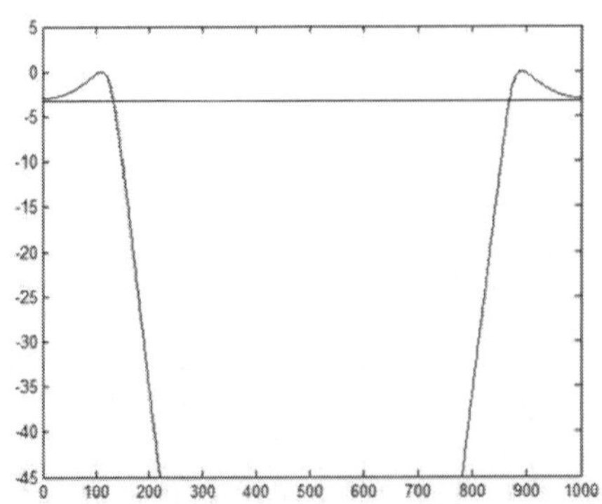

Fig. 23c. Tunable low-pass with $\omega_0 = -\pi/4$

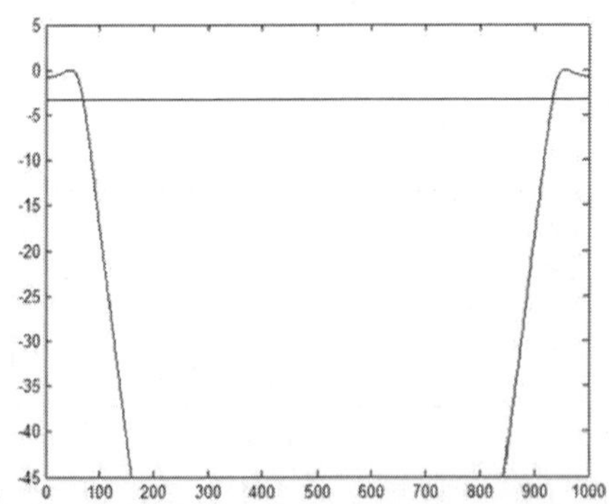

Fig. 23d. Tunable low-pass with $\omega_0 = -3\pi/8$

Fig. 23. Implementation of a tunable cut-off frequency low-pass filter using the bottom-top technique of Figure 21.

4.2 Tunable filters with poles and zeros clustered together on the unit circle

One of the most powerful applications of the Bottom-Top Tunable Complex Heterodyne Technique is its ability to implement the very important tunable center-frequency band-stop filter. Such filters, when made adaptive using the techniques of section 6 of this chapter, are very important in the design of adaptive narrow-band noise attenuation circuits. The Bottom-Top structure of Figure 21 is particularly well suited to the implementation of such filters using any of the designs that result in a cluster of poles and zeros on the unit circle. This is best accomplished by the design of narrow-band notch filters centered at $\pi/2$. All of the IIR design techniques work well for this case including Butterworth, Chebyshev, Inverse Chebyshev and Elliptical Filters.

As an example, we design a Butterworth 5th order band-stop filter and tune it from DC to the Nyquist frequency. In MatLab we use [b,a]=butter(5,[0.455 0.545],'stop'); to obtain the coefficients for the prototype filter. We then use the m-file BOTTOMTOP as before to split the poles and zeros into the proper places in the circuit of Figure 21. Finally, we run the MatLab m-file CMPLXHET to obtain the results shown in Figures 24 and 25.

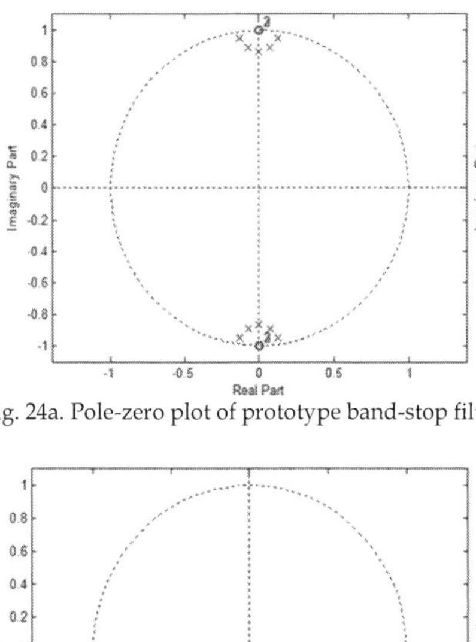

Fig. 24a. Pole-zero plot of prototype band-stop filter

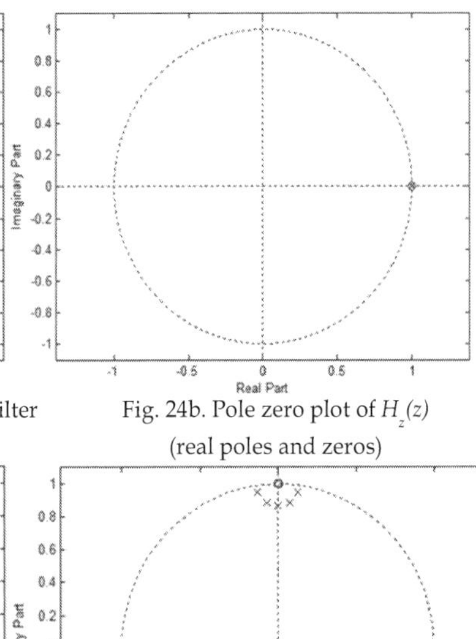

Fig. 24b. Pole zero plot of $H_z(z)$ (real poles and zeros)

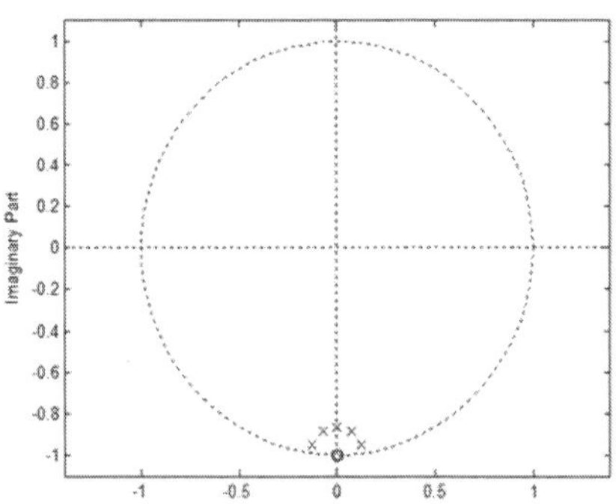

Fig. 24c. Pole-zero plot of $H_B(z)$ (bottom poles & zeros)

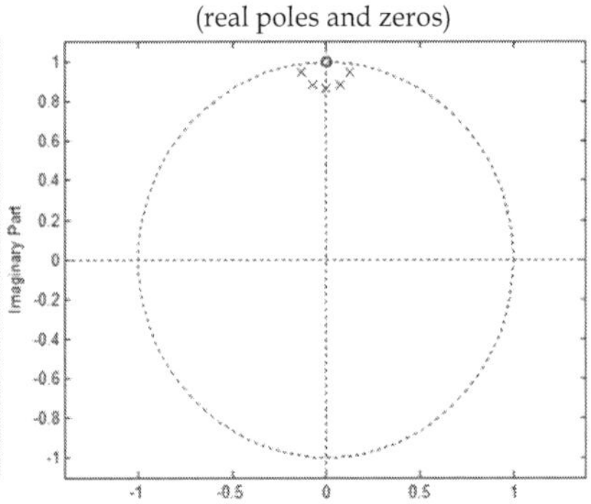

Fig. 24d. Pole zero plot of $H_T(z)$ (top poles & zeros)

Fig. 24. Distribution of poles and zeros for 5th order butterworth band-stop filter centered at $\pi/2$. Notice how the poles and zeros are clustered on the unit circle. This is the ideal case of use of the bottom-top tunable complex heterodyne filter circuit of Figure 21.

Figure 24 shows the poles and zeros clustered in the z-plane on the unit circle. Figure 24a. shows the poles and zeros of the prototype 5th order Butterworth band-stop filter centered at $\pi/2$ designed by [b,a]=butter(5,[0.455 0.545],'stop');. Figure 24b shows the poles and zeros assigned to $H_z(z)$ by the MatLab m-file BOTTOMTOP. Similarly, Figures 24c and 24d show the poles and zeros assigned by the MatLab m-file BOTTOMTOP to $H_B(z)$ and $H_T(z)$ respectively. Figure 25 shows the MatLab simulation of the Bottom-Top Tunable Complex Heterodyne Filter as implemented by the circuit of Figure 21 in the MatLab m-file CMPLXHET. The band-stop center frequency is fully tunable from DC to the Nyquist frequency. The tuned band-stop filter is identical to the prototype band-stop filter. Furthermore, this works for any band-stop design with clustered poles and zeros such as Chebyshev, Inverse Chebyshev and Elliptical designs. In section 6 we shall see how to make these filters adaptive so that they can automatically zero in on narrow-band interference and attenuate that interference very effectively. Figure 25a is for $\omega_0 = 0$, Figure 25b is for $\omega_0 = -7\pi/16$, Figure 25c is for $\omega_0 = -3\pi/16$ and Figure 25d is for $\omega_0 = 5\pi/16$. Note the full tenability form DC to Nyquist.

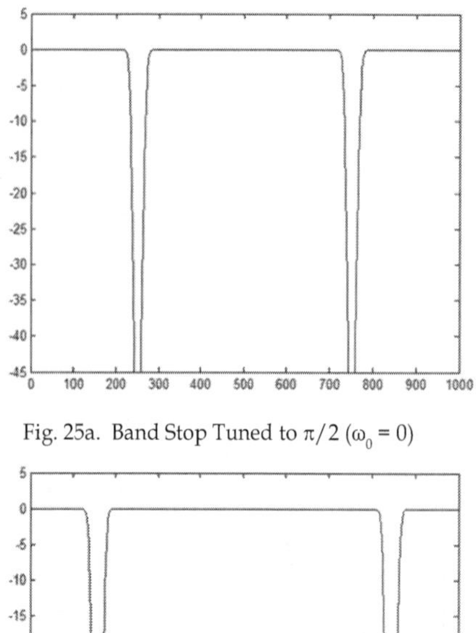

Fig. 25a. Band Stop Tuned to $\pi/2$ ($\omega_0 = 0$)

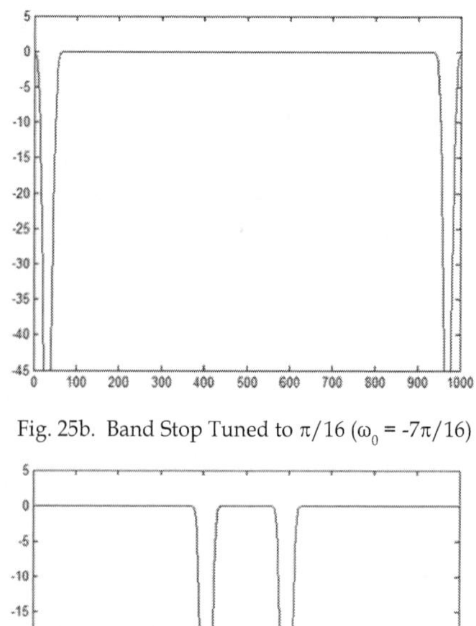

Fig. 25b. Band Stop Tuned to $\pi/16$ ($\omega_0 = -7\pi/16$)

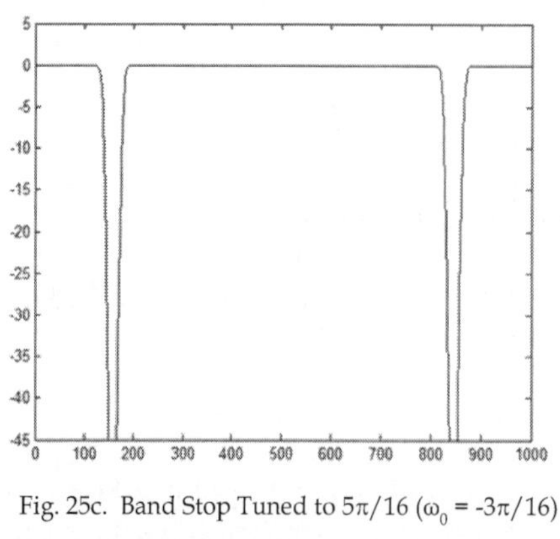

Fig. 25c. Band Stop Tuned to $5\pi/16$ ($\omega_0 = -3\pi/16$)

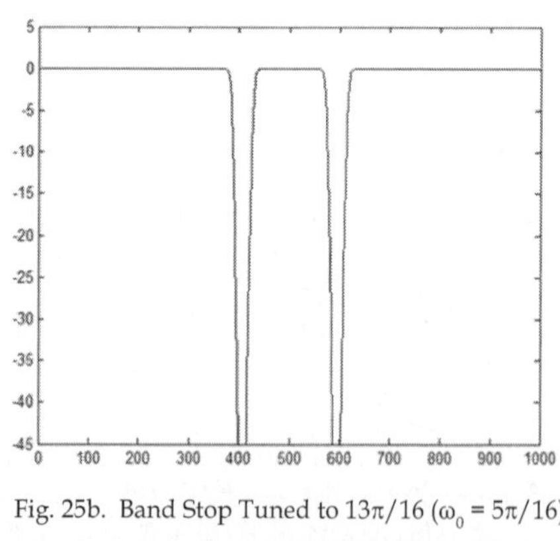

Fig. 25b. Band Stop Tuned to $13\pi/16$ ($\omega_0 = 5\pi/16$)

Fig. 25. Butterworth tunable band-stop filter implemented using bottom-top tunable complex heterodyne technique. Note that the band-stop filter is fully tunable from DC to the Nyquist frequency.

4.3 Summary of bottom-top tunable complex heterodyne filter (Cho's technique)

The Bottom-Top Complex Heterodyne Technique is the most flexible of the heterodyne filter circuits allowing the design of tunable center frequency band-pass, band-stop and notch filter, tunable cut-off frequency low-pass and high-pass filters and tunable bandwidth band-pass and band-stop filters. However, the technique is particularly useful in designing full tunable band-stop filters with characteristics identical to the prototype filter but tunable from DC to the Nyquist frequency.

Figure 21 is the basic Bottom-Top Complex Heterodyne Circuit used to implement these filters in software or hardware. A practical implementation of this circuit has been reported in the literature in a paper appearing in the proceedings of the IEEE International Symposium on Circuit and Systems (Cho, et. al., 2005). The Bottom-Top Complex Heterodyne band-stop filters reported in this paper are aimed at narrow-band attenuation in spread-spectrum radio receivers. In section 6 of this chapter we shall show how to make these tunable filters adaptive so that they can automatically very center frequency, cut-off frequency or bandwidth to adapt to various signal processing needs.

5. Nyquist tunable complex heterodyne filter technique (Soderstrand's technique)

The final technique for designing Tunable Complex Heterodyne Filters makes use of a modified version of the circuit in Figure 21 shown in Figure 26.

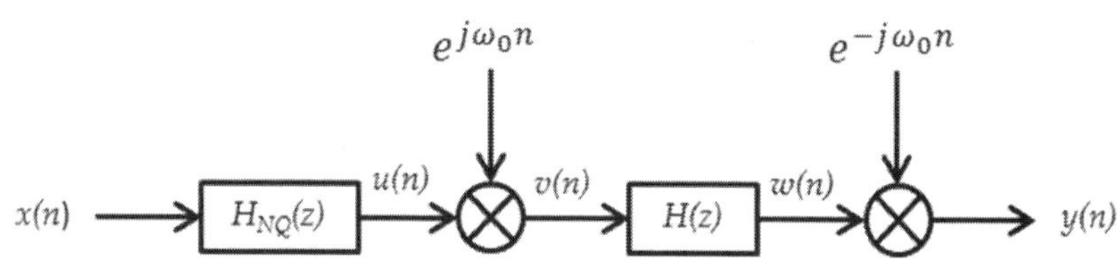

Fig. 26. Nyquist tunable complex heterodyne filter circuit (Soderstrand's technique)

In the circuit of Figure 26 the signal is first passed through $H_{NQ}(z)$, a complex-coefficient digital filter that removes all frequencies from the bottom half of the unit circle in z-plane. Thus this filter removes the negative frequencies or equivalently the frequencies above the Nyquist frequency. Such a filter is easily designed in MatLab by designing a low-pass filter with cut-off frequency of $\pi/2$ and then rotating it in the z-plane so as to pass positive frequencies (frequencies above the real axis in the z-plane) and to attenuate negative frequencies (frequencies below the unit circle in the z-plane).

5.1 Design of the Nyquist Filter $H_{NQ}(z)$

The Nyquist Filter will normally be the same filter regardless of what tunable filter we are realizing. Choice of the Nyquist Filter depends primarily on hardware or software considerations for the target application. If phase is not critical, an IIR Nyquist Filter can be designed using MatLab functions BUTTER, CHEBY, CHEBY2 or ELLIP. However, in many applications phase is of great importance and the Nyquist Filter needs to be designed using the Parks McClellan linear phase technique implemented in MatLab with FIRPM. For our examples we shall assume that we need a Nyquist Filter with 60db attenuation of the negative frequencies and no more than 1db ripple in the pass-band (positive frequencies). We shall choose a 64-tap filter, although excellent results can be obtained with many fewer taps.

The first step in the design of the Nyquist Filter is to use FIRPM to design a low-pass filter with cut-off frequency at $\pi/2$ with the desired specifications (60db stop-band attenuation and 1db ripple in the pass-band, and 3db attenuation at DC):

alp=1;blp=firpm(64,[0 0.45 0.55 1],[1 1 0 0],[1 2]);

Figure 27a shows the pole-zero plot of this low-pass filter and Figure 27c shows the frequency response. Note the attenuation at DC is 5db rather than the desired 3db. We shall see this show up in the tunable filter later. In practice we would assure 3db - but we have deliberately left it at 5db to show the effect. We then use MatLab m-file NQFILTER to rotate the low-pass filter by 90 degrees in the z-plane to create the Nyquist Filter whose pole-zero plot is shown in Figure 27b and frequency response in Figure 27d.

```
% NQFILTER
% This script rotates a low-pass filter with a
% cut-off frequency at 0.5 (pi/2) by phi radians
% in the z-plane to create a complex-coefficient
% digital filter that removes the frequencies in
% the lower half of the z-plane (phi = pi/2).
% INPUTS:  [blp,alp] = lowpass filter with 0.5 cut-off
%           phi =  (suggest pi/2)
% OUTPUTS:
%          [bnq,anq] = the complex-coefficents of
%                      the Nyquist filter
clear nb na bnq anq
nb = length(blp);
na = length(alp);
if nb > 1
    for index=1:nb
        bnq(index)=blp(index)*exp(1i*(index-1)*(phi));
    end
else
    bnq = 1;
end
if na > 1
    for index=1:na
        anq(index)=alp(index)*exp(1i*(index-1)*(phi));
    end
else
    anq = 1;
end
```

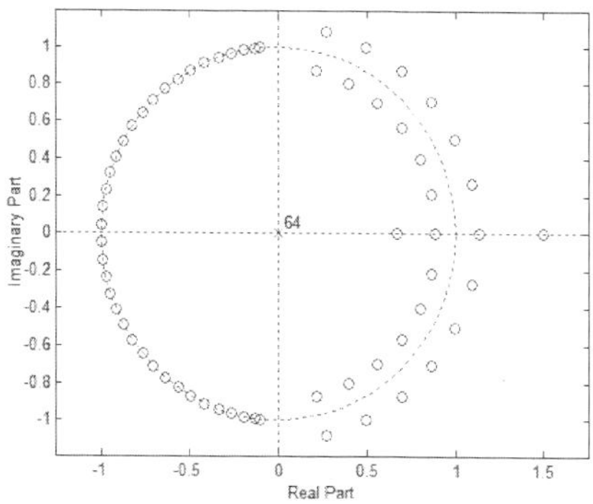

Fig. 27a. Pole-zero plot of low-pass filter

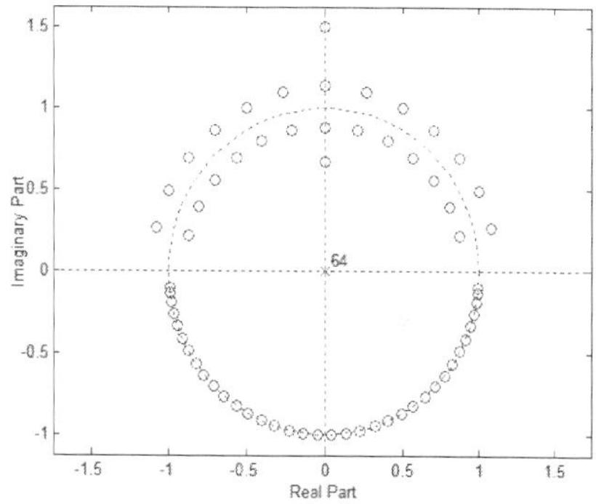

Fig. 27b. Pole-zero plot of nyquist filter

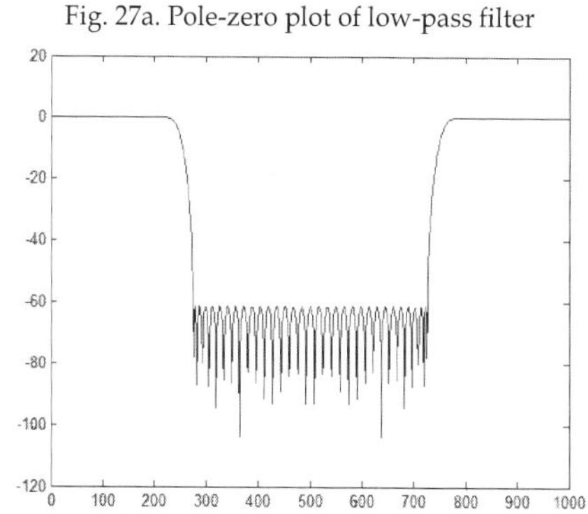

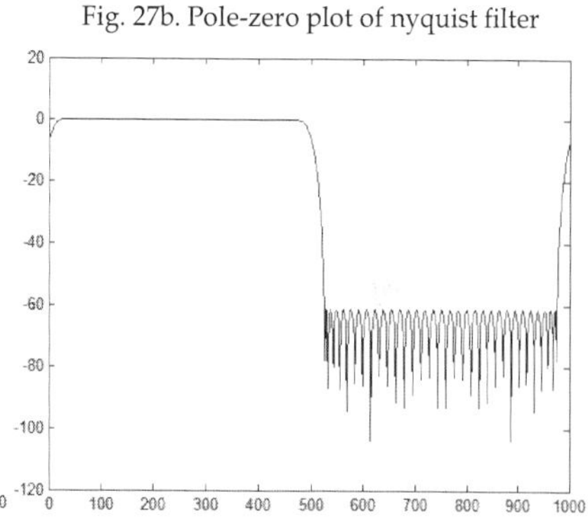

Fig. 27c. Frequency response plot of low-pass filter Fig. 27d. Frequency response plot of nyquist filter

Fig. 27. Design of a nyquist filter by rotating a 64-tap parks McClellan linear-phase filter with cut-off frequency at $\pi/2$ by 90 degrees in the z-plane to obtain a filter that attenuates all negative frequencies.

5.2 Novel technique for tuning a complex heterodyne prototype filter (Soderstrand's technique)

Once the negative frequencies have been removed from the input signal, the problem of tuning the filter becomes much simpler. Any prototype filter H(z) may be rotated from its center at DC to its center at ω_0 through the standard rotation technique of Figure 7. This is exactly what is done in the Nyquist Tunable Complex Heterodyne Circuit of Figure 26. The potential problem, however, is that we obtain a filter with all the poles and zeros in the upper half of the z-plane and none in the lower half. Hence the output, y(n), will consist of complex numbers. The novelty of Soderstrand's Technique is that the mirror image poles and zeros needed in the bottom half of the z-plane can be easily created by simply taking the real part of the output y(n). Since we only need the real part of the output, this also simplifies the hardware because we can use the simplified circuit of Figure 6d in the last stage of the circuit of Figure 26. The simulation of the circuit of Figure 26 is accomplished in MatLab with the m-file NQHET:

```
% NQHET  (Lab book p. 129 12/11/2010)
% Function to implement Cho complex heterodyne filter
% Set the following inputs before calling NQHET:
%       inp = 0 (provide input file inpf)
%           = 1 (impulse response)
%       npoints = number of points in input
%       w0 = heterodyne frequency
%       [bnq,anq] = coefficients of the Nyquist Filter
%       [b,a] = coefficients of filter H(z)
%
% OUTPUTS:  hdb = frequency response of the filter
%           udb, vdb, wdb, ydb
clear y ydb yout hdb u udb v vdb w wdb
if inp==1
    for index=1:npoints
        inpf(index)=0;
    end
    inpf(1)=1;
end
u=filter(bnq,anq,inpf);
for index=1:npoints
    v(index)=u(index)*exp(-1i*w0*(index-1));
end
w=filter(b,a,v);
for index=1:npoints
    y(index)=w(index)*exp(1i*w0*(index-1));
end
udb=20*log10(abs(fft(u)));
vdb=20*log10(abs(fft(v)));
wdb=20*log10(abs(fft(w)));
ydb=20*log10(abs(fft(y)));
yout=2*real(y);
hdb=20*log10(abs(fft(yout)));
plot(hdb,'k')
```

5.3 Example design of nyquist tunable complex heterodyne filter using circuit of Figure 26 (Soderstrand's technique)

The Nyquist Technique is very general and can rotate any type filter, IIR of FIR, low-pass, high-pass, band-pass or band-stop. However, one of the most important uses of the Nyquist Complex Heterodyne Filter is the design of a tunable band-stop filter that can be used to attenuate narrow-band interference in spread-spectrum receivers. To design tunable stop-band filters, the prototype filter, *H(z),* must be a high-pass filter with cut-off frequency set to one-half the desired bandwidth of the desired tunable band-stop filter. The high-pass prototype filter should have the same stop-band attenuation and pass-band ripple as the desired tunable band-stop filter as all characteristics of the prototype filter are maintained in the tunable filter. The MatLab instruction to design the prototype high-pass filter is

a=1;b=firpm(64,[0 0.05 0.15 1],[0 0 1 1],[1 30]);

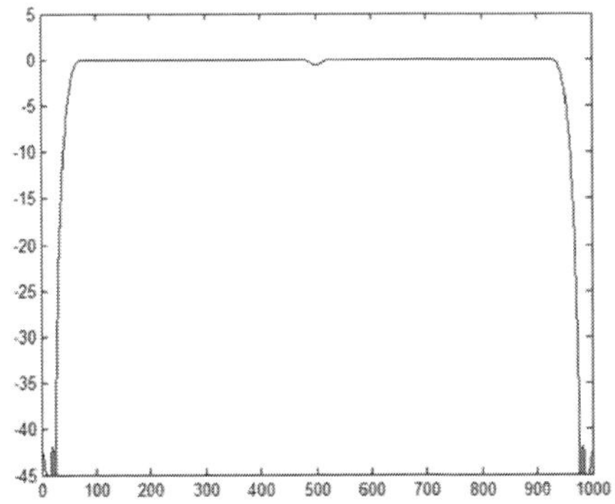

Fig. 28a. Nyquist tunable band-stop $\omega_0 = 0$

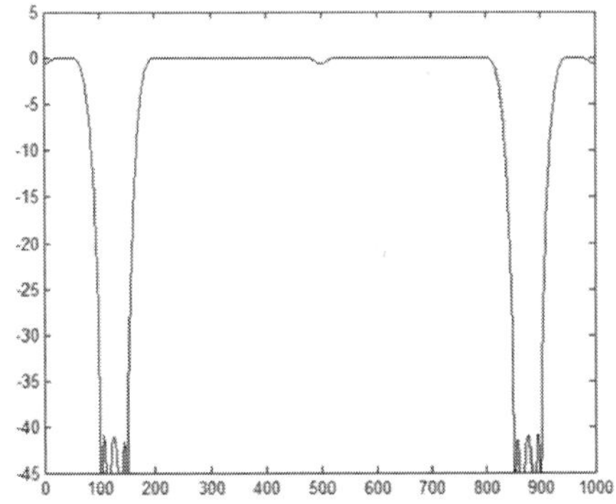

Fig. 28b. Nyquist tunable band-stop $\omega_0 = \pi/4$

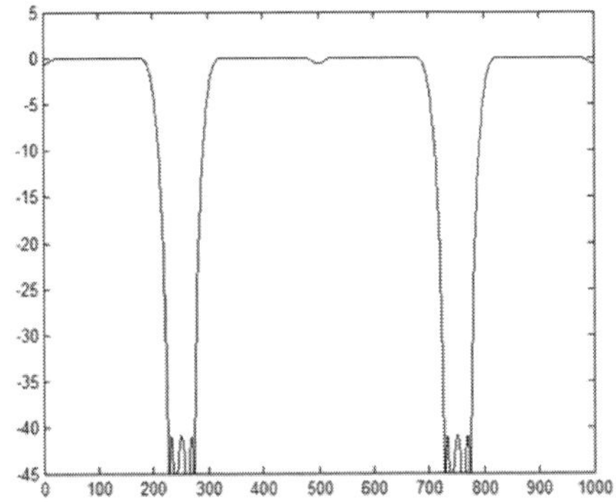

Fig. 28c. Nyquist tunable band-stop $\omega_0 = \pi/2$

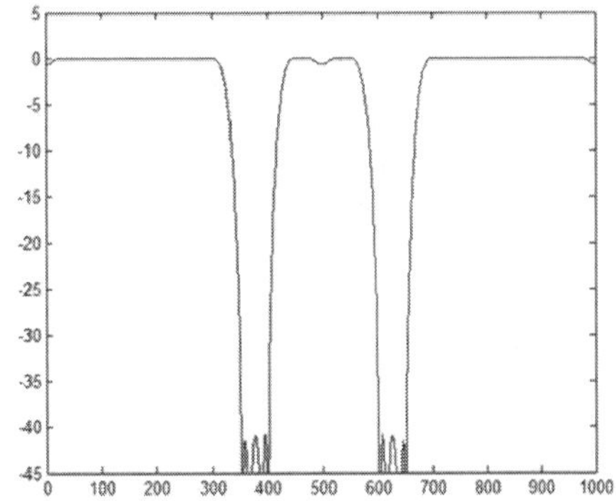

Fig. 28d. Nyquist tunable band-stop $\omega_0 = 3\pi/4$

Fig. 28. Example of nyquist tunable complex heterodyne filter (Soderstrand's technique) for a tunable band-stop filter with 40db attenuation in the stop band, less than .1 db ripple in the pass-band and bandwidth $\pi/10$.

Figure 28 shows the MatLab simulation of the Nyquist Tunable Complex Heterodyne Filter of the circuit of Figure 26. This is fully tunable from DC to the Nyquist frequency. For example, to get the plot of Figure 28d, we use:

```
inp=1;npoints=1000;w0=3*pi/4;nqhet;
```

Notice the dip at DC and the Nyquist Frequency. This is due to the Nyquist Filter not having 3db attenuation at DC. We deliberately allowed the attenuation to be 5db to demonstrate the effect of not having 3db attenuation at DC in the Nyquist filter. However, the effect is negligible only causing a ripple of less than 1db. If the attenuation were greater, the dip would be greater. If the attenuation is less than 3db, we would see a upward bulge at DC and the Nyquist frequency in Figure 27. The tunable filter has the same stop-band attenuation and pass-band ripple as the prototype filter except for this added ripple due to the Nyquist filter. The bandwidth of the stop-band is twice the bandwidth of the prototype filter.

5.4 Summary of nyquist tunable complex heterodyne filter (Sodestrand's technique)

The Nyquist Complex Heterodyne Technique has the advantage of using the least hardware or software of any of the complex heterodyne filter techniques. The technique is particularly useful in designing full tunable band-stop filters with characteristics identical to the prototype filter but tunable from DC to the Nyquist frequency.

Figure 26 is the basic Nyquist Complex Heterodyne Circuit used to implement these filters in software or hardware. A practical implementation of this circuit has been reported in the literature in a paper appearing in the proceedings of the International System on a Chip Conference (Soderstrand & Cho, 2009). The Nyquist Complex Heterodyne band-stop filters reported in this paper are aimed at narrow-band attenuation in spread-spectrum radio receivers. In section 6 of this chapter we shall show how to make these tunable filters adaptive so that they can automatically very center frequency, cut-off frequency or bandwidth to adapt to various signal processing needs.

6. Making the tunable filters adaptive

While tunable filters may be of interest in themselves, the primary interest in Tunable Complex Heterodyne Filters is to make them into Adaptive Complex Heterodyne Filters that can automatically detect interference and adapt the tunable filter to the correct place to attenuate the interference. In this section we shall look at how to adapt tunable complex heterodyne band-stop or notch filters to attenuate narrow-band noise in wide-band communication systems such as Frequency Hopping (FHSS) and Direct Sequence Spread Spectrum (DSSS) receivers. This approach is based on a series of papers presented at international conferences (Nelson, et. al., 1997, Soderstrand 2006, 2007, 2010a, 2010b) and two patents (White, et.al. 1999, White, et.al. 2003).

6.1 Narrow-band interference detection circuit

Figure 29 shows the circuit used to make the tunable heterodyne filters into adaptive heterodyne filters. The input x(n) is simultaneously provided to an Attenuation Frequency

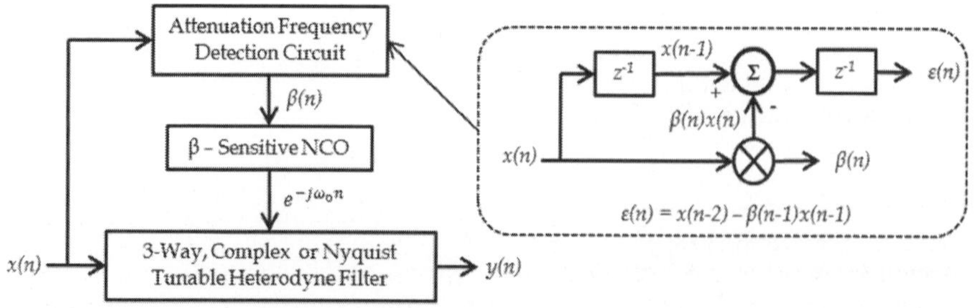

Fig. 29. Narrow-band interference detection circuit to turn tunable complex heterodyne filters into adaptive complex heterodyne filters.

Detection Circuit and to the Tunable Complex Heterodyne Filter. The Attenuation Frequency Detection Circuit (shown in inset) is a simple second-order FIR LMS adaptive notch filter. Because the detection circuit is FIR it will identify the interference without bias. Furthermore, this simple second-order FIR filter is known to be robust and to converge quickly on the correct frequency. However, the simple second-order FIR filter does not provide an adequate attenuator for the narrow-band interference because it attenuates too much of the desired signal. Therefore we only use the detection circuit to determine the value of β needed to generate the complex heterodyne tuning signal $e^{-j\omega_0 n}$. This value of β is fed to a numerically controlled complex oscillator that produces the complex heterodyne signal $e^{-j\omega_0 n}$.

6.2 Comparison of adaptive three-way complex heterodyne band-stop filter to adaptive gray markel lattice

To illustrate the performance of adaptive complex heterodyne filters, we shall set up a simulation in MatLab to compare the performance of the Three-Way Complex Heterodyne Filter to the very popular Gray-Markel Lattice (Gray, 1973, Petraglia, 1994). Figure 30 shows the simulation test setup.

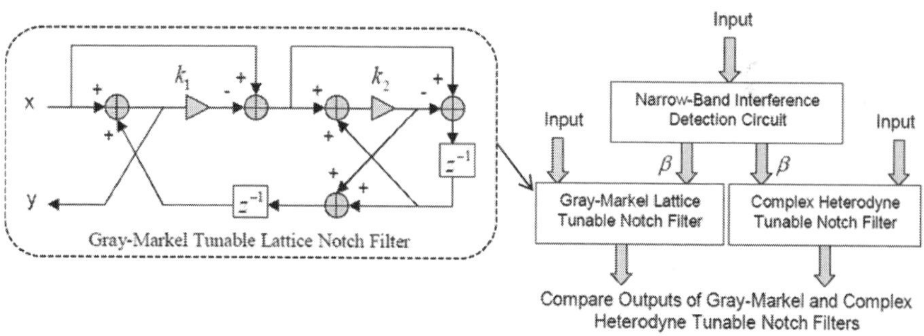

Fig. 30. Test setup for simulation in MatLab of a comparison of adaptive complex heterodyne filters to adaptive gray-markel lattice filters.

Figure 31 shows plots of the energy leakage during a transition of the narrow-band interference from one frequency to another. Both the Gray Markel and the Complex Heterodyne Adaptive Filters track the interference very well. However, in large transitions such as those shown in Figure 31a (transition from frequency $\pi/24$ to $11\pi/24$) and Figure 31b (transition from $\pi/12$ to $5\pi/12$) the Adaptive Complex Heterodyne Filter provides more attenuation of the narrow-band interference than the Gary-Markel Adaptive Filter. In the case of Figure 31a, the difference is about 20db and in the case of Figure 31b it is only about 10db. However, these represent significant differences in the ability to attenuate a fast moving signal. On the smaller transitions of Figure 31c (transition from $\pi/8$ to $3\pi/8$) and Figure 31d. (transition from $\pi/4$ to $\pi/8$) there is little difference between the two filters (although the Gray-Markel adaptive filter is a bit smoother in the transition). The point of this simulation is to show that Adaptive Heterodyne Filters offer an excellent alternative to currently used adaptive filters such as the Gray-Markel adaptive filter.

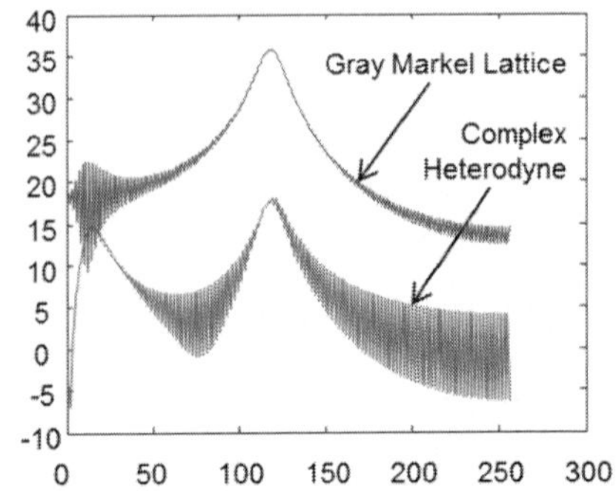

Fig. 31a. Transition from $\pi/24$ to $11\pi/24$

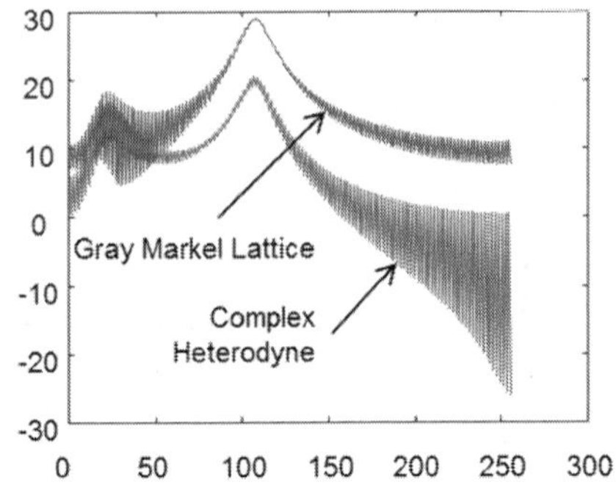

Fig. 31b. Transition from $\pi/12$ to $5\pi/12$

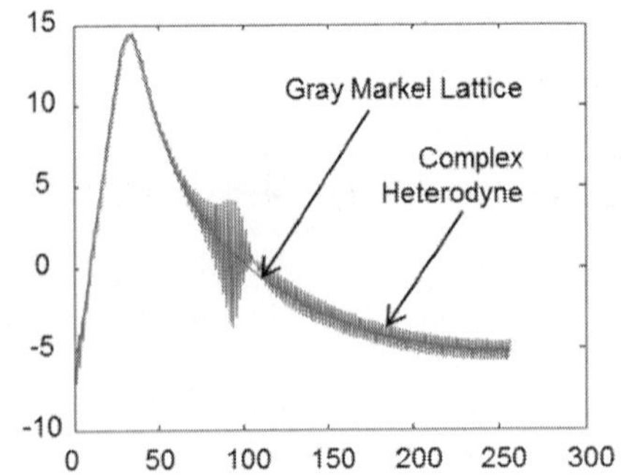

Fig. 31c. Transition from $\pi/8$ to $3\pi/8$

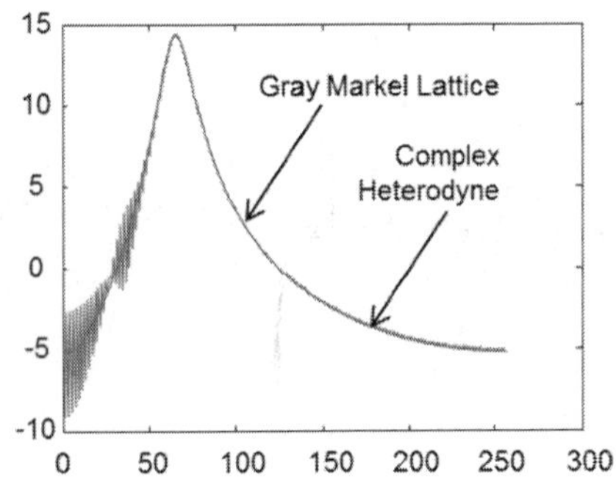

Fig. 31d. Transition from $\pi/4$ to $\pi/8$

Fig. 31. Comparison of gray-markel and complex heterodyne adaptive filters while tracking a moving signal.

7. Summary and conclusions

In this chapter we have explored four techniques for designing tunable filters using a heterodyne signal as the tuning agent:

1. The **Simple Tunable Heterodyne Filter** of Figure 2 requires only two real heterodyne operations, but is limited to tuning the center frequency of narrow-band band-pass filters. However, this is the preferred technique for designing tunable band-pass filters unless the bandwidth of the filter is too large to accommodate the requirements of Figure 2.
2. The **Three-Way Tunable Complex Heterodyne Filter** (Azam's Technique) of Figure 9 requires three complex heterodyne operations, but is able to implement tunable center-frequency band-stop and notch filters, tunable cut-off low-pass and high-pass filter, and tunable bandwidth band-stop and notch filters. However, it is not suitable for tunable center frequency band-pass filters.

3. The **Bottom-Top Tunable Complex Heterodyne Filter** (Cho's Technique) of Figure 21 has all the other tunable heterodyne filters as special cases. This is the most flexible tunable heterodyne filter, but also requires the most hardware.
4. The **Nyquist Tunable Complex Heterodyne Filter** (Soderstrand's Technique) of Figure 26 is ideally suited for implanting center-frequency tunable filters. Center-frequency tunable Band-pass and band-stop filters are most suited to this technique. This technique is able to implement full tunable filters from DC to the Nyquist frequency.

By matching the proper technique above to the particular application it is possible to design extremely efficient tunable filters and then make use of techniques like the one outlined in section 6 to make those tunable filters adaptive. The example of section 6 is typical of what can be accomplished using these new tunable heterodyne filters.

8. References

Azam, Azad, Dhinesh Sasidaran, Karl Nelson, Gary Ford, Louis Johnson and Michael Soderstrand (2000), Single-Chip Tunable Heterodyne Notch Filters Implemented in FPGA's, *IEEE International Midwest Symposium on Circuits and Systems,* Lansing, MI, August 8-11, 2000.

Butler, Lloyd, (1989) *Introduction to the Superheterodyne Receiver,* Amateur Radio, March 1989, available from http://users.tpg.com.au/users/ldbutler/Superhet.htm, accessed 12/11/2010.

Cho, Grace Yoona, (2005) Louis G. Johnson & Michael A. Soderstrand, New Complex-Arithmetic Heterodyne Filter, *IEEE International Symposium on Circuits and Systems,* vol. 3, pp. 593-596, May, 2005.

Coulson, A.J. (2004) Narrowband Interference in Pilot Symbol Assisted OFDM Systems, *IEEE Transactions on Wireless Communications,* vol. 3, no. 6, pp. 2277-2287, November 2004.

Dorf, Richard C. & Zhen, Wan (2000) The z-Transform, In: R.C. Dorf, The Electrical Engineering Handbook, CRC Press, available at http://www.4shared.com/document/VA837U3Q/ebook_-_Electrical_Engineering.html, Chapter 8, section 8.2, ISBN 978-0-84-93018-8.

Duman, Tolga M., (2005) Analog and Digital Communications, In: R.C. Dorf, *The Engineering Handbook,* 2nd Ed, CRC Press, chapter 135, ISBN 0-8493-1586-7.

Etkin, R, Parekh, A & Tse, D, (2005) Spectrum Sharing for Unlicensed Bands, *Proceedings of the 43rd Allerton Conference on Communications, Control and Computing,* ISBN 978-1-60-423491-6, Monticello, Illinois, September 2005.

Gray, A.H. Jr., (1973) & John D. Markel, Digital Lattice and Ladder Filter Synthesis, *IEEE Transactions on Audio,* vol. AU-21, no. 6, pp. 491-500, Dec 1973.

McCune, Earl, (2000) DSSS vs. FHSS Narrowband Interference Performance Issues, *mobile Development and Design,* September 1, 2000, available from http://mobiledevdesign.com/hardware_news/radio_dsss_vs_fhss/

Nelson, K.E., (1997), P-V.N. Dao, M.A. Soderstrand, S.A. White, J.P. Woodard, A Modified Fixed-Point Computational Gradient Descent Gray-Markel Notch Filter Method for

Sinusoidal Detection and Attenuation," *IEEE International Symposium on Circuits and Systems,* ISCAS '97, June 9-12, 1997, pp. 2525-2528.

Peha, Jon M., (1998) Spectrum Management Policy Options, *IEEE Communications Surveys,* vol. 1, no. 1, 4th quarter, 1998.

Peha, Jon M. (2000) The Path Towards Efficient Coexistence in unlicensed Spectrum, *IEEE 802.16 Wireless Hish-Speed Unlicensed Metropolitan Area network Standards,* April, 2000.

Petraglia, Mariane, (1994), Sanjit Mitra & Jacques Szczupak, Adaptive Sinusoid Detection Using IIR Notch Filters and Multirate Techniques, IEEE Trans CAS - 11, vol. 41, no. 11, pp. 709-717, Nov 1994.

Roberts, Michael J. (2007) *Derivation of the Properties of the z-Transform,* Web Appendix O, p. O-3, February 18, 2007, available from http://www.ece.utk.edu/~roberts/WebAppendices/O-zTransformDerivations.pdf.

Soderstrand, Michael A. (2006) Steven R. Phillips, Grace Yoona Cho & David JungPa Lee, Adaptive Notch Filters Using Complex Heterodyne Approach, *IEEE International Midwest Symposium on Circuits and Systems (MWSCAS),* San Juan Puerto Rico, August 6-9, 2006.

Soderstrand, Michael A. (2007) & W. Kenneth Jenkins, Comparison of Two Techniques for Attenuation of Narrow-Band Interference in Spread-Spectrum Communications Systems, *IEEE International Midwest Symposium on Circuits and Systems (MWSCAS),* Montreal, Canada, August 5-8, 2007.

Soderstrand, Michael A. (2009) & Grace Yoona Cho, A Novel Structure for Tunable Complex Heterodyne Filters, *International System on a Chip Conference (ISOCC),* Busan, Korea, November, 2009.

Soderstrand, Michael A. (2010a) Future of Wireless Tutorial, *IEEE International Midwest Symposium on Circuits and Systems (MWSCAS),* Seattle, WA, August 1-4, 2010..

Soderstrand, Michael A. (2010b) Noise Reduction Communication Circuits, *International System on a Chip Conference (ISOCC),* Incheon, Korea, November, 2010.

White, S.A., (1999) J.P. Woodward, M.A. Soderstrand, K.E. Nelson and P.V.N. Dao, "Adaptive Removal of Resonance Induced Noise", U.S. Patent No. 5960091, Sept. 28, 1999.

White, S.A., (2003) J.P. Woodward, M.A. Soderstrand, K.E. Nelson and P.V.N. Dao, "Adaptive Removal of Resonance Induced Noise (modified)", U.S. Patent No. 6,011,602, August 26, 2003